INSTRUCTOR GUIDE

DISCARD

Campbell Biology: Concepts & Connections

SEVENTH EDITION

Reece • Taylor • Simon • Dickey

Edward J. Zalisko

BLACKBURN COLLEGE

Benjamin Cummings

Boston   Columbus   Indianapolis   New York   San Francisco   Upper Saddle River

Amsterdam   Cape Town   Dubai   London   Madrid   Milan   Munich   Paris   Montréal   Toronto

Delhi   Mexico City   São Paulo   Sydney   Hong Kong   Seoul   Singapore   Taipei   Tokyo

Editor-in-Chief, Biology: Beth Wilbur
Executive Editor: Chalon Bridges
Senior Editorial Manager: Ginnie Simione Jutson
Senior Supplements Project Editor: Susan Berge
Project Editor: Kim Wimpsett
Editorial Assistant: Rachel Brickner
Marketing Manager: Lauren Garritson
Managing Editor, Production: Michael Early
Production Project Manager: Jane Brundage
Production Management and Composition: Integra
Cover Production: Seventeenth Street Studios
Manufacturing Buyer: Michael Penne
Text and Cover Printer: Bind-Rite, Robbinsville

Cover Photo Credit: Ring-tailed lemur (Lemur catta) looking down from large spiny plant, Itampolo, South Madagascar; Inaki Relanzon/Nature Picture Library.

ISBN 10: 0-321-74207-9
ISBN 13: 978-0-321-74207-0

Benjamin Cummings
is an imprint of

www.pearsonhighered.com   1 2 3 4 5 6 7 8 9 10—BRR—15 14 13 12 11

Contents

Author's Foreword

One of the greatest challenges facing instructors in any discipline is to remember what it was like before we understood the subject at hand. What were the mental obstacles we encountered on our way to understanding? What was it that we saw, heard, read, or touched that helped us make connections? What do we wish someone had said or explained?

Learning styles vary, and the experiences of our lives are unique. As teachers, we struggle to explain and connect the old to the new. The sections in this instructor's guide titled "Student Misconceptions and Concerns" and "Teaching Tips" are intended to give teachers, old and new, something to think about as you prepare and teach your course. Although these sections were written with a beginning instructor in mind, there should be something here for everyone to use. The field of biology is broad and fluid, offering new challenges in many diverse fields. For those of us with years of experience, a new twist or an opportunity to explain something in a different way can enliven our classes and refresh our efforts in the classroom.

It is my hope that you will find much here to consider to make biology more meaningful and relevant to your students.

If you would like to share your insights and tips for possible inclusion in future editions, your generous advice is most welcome and appreciated. We have so much to learn from each other.

Ed Zalisko, Ph.D.

Professor of Biology

Blackburn College

Forward suggestions to ezali@blackburn.edu. Please note *Campbell Biology: Concepts & Connections Instructor Guide* in the subject area of your email.

Instructor Supplements

Following is a list of *Campbell Biology: Concepts & Connections,* Seventh Edition, print and media supplements available to instructors.

Instructor Resource DVD Set

978-0-321-71882-2 / 0-321-71882-8

This DVD set combines all the instructor media for *Campbell Biology: Concepts & Connections,* Seventh Edition, into one chapter-by-chapter resource including PowerPoint slides, animations, Discovery Channel video clips, lecture presentations, lecture questions to stimulate class discussions, quiz games, and digital transparencies. The Test Bank provides a variety of test questions, many art- or scenario-based, in both TestGen and Microsoft Word.

Instructor Guide

978-0-321-74207-0 / 0-321-74207-9

This comprehensive guide provides instructors with chapter-by-chapter objectives, key terms, word roots, lecture outlines, student misconceptions and concerns, and teaching tips.

Blackboard

978-0-321-71884-6 / 0-321-71884-4
www.pearsonhighered.com/elearning

All the content available through the Premium Website is available in the Blackboard course management system.

Blackboard Premium

978-0-321-70921-9 / 0-321-70921-7

MasteringBiology

978-0-321-71886-0 / 0-321-71886-0
www.masteringbiology.com

MasteringBiology is an online assessment and tutorial system designed to help instructors teach more efficiently and pedagogically proven to help students learn. It helps instructors maximize class time with customizable, easy-to-assign, and automatically graded assessments that motivate students to learn outside of class and arrive prepared for lecture. The powerful gradebook provides unique insight into student and class performance even before the first test. As a result, instructors can spend class time where students need it most. The Mastering system empowers students to take charge of their learning through activities aimed at different learning styles and engages them in learning science through practice and step-by-step guidance—at their convenience, 24/7.

MasteringBiology with Pearson eText

978-0-321-70920-2 / 0-321-70920-9

This includes all the features of MasteringBiology in addition to Pearson eText content.

MasteringBiology with Enhanced Course Management

978-0-321-78084-3 / 0-321-78084-1

This includes all the features of MasteringBiology in addition to Pearson's own course-management system.

TestGen Computerized Test Bank

978-0-321-71881-5 / 0-321-71881-X

The Test Bank in TestGen provides a variety of test questions, many art- or scenario-based.

CHAPTER **1**

Biology: Exploring Life

Chapter Objectives

Opening Essay

Explain why Madagascar has so many species of lemurs.

Themes in the Study of Biology

1.1 Describe seven properties common to all life.

1.2 Describe the levels of biological organization from molecules to the biosphere, noting the interrelationships between levels.

1.2 Define the concept of emergent properties and describe an example of it.

1.3 Explain why cells are a special level in biological organization. Compare prokaryotic and eukaryotic cells.

1.4 Compare the dynamics of nutrients and energy in an ecosystem.

Evolution, the Core Theme of Biology

1.5 Explain how DNA encodes a cell's information.

1.6 Compare the three domains of life. Distinguish between the three multicellular kingdoms within Eukarya.

1.7 Describe the process and products of natural selection. Explain why individuals cannot evolve.

The Process of Science

1.8 Distinguish between quantitative and qualitative data. Compare the definitions and use of inductive and deductive reasoning in scientific investigations.

1.8 Distinguish between a scientific theory and a hypothesis.

1.8 Distinguish between the scientific definition and common use of the word *theory*.

1.9 Describe the structure of a controlled experiment and give an example.

Biology and Everyday Life

1.10 Compare the goals of science and technology. Explain why an understanding of science is essential to our lives.

1.11 Explain how evolution impacts the lives of all humans.

Lecture Outline

I. Introduction

  A. Lemurs are primates that

    1. are known for their distinctive tails, dark eye patches, and muzzles,

    2. live in Madagascar, and

    3. have ancestors who floated to Madagascar about 60 million years ago and diversified in a world

      a. relatively free of predators and competitors and

      b. with many different habitats.

II. Themes in the Study of Biology

  A. 1.1 All forms of life share common properties

    1. Biology is the scientific study of life.

    2. Properties of life include

      a. Order—the highly ordered structure that typifies life,

      b. Reproduction—the ability of organisms to reproduce their own kind,

      c. Growth and development—consistent growth and development controlled by inherited DNA,

      d. Energy processing—the use of chemical energy to power an organism's activities and chemical reactions,

      e. Response to the environment—an ability to respond to environmental stimuli,

      f. Regulation—an ability to control an organism's internal environment within limits that sustain life, and

      g. Evolutionary adaptation—adaptations evolve over many generations as individuals with traits best suited to their environments have greater reproductive success and pass their traits to offspring.

  B. 1.2 In life's hierarchy of organization, new properties emerge at each level

    1. Biological organization unfolds as follows:

      a. Biosphere—all of the environments on Earth that support life,

      b. Ecosystem—all the organisms living in a particular area and the physical components with which the organisms interact,

      c. Community—the entire array of organisms living in a particular ecosystem,

      d. Population—all the individuals of a species living in a specific area,

      e. Organism—an individual living thing,

      f. Organ system—several organs that cooperate in a specific function,

      g. Organ—a structure that is composed of tissues and that provides a specific function for the organism,

      h. Tissues—a group of similar cells that perform a specific function,

      i. Cells—the fundamental unit of life,

      j. Organelle—a membrane-bound structure that performs a specific function in a cell, and

      k. Molecule—a cluster of small chemical units called atoms held together by chemical bonds.

    2. Emergent properties are

      a. new properties that arise in each step upward in the hierarchy of life,

      b. from the arrangement and interactions among component parts.

C. 1.3 Cells are the structural and functional units of life

   1. Cells are the level at which the properties of life emerge.

   2. A cell can

      a. regulate its internal environment,

      b. take in and use energy,

      c. respond to its environment,

      d. develop and maintain its complex organization, and

      e. give rise to new cells.

   3. All cells

      a. are enclosed by a membrane that regulates the passage of materials between the cell and its surroundings and

      b. use DNA as their genetic information.

   4. There are two basic types of cells.

      a. Prokaryotic cells

        i. were the first to evolve,

        ii. are simpler, and

        iii. are usually smaller than eukaryotic cells.

      b. Eukaryotic cells

        i. contain membrane-enclosed organelles, including a nucleus containing DNA, and

        ii. are found in plants, animals, and fungi.

   5. Systems biology models the complex interactions of biological systems, ranging

      a. from the functioning of the biosphere

      b. to the complex molecular machinery of a cell.

   6. Cells illustrate another theme in biology: the correlation of structure and function.

   7. Structure is related to function at all levels of biological organization.

D. 1.4 Living organisms interact with their environment, exchanging matter and energy

   1. Living organisms interact with their environments, which include

      a. other organisms and

      b. physical factors.

   2. In most ecosystems

      a. plants are the *producers* that provide the food,

      b. *consumers* eat plants and other animals, and

      c. *decomposers* act as recyclers, changing complex matter into simpler mineral nutrients.

   3. The dynamics of ecosystems include two major processes:

      a. The recycling of chemical nutrients from the atmosphere and soil through producers, consumers, and decomposers back to the environment.

      b. The one-way flow of energy through an ecosystem, entering as sunlight, converted to chemical energy by producers, passed on to consumers, and exiting as heat.

III. Evolution, the Core Theme of Biology

A. 1.5 The unity of life is based on DNA and a common genetic code

   1. All cells have DNA, the chemical substance of genes.

   2. Genes

      a. are the unit of inheritance that transmits information from parents to offspring,

      b. are grouped into very long DNA molecules called chromosomes, and

      c. control the activities of a cell.

3. A species' genes are coded in the sequences of the four building blocks making up DNA's double helix.
   a. All forms of life use essentially the same code to translate the information stored in DNA into proteins.
   b. The diversity of life arises from differences in DNA sequences.
B. 1.6 The diversity of life can be arranged into three domains
   1. We can think of biology's enormous scope as having two dimensions.
      a. The "vertical" dimension is the size scale that stretches from molecules to the biosphere.
      b. The "horizontal" dimension spans across the great diversity of organisms existing now and over the long history of life on Earth.
   2. Diversity is the hallmark of life.
      a. Biologists have identified about 1.8 million species.
      b. Estimates of the actual number of species ranges from 10–100 million.
   3. Taxonomy names species and classifies them into a system of broader groups.
   4. The diversity of life can be arranged into three **domains**.
      a. **Bacteria** are the most diverse and widespread prokaryotes.
      b. **Archaea** are prokaryotes that often live in Earth's extreme environments.
      c. **Eukarya** have eukaryotic cells and include
         i. single-celled protists and
         ii. multicellular fungi, animals, and plants.
C. 1.7 Evolution explains the unity and diversity of life
   1. The history of life, as documented by fossils, is a saga of a changing Earth
      a. billions of years old and
      b. inhabited by an evolving cast of life forms.
   2. Evolution accounts for life's dual nature of
      a. kinship and
      b. diversity.
   3. In 1859, Charles Darwin published the book *On the Origin of Species by Means of Natural Selection*, which articulated two main points.
      a. A large amount of evidence supports the idea of evolution, that species living today are descendants of ancestral species in what Darwin called "descent with modification."
      b. **Natural selection** is a mechanism for evolution.
   4. Natural selection was inferred by connecting two observations.
      a. Individuals in a population vary in their traits, many of which are passed on from parents to offspring.
      b. A population can produce far more offspring than the environment can support.
   5. From these observations, Darwin inferred that
      a. those individuals with heritable traits best suited to the environment are more likely to survive and reproduce than less well-suited individuals,
      b. as a result of this unequal reproductive success over many generations, an increasing proportion of individuals will have the advantageous traits, and
      c. the result will be evolutionary adaptation, the accumulation of favorable traits in a population over time.

IV. The Process of Science

A. 1.8 Scientific inquiry is used to ask and answer questions about nature

1. The word *science* is derived from a Latin verb meaning "to know." Science is a way of knowing.

2. Scientists

   a. use **inductive reasoning** to draw general conclusions from many observations and

   b. **deductive reasoning** to come up with ways to test a **hypothesis**, a proposed explanation for a set of observations. The logic flows from general premises to the specific results we should expect if the premises are true.

3. How is a theory different from a hypothesis? A scientific **theory** is

   a. much broader in scope than a hypothesis,

   b. usually general enough to generate many new, specific hypotheses, which can then be tested, and

   c. supported by a large and usually growing body of evidence.

B. 1.9 Scientists form and test hypotheses and share their results

1. We solve everyday problems by using hypotheses.

   a. A common example would be the reasoning we use to answer the question, "Why doesn't a flashlight work?"

   b. Using deductive reasoning we realize that the problem is either (1) the bulb or (2) the batteries.

   c. Further, a hypothesis must be

      i. testable and

      ii. falsifiable.

   d. In this example, two hypotheses are tested.

2. An actual research project demonstrates the process of science.

3. Scientists began with a set of observations and generalizations that

   a. poisonous animals are brightly colored and

   b. imposters resemble poisonous species but are actually harmless.

4. They then tested the hypothesis that mimics benefit because predators confuse them with the harmful species.

5. The scientists conducted a **controlled experiment**, comparing

   a. an experimental group consisting of artificial king snakes and

   b. a control group consisting of artificial brown snakes.

   c. The groups differed only by one factor, the coloration of the artificial snakes.

   d. The data fit the key prediction of the mimicry hypothesis.

6. Science is a social activity with most scientists working in teams.

7. Scientists share information in many ways.

8. Science seeks natural causes for natural phenomena.

   a. The scope of science is limited to the study of structures and processes that we can directly observe and measure.

   b. Hypotheses about supernatural forces or explanations are outside the bounds of science because they generate hypotheses that cannot be tested by science.

V. Biology and Everyday Life

A. 1.10 CONNECTION: Biology, technology, and society are connected in important ways

1. Many issues facing society are related to biology. Most involve our expanding technology.

2. The basic goals of science and technology differ.

    a. The goal of science is to understand natural phenomena.

    b. The goal of **technology** is to apply scientific knowledge for some specific purpose.

  3. Although their goals differ, science and technology are interdependent.

    a. Technological advances stem from scientific research.

    b. Research benefits from new technologies.

B. 1.11 EVOLUTION CONNECTION: Evolution is connected to our everyday lives

  1. Evolution is a core theme of biology.

  2. Evolutionary theory is useful in

    a. medicine,

    b. agriculture,

    c. forensics, and

    d. conservation.

  3. Human-caused environmental changes are powerful selective forces that affect the evolution of many species, including

    a. antibiotic-resistant bacteria,

    b. pesticide-resistant pests,

    c. endangered species, and

    d. increasing rates of extinction.

Chapter Guide to Teaching Resources

Themes in the Study of Biology (1.1–1.4)

Student Misconceptions and Concerns

- Many students enter our courses with a limited appreciation of the diversity of life. Ask any group of freshmen at the start of the semester to write down the first type of animal that comes to mind, and the most frequent response is a mammal. As the diversity of life is explored, the common heritage of biological organization can be less, and not more, apparent. The diverse forms, habits, and ecological interactions overwhelm our senses with striking distinctions. Emphasizing the diversity and the unifying aspects of life is necessary for a greater understanding of the rich evolutionary history of life on Earth. (1.1–1.4)

- We live in a world that is largely understood by what we can distinguish and identify with our naked senses. However, the diversity of life and the levels of biological organization extend well below the scale of our unaided perceptions. For many students, appreciating the diversity of the microscopic world is abstract, nearly on par with an understanding of the workings of atoms and molecules. The ability to examine the microscopic details of the world of our students (the surface of potato chips, the structure of table salt and sugar, the details of a blade of grass) can be an important sensory extension that prepares the mind for greater comprehension of these minute biological details. (1.1–1.4)

Teaching Tips

- Consider asking students to bring to class a page or two of some article about biology that appeared in the media in the last month. Alternatively, you could have each student e-mail a Web address of a recent biology-related news event to you. You might even have them e-mail relevant articles to you for each of the main topics you address throughout the semester. (1.1–1.4)

- The scientific organization Sigma Xi offers a free e-mail summary of the major science news articles appearing each weekday in major U.S. news media. The first paragraph or so of each article is included in the e-mail with a hyperlink to the rest of the article. The diverse topics are an excellent way to learn of general scientific announcements and reports. Typically, 5–10 articles are cited in each e-mail. To sign up for this free service, go to www.sigmaxi.org/programs/public/instruct.html. (1.1–1.4)

- The seven characteristics of life described in Module 1.1 can easily become another list to memorize. Exercises that require reflection and analysis of these significant traits can help to make this list more meaningful. Consider challenging your students to identify each property in the life of a butterfly or other common form of life (or perhaps a school mascot, if appropriate). (1.1)

- For a chance to add a little math to the biological levels of organization, consider calculating the general scale differences between each level of biological organization. For example, are cells generally 5, 10, 50, or 100 times larger in diameter than organelles? Are organelles generally 5, 10, 50, or 100 times larger than macromolecules? For some levels of organization, such as ecosystems, communities, and populations, size/scale differences are perhaps less relevant and more problematic to consider. However, at the smaller levels, the sense of scale might enhance an appreciation for levels of biological organization. (1.2)

- The U.S. Census Bureau maintains updated population clocks that estimate the U.S. and world populations on its website at www.census.gov/main/www/popclock.html. If students have an accurate general idea of the population of the United States, statistics about the number of people affected with a disease or disaster become more significant. For example, the current population of the United States is more than 311 million (in 2011). It is currently estimated that about one million people in the United States are infected with HIV. The number of people infected with HIV is impressive and concerning, but not perhaps as meaningful as realizing that the number of people infected represents about one out of every 311 people in the United States. Although the infected people are not evenly distributed among geographic and ethnic groups, if you apply this generality to the enrollments in your classes, the students might better appreciate the tremendous impact of the infection. (1.2)

- Here is a simple way to contrast the relative size of prokaryotic and eukaryotic cells. Mitochondria and chloroplasts are thought to have evolved by endosymbiosis (see Chapter 16). Thus, mitochondria and chloroplasts are about the size of bacteria, contained within a plant cell. A figure of a plant cell therefore provides an immediate comparison of these sizes, not side-by-side, but one inside the other! (1.3)

- Examples of biological form and function relationships are nearly endless. Those immediately apparent to your students will be easiest to comprehend. Have your students examine (in photos or in specimens) the teeth of various vertebrates. The diet of these animals is implied by the shape of the teeth (sharp teeth in carnivorous cats and blunted molars in a rat). Sliding your tongue over your teeth reveals our omnivorous history, with sharp canine teeth for slicing flesh and flat rear molars well suited for grinding plant material. (1.3)

- Help the class think through the diverse interactions between an organism and its environment. In class, select an organism and have the class develop a list of environmental components that interact with the organism. Items in this list will likely fall into living and nonliving categories. (1.4)

- Perhaps you have seen and can find a photo of a glass enclosed miniature ecosystem, likely containing some plants and shrimp. These are sometimes called a "shrimp biosphere," "Aqua-Biosphere," or "Ecosphere." Present this system to your students and challenge them to explain the dynamics of energy and nutrients in this system. Such an analysis will reveal that energy flows through but nutrients cycle within this system. (1.4)

Evolution, the Core Theme of Biology (1.5–1.7)

Student Misconceptions and Concerns

- Students likely have heard the terms chromosome, DNA, and gene. But distinguishing between a chromosome and DNA is often difficult for students, and defining a gene has been problematic even for scientists. Consider spending additional time to distinguish between these terms and note how our understanding has dramatically changed in the last 60 years. (1.5)

- As noted in the text, the classification of life has changed significantly in recent years. Many of your students may have used outdated materials in high school, increasingly common in difficult financial times. Therefore, the current descriptions may be contrary to schemes already understood by your students. Noting these revisions in classification can also be an opportunity to reflect on the nature of science, as new information is used to revise our understandings. (1.6)

- Students often misunderstand the basic process of evolution and instead express a Lamarckian point of view. Organisms do not evolve structures deliberately or out of want or need, and individuals do not evolve. Evolution is a passive process in which the environment favors one or more variations of a trait that naturally exist within a population. (1.7)

- Students often believe that Charles Darwin was the first to suggest that life evolves; the early contributions by Greek philosophers and the work of Jean-Baptiste de Lamarck and others may be unappreciated. Consider emphasizing this earlier work in your introduction to Darwin's contributions. (1.7)

Teaching Tips

- The authors make an analogy between the four bases used to form genes and the 26 letters of the English alphabet used to create words and sentences. One could also make an analogy between the four bases and trains composed of four different types of railroad cars (perhaps an engine, boxcar, tanker, and caboose). Imagine how many different types of trains one could make using just 100 rail cars of four different types. (The answer is 4^{100}.) (1.5)

- An excellent introduction to the domains and kingdoms of life is presented at www.ucmp.berkeley.edu/exhibits/historyoflife.php. (1.6)

- Many resources related to Charles Darwin are available on the Internet.
  a. General evolution resources:
    http://evolution.berkeley.edu
    www.ncse.com
    http://nationalacademies.org/evolution

b. An outstanding source for Darwin's writings and other resources can be found at http://darwin.amnh.org

c. The complete works of Charles Darwin can be found at http://darwin-online.org.uk/life20.html

d. Details about Charles Darwin's home are located at http://williamcalvin.com/bookshelf/down_hse.htm

e. An extensive Usenet newsgroup devoted to the discussion and debate of biological and physical origins is at www.talkorigins.org. (1.7)

- Many games model aspects of natural selection. Here is one that is appropriate for a laboratory exercise. Purchase several bags of dried grocery store beans of diverse sizes and colors. Large lima beans, small white beans, red beans, and black beans are all good options. Consider the beans food for the "predatory" students. To begin, randomly distribute (throw) 100 beans of each of four colors onto a green lawn. Allow individual students to collect beans over a set period, perhaps 2 minutes. Then count the total number of each color of bean collected. Assume that the beans remaining undetected (still in the lawn) reproduce by doubling in number. Calculate the number of beans of each color remaining in the field. For the next round, count out the number of each color to add to the lawn such that the new totals on the lawn will double the number of beans that students did not find in the first "generation." Before each predatory episode, record the total number of each color of beans that have "survived" in the field. Then toss out the new beans and let your student predators search for another round (generation). Repeat the process for at least three or four generations. Note what colors of beans have been favored by the environment. Apply Darwin's observations and inferences to this exercise. Ask students to speculate which colors might have been favored during another season of the year or in another location, such as a parking lot. (1.7)

The Process of Science (1.8–1.9)

Student Misconceptions and Concerns

- The common use of the terms law and theory by the public often blur the stricter definitions of these terms in science. In general, laws describe and theories explain. Both are typically well-established concepts in science. A free online publication by the National Academy of Sciences helps to define these and related terms more carefully. See Chapter 1 of Teaching about Evolution and the Nature of Science at www.nap.edu/readingroom/books/evolution98/. (1.8)

- The authors' distinction between natural and supernatural explanations is essential to understanding the power and limits of scientific explanations. This distinction is important when distinguishing between science and supernatural explanations for the origin of life and the generation of biodiversity. (1.9)

- Contrasting the concept of faith with the tentative nature of science can help to define and distinguish science from other ways of knowing. Students sometimes enter science classes expecting absolutes of facts and rigid dogma. Instead, scientific knowledge reflects tentative knowledge with degrees of confidence closely correlated to the related evidence. (1.9)

Teaching Tips

- Consider using a laboratory exercise to have your students plan and perhaps conduct a scientific investigation. Emphasize the processes and not the significance of the questions. Students can conduct descriptive surveys of student behavior (use of pens or pencils for taking notes, use of backpacks), or test hypotheses using controlled trials. Students will need some supervision and advice while planning and conducting their experiments. (1.8)

- Have your students explain why a coordinated conspiracy promoting a specific idea in science is unlikely to succeed. Have your students describe aspects of science that would check fraudulent or erroneous claims and/or political efforts. (1.8–1.9)

- Consider presenting your class with descriptions of several scientific investigations that you have written or found described in the media. Edit or include numerous examples of improper methodology (small sample size, several variables existing between the control and experimental groups, failure to specifically test the hypothesis, etc.). Let small groups or individuals analyze the experiments in class to identify the flaws. This critical analysis allows students the opportunity to suggest the characteristics of good investigations in class. (1.9)

Biology and Everyday Life (1.10–1.11)

Student Misconceptions and Concerns

- Many students will be unable to distinguish between science and technology before reading through this textbook chapter. The discussion in Module 1.10 makes several distinctions worth emphasizing which may promote interest in your course. (1.10)

- Few students are likely to understand the tremendous benefits that result from an understanding of evolution. For some, evolution may seem like an abstract concept that is still up for debate. Yet evolution, like gravity, is a daily part of our lives, recognized or not. (1.11)

Teaching Tips

- Looking around your classroom, consider immediate examples of technology. Perhaps a video projector, a telephone, a wall clock, or other devices are available for quick reference (or perhaps your students are distracted by technology they brought with them). Then challenge your students to suggest examples of science in their immediate world, which is important to them. (These might include dietary guidelines, other suggestions to improve health and fitness, and medications.) (1.10)

- Module 1.11 lists many of the major human challenges impacted by evolution. Our ability to feed ourselves, respond to infectious disease, and understand the interrelationships of our crops, agricultural animals, pets, and each other, are all enriched by an appreciation of evolution. Understanding evolution permits us to work more deliberately in our evolving world. (1.11)

Key Terms

Archaea	biosphere	controlled experiment
Bacteria	cell	deductive reasoning
biology	community	domains

ecosystem   inductive reasoning   population
emergent properties   molecule   prokaryotic cells
Eukarya   natural selection   systems biology
eukaryotic cells   organ system   technology
evolution   organelle   theory
genes   organism   tissues
hypothesis   organs

Word Roots

bio- = life (*biosphere*: all the environments on Earth that support life); **-logy** = the scientific study of a subject (*biology*: the scientific study of life)

-ell = small (*organelle*: a membrane-bound structure that performs a specific function in a cell)

eu- = true; **karyo-** = nucleus (*eukaryotic cell*: a cell with a membrane-enclosed nucleus and other membrane-enclosed organelles)

pro- = before (*prokaryotic cell*: a cell that has no nucleus)

tech- = skill or art (*technology*: the practical application of scientific knowledge)

CHAPTER 2

The Chemical Basis of Life

Chapter Objectives

Opening Essay

Explain why an understanding of chemistry and the properties of water are important aspects of biology.

Elements, Atoms, and Compounds

2.1 Define matter, an element, a compound, and a trace element.

2.2 Explain how and why iodine, fluoride, and iron are added to the human diet.

2.3 Distinguish between the size, location, and properties of protons, electrons, and neutrons.

2.3 Define the atomic number and mass number of an atom.

2.3 Define an isotope and explain what makes some isotopes radioactive.

2.4 Describe the uses and dangers of radioactive isotopes.

Chemical Bonds

2.5 Explain how the electron configuration of an atom influences its chemical behavior.

2.6–2.8 Distinguish between covalent bonds, nonpolar polar covalent bonds, polar covalent bonds, hydrogen bonds, and ionic bonds, noting their relative strengths and how and where they form.

2.9 Explain the significance of chemical reactions. Identify the reactants and products of photosynthesis.

Water's Life-Supporting Properties

2.10–2.13 Describe the special properties of water that make it vital to living systems. Explain how these properties are related to hydrogen bonding.

2.10 Define and distinguish between cohesion, adhesion, and surface tension.

2.11 Define and distinguish between heat and temperature. Explain how sweating helps to cool your body.

2.12 Explain why ice floats.

2.13 Define a solute, a solvent, and a solution.

2.14 Explain how acids and bases directly or indirectly affect the hydrogen ion concentration of a solution.

2.14 Explain the basis of the pH scale.

2.14 Explain how buffers function.

2.15 Describe the causes and consequences of acid precipitation and ocean acidification.

2.16 Explain why the search for extraterrestrial life centers on the search for water.

Lecture Outline

I. Introduction

   A. Chemicals are the stuff that make up

      1. our bodies,

      2. the bodies of other organisms, and

      3. the physical environment.

   B. Life's chemistry is tied to water.

      1. Life first evolved in water.

      2. All living organisms require water.

      3. The chemical reactions of your body occur in cells consisting of 70–95% water.

II. Elements, Atoms, and Compounds

   A. 2.1 Organisms are composed of elements, in combinations called compounds

      1. Living organisms are composed of **matter**, which is anything that occupies space and has <u>mass (weight)</u>.

      2. Matter is composed of chemical elements.

         a. An **element** is a substance that cannot be broken down to other substances.

         b. There are 92 elements in nature—only a few exist in a pure state.

      3. A **compound** is a substance consisting of two or more different elements in a fixed ratio.

      4. Compounds are more common than pure elements.

      5. Sodium chloride, table salt, is a common compound of equal parts of sodium (Na) and chlorine (Cl).

      6. About 25 elements are essential to life.

      7. Four elements make up about 96% of the weight of most living organisms. These are

         a. oxygen,

         b. carbon,

         c. hydrogen, and

         d. nitrogen.

      8. **Trace elements** are essential but are only needed in minute quantities.

   B. 2.2 CONNECTION: Trace elements are common additives to food and water

      1. Some trace elements are required to prevent disease.

         a. Without iron, your body cannot transport oxygen.

         b. An iodine deficiency prevents production of thyroid hormones, resulting in goiter.

      2. Fluoride is added to municipal water and dental products to help reduce tooth decay.

      3. Several chemicals are added to food to

         a. help preserve it,

         b. make it more nutritious, and/or

         c. make it look better.

      4. Check out the "Nutrition Facts" label on foods and drinks you purchase.

   C. 2.3 Atoms consist of protons, neutrons, and electrons

      1. Each element consists of one kind of atom.

      2. An **atom** is the smallest unit of matter that still retains the properties of an element.

      3. Three subatomic particles in atoms are relevant to our discussion of the properties of elements.

         a. **Protons** are positively charged.

         b. **Electrons** are negatively charged.

      c. **Neutrons** are electrically neutral.

  4. Neutrons and protons are packed into an atom's **nucleus**.

  5. Electrons orbit the nucleus.

  6. The negative charge of electrons and the positive charge of protons keep electrons near the nucleus.

  7. The number of protons is the atom's **atomic number**.

  8. An atom's **mass number** is the sum of the number of protons and neutrons in the nucleus.

  9. The **atomic mass** is approximately equal to its mass number.

  10. Although all atoms of an element have the same atomic number, some differ in mass number.

  11. Different **isotopes** of an element have

      a. the same number of protons,

      b. but different numbers of neutrons.

  12. Different isotopes of an element behave identically in chemical reactions.

  13. In **radioactive isotopes**, the nucleus decays spontaneously, giving off particles and energy.

D. 2.4 CONNECTION: Radioactive isotopes can help or harm us

  1. Living cells cannot distinguish between isotopes of the same element.

      a. Therefore, radioactive compounds in metabolic processes can act as tracers.

      b. This radioactivity can be detected by instruments.

      c. Using these instruments, the fate of radioactive tracers can be monitored in living organisms.

  2. Radioactive tracers are frequently used in medical diagnosis.

  3. Sophisticated imaging instruments are used to detect them.

      a. An imaging instrument that uses positron-emission tomography (PET) detects the location of injected radioactive materials.

      b. PET is useful for diagnosing heart disorders, cancer, and in brain research.

  4. In addition to benefits, there are also dangers associated with using radioactive substances.

      a. Uncontrolled exposure can cause damage to some molecules in a living cell, especially DNA.

      b. Chemical bonds are broken by the emitted energy, which causes abnormal bonds to form.

III. Chemical Bonds

A. 2.5 The distribution of electrons determines an atom's chemical properties

  1. Of the three subatomic particles—protons, neutrons, and electrons—only electrons are directly involved in chemical activity.

  2. Electrons occur in energy levels called **electron shells**.

      a. Information about the distribution of electrons is found in the periodic table of the elements.

  3. An atom may have one, two, or three electron shells surrounding the nucleus.

      a. The number of electrons in the outermost shell determines the chemical properties of the atom.

      b. Atoms whose outer shells are not full tend to interact with other atoms, participating in chemical reactions.

4. Atoms with incomplete outer shells tend to react so that both atoms end up with completed outer shells.

5. These atoms may react with each other by sharing, donating, or receiving electrons.

6. These interactions usually result in atoms staying close together, held by attractions called **chemical bonds**.

B. 2.6 Covalent bonds join atoms into molecules through electron sharing

1. The strongest kind of chemical bond is a **covalent bond** in which two atoms share one or more outer-shell electrons.

2. Two or more atoms held together by covalent bonds form a **molecule**.

3. A covalent bond connects two hydrogen atoms in a molecule of the gas H_2.

4. There are four alternative ways to represent common molecules.

5. Atoms in a covalently bonded molecule continually compete for shared electrons.

   a. The attraction (pull) for shared electrons is called **electronegativity**.

   b. More electronegative atoms pull harder.

6. In molecules of only one element, the pull toward each atom is equal, because each atom has the same electronegativity.

7. The bonds formed are called **nonpolar covalent bonds**.

8. Water has atoms with different electronegativities.

   a. Oxygen attracts the shared electrons more strongly than hydrogen.

   b. So, the shared electrons spend more time near oxygen.

   c. The oxygen atom has a slightly negative charge and the hydrogen atoms have a slightly positive charge.

   d. The result is a **polar covalent bond**.

   e. Because of these polar covalent bonds, water is a **polar molecule**.

C. 2.7 Ionic bonds are attractions between ions of opposite charge

   a. An **ion** is an atom or molecule with an electrical charge resulting from gain or loss of electrons.

   b. When an electron is lost, a positive charge results.

   c. When an electron is gained, a negative charge results.

1. Two ions with opposite charges attract each other.

   a. When the attraction holds the ions together, it is called an **ionic bond**.

   b. **Salt** is a synonym for an ionic compound.

D. 2.8 Hydrogen bonds are weak bonds important in the chemistry of life

1. Most large molecules are held in their three-dimensional functional shape by weak bonds.

2. Hydrogen, as part of a polar covalent bond, has a partial positive charge.

3. The charged regions on molecules are electrically attracted to oppositely charged regions on neighboring molecules.

4. Because the positively charged region is always a hydrogen atom, the bond is called a **hydrogen bond**.

E. 2.9 Chemical reactions make and break chemical bonds

1. Remember that the structure of atoms and molecules determines the way they behave.

   a. Remember that atoms combine to form molecules.

   b. Hydrogen and oxygen can react to form water:

$$2H_2 + O_2 \rightarrow 2H_2O$$

2. The formation of water from hydrogen and oxygen is an example of a **chemical reaction**.

3. The **reactants** (H_2 and O_2) are converted to H_2O, the **product**.

4. Chemical reactions do not create or destroy matter.

5. Chemical reactions only rearrange matter.

6. Photosynthesis is a chemical reaction that is essential to life on Earth.

    a. Carbon dioxide (from the air) reacts with water.

    b. Sunlight powers the conversion to produce the products glucose and oxygen.

IV. Water's Life-Supporting Properties

A. 2.10 Hydrogen bonds make liquid water cohesive

1. The tendency of molecules of the same kind to stick together is **cohesion**.

    a. Cohesion is much stronger for water than other liquids.

    b. Most plants depend upon cohesion to help transport water and nutrients from their roots to their leaves.

2. The tendency of two kinds of molecules to stick together is **adhesion**.

3. Cohesion is related to **surface tension**—a measure of how difficult it is to break the surface of a liquid.

    a. Hydrogen bonds give water high surface tension, making it behave as if it were coated with an invisible film.

    b. Water striders stand on water without breaking the water surface.

B. 2.11 Water's hydrogen bonds moderate temperature

1. Because of hydrogen bonding, water has a greater ability to resist temperature change than other liquids.

    a. Heat is the energy associated with movement of atoms and molecules in matter.

    b. Temperature measures the intensity of heat.

2. Heat is released when hydrogen bonds form.

3. Heat must be absorbed to break hydrogen bonds.

4. When a substance evaporates, the surface of the liquid that remains behind cools down, in the process of **evaporative cooling**.

5. This cooling occurs because the molecules with the greatest energy leave the surface.

C. 2.12 Ice is less dense than liquid water

1. Water can exist as a gas, liquid, or solid.

2. Water is less dense as a solid than a liquid because of hydrogen bonding.

3. When water freezes, each molecule forms a stable hydrogen bond with its neighbors.

    a. As ice crystals form, the molecules are less densely packed than in liquid water.

    b. Because ice is less dense than water, it floats.

D. 2.13 Water is the solvent of life

1. A **solution** is a liquid consisting of a uniform mixture of two or more substances.

    a. The dissolving agent is the **solvent**.

    b. The substance that is dissolved is the **solute**.

    c. An **aqueous solution** is one in which water is the solvent.

2. Water's versatility as a solvent results from the polarity of its molecules.

3. Polar or charged solutes dissolve when water molecules surround them, forming aqueous solutions.

4. Table salt is an example of a solute that will go into solution in water.

E. 2.14 The chemistry of life is sensitive to acidic and basic conditions

1. In aqueous solutions, a small percentage of water molecules break apart into ions.

    a. Some are hydrogen ions (H^+).

    b. Some are hydroxide ions (OH^-).

  c. Both types are very reactive.
 2. A compound that releases H^+ to a solution is an **acid**.
 3. A compound that accepts H^+ is a **base**.
 4. The **pH scale** describes how acidic or basic a solution is.
  a. The pH scale ranges from 0 to 14, with zero the most acidic and 14 the most basic.
  b. Each pH unit represents a tenfold change in the concentration of H^+.
 5. A **buffer** is a substance that minimizes changes in pH. Buffers
  a. accept H+ when it is in excess and
  b. donate H^+ when it is depleted.
F. 2.15 CONNECTION: Acid precipitation and ocean acidification threaten the environment
 1. When we burn fossil fuels (coal, oil, and gas), air-polluting compounds and CO_2 are released into the atmosphere.
  a. Sulfur and nitrous oxides react with water in the air to form acids.
  b. These acids fall to Earth as **acid precipitation**, which is rain, snow, or fog with a pH lower than 5.2.
  c. CO_2 dissolving in seawater lowers ocean pH in a process known as **ocean acidification**.
G. 2.16 EVOLUTION CONNECTION: The search for extraterrestrial life centers on the search for water
 1. The emergent properties of water support life on Earth.
 2. When astrobiologists search for signs of extraterrestrial life on distant planets, they look for evidence of water.
 3. The National Aeronautics and Space Administration (NASA) have found evidence that water was once abundant on Mars.

Chapter Guide to Teaching Resources

Elements, Atoms, and Molecules (2.1–2.4)

Student Misconceptions and Concerns

- The dangers posed by certain chemicals in our food and broader environment have some-times misled people to associate chemicals with harm. People might not want chemicals added to their food or in their environment. Students often fail to appreciate the chemical nature of our bodies and our world and the potential harm or benefits of naturally occur-ring chemistry. They often fail to understand why "natural" does not necessarily mean good. (Consider presenting a long list of naturally occurring toxins to make this point.) Your class may benefit from a class discussion of these misconceptions about our attitudes toward chemicals. (2.1–2.4)

- Students with limited backgrounds in chemistry and physics might struggle with basic concepts of mass, weight, compounds, elements, and isotopes. It may also be early in the semester when mature study habits have not yet developed. Consider passing along basic studying advice and tips to help students master these early chemistry concepts. In-class quizzes (graded or not) or a few homework problems will also provide reinforcing practice. (2.3)

Teaching Tips

- The text notes the unique properties of pure sodium, pure chlorine, and the compound sodium chloride formed when the two bond together. Consider challenging your students to think of other simple examples of new properties that result when a compound is formed. (For example, water, formed from hydrogen and oxygen, and rust, formed from iron and oxygen.) (2.1)

- Students might be interested in the following aside: One of the challenges of raising captive, exotic animals is meeting the unique dietary requirements of a species. A zoo may struggle to keep a particular animal because zoologists have not identified all of the trace elements required in the animal's diet. (2.1–2.2)

- Many breakfast cereals are fortified with iron (see Figure 2.2c). As noted in Module 2.2, you can crush the cereal and extract distinct iron particles with a magnet. An overhead projector or video imaging device should clearly reveal the iron particles stuck to the magnet. This short practical demonstration can help connect a concrete example to an abstract concept. (2.2)

- Here is a comparison that helps make the point about the differences in mass of protons and electrons. If a proton were as massive as a bowling ball, an electron would be the mass of a Lifesaver. (This is calculated by considering a 15-pound bowling ball, a Lifesaver with mass of 0.12 ounces, and the mention in Module 2.3 that an electron is about 1/2,000 the mass of a proton.) (2.3)

- The text in Module 2.3 makes an analogy regarding the size of a helium atom. The text notes that if a helium atom were the size of Yankee Stadium, the nucleus would be about the size of a fly in center field, and the two electrons would be like tiny gnats buzzing around the stadium. This analogy helps to relate the great distances between parts of an atom. Consider modifying the analogy to any local stadium in your region. Such concrete examples help to relate abstract concepts. (2.3)

- After sharing Teaching Tips 4 and 5, consider asking your students to compare the mass of the gnat orbiting Yankee Stadium to the mass of the fly in center field. If a proton or neutron is about 2,000 times more massive than an electron, how does the mass of a helium nucleus compare to the mass of one of its electrons? (2.3)

- The text notes the use of radioactive isotopes in dating fossils but references Module 15.5 for further discussion. If your course does not include Chapter 15, consider explaining this process at this point in your course. (2.3)

- The half-lives of many radioactive substances, especially those used for dating fossils, might lead some students to expect very long periods of decay for any radioactive substance. This might even be alarming if students are someday asked to consume a radioactive substance for a medical test. However, some medically significant isotopes have relatively short half-lives. Radioactive iodine-131 is often used to diagnose or treat certain thyroid problems. Its half-life of eight days means that it will decay quickly. (2.4)

- Depending upon where you are teaching, radon in homes may be a common problem and significant health risk. If you are in a high radon region, consider adding details about home remediation methods and expenses, or have students research the topic and report back. (2.4)

Chemical Bonds (2.5–2.9)

Student Misconceptions and Concerns

- Students with limited backgrounds in chemistry will benefit from a discussion of Table 2.6 and the differences and limitations of representing atomic structure. The contrast in Table 2.6 is a good beginning for such a discussion. In addition to comparing how the positions of electrons are depicted, note the problems with the sense of scale as discussed in Module 2.3. (2.6)

- Students may misunderstand the chemical shorthand equation of photosynthesis presented in Module 2.9. As noted in the text, this overall equation does not include many smaller steps and reactions that occur in photosynthesis. If you discuss additional details of photosynthesis in your course, you might mention that you will add more to this equation at a later time. (2.9)

- A common student misconception is that energy is produced by a chemical reaction. When introducing chemical reactions, consider addressing the conservation of energy (the first law of thermodynamics) and the investment and release of energy in the creation and breaking of chemical bonds. (2.9)

Teaching Tips

- Consider challenging your students to suggest relationships in human lives that are analogous to each of the three types of chemical bonds (covalent, ionic, and hydrogen). Evaluating the accuracy of potential analogies requires careful analysis of the chemical bonding relationships and practices critical thinking skills. Small groups might provide immediate critiques before passing along analogies for the entire class to consider. The following is one example. (2.5–2.8)

  - Ionic and covalent bonds are different types of relationships. Consider this analogy. A woman taking out a loan has a specific relationship to her bank. She owes the bank money, something she got from the bank. A man shares an office with another man. Both look out the same window and answer the same phone. Ionic bonds are like a bank loan, in which something is borrowed. Covalent bonds are like sharing an office, with items (electrons) shared by both members of the relationship. After presenting this analogy, ask your students to modify the office analogy to represent a polar covalent bond. (Perhaps one man in the office sits closer to the window and the phone.)

- Have your students try to calculate the number of covalent bonds possible for a variety of atoms. (Carbon, for example, can form up to four covalent bonds.) Then provide the students with a list of elements and the number of outer electrons for each and have them make predictions about the chemical formula for many types of molecules. (For example, carbon could form covalent bonds with four hydrogen atoms.) (2.6)

- Modules 2.6 and 2.8 discuss the special bonding in and between water molecules. Many students do not appreciate the importance of weak chemical bonds in water and cellular chemistry. Extra time and attention may be required to address this special aspect of chemistry. (2.6 & 2.8)

- As noted in the text, chemical reactions do not create or destroy matter. Instead, they rearrange the structure and form new relationships. This is much like shuffling and dealing cards. When playing poker, cards are not created nor destroyed. Instead, new combinations are formed as the cards are dealt to the players. (2.9)

- The overall reaction of photosynthesis illustrates the investment and release of energy by chemical reactions. Consider discussing the investment of sunlight energy to create chemical bonds and the release of energy in the form of heat when plant materials are burned. (Animals invest some of the energy released by the breakdown of sugars to form new chemical bonds, such as those in ATP.) (2.9)

Water's Life-Supporting Properties (2.10–2.16)

Student Misconceptions and Concerns

- Students are unlikely to have carefully considered the four special properties of water that are apparent in our world. However, these properties are of great biological significance and are often familiar parts of our lives. The connections between these properties and personal experiences can invest great meaning into a discussion of water's properties. A homework assignment asking for examples of each of these properties in each student's experiences will require reflection and may produce meaningful illustrations. Similarly, quizzes or exam questions matching examples to a list of the properties may require high-level evaluative analysis. (2.10–2.13)

- Students at all levels struggle with the distinction between heat and temperature.

- Students might also expect that all ice is about the same temperature, 0°C. Redefining and correcting misunderstandings often takes more class time and energy than introducing previously unknown concepts. (2.12)

Teaching Tips

- Here is a way to help your students think about the sticky nature of water in their lives. Ask them to consider the need for a towel after a shower or a bath. Once we get out of the shower or bath, we have left the source of water. So why do we need the towel? A towel helps us dry off water that is still clinging to our bodies because water molecules are polar. The molecules on cell surfaces are also polar, so our skin and the water stick to each other. (2.10)

- Some students may be intrigued if you tell them that you too can stand on the surface of water—*when it is frozen*. Thus, it is necessary to note a liquid water surface when discussing surface tension. (2.10)

- Have students compare the seasonal ranges of temperatures of Anchorage and Fairbanks, Alaska. (Many websites, such as www.weather.com, provide weather information about various cities.) These two northern cities have large differences in their annual temperature ranges. Make the point that the coastal location of Anchorage moderates the temperature. (2.11)

- The following analogies may help students to understand the relationships between evaporation, heat, and temperature. (a) Ask students how the average on an exam would be affected if the brightest students didn't take the test. (b) The authors note that the performance of a track team would drop if the fastest runners did not compete. In both analogies, removing the top performers lowers the average, just as the evaporation of the most active water molecules cools the evaporative surface. (2.11)

- It's not the heat, it's the humidity. The efficiency of evaporative cooling is affected by humidity. As humidity rises, the rate of evaporation decreases, making it more difficult to cool our heat-generating bodies on a warm and humid summer day. (2.11)

- Ask your students if the ocean levels would change if ice did not float. They can try this experiment to find out, or you can begin class with the demonstration and watch the progress throughout the class period. Place several large chunks of ice in a glass and fill the glass up completely with water to the top rim. Thus, the ice cubes should be sticking up above the top of the filled glass. Will the glass overflow when the ice melts? (No.) This phenomenon is important when we consider the potential consequences of global warming. If floating glaciers melt, ocean levels will not be affected. However, if the ice over land melts, we can expect higher ocean levels. (2.12)

- Module 2.12 notes the insulating effect of ice forming at the surface of a lake. This phenomenon would not occur if ice were denser than water. Challenge students to think of other consequences from the expansion of water when it forms ice. (These include the ability to widen cracks in rocks, roads, and sidewalks!) (2.12)

- A simple demonstration of a solute dissolving in a solvent can focus students' attention on the process when discussing solutions. Using colored water and white sugar or salt may make it easier to see and reference while you are discussing the process. Such simple visual aids add life to a lecture. (You might also add corn oil to the top of the solution to demonstrate the properties of hydrophobic substances, and challenge your class to explain why oil and water do not mix.) (2.13)

- Discussions of pH are enhanced by lab activities that permit students to test the pH of everyday items (foods and household solutions). If students do not have opportunities to conduct such tests in lab, consider testing a few items during your class (pH paper or a basic pH meter will, of course, be necessary). (2.14)

- The Environmental Protection Agency (EPA) website, www.epa.gov/acidrain, includes useful information about acid rain and related science experiments. (2.15)

- In Module 2.15, the authors note that burning fossil fuels contributes to global climate change, as addressed further in Chapter 38. If your course does not include Chapter 38, consider addressing these aspects in your class discussions. (2.15)

- The SETI (Search For Extraterrestrial Intelligence) Institute's mission is "to explore, understand, and explain the origin, nature, and prevalence of life in the universe." Your students might enjoy exploring this respected scientific organization's website at www.seti.org. (2.16)

Key Terms

acid	compound	mass number
acid precipitation	covalent bond	matter
adhesion	electron	molecule
aqueous solution	electron shell	neutron
atom	electronegativity	nonpolar covalent bond
atomic mass	element	nucleus
atomic number	evaporative cooling	ocean acidification
base	heat	pH scale
buffer	hydrogen bond	polar covalent bond
chemical bond	ion	polar molecule
chemical reaction	ionic bond	product
cohesion	isotope	proton

radioactive isotope	solute	surface tension
reactant	solution	temperature
salt	solvent	trace element

Word Roots

ad- = to or toward (*adhesion*: the attraction between different kinds of molecules)

aqua- = water (*aqueous solution*: a solution in which water is the solvent)

co- = together; **-valent** = strength (*covalent bond*: an attraction between atoms that share one or more pairs of outer-shell electrons)

electro- = electricity (*electronegativity*: the attraction of a given atom for the electrons of a covalent bond)

iso- = equal (*isotope*: a variant form of an atomic element having the same number of protons and electrons but a different number of neutrons)

neutr- = neither (*neutron*: a subatomic particle with no electrical charge)

pro- = before (*proton*: a subatomic particle with a single positive electrical charge)

CHAPTER 3

The Molecules of Cells

Chapter Objectives

Opening Essay

Explain why lactose intolerance is considered normal in adult humans.

Introduction to Organic Compounds

3.1 Explain why carbon is unparalleled in its ability to form large, diverse molecules.

3.1 Define organic compounds, hydrocarbons, a carbon skeleton, and an isomer.

3.2 Describe the properties of and distinguish between the six chemical groups important in the chemistry of life.

3.3 List the four main classes of macromolecules important to life. Explain the relationship between monomers and polymers. Compare the processes of dehydration synthesis and hydrolysis.

Carbohydrates

3.4–3.7 Describe the structures, functions, properties, and types of carbohydrate molecules common in the human diet.

3.6 Explain how and why high-fructose corn syrup is produced.

Lipids

3.8–3.10 Describe the structures, functions, properties, and types of lipid molecules.

3.10 Describe the health risks associated with the use of anabolic steroids.

Proteins

3.11–3.13 Describe the structures, functions, properties, and types of proteins.

3.12 Explain how a protein's shape determines its functions.

Nucleic Acids

3.14–3.15 Compare the structures and functions of DNA and RNA, noting similarities and differences.

3.16 Describe the adaptive advantage of lactose tolerance in people of East African decent.

Lecture Outline

I. Introduction

    A. Most of the world's population cannot digest milk-based foods.

        1. These people are lactose intolerant because they lack the enzyme lactase.

        2. This illustrates the importance of biological molecules, such as lactase, in the daily functions of living organisms.

II. Introduction to Organic Compounds

    A. 3.1 Life's molecular diversity is based on the properties of carbon

        1. Diverse molecules found in cells are composed of carbon bonded to

            a. other carbons and

            b. atoms of other elements.

        2. Carbon-based molecules are called **organic compounds**.

        3. By sharing electrons, carbon can

            a. bond to four other atoms and

            b. branch in up to four directions.

        4. Methane (CH_4) is one of the simplest organic compounds.

            a. Four covalent bonds link four hydrogen atoms to the carbon atom.

            b. Each of the four lines in the formula for methane represents a pair of shared electrons.

        5. Methane and other compounds composed of only carbon and hydrogen are called **hydrocarbons**.

        6. Carbon, with attached hydrogens, can bond together in chains of various lengths.

        7. A **carbon skeleton** is a chain of carbon atoms that can be

            a. branched or

            b. unbranched.

        8. Compounds with the same formula but different structural arrangements are call **isomers**.

    B. 3.2 A few chemical groups are key to the functioning of biological molecules

        1. An organic compound has unique properties that depend upon the

            a. size and shape of the molecule and

            b. groups of atoms (functional groups) attached to it.

        2. A **functional group** affects a biological molecule's function in a characteristic way.

        3. Compounds containing functional groups are **hydrophilic** (water-loving).

        4. The functional groups are

            a. **hydroxyl group**—consists of a hydrogen bonded to an oxygen,

            b. **carbonyl group**—a carbon linked by a double bond to an oxygen atom,

            c. **carboxyl group**—consists of a carbon double-bonded to both an oxygen and a hydroxyl group,

            d. **amino group**—composed of a nitrogen bonded to two hydrogen atoms and the carbon skeleton, and

            e. **phosphate group**—consists of a phosphorus atom bonded to four oxygen atoms.

        5. An example of similar compounds that differ only in functional groups is sex hormones.

            a. Male and female sex hormones differ only in functional groups.

            b. The differences cause varied molecular actions.

            c. The result is distinguishable features of males and females.

C. 3.3 Cells make a huge number of large molecules from a limited set of small molecules

    1. There are four classes of molecules important to organisms:

        a. carbohydrates,

        b. proteins,

        c. lipids, and

        d. nucleic acids.

    2. The four classes of biological molecules contain very large molecules.

        a. They are often called **macromolecules** because of their large size.

        b. They are also called **polymers** because they are made from identical building blocks strung together.

        c. The building blocks of polymers are called **monomers**.

    3. Monomers are linked together to form polymers through **dehydration reactions**, which remove water.

    4. Polymers are broken apart by **hydrolysis**, the addition of water.

    5. All biological reactions of this sort are mediated by **enzymes**, which speed up chemical reactions in cells.

    6. A cell makes a large number of polymers from a small group of monomers. For example,

        a. proteins are made from only 20 different amino acids and

        b. DNA is built from just four kinds of nucleotides.

    7. The monomers used to make polymers are universal.

III. Carbohydrates

  A. 3.4 Monosaccharides are the simplest carbohydrates

    1. **Carbohydrates** range from small sugar molecules (monomers) to large polysaccharides.

    2. Sugar monomers are **monosaccharides**, such as those found in honey,

        a. glucose and

        b. fructose.

    3. Monosaccharides can be hooked together to form

        a. more complex sugars and

        b. polysaccharides.

    4. The carbon skeletons of monosaccharides vary in length.

        a. Glucose and fructose are six carbons long.

        b. Others have three to seven carbon atoms.

    5. Monosaccharides are

        a. the main fuels for cellular work and

        b. used as raw materials to manufacture other organic molecules.

    6. Many monosaccharides form rings.

    7. The ring diagram may be

        a. abbreviated by not showing the carbon atoms at the corners of the ring and

        b. drawn with different thicknesses for the bonds, to indicate that the ring is a relatively flat structure with attached atoms extending above and below it.

  B. 3.5 Two monosaccharides are linked to form a disaccharide

    1. Two monosaccharides (monomers) can bond to form a **disaccharide** in a dehydration reaction.

    2. The disaccharide sucrose is formed by combining

        a. a glucose monomer and

    b. a fructose monomer.

   3. The disaccharide maltose is formed from two glucose monomers.

C. 3.6 CONNECTION: What is high-fructose corn syrup, and is it to blame for obesity?

   1. Sodas or fruit drinks probably contain high-fructose corn syrup (HFCS).

   2. Fructose is sweeter than glucose.

   3. To make HFCS, glucose atoms are rearranged to make the glucose isomer, fructose.

   4. High-fructose corn syrup (HFCS) is

     a. used to sweeten many beverages and

     b. may be associated with weight gain.

   5. Good health is promoted by

     a. a diverse diet of proteins, fats, vitamins, minerals, and complex carbohydrates and

     b. exercise.

D. 3.7 Polysaccharides are long chains of sugar units

   1. Polysaccharides are

     a. macromolecules and

     b. polymers composed of thousands of monosaccharides.

   2. Polysaccharides may function as

     a. storage molecules or

     b. as structural compounds.

   3. Starch is

     a. a polysaccharide,

     b. composed of glucose monomers, and

     c. used by plants for energy storage.

   4. Glycogen is

     a. a polysaccharide,

     b. composed of glucose monomers, and

     c. used by animals for energy storage.

   5. Cellulose

     a. is a polymer of glucose and

     b. forms plant cell walls.

   6. Chitin is

     a. a polysaccharide and

     b. used by insects and crustaceans to build an exoskeleton.

   7. Polysaccharides are usually hydrophilic (water-loving).

   8. Bath towels are

     a. often made of cotton, which is mostly cellulose, and

     b. water absorbent.

IV. Lipids

A. 3.8 Fats are lipids that are mostly energy-storage molecules

   1. Lipids

     a. are water insoluble (**hydrophobic**, or water-fearing) compounds,

     b. are important in long-term energy storage,

     c. contain twice as much energy as a polysaccharide, and

     d. consist mainly of carbon and hydrogen atoms linked by nonpolar covalent bonds.

   2. Lipids differ from carbohydrates, proteins, and nucleic acids in that they are

     a. not huge molecules and

     b. not built from monomers.

3. Lipids vary a great deal in
    a. structure and
    b. function.
4. We will consider three types of lipids:
    a. fats,
    b. phospholipids, and
    c. steroids.
5. A **fat** is a large lipid made from two kinds of smaller molecules,
    a. glycerol and
    b. fatty acids.
6. A fatty acid can link to glycerol by a dehydration reaction.
    a. A fat contains one glycerol linked to three fatty acids.
    b. Fats are often called triglycerides because of their structure.
7. Some fatty acids contain one or more double bonds, forming **unsaturated fatty acids** that
    a. have one fewer hydrogen atom on each carbon of the double bond,
    b. cause kinks or bends in the carbon chain, and
    c. prevent them from packing together tightly and solidifying at room temperature.
8. Fats with the maximum number of hydrogens are called **saturated fatty acids**.
9. Unsaturated fats include corn and olive oils.
10. Most animal fats are saturated fats.
11. Hydrogenated vegetable oils are unsaturated fats that have been converted to saturated fats by adding hydrogen.
12. This hydrogenation creates **trans fats** associated with health risks.

B. 3.9 Phospholipids and steroids are important lipids with a variety of functions
   1. **Phospholipids** are
       a. structurally similar to fats and
       b. the major component of all cells.
   2. Phospholipids are structurally similar to fats.
       a. Fats contain three fatty acids attached to glycerol.
       b. Phospholipids contain two fatty acids attached to glycerol.
   3. Phospholipids cluster into a bilayer of phospholipids.
   4. The hydrophilic heads are in contact with
       a. the water of the environment and
       b. the internal part of the cell.
   5. The hydrophobic tails band in the center of the bilayer.
   6. **Steroids** are lipids in which the carbon skeleton contains four fused rings.
   7. **Cholesterol** is a
       a. common component in animal cell membranes and
       b. starting material for making steroids, including sex hormones.

C. 3.10 CONNECTION: Anabolic steroids pose health risks
   1. **Anabolic steroids**
       a. are synthetic variants of testosterone,
       b. can cause a buildup of muscle and bone mass, and
       c. are often prescribed to treat general anemia and some diseases that destroy body muscle.

2. Anabolic steroids are abused by some athletes with serious consequences, including
   a. violent mood swings,
   b. depression,
   c. liver damage,
   d. cancer,
   e. high cholesterol, and
   f. high blood pressure.

V. Proteins

A. 3.11 Proteins are made from amino acids linked by peptide bonds
   1. Proteins are
      a. involved in nearly every dynamic function in your body and
      b. very diverse, with ten of thousands of different proteins, each with a specific structure and function, in the human body.
   2. Proteins are composed of differing arrangements of a common set of just 20 amino acid monomers.
   3. **Amino acids** have
      a. an amino group and
      b. a carboxyl group (which makes it an acid).
   4. Also bonded to the central carbon is
      a. a hydrogen atom and
      b. a chemical group symbolized by R, which determines the specific properties of each of the 20 amino acids used to make proteins.
   5. Amino acids are classified as either
      a. hydrophobic or
      b. hydrophilic.
   6. Amino acid monomers are linked together
      a. in a dehydration reaction,
      b. joining carboxyl group of one amino acid to the amino group of the next amino acid, and
      c. creating a **peptide bond**.
   7. Additional amino acids can be added by the same process to create a chain of amino acids called a **polypeptide**.
B. 3.12 A protein's specific shape determines its function
   1. Probably the most important role for proteins is as **enzymes**, proteins that
      a. serve as metabolic catalysts and
      b. regulate the chemical reactions within cells.
   2. Other proteins are also important.
      a. **Structural** proteins provide associations between body parts.
      b. **Contractile** proteins are found within muscle.
      c. **Defensive** proteins include antibodies of the immune system.
      d. **Signal** proteins are best exemplified by hormones and other chemical messengers.
      e. **Receptor** proteins transmit signals into cells.
      f. **Transport** proteins carry oxygen.
      g. **Storage** proteins serve as a source of amino acids for developing embryos.
   3. A polypeptide chain contains of hundreds or thousands of amino acids linked by peptide bonds.
   4. The amino acid sequence causes the polypeptide to assume a particular shape.

5. The shape of a protein determines its specific function.

6. If a protein's shape is altered, it can no longer function.

7. In the process of **denaturation**, a polypeptide chain

    a. unravels,

    b. loses its shape, and

    c. loses its function.

8. Proteins can be denatured by changes in salt concentration, pH, or by high heat.

C. 3.13 A protein's shape depends on four levels of structure

1. A protein can have four levels of structure:

    a. primary structure

    b. secondary structure

    c. tertiary structure

    d. quaternary structure

2. The **primary structure** of a protein is its unique amino acid sequence.

    a. The correct amino acid sequence is determined by the cell's genetic information.

    b. The slightest change in this sequence may affect the protein's ability to function.

3. Protein **secondary structure** results from coiling or folding of the polypeptide.

    a. Coiling results in a helical structure called an alpha helix.

    b. A certain kind of folding leads to a structure called a pleated sheet, which dominates some fibrous proteins such as those used in spider webs.

    c. Coiling and folding are maintained by regularly spaced hydrogen bonds between hydrogen atoms and oxygen atoms along the backbone of the polypeptide chain.

4. The overall three-dimensional shape of a polypeptide is called its **tertiary structure**.

    a. Tertiary structure generally results from interactions between the R groups of the various amino acids.

    b. Disulfide bridges may further strengthen the protein's shape.

5. Two or more polypeptide chains (subunits) associate providing **quaternary structure**.

    a. Collagen is an example of a protein with quaternary structure.

    b. Collagen's triple helix gives great strength to connective tissue, bone, tendons, and ligaments.

VI. Nucleic Acids

A. 3.14 DNA and RNA are the two types of nucleic acids

1. The amino acid sequence of a polypeptide is programmed by a discrete unit of inheritance known as a **gene**.

2. Genes consist of **DNA** (**<u>d</u>eoxyribo<u>n</u>ucleic <u>a</u>cid**), a type of **nucleic acid**.

3. DNA is inherited from an organism's parents.

4. DNA provides directions for its own replication.

5. DNA programs a cell's activities by directing the synthesis of proteins.

6. DNA does not build proteins directly.

7. DNA works through an intermediary, **<u>r</u>ibo<u>n</u>ucleic <u>a</u>cid** (**RNA**).

    a. DNA is transcribed into RNA.

    b. RNA is translated into proteins.

B. 3.15 Nucleic acids are polymers of nucleotides

1. **DNA (deoxyribonucleic acid)** and **RNA (ribonucleic acid)** are composed of monomers called **nucleotides**.

2. Nucleotides have three parts:
   a. a five-carbon sugar called ribose in RNA and deoxyribose in DNA,
   b. a phosphate group, and
   c. a nitrogenous base.
3. DNA nitrogenous bases are
   a. adenine (A),
   b. thymine (T),
   c. cytosine (C), and
   d. guanine (G).
4. RNA
   a. also has A, C, and G,
   b. but instead of T, it has uracil (U).
5. A nucleic acid polymer, a polynucleotide, forms
   a. from the nucleotide monomers,
   b. when the phosphate of one nucleotide bonds to the sugar of the next nucleotide,
   c. by dehydration reactions, and
   d. by producing a repeating sugar-phosphate backbone with protruding nitrogenous bases.
6. Two polynucleotide strands wrap around each other to form a DNA **double helix**.
   a. The two strands are associated because particular bases always hydrogen bond to one another.
   b. A pairs with T, and C pairs with G, producing **base pairs**.
7. RNA is usually a single polynucleotide strand.

C. 3.16 EVOLUTION CONNECTION: Lactose tolerance is a recent event in human evolution
1. The majority of people
   a. stop producing the enzyme lactase in early childhood and
   b. do not easily digest the milk sugar lactose.
2. Lactose tolerance represents a
   a. relatively recent mutation in the human genome and
   b. survival advantage for human cultures with milk and dairy products available year-round.
3. Researchers identified three mutations that keep the lactase gene permanently turned on.
4. The mutations appear to have occurred
   a. about 7,000 years ago and
   b. at the same time as the domestication of cattle in these regions.

Chapter Guide to Teaching Resources

Introduction to Organic Compounds (3.1–3.3)

Student Misconceptions and Concerns

- General biology students might not have previously taken a chemistry course. The concept of molecular building blocks that cannot be seen can be abstract and difficult to comprehend for such students. Concrete examples from our diets and good images will increase comprehension. (3.1–3.3)

- Students might need to be reminded about the levels of biological organization. The relationship between atoms, monomers, and polymers can be confusing as each is discussed. Consider noting these relationships somewhere in the classroom (such as on the board) where students can quickly glance for reassurance. (3.1)

Teaching Tips

- One of the great advantages of carbon is its ability to form up to four bonds, permitting the assembly of diverse components and branching configurations. Challenge your students to find another element that might also permit this sort of adaptability. (Like carbon, silicon has four electrons in its outer shell.) (3.1)

- Toothpicks and gumdrops (or any other pliable small candy) permit the quick construction of chemical models. Different candy colors can represent certain atoms. The model of the methane molecule in Figure 3.1 can thus easily be demonstrated (and consumed)! (3.1)

- A drill with interchangeable drill bits is a nice analogy to carbon skeletons with different functional groups. The analogy relates the role of different functions to different structures. (3.2)

- Train cars linking together to form a train is a nice analogy to linking monomers to form polymers. Consider adding that as the train cars are joined, a puff of steam appears—a reference to water production and a dehydration reaction when linking molecular monomers. (3.3)

- The authors note that the great diversity of polymers mainly results from variable arrangements of monomers, with different sequences possible by combinations or permutations of the same monomers. Consider illustrating this by simply asking students how many different ways can we arrange the letters A, B, and C, using each letter, and only once, to form 3 lettered words. The answer is 6 permutations: ABC, ACB, BAC, BCA, CBA, CAB (the factorial of 3). And if letters can be repeated, the answer is 27 (= 3^3): AAA, BBB, CCC, ABB, ACC, etc. (3.3)

Carbohydrates (3.4–3.7)

Student Misconceptions and Concerns

- The abstract nature of chemistry can be discouraging to many students. Consider starting out this section of lecture by examining the chemical groups on a food nutrition label. Candy bars with peanuts are particularly useful, as they contain significant amounts of all three sources of calories (carbohydrates, proteins, and lipids). (3.4)

- Consider reinforcing the three main sources of calories with food items that clearly represent each group. Bring clear examples to class as visual references. For example, a can of Coke or a bag of sugar (or cotton candy) for carbohydrates, a tub of margarine for lipids, and some beef jerky for protein (although some fat and carbohydrates might also be included). (3.4–3.7)

Teaching Tips

- If your lectures will eventually include details of glycolysis and aerobic respiration, this is a good point to introduce the basic concepts of glucose as fuel. Just introducing this conceptual formula might help: eating glucose and breathing oxygen produces water and usable energy (used to build ATP) plus heat and carbon dioxide exhaled in our breath. (3.4)

- Learning the definitions of word roots is invaluable when learning science. Learning the meaning of the prefix word roots "mono" (one), "di" (two), and "poly" (many) helps to distinguish the structures of various carbohydrates. (3.5)

- The widespread use of high-fructose corn syrup can be surprising to students. Consider asking each student to bring to class a product label that indicates the use of high-fructose corn syrup (HFCS) as an ingredient. (3.6)

- Consider an assignment for students to access the Internet and find reliable sources that discuss high rates of sugar consumption in the modern diet. The key, of course, is in the quality of the resource. Consider limiting their search to established nonprofit organizations (American Cancer Society, American Heart Association, etc.) and peer-reviewed journals. (3.6)

- A simple exercise demonstrates the enzymatic breakdown of starches into sugars. If students place an unsalted cracker in their mouths, holding it in their mouths while it mixes well with saliva, they might soon notice that a sweeter taste begins to emerge. The salivary enzyme amylase begins the digestion of starches into disaccharides, which may be degraded further by other enzymes. These disaccharides are the source of the sweet taste. (3.7)

- The text notes that cellulose is the most abundant organic molecule on Earth. Ask your students why this is true. (3.7)

- The cellophane wrap often used to package foods is a biodegradable material derived from cellulose. Consider challenging students to create a list of other cellulose-derived products (such as paper). (3.7)

- An adult human may store about a half of a kilogram of glycogen in the liver and muscles of the body, depending upon recent dietary habits. A person who begins dieting might soon notice an immediate weight loss of 2–4 pounds (1–2 kilograms) over several days, reflecting reductions in stored glycogen, water, and intestinal contents (among other factors). (3.7)

Lipids (3.8–3.10)

Student Misconceptions and Concerns

- Students may struggle with the concept that a pound of fat contains more than twice the calories of a pound of sugar. It might seem that a pound of food would potentially add on a pound of weight. Other students may have never understood the concept of calories in the diet, simply following general guidelines of avoiding fatty foods. Furthermore, fiber and water have no caloric value but add to the weight of food. Consider class discussions that explore student misconceptions about calories, body weight, and healthy diets. (3.8)

- Students might struggle to extrapolate the properties of lipids to their roles in an organism. Ducks float because their feathers repel water instead of attracting it. Hair on our heads remains flexible because of oils produced in our scalp. Examples such as these help connect the abstract properties of lipids to concrete examples in our world. (3.8–3.10)

Teaching Tips

- The text in Module 3.8 notes the common observation that vinegar and oil do not mix in this type of salad dressing. A simple demonstration can help make this point. In front of the class, mix together colored water and a yellow oil (corn or canola oil work well). Shake up the mixture and then watch as the two separate. (You may have a mixture already made ahead of time that remains separated; however, the dye may bleed between the oil and the water.) Placing the mixture on an overhead projector or other well-illuminated imaging device makes for a dramatic display of hydrophobic activity! (3.8)

- The text notes that a gram of fat stores more than twice the energy of a gram of polysaccharide, such as starch. You might elaborate with a simple calculation to demonstrate how a person's body weight would vary if the energy stored in body fat were stored in carbohydrates instead. If a 100-kg man carried 25% body fat, he would have 25 kg of fat in his body. Fat stores about 2.25 times more energy per gram than carbohydrate. What would be the weight of the man if he stored the energy in the fat in the form of carbohydrate? ($2.25 \times 25 = 56.25$ kg of carbohydrate + 75 kg (nonfat body weight) = 131.25 kg, an increase of 31.25%). (3.8)

- Margarine in stores commonly comes in liquid spray or squeeze containers, in tubs, and in sticks. These forms reflect increasing amounts of hydrogenation, gradually increasing the stiffness from a liquid, to a firmer spread, to a firm stick of margarine. As noted in the text, recent studies have suggested that unsaturated oils become increasingly unhealthy as they are hydrogenated. Students might therefore remember that as margarine products increase in stiffness, they generally become less healthy. Public attention to hydrogenation and the health risks of the resulting trans fats are causing changes in the use of products containing trans fats. (3.8)

- Before explaining the properties of a polar molecule such as a phospholipid, have students predict the consequences of adding phospholipids to water. See if the class can generate the two most common configurations: (1) a lipid bilayer encircling water (water surrounding the bilayer and water contained internally) and (2) a micelle (polar heads in contact with water and hydrophobic tails clustered centrally). (3.9)

- The consequences of steroid abuse will likely be of great interest to your students. However, the reasons for the damaging consequences might not be immediately clear. As time permits, consider noting the diverse homeostatic mechanisms that normally regulate the traits affected by steroid abuse. (3.10)

Proteins (3.11–3.13)

Student Misconceptions and Concerns

- The functional significance of protein shape is an abstract molecular example of form and function relationships, which might be new to some students. The binding of an enzyme to its substrate is a type of molecular handshake, which permits specific interactions. To help students think about form and function relationships, share some concrete analogies in their lives—perhaps flathead and Phillips screwdrivers that match the proper type of screws or the fit of a hand into a glove. (3.12)

Teaching Tips

- Many analogies help students appreciate the diversity of proteins that can be made from just 20 amino acids. The authors note that our language uses combinations of 26 letters to form words. Proteins are much longer "words," creating even more diversity. Another analogy is to trains. This builds upon the earlier analogy when polymers were introduced. Imagine making different trains about 100 cars long, using any combination of 20 types of railroad cars. Mathematically, the number of possible trains is 20^{100}, a number beyond imagination. (3.11)

- The authors note that the difference between a polypeptide and a protein is analogous to the relationship between a long strand of yarn and a sweater knitted from yarn. Proteins are clearly more complex! (3.11)

- Most cooking results in changes in the texture and color of food. The brown color of a cooked steak is the product of the denaturation of proteins. Fixatives such as formalin also denature proteins and cause color changes. Students who have dissected vertebrates will realize that the brown color of the muscles makes it look as if the animal has been cooked. (3.12)

- An examination of the fabrics and weave of a sweater might help students understand the levels of protein structure. Although not a perfect analogy, levels of organization can be better appreciated. Teasing apart a single thread reveals a simpler organization of smaller fibers woven together. In turn, threads are interlaced into a connected fabric, which may be further twisted and organized into a pattern or structural component of a sleeve. Challenge students to identify the limits of this analogy and identify aspects of protein structure not included (such as the primary structure of a protein, its sequence of amino acids). (3.13)

Nucleic Acids (3.14–3.16)

Student Misconceptions and Concerns

- Module 3.14 is the first time the authors present the concept of transcription and translation, discussed extensively in later chapters. The basic conceptual flow of information from DNA to RNA to proteins is essential to these later discussions. (3.14)

- The evolution of lactose tolerance within human groups in East Africa does not represent a deliberate decision, yet this evolutionary change appears logical. Many students perceive adaptations as deliberate events with purpose. As students develop a better understanding of the mechanisms of evolution, it will be important to point out that mutations arise by chance, with the culling hand of natural selection favoring traits that convey an advantage. Organisms cannot plan evolutionary change. (3.16)

Teaching Tips

- The "NA" in the acronyms DNA and RNA stands for "nucleic acid." Students often do not make this association without assistance. (3.14)

- When discussing the sequence of nucleotides in DNA and RNA, consider challenging your students with the following questions based upon prior analogies. If the 20 possible amino acids in a polypeptide represent "words" in a long polypeptide sentence, how many possible words are in the language of a DNA molecule? (Answer: Four nucleotides, GCAT, are possible). Are these the same "words" used in RNA? (Answer: No. Uracil substitutes for thymine.) (3.15)

- The research revealing the separate evolution of lactose tolerance into human adulthood in several parts of the world provide another opportunity to help students understand the process of natural selection. Consider using this example to walk students through the steps of this evolutionary change. Help students to understand that people did not choose to be lactose tolerant as adults. Instead, the environment of nutritious dairy products created an adaptive advantage for those people fortunate enough to possess the lactose tolerant mutation. (3.16)

Key Terms

amino acid
amino group
anabolic steroid
carbohydrate
carbon skeleton
carbonyl group
carboxyl group
cellulose
chitin
cholesterol
dehydration reaction
denaturation
deoxyribonucleic acid (DNA)
disaccharide
double helix
enzyme
fat

functional group
gene
glycogen
hydrocarbon
hydrolysis
hydrophilic
hydrophobic
hydroxyl group
isomers
lipid
macromolecule
methyl group
monomer
monosaccharide
nucleic acid
nucleotide
organic compound
peptide bond

phosphate group
phospholipid
polymer
polypeptide
polysaccharide
primary structure
protein
quaternary structure
ribonucleic acid (RNA)
saturated fatty acid
secondary structure
starch
steroid
tertiary structure
trans fat
unsaturated fatty acid

Word Roots

de- = without or remove; **hydro-** = water (*dehydration reaction*: a chemical process in which two molecules become covalently bonded to each other with the removal of a water molecule)

di- = two; **-sacchar** = sugar (*disaccharide*: a sugar molecule consisting of two monosaccharides linked by a dehydration reaction)

carb- = coal (*carboxyl group*: a functional group in an organic molecule, consisting of an oxygen atom double-bonded to a carbon atom that is also bonded to a hydroxyl group)

glyco- = sweet (*glycogen*: an extensively branched polysaccharide of many glucose monomers that serves as an energy-storage molecule in animal liver and muscle cells)

hydro- = water (*hydrocarbon*: a chemical compound composed only of the elements carbon and hydrogen)

iso- = equal (*isomer*: one of several organic compounds with the same molecular formula but different structures and, therefore, different properties)

-lyse = break (*hydrolysis*: a chemical process in which polymers are broken down by the chemical addition of water molecules to the bonds linking their monomers)

macro- = large (*macromolecule*: a giant molecule in a living organism formed by the joining of smaller molecules)

mono- = single; **-mer** = part (*monomer*: a chemical subunit that serves as a building block of a polymer)

-philos = loving (*hydrophilic*: "water-loving": refers to polar, or charged, molecules [or parts of molecules] that are soluble in water)

-phobos = fearing (*hydrophobic*: "water-fearing": refers to nonpolar molecules [or parts of molecules] that do not dissolve in water)

poly- = many (*polymer*: a large molecule consisting of many monomers covalently joined together in a chain; polysaccharide: many monosaccharides joined together)

quatr- = four (*quaternary structure*: the fourth level of protein structure; the shape resulting from the association of two or more polypeptide subunits)

terti- = three (*tertiary structure*: the third level of protein structure; the overall, three-dimensional shape of a polypeptide due to interactions of the R groups of the amino acids making up the chain)

CHAPTER 4

A Tour of the Cell

Chapter Objectives

Opening Essay

Explain what is unique about the cellular level of biological organization.

Introduction to the Cell

4.1   Compare the designs of and images produced by a light microscope, a scanning electron microscope, and a transmission electron microscope. Distinguish between magnification and resolving power.

4.1   Describe the two parts of cell theory.

4.2   Explain why there are upper and lower limits to cell size.

4.2   Describe the hydrophobic and hydrophilic components of a plasma membrane and relate these regions to the functions of the plasma membrane.

4.3   Distinguish between the structures of prokaryotic and eukaryotic cells.

4.4   Explain why compartmentalization is important in eukaryotic cells.

4.4   Compare the structures of plant and animal cells. Note the function of each cell part.

4.4   Describe the structures and functions of the four compartments of eukaryotic cells.

The Nucleus and Ribosomes

4.5   Describe the structure and functions of the nucleus and nucleolus. Explain how DNA is packaged inside of the nucleus.

4.6   Describe the functions of ribosomes. Explain why some ribosomes are free in the fluid of the cytoplasm while others are bound to the endoplasmic reticulum or nuclear envelope.

The Endomembrane System

4.7–4.12   Describe the structures and functions of the components of the endomembrane system, including smooth and rough endoplasmic reticulum, Golgi apparatus, lysosomes, vacuoles, and peroxisomes.

Energy-Converting Organelles 4.13–4.15

4.13–4.14   Compare the structures and functions of chloroplasts and mitochondria.

4.15   Describe the evidence that suggests that mitochondria and chloroplasts evolved by endosymbiosis.

The Cytoskeleton and Cell Surfaces 4.16–4.22

4.16 Compare the structures and functions of microfilaments, intermediate filaments, and microtubules.

4.17 Relate the structure of cilia and flagella to their functions.

4.18 Describe examples of environmental and genetic causes of infertility in men.

4.19 Relate the structure of the extracellular matrix to its functions.

4.20 Compare the structures and functions of tight junctions, anchoring junctions, and gap junctions.

4.21 Relate the structures of plant cell walls and plasmodesmata to their functions.

4.22 Describe the four functional categories of organelles in eukaryotic cells.

4.22 Describe the fundamental features of all organisms.

Lecture Outline

I. Introduction

A. Cells are the simplest collection of matter that can live.

B. Cells were first observed by Robert Hooke in 1665.

C. Working with more refined lenses, Antoni van Leeuwenhoek later described

  1. blood,

  2. sperm, and

  3. organisms living in pond water.

D. Since the days of Hooke and Leeuwenhoek, improved microscopes have vastly expanded our view of the cell.

II. Introduction to the Cell

A. 4.1 Microscopes reveal the world of the cell

  1. A variety of microscopes have been developed for a clearer view of cells and cellular structure.

  2. The most frequently used microscope is the **light microscope** (**LM**)—like the one used in biology laboratories.

    a. Light passes through a specimen, then through glass lenses, and finally light is projected into the viewer's eye.

    b. Specimens can be magnified up to 1,000 times the actual size of the specimen.

  3. *Magnification* is the increase in the apparent size of an object.

  4. *Resolution* is a measure of the clarity of an image. In other words, it is the ability of an instrument to show two close objects as separate.

  5. Microscopes have limitations.

    a. The human eye and the microscope have limits of resolution—the ability to distinguish between small structures.

    b. Therefore, the light microscope cannot provide the details of a small cell's structure.

  6. Using light microscopes, scientists studied

    a. microorganisms,

    b. animal and plant cells, and

    c. some structures within cells.

7. In the 1800s, these studies led to **cell theory**, which states that
   a. all living things are composed of cells and
   b. all cells come from other cells.
8. Beginning in the 1950s, scientists started using a very powerful microscope called the **electron microscope** (**EM**) to view the ultrastructure of cells.
   a. Instead of light, EM uses a beam of electrons.
9. Electron microscopes can
   a. resolve biological structures as small as 2 nanometers and
   b. magnify up to 100,000 times.
10. **Scanning electron microscopes (SEM)** study the detailed architecture of cell surfaces.
11. **Transmission electron microscopes (TEM)** study the details of internal cell structure.
12. Differential interference light microscopes amplify differences in density so that structures in living cells appear almost three-dimensional.

B. 4.2 The small size of cells relates to the need to exchange materials across the plasma membrane
   1. Cell size must
      a. be large enough to house DNA, proteins, and structures needed to survive and reproduce, but
      b. remain small enough to allow for a surface-to-volume ratio that will allow adequate exchange with the environment.
   2. The **plasma membrane** forms a flexible boundary between the living cell and its surroundings.
   3. Phospholipids form a two-layer sheet called a phospholipid bilayer in which
      a. hydrophilic heads face outward, exposed to water, and
      b. hydrophobic tails point inward, shielded from water.
   4. Membrane proteins are either
      a. attached to the membrane surface or
      b. embedded in the phospholipid bilayer.
   5. Some proteins form channels or tunnels that shield ions and other hydrophilic molecules as they pass through the hydrophobic center of the membrane.
   6. Other proteins serve as pumps, using energy to actively transport molecules into or out of the cell.

C. 4.3 Prokaryotic cells are structurally simpler than eukaryotic cells
   1. Bacteria and archaea are **prokaryotic** cells.
   2. All other forms of life are composed of **eukaryotic** cells.
      a. Prokaryotic and eukaryotic cells have
         i. a plasma membrane and
         ii. one or more chromosomes and ribosomes.
      b. Eukaryotic cells have a
         i. membrane-bound nucleus and
         ii. number of other organelles.
      c. Prokaryotes have a nucleoid and no true organelles.
   3. The DNA of prokaryotic cells is coiled into a region called the **nucleoid**, but no membrane surrounds the DNA.

4. The surface of prokaryotic cells may

    a. be surrounded by a chemically complex cell wall,

    b. have a capsule surrounding the cell wall,

    c. have short projections that help attach to other cells or the substrate, or

    d. have longer projections called **flagella** that may propel the cell through its liquid environment.

D. 4.4 Eukaryotic cells are partitioned into functional compartments

    1. The structures and organelles of eukaryotic cells perform four basic functions.

        a. The nucleus and ribosomes are involved in the genetic control of the cell.

        b. The endoplasmic reticulum, Golgi apparatus, lysosomes, vacuoles, and peroxisomes are involved in the manufacture, distribution, and breakdown of molecules.

        c. Mitochondria in all cells and chloroplasts in plant cells are involved in energy processing.

        d. Structural support, movement, and communication between cells are functions of the cytoskeleton, plasma membrane, and cell wall.

    2. The internal membranes of eukaryotic cells partition it into compartments.

    3. Cellular metabolism, the many chemical activities of cells, occurs within organelles.

    4. Almost all of the organelles and other structures of animals cells are present in plant cells.

    5. A few exceptions exist.

        a. Lysosomes and centrioles are not found in plant cells.

        b. Plant but not animal cells have

            i. a rigid cell wall,

            ii. chloroplasts, and

            iii. a central vacuole.

III. The Nucleus and Ribosomes

    A. 4.5 The nucleus is the cell's genetic control center

        1. The **nucleus**

            a. contains most of the cell's DNA and

            b. controls the cell's activities by directing protein synthesis by making messenger RNA (mRNA).

        2. DNA is associated with many proteins in structures called **chromosomes**.

        3. The **nuclear envelope**

            a. is a double membrane and

            b. has pores that allow material to flow in and out of the nucleus.

        4. The nuclear envelope is attached to a network of cellular membranes called the endoplasmic reticulum.

        5. The **nucleolus** is

            a. a prominent structure in the nucleus and

            b. the site of ribosomal RNA (rRNA) synthesis.

    B. 4.6 Ribosomes make proteins for use in the cell and export

        1. Ribosomes are involved in the cell's protein synthesis.

            a. Ribosomes are synthesized from rRNA produced in the nucleolus.

            b. Cells that must synthesize large amounts of protein have a large number of ribosomes.

2. Some ribosomes are free ribosomes; others are bound.

   a. *Free ribosomes* are

      i. suspended in the cytoplasm and

      ii. typically involved in making proteins that function within the cytoplasm.

   b. *Bound ribosomes* are

      i. attached to the endoplasmic reticulum (ER) associated with the nuclear envelope and

      ii. associated with proteins packed in certain organelles or exported from the cell.

IV. The Endomembrane System

A. 4.7 Overview: Many cell organelles are connected through the endomembrane system

   1. Many of the membranes within a eukaryotic cell are part of the **endomembrane system**.

   2. Some of these membranes are physically connected and some are related by the transfer of membrane segments by tiny **vesicles** (sacs made of membrane).

   3. Many of these organelles work together in the

      a. synthesis,

      b. storage, and

      c. export of molecules.

   4. The **endomembrane system** includes

      a. the nuclear envelope,

      b. endoplasmic reticulum (ER),

      c. Golgi apparatus,

      d. lysosomes,

      e. vacuoles, and

      f. the plasma membrane.

B. 4.8 The endoplasmic reticulum is a biosynthetic factory

   1. There are two kinds of endoplasmic reticulum—smooth and rough.

      a. **Smooth ER** lacks attached ribosomes.

      b. **Rough ER** lines the outer surface of membranes.

      c. Although physically interconnected, smooth and rough ER differ in structure and function.

   2. Smooth ER is involved in a variety of diverse metabolic processes.

      a. Smooth ER produces enzymes important in the synthesis of lipids, oils, phospholipids, and steroids.

      b. Other enzymes help process drugs, alcohol, and other potentially harmful substances.

      c. Some smooth ER helps store calcium ions.

   3. Rough ER makes

      a. additional membrane for itself and

      b. proteins destined for secretions.

C. 4.9 The Golgi apparatus finishes, sorts, and ships cell products

   1. The Golgi apparatus serves as a molecular warehouse and finishing factory for products manufactured by the ER.

      a. Products travel in transport vesicles from the ER to the Golgi apparatus.

      b. One side of the Golgi apparatus functions as a receiving dock for the product and the other as a shipping dock.

      c. Products are modified as they go from one side of the Golgi apparatus to the other and travel in vesicles to other sites.

D. 4.10 Lysosomes are digestive compartments within a cell

1. A **lysosome** is a membranous sac containing digestive enzymes.
    a. The enzymes and membrane are produced by the ER and transferred to the Golgi apparatus for processing.
    b. The membrane serves to safely isolate these potent enzymes from the rest of the cell.
2. Lysosomes help digest food particles engulfed by a cell.
    a. A food vacuole binds with a lysosome.
    b. The enzymes in the lysosome digest the food.
    c. The nutrients are then released into the cell.
3. Lysosomes also help remove or recycle damaged parts of a cell.
    a. The damaged organelle is first enclosed in a membrane vesicle.
    b. Then a lysosome
        i.   fuses with the vesicle,
        ii. dismantles its contents, and
        iii. breaks down the damaged organelle.

E. 4.11 Vacuoles function in the general maintenance of the cell

1. **Vacuoles** are large vesicles that have a variety of functions.
    a. Some protists have contractile vacuoles that help to eliminate water from the protist.
    b. In plants, vacuoles may
        i.   have digestive functions,
        ii. contain pigments, or
        iii. contain poisons that protect the plant.

F. 4.12 A review of the structures involved in manufacturing and breakdown

V. Energy-Converting Organelles

A. 4.13 Mitochondria harvest chemical energy from food

1. **Mitochondria** are organelles that carry out cellular respiration in nearly all eukaryotic cells.
2. Cellular respiration converts the chemical energy in foods to chemical energy in **ATP** (adenosine triphosphate).
3. Mitochondria have two internal compartments.
    a. The intermembrane space is the narrow region between the inner and outer membranes.
    b. The **mitochondrial matrix** contains
        i.   the mitochondrial DNA,
        ii. ribosomes, and
        iii. many enzymes that catalyze some of the reactions of cellular respiration.

B. 4.14 Chloroplasts convert solar energy to chemical energy

1. **Chloroplasts** are the photosynthesizing organelles of all photosynthesizing eukaryotes.
2. Photosynthesis is the conversion of light energy from the sun to the chemical energy of sugar molecules.
3. Chloroplasts are partitioned into compartments.
    a. Between the outer and inner membrane is a thin intermembrane space.

    b. Inside the inner membrane is

        i. a thick fluid called **stroma** that contains the chloroplast DNA, ribosomes, and many enzymes; and

        ii. a network of interconnected sacs called **thylakoids**.

        iii. In some regions, thylakoids are stacked like poker chips. Each stack is called a **granum**, where green chlorophyll molecules trap solar energy.

C. 4.15 EVOLUTION CONNECTION: Mitochondria and chloroplasts evolved by endosymbiosis

    1. Mitochondria and chloroplasts have

        a. DNA and

        b. ribosomes.

    2. The structure of this DNA and these ribosomes is very similar to that found in prokaryotic cells.

    3. The **endosymbiont theory** proposes that

        a. mitochondria and chloroplasts were formerly small prokaryotes and

        b. they began living within larger cells.

VI. The Cytoskeleton and Cell Surfaces

A. 4.16 The cell's internal skeleton helps organize its structure and activities

    1. Cells contain a network of protein fibers, called the **cytoskeleton**, which functions in structural support and motility.

    2. Scientists believe that motility and cellular regulation result when the cytoskeleton interacts with proteins called motor proteins.

    3. The cytoskeleton is composed of three kinds of fibers.

        a. Microfilaments (actin filaments) support the cell's shape and are involved in motility.

        b. Intermediate filaments reinforce cell shape and anchor organelles.

        c. Microtubules (made of tubulin) give the cell rigidity and act as tracks for organelle movement.

B. 4.17 Cilia and flagella move when microtubules bend

    1. While some protists have flagella and **cilia** that are important in locomotion, some cells of multicellular organisms have them for different reasons.

        a. Cells that sweep mucus out of our lungs have cilia.

        b. Animal sperm are flagellated.

    2. A flagellum, longer than cilia, propels a cell by an undulating, whiplike motion.

    3. Cilia work more like the oars of a crew boat.

    4. Although differences exist, flagella and cilia have a common structure and mechanism of movement.

    5. Both flagella and cilia are made of microtubules wrapped in an extension of the plasma membrane.

    6. A ring of nine microtubule doublets surrounds a central pair of microtubules. This arrangement is

        a. called the 9 + 2 pattern and

        b. anchored in a basal body with nine microtubule triplets arranged in a ring.

7. Cilia and flagella move by bending motor proteins called dynein feet.

    a. These feet attach to and exert a sliding force on an adjacent doublet.

    b. The arms then release and reattach a little further along and repeat this time after time.

    c. This "walking" causes the microtubules to bend.

C. 4.18 CONNECTION: Problems with sperm motility may be environmental or genetic

    1. In developed countries over the last 50 years, there has been a decline in sperm quality.

    2. The causes of this decline may be

        a. environmental chemicals or

        b. genetic disorders that interfere with the movement of sperm and cilia. Primary ciliary dyskinesia (PCD) is a rare disease characterized by recurrent infections of the respiratory tract and immotile sperm.

D. 4.19 The extracellular matrix of animal cells functions in support and regulation

    1. Animal cells synthesize and secrete an elaborate **extracellular matrix (ECM)** that

        a. helps hold cells together in tissues and

        b. protects and supports the plasma membrane.

    2. The ECM may attach to a cell through glycoproteins that then bind to membrane proteins called **integrins**. Integrins span the plasma membrane and connect to microfilaments of the cytoskeleton.

E. 4.20 Three types of cell junctions are found in animal tissues

    1. Adjacent cells communicate, interact, and adhere through specialized junctions between them.

        a. **Tight junctions** prevent leakage of extracellular fluid across a layer of epithelial cells.

        b. **Anchoring junctions** fasten cells together into sheets.

        c. **Gap junctions** are channels that allow molecules to flow between cells.

F. 4.21 Cell walls enclose and support plant cells

    1. A plant cell, but not an animal cell, has a rigid **cell wall** that

        a. protects and provides skeletal support that helps keep the plant upright against gravity and

        b. is primarily composed of cellulose.

    2. Plant cells have cell junctions called **plasmodesmata** that serve in communication between cells.

G. 4.22 Review: Eukaryotic cell structures can be grouped on the basis of four basic functions

    1. Eukaryotic cell structures can be grouped on the basis of four functions:

        a. genetic control,

        b. manufacturing, distribution, and breakdown,

        c. energy processing, and

        d. structural support, movement, and communication between cells.

Chapter Guide to Teaching Resources

Introduction to the Cell (4.1–4.4)

Student Misconceptions and Concerns

- Students can easily feel overwhelmed by the large numbers of structures and related functions in this chapter. For such students, Module 4.22 might be the best place to start when approaching this chapter. Students might best comprehend the content in Chapter 4 by reviewing the categories of organelles and related functions in Table 4.22 and referring to it regularly as the chapter is studied and/or discussed. (4.1–4.4)

- Students typically cannot distinguish between the concepts of resolution and magnification. However, pixels and resolution of digital images can help clarify the distinction. Consider printing the same image at high and low resolution and enlarging the same image at two different levels of resolution. The second Teaching Tip that follows suggests another related exercise. (4.1)

- Students often think of the function of cell membranes as mainly containment, like that of a plastic bag. Consider relating the functions of membranes to our human skin. (For example, both membranes and our skin detect stimuli, engage in gas exchange, and serve as sites of excretion and absorption.) (4.2)

Teaching Tips

- Challenge students to identify other examples of technology that have extended our senses. Chemical probes can identify what we cannot taste, listening devices detect what we do not normally hear, night vision and ultraviolet (UV) cameras see or magnify wavelengths beyond our vision, etc. Students can be assigned the task of preparing a short report on one of these technologies. (4.1)

- Here is a chance to demonstrate resolving power in the classroom. Use a marker and your classroom marker board to make several pairs of dots separated by shorter and shorter distances. Start out with two dots clearly separated apart—perhaps by 4–5 cm—and end with a pair of dots that touch. Label them a, b, c, etc. Ask your students to indicate the letters of the pairs of points that they can distinguish as separate; this is the definition of resolution for their eyes (they need not state their answers publicly, to avoid embarrassment). (4.1)

- Most biology laboratories have two types of microscopes for student use: a dissection (or stereo-) microscope, and a compound light microscope using microscope slides. The way these scopes function parallels the workings of electron microscopes. Dissection microscopes are like an SEM—both rely upon a beam reflected off a surface. As you explain this to your class, hold up an object, identify a light source in the room, and explain that our eyes see most images when our eyes detect light that has reflected off the surface of an object. Compound light microscopes are like TEMs, in which a beam is transmitted through a thin sheet of material. If you have an overhead or other strong light source, hold up a piece of paper between your eye and the light source. You will see the internal detail of the paper as light is transmitted through the paper to your eye . . . the same way a compound light microscope or TEM works! (4.1)

- Even in college, students still struggle with the metric system. When discussing the scale of life, consider bringing a meter stick to class. The ratio of a meter to a millimeter is the same as the ratio of a millimeter to a micron: 1,000 to 1. (4.2)

- Here is another way to explain surface-to-volume ratios. Have your class consider this situation. You purchase a set of eight coffee mugs, each in its own cubic box, for a wedding present. You can wrap the eight boxes together as one large cube, or wrap each of the eight boxes separately. Either way, you will be wrapping the same volume. However, wrapping the mugs separately requires much more paper. This is because the surface-to-volume ratio is greater for smaller objects. (4.2)

- The hydrophobic and hydrophilic ends of a phospholipid molecule create a lipid bilayer. The hydrophobic edges of the layer will naturally seal to other such edges, eventually wrapping a sheet into a sphere that can enclose water (a simple cell). Furthermore, because of these hydrophobic properties, lipid bilayers are also self-healing. That the properties of phospholipids emerge from their organization is worth emphasizing to students. (4.2)

- You might wish to share a very simple analogy that works very well for some students. A cell membrane is a little like a peanut butter and jelly sandwich with jelly beans poked into it. The bread represents the hydrophilic portions of the bilayer (and bread does indeed quickly absorb water). The peanut butter and jelly represent the hydrophobic regions (and peanut butter, containing plenty of oil, is generally hydrophobic). The jelly beans stuck into the sandwich represent proteins variously embedded partially into or completely through the membrane. Transport proteins would be like the jellybeans that poke completely through the sandwich. Analogies are rarely perfect. Challenge your students to critique this analogy by finding exceptions. (For example, this analogy does not include a model of the carbohydrates on the cell surface.) (4.2)

- A visual comparison of prokaryotic and eukaryotic cells, such as that found in Figure 1.4, can be very helpful when discussing the key differences between these cell types. These cells are strikingly different in size and composition. Providing students with a visual reference point rather than simply listing these traits will help them better retain this information. (4.3)

- Students might wrongly conclude that prokaryotes are typically one-tenth the volume of eukaryotic cells. A difference in diameter of a factor of ten translates into a much greater difference in volume. If students recall enough geometry, you may want to challenge them to calculate the difference in the volume of two cells with diameters that differ by a factor of ten (the answer is about 1,000x). (4.3)

- Germs—here is a term that we learn early in our lives but that is rarely well defined. Students may appreciate a biological explanation. The general use of germs is a reference to anything that causes disease. This may be a good time to sort the major disease-causing agents into three categories: (1) bacteria (prokaryotes), (2) viruses (not yet addressed), and (3) single-celled and multicellular eukaryotes (athlete's foot is a fungal infection; malaria is caused by a unicellular eukaryote). (4.3)

- Module 4.3 mentions how antibiotics can specifically target prokaryotic but not eukaryotic cells, providing a good segue into discussion of the evolution of antibiotic resistance. Teaching tips and ideas for related lessons can be found at http://www.pbs.org/wgbh/evolution/educators/lessons/lesson6/act1.html. (4.3)

- Some instructors have found that challenging students to come up with analogies for the many eukaryotic organelles is a highly effective teaching method. Students may wish to construct one inclusive analogy between a society or factory and a cell or construct separate analogies for each organelle. As with any analogy, it is important to list the similarities and exceptions. (4.4)

The Nucleus and Ribosomes (4.5–4.6)

Student Misconceptions and Concerns

- Students often enter college with misunderstandings about the interrelationship between DNA, a chromosome, and a replicated chromosome often photographed just prior to mitosis or meiosis. Consider specifically distinguishing between these important cellular components early in your discussions of the nucleus. (4.5).

- Conceptually, some students seem to benefit from the well-developed cell-factory analogy developed in the text. The use of this analogy in lecture might help to anchor these relationships. As mentioned before, challenge students to find exceptions in the analogy, an exercise that promotes critical thinking. (4.5–4.6)

Teaching Tips

- Not all human cells have 46 chromosomes per human cell. Some of your more knowledgeable students may like to guess the exceptions. These include gametes, some of the cells that produce gametes, and adult red blood cells in mammals. (4.5)

- If you wish to continue the text's factory analogy, nuclear pores might be said to function most like the door to the boss's office. Through these doors, directions to the rest of the factory, including ribosomal components, are transmitted. (4.5–4.6)

- Noting the main flow of genetic information on the board as DNA to RNA to protein will provide a useful reference for students when explaining these processes. As a review, have students note where new molecules of DNA, rRNA, mRNA, ribosomes, and proteins are produced in a cell. (4.5–4.6)

- If you want to challenge your students further, ask them to consider the adaptive advantage of using mRNA to direct the production of proteins instead of using DNA directly. One advantage is that DNA is better protected in the nucleus and that mRNA, exposed to more damaging cross-reactions in the cytosol, is the temporary working copy of the genetic material. In some ways, this is like making a working photocopy of an important document, keeping the original copy safely stored away (perhaps like the U.S. Constitution). (4.5–4.6)

- Consider challenging your students to explain how we can have four main types of organic molecules functioning in specific roles in our cells, yet DNA and RNA only specifically dictate the generation of proteins (and more copies of DNA and RNA). How is the production of specific types of carbohydrates and lipids in cells controlled? (Answer: primarily by the specific properties of enzymes.) (4.5–4.6)

The Endomembrane System (4.7–4.12)

Student Misconceptions and Concerns

- Students can have trouble relating many cell organelles to their diverse functions. They may not realize that Modules 4.7–4.12 introduce the primary organelles in the general order that they function in the production and release of secretory proteins. Products and information generally move from the central nucleus to the rough ER, through the more peripherally located Golgi apparatus and the secretory vesicles, and finally to the outer plasma membrane. Emphasizing the flow from center to periphery in this process can help students to remember the function of individual organelles as they recall the steps of the sequence. (4.7–4.12)

- Conceptually, some students seem to benefit from the well-developed cell-factory analogy developed in the text. The use of this analogy in lecture might help to anchor these relationships. As mentioned before, challenge students to find exceptions in the analogy, an exercise that promotes critical thinking. (4.7–4.12)

Teaching Tips

- Point out to your students that the endoplasmic reticulum is continuous with the outer nuclear membrane. This explains why the ER is usually found close to the nucleus. (4.7)

- Students often learn that a human body can build up a tolerance to a drug. Here, in Module 4.8, students learn about one of the specific mechanisms of this response. Liver cells exposed to certain toxins or drugs increase the amount of smooth ER, which functions in the processing of these chemicals. Thus, there is a structural and functional explanation to the development of drug tolerance. (4.8)

- If you continue the factory analogy, the addition of a molecular tag by the Golgi apparatus is like adding address labels in the shipping department of a factory. (4.9)

- Some people think that the Golgi apparatus looks like a stack of pita bread. (4.9)

- As noted in Module 4.10, lysosomes help to recycle damaged cell components. Challenge your students to explain why this is adaptive. Recycling, whether in human society or in our cells, can be an efficient way to reuse materials. The recycled components, which enter the lysosomes in a highly organized form, would require a much greater investment to produce from "scratch." (4.10)

- Challenge your students to identify animal cell organelles other than mitochondria and chloroplasts that are not involved in the synthesis of proteins. (Lysosomes, vacuoles, and peroxisomes are also not involved in protein synthesis.) (4.11)

- Challenge students to suggest two changes in cell structure associated with high exposure to drugs or harmful compounds. These were discussed in separate modules. (Answer: increased amounts of SER and abundant peroxisomes.) (4.12)

Energy-Converting Organelles (4.13–4.15)

Student Misconceptions and Concerns

- Students often mistakenly think that chloroplasts are a substitute for mitochondria in plant cells. They might think that cells either have mitochondria or they have chloroplasts. You might challenge this thinking by asking how plant cells generate ATP at night. (4.13–4.14)

- The evidence that mitochondria and chloroplasts evolved from free-living prokaryotes is further supported by the small size of these organelles, similar to the size of a prokaryote. Mitochondria and chloroplasts are therefore helpful in comparing the general size of eukaryotic and prokaryotic cells. You might think of these organelles as built-in comparisons. (4.15)

Teaching Tips

- ATP functions in cells much like money functions in modern societies. Each holds value that can be generated in one place and spent in another. This analogy has been very helpful for many students. (4.13)

- Mitochondria and chloroplasts are each wrapped by multiple membranes. In both organelles, the innermost membranes are the sites of greatest molecular activity and the outer membranes have fewer significant functions. This makes sense when we consider that the outer membranes correspond to the plasma membrane of the eukaryotic cells that originally wrapped the free-living prokaryotes during endocytosis. Biology makes sense in light of evolution. (4.13–4.15)

- Mitochondria and chloroplasts are not cellular structures that are synthesized in a cell like ribosomes and lysosomes. Instead, mitochondria only come from other mitochondria and chloroplasts only come from other chloroplasts. This is further evidence of the independent evolution of these organelles from free-living ancestral forms. (4.15)

The Cytoskeleton and Cell Surfaces (4.16–4.22)

Student Misconceptions and Concerns

- Students often regard the fluid of the cytoplasm as little more than cell broth, a watery fluid that suspends the organelles. The diverse functions of thin, thick, and intermediate filaments are rarely appreciated before college. Module 4.16 describes the dynamic and diverse functions of the cytoskeleton. (4.16)

- Students often think that the cilia on the cells lining our trachea function like a comb, removing debris from the air. Except in cases of disease or damage, these respiratory cilia are covered by mucus. Cilia do not reach the air to comb it free of debris. Instead, these cilia sweep dirty mucus up our respiratory tracts to be expelled or swallowed. (4.17)

- The structure and functions of the extracellular matrix (ECM) are closely associated with the cells that it contacts. Students might suspect that like roots from a tree, cells are anchored to the matrix indefinitely. However, some cells can detach from the ECM and migrate great distances, often following molecular trails (such as fibronectin and laminin) that direct them along the journey. (4.19)

Teaching Tips

- Analogies between the infrastructure of human buildings and the cytoskeleton are limited by the dynamic nature of the cytoskeleton. Few human structures have a structural frame-work that is routinely constructed, deconstructed, and then reconstructed in a new configu-ration on a regular basis. (Tents are often constructed, deconstructed, and then reconstructed repeatedly, but typically rely upon the same basic design.) Thus, caution is especially warranted when using such analogies. (4.16)

- Students might enjoy this brief class activity. Have everyone in the class clear their throats at the same time. Wait a few seconds. Have them notice that after clearing, they swal-lowed. The mucus that trapped debris is swept up the trachea by cilia. When we clear our throats, this dirty mucus is disposed of down our esophagus and among the strong acids of our stomach! (4.17)

- Primary ciliary dyskinesia results in nonmotile cilia. Module 4.18 describes infertility in males due to immotile sperm. Challenge your students to suggest reasons why this same disease might reduce fertility in an affected woman. (In the oviduct, cilia convey the egg along the oviduct toward the uterus.) (4.18)

- The extracellular matrix forms a significant structural component of many connective tissues, including cartilage and bone. Many of the properties of cartilage and bone are directly related to the large quantities of material sandwiched between the bone (osteocyte) and cartilage (chondrocyte) cells. (4.19)

- Tight junctions form a seal that prevents the movement of fluids past the region of the junction. Functionally, this is similar to the lengthy zipper-like seal at the top of common plastic food storage bags. (4.20)

- Consider challenging your students to suggest analogies to the structure and function of plasmodesmata (perhaps air ducts between offices in a building). Consider discussing the advantages of interconnected cytoplasms. (4.21)

- The text in Module 4.21 compares the fibers-in-a-matrix construction of a plant cell wall to fiberglass. Students familiar with highway construction or the pouring of concrete might also be familiar with the frequent use of reinforcing bar (rebar) to similarly reinforce concrete. (4.21)

- The chapter ends noting the three fundamental features of all organisms. Challenge students to explain if viruses are organisms according to this definition. (4.22)

- Some students might benefit by creating a concept map integrating the information in Table 4.22. Such a map would note the components of a cell interconnected by lines and relationships between these cellular components. Such techniques may also be beneficial in later chapters, depending upon the learning style of particular students. (4.22)

Key Terms

cell theory
cell wall
cellular metabolism
central vacuole
centriole
chloroplast
chromatin
chromosome
cilia
crista (plural, cristae)
cytoplasm
cytoskeleton
electron microscope (EM)
endomembrane system
endoplasmic reticulum (ER)
endosymbiont theory
eukaryotic cell

extracellular matrix (ECM)
flagellum (plural, flagella)
glycoprotein
Golgi apparatus
granum (plural, grana)
integrins
intermediate filament
light microscope (LM)
lysosome
microfilament
microtubule
mitochondrial matrix
mitochondrion (plural, mitochondria)
nuclear envelope
nucleoid
nucleolus
nucleus (plural, nuclei)
organelle

peroxisome
plasma membrane
plasmodesma (plural, plasmodesmata)
prokaryotic cell
ribosome
rough endoplasmic reticulum
scanning electron microscope (SEM)
smooth endoplasmic reticulum
stroma
thylakoid
transmission electron microscope (TEM)
transport vesicle
vacuole
vesicle

Word Roots

centri- = center (*centriole*: an animal cell structure composed of cylinders of microtubule triplets; within the cell's centrosome, a pair of centrioles function in cell division)

chloro- = green; **-plast** = molded (*chloroplast*: the site of photosynthesis in plants and algae)

cili- = hair (*cilium*: a short hair-like cellular appendage with a microtubule core, specialized for locomotion)

cyto- = cell; **-plasm** = fluid (*cytoplasm*: everything inside a cell between the plasma membrane and the nucleus, consisting of a semifluid medium and organelles)

-ell = small (*organelle*: a membrane-enclosed structure with a specialized function within a cell)

endo- = inner; **sym-** = together; **bios-** = living (*endosymbiosis*: when one organism lives inside another organism; the process by which the mitochondria and chloroplasts of eukaryotic cells probably evolved)

eu- = true; **karyo-** = nucleus (*eukaryotic cell*: a cell with a membrane-enclosed nucleus and other membrane-enclosed organelles)

extra- = outside (*extracellular matrix*: the substance in which animal tissue cells are embedded)

flagell- = whip (*flagellum*: a long whip-like cellular appendage specialized for locomotion)

glyco- = sweet (*glycoprotein*: a macromolecule consisting of one or more polypeptides linked to short chains of sugars)

lyso- = loosen (*lysosome*: a digestive organelle containing hydrolytic enzymes used by eukaryotic cells to digest food and wastes)

micro- = small; **-tubul** = a little pipe (*microtubule*: a straight, hollow tube of globular proteins in the cytoskeleton of eukaryotic cells that support the structure and movement of cilia and flagella)

micro- = small; **-graph** = write (*micrograph*: a photograph taken through a microscope)

nucle- = nucleus; **-oid** = like (*nucleoid*: a dense region of DNA in a prokaryotic cell); a band or bond (*plasmodesmata*: an open channel in a plant cell wall)

pro- = before (*prokaryotic cell*: a cell that has no nucleus)

-soma = a body (*chromosome*: the structure carrying the genetic material found in the nucleus of a eukaryotic cell)

thylaco- = sac or pouch (*thylakoid*: a flattened membranous sac inside the chloroplast that serves as the site of the light reactions of photosynthesis)

trans- = across; **-port** = a harbor; **vesic-** = sac or bladder (*transport vesicle*: a membranous compartment used to enclose and transport materials from one part of a cell to another)

vacu- = empty (*vacuole*: a membrane-enclosed sac that is part of the endomembrane system of a eukaryotic cell)

CHAPTER 5

The Working Cell

Chapter Objectives

Opening Essay

Explain how organisms produce and use bioluminescence to attract mates or prey, repulse predators, or communicate.

Membrane Structure and Function

5.1   Describe the fluid mosaic structure of cell membranes.

5.1   Describe the diverse functions of membrane proteins.

5.2   Relate the structure of phospholipid molecules to the structure and properties of cell membranes.

5.2   Explain how the properties of phospholipids spontaneously form membranes.

5.3   Define diffusion and describe the process of passive transport.

5.4   Explain how osmosis can be defined as the diffusion of water across a membrane.

5.5   Distinguish between hypertonic, hypotonic, and isotonic solutions.

5.5   Explain how animal and plants cells change when placed into hypertonic or hypotonic solutions.

5.6   Explain how transport proteins facilitate diffusion.

5.7   Describe the function of aquaporins in cell membranes.

5.8   Compare the processes of facilitated diffusion and active transport.

5.9   Distinguish between exocytosis, endocytosis, phagocytosis, pinocytosis, and receptor-mediated endocytosis.

Energy and the Cell

5.10   Define and compare kinetic energy, potential energy, chemical energy, and heat.

5.10   Define the first and second laws of thermodynamics. Explain how these laws of thermodynamics relate to energy use in a cell.

5.11   Define and compare endergonic and exergonic reactions. Explain how cells use cellular respiration and energy coupling to survive.

5.12   Describe the three main types of cellular work.

5.12   Explain how ATP functions as an energy shuttle.

How Enzymes Function

5.13   Define activation energy and explain how enzymes speed up chemical reactions.

5.14   Describe the structure of an enzyme-substrate interaction.

5.14   Explain how the cellular environment affects enzyme activity.

5.15 Explain how competitive and noncompetitive inhibitors alter an enzyme's activity.

5.15 Describe the process of feedback inhibition.

5.16 Explain how certain drugs, pesticides, and poisons can affect enzymes.

Lecture Outline

I. Introduction

A. Some organisms use energy-converting reactions to produce light in a process called bioluminescence.

1. Many marine invertebrates and fishes use bioluminescence to hide themselves from predators.

2. Scientists estimate that 90% of deep-sea marine life produces bioluminescence.

B. The light is produced from chemical reactions that convert chemical energy into visible light.

C. Bioluminescence is an example of the multitude of energy conversions that a cell can perform.

D. Many of a cell's reactions

1. take place in organelles and

2. use enzymes embedded in the membranes of these organelles.

E. This chapter addresses how working cells use membranes, energy, and enzymes.

II. Membrane Structure and Function

A. 5.1 Membranes are fluid mosaics of lipids and proteins with many functions

1. Membranes are composed of

   a. a bilayer of phospholipids with

   b. embedded and attached proteins,

   c. in a structure biologists call a **fluid mosaic**.

2. Many phospholipids are made from unsaturated fatty acids that have kinks in their tails.

3. These kinks prevent phospholipids from packing tightly together, keeping them in liquid form.

4. In animal cell membranes, cholesterol helps

   a. stabilize membranes at warmer temperatures and

   b. keep the membrane fluid at lower temperatures.

5. Membrane proteins perform many functions.

   a. Some proteins help maintain cell shape and coordinate changes inside and outside the cell through their attachment to the cytoskeleton and extracellular matrix.

   b. Some proteins function as receptors for chemical messengers from other cells.

   c. Some membrane proteins function as enzymes.

   d. Some membrane glycoproteins are involved in cell to cell recognition.

   e. Membrane proteins may participate in the intercellular junctions that attach adjacent cells to each other.

   f. Membranes may exhibit **selective permeability**, allowing some substances to cross more easily than others.

B. 5.2 EVOLUTION CONNECTION: Membranes form spontaneously, a critical step in the origin of life
  1. Phospholipids, the key ingredient of biological membranes, spontaneously self-assemble into simple membranes.
  2. The formation of membrane-enclosed collections of molecules was a critical step in the evolution of the first cells.
C. 5.3 Passive transport is diffusion across a membrane with no energy investment
  1. Diffusion is the tendency of particles to spread out evenly in an available space.
    a. Particles move from an area of more concentrated particles to an area where they are less concentrated.
    b. This means that particles diffuse down their **concentration gradient**.
    c. Eventually, the particles reach equilibrium where the concentration of particles is the same throughout.
  2. Diffusion across a cell membrane does not require energy, so it is called **passive transport**.
  3. The concentration gradient itself represents potential energy for diffusion.
D. 5.4 Osmosis is the diffusion of water across a membrane
  1. One of the most important substances that crosses membranes is water.
  2. The diffusion of water across a selectively permeable membrane is called **osmosis**.
  3. If a membrane permeable to water but not a solute separates two solutions with different concentrations of solute,
    a. water will cross the membrane,
    b. moving down its own concentration gradient,
    c. until the solute concentration on both sides is equal.
E. 5.5 Water balance between cells and their surroundings is crucial to organisms
  1. Tonicity is a term that describes the ability of a solution to cause a cell to gain or lose water.
  2. Tonicity mostly depends on the concentration of a solute on both sides of the membrane.
  3. How will animal cells be affected when placed into solutions of various tonicities? When an animal cell is placed into
    a. an **isotonic** solution, the concentration of solute is the same on both sides of a membrane, and the cell volume will not change,
    b. a **hypotonic** solution, the solute concentration is lower outside the cell, water molecules move into the cell, and the cell will expand and may burst, or
    c. a **hypertonic** solution, the solute concentration is higher outside the cell, water molecules move out of the cell, and the cell will shrink.
  4. For an animal cell to survive in a hypotonic or hypertonic environment, it must engage in **osmoregulation**, the control of water balance.
  5. The cell walls of plant cells, prokaryotes, and fungi, make water balance issues somewhat different.
    a. The cell wall of a plant cell exerts pressure that prevents the cell from taking in too much water and bursting when placed in a hypotonic environment.
    b. But in a hypertonic environment, plant and animal cells both shrivel.

F. 5.6 Transport proteins can facilitate diffusion across membranes
  1. Hydrophobic substances easily diffuse across a cell membrane.
  2. However, polar or charged substances do not easily cross cell membranes and, instead, move across membranes with the help of specific transport proteins in a process called **facilitated diffusion**, which
      a. does not require energy and
      b. relies on the concentration gradient.
  3. Some proteins function by becoming a hydrophilic tunnel for passage of ions or other molecules.
  4. Other proteins bind their passenger, change shape, and release their passenger on the other side.
  5. In both of these situations, the protein is specific for the substrate, which can be sugars, amino acids, ions, and even water.
  6. Because water is polar, its diffusion through a membrane's hydrophobic interior is relatively slow.
  7. The very rapid diffusion of water into and out of certain cells is made possible by a protein channel called an **aquaporin**.

G. 5.7 SCIENTIFIC DISCOVERY: Research on another membrane protein led to the discovery of aquaporins
  1. Dr. Peter Agre received the 2003 Nobel Prize in chemistry for his discovery of aquaporins.
  2. His research on the Rh protein used in blood typing led to this discovery.

H. 5.8 Cells expend energy in the active transport of a solute
  1. In active transport, a cell
      a. must expend energy to
      b. move a solute against its concentration gradient.

I. 5.9 Exocytosis and endocytosis transport large molecules across membranes
  1. A cell uses two mechanisms to move large molecules across membranes.
      a. Exocytosis is used to export bulky molecules, such as proteins or polysaccharides.
      b. Endocytosis is used to import substances useful to the livelihood of the cell.
  2. In both cases, material to be transported is packaged within a vesicle that fuses with the membrane.
  3. There are three kinds of endocytosis.
      a. Phagocytosis is the engulfment of a particle by wrapping cell membrane around it, forming a vacuole.
      b. Pinocytosis is the same thing except that fluids are taken into small vesicles.
      c. Receptor-mediated endocytosis uses receptors in a receptor-coated pit to interact with a specific protein, initiating the formation of a vesicle.

III. Energy and the Cell

A. 5.10 Cells transform energy as they perform work
  1. Cells are small units, a chemical factory, housing thousands of chemical reactions.
  2. Cells use these chemical reactions for
      a. cell maintenance,
      b. manufacture of cellular parts, and
      c. cell replication.
  3. **Energy** is the capacity to cause change or to perform work.

4. There are two kinds of energy.
   a. **Kinetic energy** is the energy of motion.
   b. **Potential energy** is energy that matter possesses as a result of its location or structure.
5. **Heat**, or thermal energy, is a type of kinetic energy associated with the random movement of atoms or molecules.
6. Light is also a type of kinetic energy and can be harnessed to power photosynthesis.
7. Chemical energy is the potential energy available for release in a chemical reaction. It is the most important type of energy for living organisms to power the work of the cell.
8. **Thermodynamics** is the study of energy transformations that occur in a collection of matter.
9. Scientists use the word
   a. *system* for the matter under study and
   b. *surroundings* for the rest of the universe.
10. Two laws govern energy transformations in organisms. According to the
   a. **first law of thermodynamics**, energy in the universe is constant, and
   b. **second law of thermodynamics**, energy conversions increase the disorder of the universe.
11. **Entropy** is the measure of disorder or randomness.
12. Cells use oxygen in reactions that release energy from fuel molecules.
13. In **cellular respiration**, the chemical energy stored in organic molecules is converted to a form that the cell can use to perform work.

B. 5.11 Chemical reactions either release or store energy
   1. Chemical reactions either
      a. release energy (**exergonic reactions**) or
      b. require an input of energy and store energy (**endergonic reactions**).
   2. Exergonic reactions release energy.
      a. These reactions release the energy in covalent bonds of the reactants.
      b. Burning wood releases the energy in glucose as heat and light.
      c. Cellular respiration
         i.   involves many steps,
         ii. releases energy slowly, and
         iii. uses some of the released energy to produce ATP.
   3. An **endergonic reaction**
      a. requires an input of energy and
      b. yields products rich in potential energy.
   4. Endergonic reactions
      a. begin with reactant molecules that contain relatively little potential energy but
      b. end with products that contain more chemical energy.
   5. Photosynthesis is a type of endergonic process.
      a. Energy-poor reactants, carbon dioxide, and water are used.
      b. Energy is absorbed from sunlight.
      c. Energy-rich sugar molecules are produced.
   6. A living organism carries out thousands of endergonic and exergonic chemical reactions.
   7. The total of an organism's chemical reactions is called **metabolism**.

8. A **metabolic pathway** is a series of chemical reactions that either
    a. builds a complex molecule or
    b. breaks down a complex molecule into simpler compounds.
9. **Energy coupling** uses the
    a. energy released from exergonic reactions to drive
    b. essential endergonic reactions,
    c. usually using the energy stored in ATP molecules.
C. 5.12 ATP drives cellular work by coupling exergonic and endergonic reactions
    1. **ATP**, adenosine triphosphate, powers nearly all forms of cellular work.
    2. ATP consists of
        a. the nitrogenous base adenine,
        b. the five-carbon sugar ribose, and
        c. three phosphate groups.
    3. Hydrolysis of ATP releases energy by transferring its third phosphate from ATP to some other molecule in a process called **phosphorylation**.
    4. Most cellular work depends on ATP energizing molecules by phosphorylating them.
    5. There are three main types of cellular work:
        a. chemical,
        b. mechanical, and
        c. transport.
    6. ATP drives all three of these types of work.
    7. ATP is a renewable source of energy for the cell.
    8. In the ATP cycle, energy released in an exergonic reaction, such as the breakdown of glucose, is used in an endergonic reaction to generate ATP.

IV. How Enzymes Function

A. 5.13 Enzymes speed up the cell's chemical reactions by lowering energy barriers
    1. Although biological molecules possess much potential energy, it is not released spontaneously.
        a. An energy barrier must be overcome before a chemical reaction can begin.
        b. This energy is called the **activation energy** (E_A).
    2. We can think of E_A
        a. as the amount of energy needed for a reactant molecule to move "uphill" to a higher energy but an unstable state
        b. so that the "downhill" part of the reaction can begin.
    3. One way to speed up a reaction is to add heat,
        a. which agitates atoms so that bonds break more easily and reactions can proceed but
        b. could kill a cell.
    4. Enzymes
        a. function as biological catalysts by lowering the E_A needed for a reaction to begin,
        b. increase the rate of a reaction without being consumed by the reaction, and
        c. are usually proteins, although some RNA molecules can function as enzymes.
B. 5.14 A specific enzyme catalyzes each cellular reaction
    1. An enzyme
        a. is very selective in the reaction it catalyzes and
        b. has a shape that determines the enzyme's specificity.
    2. The specific reactant that an enzyme acts on is called the enzyme's **substrate**.
    3. A substrate fits into a region of the enzyme called the **active site**.

4. Enzymes are specific because their active site fits only specific substrate molecules.

5. For every enzyme, there are optimal conditions under which it is most effective.

6. Temperature affects molecular motion.

   a. An enzyme's optimal temperature produces the highest rate of contact between the reactants and the enzyme's active site.

   b. Most human enzymes work best at 35–40°C.

7. The optimal pH for most enzymes is near neutrality.

8. Many enzymes require nonprotein helpers called **cofactors**, which

   a. bind to the active site and

   b. function in catalysis.

9. Some cofactors are inorganic, such as zinc, iron, or copper.

10. If a cofactor is an organic molecule, such as most vitamins, it is called a **coenzyme**.

C. 5.15 Enzyme inhibitors can regulate enzyme activity in a cell

   1. A chemical that interferes with an enzyme's activity is called an inhibitor.

   2. **Competitive inhibitors**

      a. block substrates from entering the active site and

      b. reduce an enzyme's productivity.

   3. **Noncompetitive inhibitors**

      a. bind to the enzyme somewhere other than the active site,

      b. change the shape of the active site, and

      c. prevent the substrate from binding.

   4. Enzyme inhibitors are important in regulating cell metabolism.

   5. In some reactions, the product may act as an inhibitor of one of the enzymes in the pathway that produced it. This is called **feedback inhibition**.

D. 5.16 CONNECTION: Many drugs, pesticides, and poisons are enzyme inhibitors

   1. Many beneficial drugs act as enzyme inhibitors, including

      a. Ibuprofen, inhibiting the production of prostaglandins,

      b. some blood pressure medicines,

      c. some antidepressants,

      d. many antibiotics, and

      e. protease inhibitors used to fight HIV.

   2. Enzyme inhibitors have also been developed as pesticides and deadly poisons for chemical warfare.

Chapter Guide to Teaching Resources

Membrane Structure and Function (5.1–5.9)

Student Misconceptions and Concerns

- For students with limited science backgrounds, concepts such as diffusion and osmosis can take considerable time to fully understand and apply. Instructors often struggle to remember a time in their lives when they did not know about such fundamental scientific principles. Consider spending extra time to illustrate and demonstrate these key processes to the class. Consider short interactive class exercises in which students create analogies or think of examples of these principles in their lives. (5.3–5.4)

- Students easily confuse the term hypertonic and hypotonic. One challenge is to get them to understand that these are relative terms, such as heavier, darker, or fewer. No single object is heavier, no single cup of coffee is darker, and no single bag of M&M's has fewer candies. Such terms only apply when comparing two or more items. A solution with a higher concentration than another solution is hypertonic to that solution. However, the same solution might also be hypotonic to a third solution. (5.5)

Teaching Tips

- You might wish to share a very simple analogy that seems to work well for some students. A cell membrane is a little like a peanut butter and jelly sandwich with jelly beans poked into it. The bread represents the hydrophilic portions of the bilayer (and bread does indeed quickly absorb water). The peanut butter and jelly represent the hydrophobic regions (and peanut butter, containing plenty of oil, is generally hydrophobic). The jelly beans stuck into the sandwich represent proteins variously embedded partially into or completely through the membrane. Transport proteins would be like the jelly beans that poke completely through the sandwich. Analogies are rarely perfect. Challenge your students to critique this analogy by finding exceptions. (For example, this analogy does not include a model of the carbohydrates on the cell surface.) (5.1)

- The hydrophobic and hydrophilic ends of a phospholipid molecule create a lipid bilayer. The hydrophobic edges of the layer will also seal to other such edges, eventually wrapping a sheet into a sphere that can enclose water. Furthermore, because of these hydrophobic properties, lipid bilayers are naturally self-healing. All of these properties emerge from the structure of phospholipids. (5.2)

- Students often benefit from reminders of diffusion in their lives. Smells can usually be traced back to their sources—the smell of dinner on the stove, the scent of perfume or cologne from a bottle, the smoke drifting away from a campfire. These scents are strongest nearest the source and weaker as we move away. (5.3)

- Consider demonstrating simple diffusion. A large jar of water and a few drops of dark-colored dye work well over the course of a lecture period. Alternatively, release a strong scent of cologne or peppermint or peel part of an orange in the classroom and have students raise their hands as they first detect the smell. Students nearest the source will raise their hands before students farther away. The fan from an active overhead projector or overhead vent may bias the experiment a bit, so be aware of any directed movements of air in your classroom that might disrupt this demonstration. (5.3)

- Your students may have noticed that the skin of their fingers wrinkles after taking a long shower or bath, or after washing dishes. The skin wrinkles because it is swollen with water but still tacked down at some points. Through osmosis, water moves into the epidermal skin cells. Our skin is hypertonic to these solutions, producing the swelling that appears as large wrinkles. Oils inhibit the movement of water into our skin. Thus, soapy water results in wrinkling faster than plain water because the soap removes the natural layer of oil from our skin. (5.4)

- The word root hypo means below. Thus, a hypodermic needle injects substances below the dermis. Students might best remember that hypotonic solutions have concentrations of solutes below that of the other solution(s). (5.5)

- After introducing the idea of hypertonic and hypotonic solutions, you may wish to challenge your students with the following: A salmon might swim from the ocean up a freshwater stream to reproduce. The salmon is moving from a _____ environment to a _____ environment. (Answers: hypertonic, hypotonic) (5.5)

- The effects of hypertonic and hypotonic solutions can be demonstrated if students soak carrot sticks, long slices of potato, or celery in hypertonic and hypotonic solutions. These also make nice class demonstrations. (5.5)

- The text notes that "The greater the number of transport proteins for a particular solute in a membrane, the faster the solute's rate of diffusion across the membrane." This is similar to a situation that might be more familiar to your students. The more ticket-takers present at the entrance to a stadium, the faster the rate of movement of people into the stadium. (5.6)

- The functional significance of aquaporins in cell membranes is somewhat like open windows in a home. Even without windows, air moves slowly into and out of a home. Open windows and aquaporins facilitate the process of these movements, speeding them up. (5.7)

- Active transport uses energy to move a solute against its concentration gradient. Challenge your students to think of the many possible analogies to this situation, for example, bailing out a leaky boat by moving water back to a place (outside the boat) where water is more concentrated. An alternative analogy might be the herding of animals, which requires work to keep the organisms concentrated and counteract their natural tendency to spread out. (5.8)

- Students familiar with city subway toll stations might think of some gate mechanisms that work similarly to the proteins regulating active transport. A person steps up to a barrier and inserts payment (analogous to ATP input), and the gate changes shape, permitting passage to the other side. Even a simple turnstile system that requires payment is generally similar. (5.8)

- Students carefully considering exocytosis may notice that membrane from secretory vesicles is added to the plasma membrane. Consider challenging your students to identify mechanisms that balance out this enlargement of the cell surface. (Endocytosis "subtracts" area from the cell surface. It is a major factor balancing out the additional membrane supplied by exocytosis.) (5.9)

Energy and the Cell (5.10–5.12)

Student Misconceptions and Concerns

- Students with limited exposure to physics may have never understood the concepts of energy and the conservation of energy or distinguished between potential and kinetic energy. Understanding such broad and new abstract concepts requires time and concrete examples. (5.10–5.12)

- All too often we hear or read that some thing or reaction creates energy. We might hear or read that a power plant "produces" energy or that mitochondria "make" energy. Even in our classroom conversations, we may occasionally slip into this error. When discussing the first law of thermodynamics, consider emphasizing the inaccuracy of such statements. (5.11)

- Although typically familiar with the concept of dietary calories, students often struggle to think of calories as a source of potential energy. For many students, it is not clear that potential energy is stored in food as calories. (5.11)

- Energy coupling at the cellular level may be new to many students, but it is a familiar concept when related to the use of money in our society. Students might be discouraged if the only benefit of work was the ability to make purchases from the employer. (We all might soon tire of a fast-food job that only paid its employees in food!) Money permits the coupling of a generation of value (a paycheck, analogous to an energy-releasing reaction) to an energy-consuming reaction (money, which allows us to make purchases in distant locations). This idea of earning and spending is a common concept we all know well. (5.12)

Teaching Tips

- In our daily lives, we rely upon many energy transformations. On our classroom walls, a clock converts electrical energy to mechanical energy to sweep the hands around the clock's face (unless it is digital!). Our physical (mechanical) activities walking to and from the classroom rely upon the chemical energy from our diet. This chemical energy in our diet also helps us maintain a steady body temperature (heat). Consider challenging your students to come up with additional examples of such common energy conversions in their lives. (5.10)

- Some students can relate well to the concept of entropy as applied to the room where they live. Despite cleaning up and organizing the room on a regular (or irregular) basis, the room becomes increasingly disorganized, a victim of entropy, until another energy input (or effort) is exerted to make the room more orderly again. Students might even get to know entropy as the "dorm room effect." (5.10)

- The heat produced by the engine of a car is typically used to heat the car during cold weather. However, is this same heat available in warmer weather? Students are often unaware that their car "heaters" work very well in the summer too. Just as exercise can warm us when it is cold, the same extra heat is released when we exercise in warm conditions. A car engine in the summer struggles to dissipate heat in the same way that a human struggles to cool off after exercising when weather is warm. (5.10)

- Here is a question that might make cellular respiration a little more meaningful to your students. Ask your students why they feel warm when it is 30°C (86°F) outside if their core body temperature is 37°C (98.6°F). Shouldn't they feel cold? The answer is, our bodies are always producing heat. At these higher temperatures, we are producing more heat than we need to maintain a core body temperature around 37°C. Thus, we sweat and behave in ways that help release our extra heat generated in cellular respiration. (5.10)

- The same mass of fat stores nearly twice as many calories (about 9 kcal per gram) as an equivalent mass of protein or carbohydrates (about 4.5–5 kcal per gram). Thus, when comparing equal masses of fat, protein, and lipid, the fat has nearly twice the potential energy. Fat is therefore an efficient way to store energy in animals and many plants. To store an equivalent amount of energy in the form of carbohydrates or proteins would require about twice the mass, adding a significant burden to the organism's structure. (For example, if you were 20 lbs overweight, you would be nearly 40 lbs overweight if the same energy were stored as carbohydrates or proteins instead of fat). (5.11)

- The amount of energy each adult human needs to generate the ATP required in a day is tremendous. Here is a calculation that has impressed many students. Depending upon the size and activity of a person, a human might burn 2,000 dietary calories (kilocalories) a day. This is enough energy to raise the temperature of 20 liters of liquid water from 0° to

100°C. This is something to think about the next time you heat water on the stove! If you can bring in ten 2-liter bottles, you can help students visualize how much liquid water can be raised from 0° to 100°C. (Note: 100 calories raises about 1 liter of water 100°C, but it takes much more energy to melt ice or to convert boiling water into steam.) (5.11–5.12)

- When introducing ATP and ADP, consider asking your students to think of the terms as A-3-P and A-2-P, noting that the word roots "tri" = 3 and "di" = 2. It might help students to keep track of the number of phosphates more easily. (5.12)

- Recycling is essential in cell biology. Damaged organelles are broken down intracellularly and chemical components, the monomers of the cytoskeleton, and ADP are routinely recycled. There are several advantages common to human recycling of garbage and cellular recycling. Both save energy by avoiding the need to remanufacture the basic units, and both avoid an accumulation of waste products that could interfere with other "environmental" chemistry (the environment of the cell or the environment of the human population). (5.12)

How Enzymes Function (5.13–5.16)

Student Misconceptions and Concerns

- For students not previously familiar with activation energy, analogies can make all the difference. Activation energy can be thought of as a small input that is needed to trigger a large output. This is like (a) an irritated person who needs only a bit more frustration to explode in anger, (b) small waves that lift debris over a dam, or (c) lighting a match around lighter fluid. In each situation, the output is much greater than the input. (5.13)

- The specific interactions of enzymes and substrates can be illustrated with simple physical models. Many students new to these concepts will benefit from several forms of explanation, including diagrams such as those in the textbook, physical models, and the opportunity to manipulate or create their own examples. Just like pitching a tent, new concepts are best constructed with many lines of support. (5.14–5.15)

Teaching Tips

- The information in DNA is used to direct the production of RNA, which in turn directs the production of proteins. However, in Chapter 3, four different types of biological molecules were noted as significant components of life. Students who think this through might wonder, and you could point out that DNA does not directly control the production of carbohydrates and lipids. So how does DNA exert its influence over the synthesis of these two chemical groups? The answer is largely by way of enzymes, proteins with the ability to promote the production of carbohydrates and lipids. (5.13–5.15)

- The text notes that the relationship between an enzyme and its substrate is like a handshake, with each hand generally conforming to the shape of the other. This induced fit is also like the change in shape of a glove when a hand is inserted. The glove's general shape matches the hand, but the final "fit" requires some additional adjustments. (5.14)

- Enzyme inhibitors that block the active site are like (a) a person sitting in your assigned theater seat or (b) a car parked in your parking space. Analogies for inhibitors that change the shape of the active site are more difficult to imagine. Consider challenging your students to think of such analogies. (Perhaps someone adjusting the driver seat of the car differently from your preferences and then leaving it that way when you try to use the car.) (5.15)

- Feedback inhibition relies upon the negative feedback of the accumulation of a product. Ask students in class to suggest other products of reactions that inhibit the process that made them when the product reaches high enough levels. (Gas station pumps routinely shut off when a high level of gasoline is detected. Furnaces typically turn off when enough heat has been produced.) (5.15)
- Challenge your class to identify advantages of specific enzyme inhibitors for pest control. These advantages include (a) the ability to target chemical reactions of only certain types of pest organisms and (b) the ability to target chemical reactions that are found in insects but not in humans. (5.16)

Key Terms

active site	entropy	noncompetitive inhibitor
activation energy	enzyme	osmoregulation
active transport	exergonic reaction	osmosis
ATP	exocytosis	passive transport
aquaporin	facilitated diffusion	phagocytosis
cellular respiration	feedback inhibition	phosphorylation
chemical energy	first law of thermodynamics	pinocytosis
coenzyme	fluid mosaic	potential energy
cofactor	heat	receptor-mediated endocytosis
competitive inhibitor	hypertonic	second law of thermodynamics
concentration gradient	hypotonic	selective permeability
diffusion	induced fit	substrate
endergonic reaction	isotonic	thermodynamics
endocytosis	kinetic energy	tonicity
energy coupling	metabolic pathway	
energy	metabolism	

Word Roots

aqua- = water; **-pori** = a small opening (*aquaporin*: a transport protein in the plasma membrane of a plant or animal cell that facilitates the diffusion of water across the membrane)

co- = together (*cofactor*: a nonprotein molecule or ion that is required for the proper functioning of an enzyme)

endo- = inner, within (*endergonic reaction*: an energy-requiring chemical reaction that yields products with more potential energy than the reactants); **cyto-** = cell (*endocytosis*: cellular uptake of molecules or particles via formation of new vesicles from the plasma membrane)

exo- = outer (*exergonic reaction*: an energy-releasing chemical reaction in which the reactants contain more potential energy than the products; *exocytosis*: the movement of materials out of the cytoplasm of a cell by the fusion of vesicles with the plasma membrane)

hyper- = exceeding; **-tonus** = tension (*hypertonic*: a solution with a higher concentration of solutes)

hypo- = lower (*hypotonic*: a solution with a lower concentration of solutes)

iso- = same (*isotonic*: solutions with equal concentrations of solutes)

kinet- = movement (*kinetic energy*: the energy of motion)

osmo- = pushing (*osmosis*: the diffusion of water across a selectively permeable membrane)

phago- = eat (*phagocytosis*: cellular "eating," a type of endocytosis in which a cell engulfs macromolecules, other cells, or particles into its cytoplasm)

pino- = drink (*pinocytosis*: cellular "drinking," a type of endocytosis in which the cell takes fluid and dissolved solutes into small membranous vesicles)

therm- = heat (*thermodynamics*: the study of the energy transformations that occur in a collection of matter)

CHAPTER 6

How Cells Harvest Chemical Energy

Chapter Objectives

Opening Essay

Describe the main reactants and products of cellular respiration.

Cellular Respiration: Aerobic Harvesting of Energy

6.1 Compare the processes and locations of cellular respiration and photosynthesis. Explain why it is accurate to say that life on Earth is solar-powered.

6.2 Explain how breathing and cellular respiration are related.

6.3 Provide the overall chemical equation for cellular respiration. Compare the efficiency of this process in cells to the efficiency of a gasoline automobile engine.

6.4 Explain how the human body uses its daily supply of ATP.

6.5 Explain how the energy in a glucose molecule is released during cellular respiration.

6.5 Explain how redox reactions are used in cellular respiration.

6.5 Describe the general roles of dehydrogenase, NADH, and the electron transport chain in cellular respiration.

Stages of Cellular Respiration

6.6 List the cellular regions where glycolysis, the citric acid cycle, and oxidative phosphorylation occur. Note whether substrate-level phosphorylation or chemiosmosis occur at each of these sites.

6.7–6.12 Compare the reactants, products, and energy yield of the three stages of cellular respiration.

6.11 Explain how rotenone, cyanide, carbon monoxide, oligomycin, and uncouplers interrupt critical events in cellular respiration.

Fermentation: Anaerobic Harvesting of Energy

6.13 Compare the reactants, products, and energy yield of alcohol and lactic acid fermentation. Distinguish between strict anaerobes and facultative anaerobes.

6.14 Describe the evolutionary history of glycolysis.

Connections Between Metabolic Pathways

6.15 Explain how carbohydrates, fats, and proteins are used as fuel for cellular respiration. Explain why a gram of fat yields more ATP than a gram of starch or protein.

6.16 Explain how nutrients are used in biosynthesis.

Lecture Outline

I. Introduction

  A. In eukaryotes, cellular respiration

    1. harvests energy from food,

    2. yields large amounts of ATP, and

    3. uses ATP to drive cellular work.

  B. A similar process takes place in many prokaryotic organisms.

II. Cellular Respiration: Aerobic Harvesting of Energy

  A. 6.1 Photosynthesis and cellular respiration provide energy for life

    1. Life requires energy.

    2. In almost all ecosystems, energy ultimately comes from the sun.

    3. In photosynthesis,

      a. some of the energy in sunlight is captured by chloroplasts,

      b. atoms of carbon dioxide and water are rearranged, and

      c. glucose and oxygen are produced.

    4. In cellular respiration

      a. glucose is broken down to carbon dioxide and water, and

      b. the cell captures some of the released energy to make ATP.

    5. Cellular respiration takes place in the mitochondria of eukaryotic cells.

  B. 6.2 Breathing supplies O_2 for use in cellular respiration and removes CO_2

    1. Respiration, as it relates to breathing, and cellular respiration are not the same.

      a. Respiration, in the breathing sense, refers to an exchange of gases. Usually an organism brings in oxygen from the environment and releases waste CO_2.

      b. Cellular respiration is the aerobic (oxygen requiring) harvesting of energy from food molecules by cells.

  C. 6.3 Cellular respiration banks energy in ATP molecules

    1. Cellular respiration is an exergonic process that transfers energy from the bonds in glucose to form ATP.

    2. Cellular respiration

      a. produces up to 32 ATP molecules from each glucose molecule and

      b. captures only about 34% of the energy originally stored in glucose.

    3. Other foods (organic molecules) can also be used as a source of energy.

  D. 6.4 CONNECTION: The human body uses energy from ATP for all its activities

    1. The average adult human needs about 2,200 kcal of energy per day.

      a. About 75% of these calories are used to maintain a healthy body.

      b. The remaining 25% is used to power physical activities.

    2. A **kilocalorie (kcal)** is

      a. the quantity of heat required to raise the temperature of 1 kilogram (kg) of water by 1°C,

      b. the same as a food Calorie, and

      c. used to measure the nutritional values indicated on food labels.

  E. 6.5 Cells tap energy from electrons "falling" from organic fuels to oxygen

    1. The energy necessary for life is contained in the arrangement of electrons in chemical bonds in organic molecules.

    2. An important question is how do cells extract this energy?

3. When the carbon-hydrogen bonds of glucose are broken, electrons are transferred to oxygen.
   a. Oxygen has a strong tendency to attract electrons.
   b. An electron loses potential energy when it "falls" to oxygen.
4. Energy can be released from glucose by simply burning it.
5. The energy is dissipated as heat and light and is not available to living organisms.
6. On the other hand, cellular respiration is the controlled breakdown of organic molecules.
7. Energy is
   a. gradually released in small amounts,
   b. captured by a biological system, and
   c. stored in ATP.
8. The movement of electrons from one molecule to another is an oxidation-reduction reaction, or **redox reaction**. In a redox reaction,
   a. the loss of electrons from one substance is called **oxidation**,
   b. the addition of electrons to another substance is called **reduction**,
   c. a molecule is oxidized when it loses one or more electrons, and
   d. reduced when it gains one or more electrons.
9. A cellular respiration equation is helpful to show the changes in hydrogen atom distribution.
10. Glucose
    a. loses its hydrogen atoms and
    b. becomes oxidized to CO_2.
11. Oxygen
    a. gains hydrogen atoms and
    b. becomes reduced to H_2O.
12. Enzymes are necessary to oxidize glucose and other foods.
13. NAD^+
    a. is an important enzyme in oxidizing glucose,
    b. accepts electrons, and
    c. becomes reduced to NADH.
14. There are other electron "carrier" molecules that function like NAD^+.
    a. They form a staircase where the electrons pass from one to the next down the staircase.
    b. These electron carriers collectively are called the **electron transport chain**.
    c. As electrons are transported down the chain, ATP is generated.

III. Stages of Cellular Respiration

A. 6.6 Overview: Cellular respiration occurs in three main stages
   1. Cellular respiration consists of a sequence of steps that can be divided into three stages.
      a. Stage 1 – Glycolysis
      b. Stage 2 – Pyruvate oxidation and citric acid cycle
      c. State 3 – Oxidative phosphorylation
   2. Stage 1: Glycolysis
      a. occurs in the cytoplasm,
      b. begins cellular respiration, and

    c. breaks down glucose into two molecules of a three-carbon compound called pyruvate.

  3. Stage 2: The citric acid cycle

    a. takes place in mitochondria,

    b. oxidizes pyruvate to a two-carbon compound, and

    c. supplies the third stage with electrons.

  4. Stage 3: Oxidative phosphorylation

    a. involves electrons carried by NADH and $FADH_2$,

    b. shuttles these electrons to the electron transport chain embedded in the inner mitochondrial membrane,

    c. involves chemiosmosis, and

    d. generates ATP through oxidative phosphorylation associated with **chemiosmosis**.

B. 6.7 Glycolysis harvests chemical energy by oxidizing glucose to pyruvate

  1. In **glycolysis**,

    a. a single molecule of glucose is enzymatically cut in half through a series of steps,

    b. two molecules of pyruvate are produced,

    c. two molecules of NAD^+ are reduced to two molecules of NADH, and

    d. a net of two molecules of ATP is produced.

  2. ATP is formed in glycolysis by **substrate-level phosphorylation** during which

    a. an enzyme transfers a phosphate group from a substrate molecule to ADP and

    b. ATP is formed.

  3. The compounds that form between the initial reactant, glucose, and the final product, pyruvate, are called **intermediates**.

  4. The steps of glycolysis can be grouped into two main phases.

    a. In steps 1–4, the energy investment phase,

      i. energy is consumed as two ATP molecules are used to energize a glucose molecule,

      ii. which is then split into two small sugars that are now primed to release energy.

    b. In steps 5–9, the energy payoff,

      i. two NADH molecules are produced for each initial glucose molecule, and

      ii. ATP molecules are generated.

C. 6.8 Pyruvate is oxidized prior to the citric acid cycle

  1. The pyruvate formed in glycolysis is transported from the cytoplasm into a mitochondrion where

    a. the citric acid cycle and

    b. oxidative phosphorylation will occur.

  2. Two molecules of pyruvate are produced for each molecule of glucose that enters glycolysis.

  3. Pyruvate does not enter the citric acid cycle, but undergoes some chemical grooming in which

    a. a carboxyl group is removed and given off as CO_2,

    b. the two-carbon compound remaining is oxidized while a molecule of NAD^+ is reduced to NADH,

    c. coenzyme A joins with the two-carbon group to form acetyl coenzyme A, abbreviated as **acetyl CoA**, and

    d. acetyl CoA enters the citric acid cycle.

D. 6.9 The citric acid cycle completes the oxidation of organic molecules, generating many NADH and FADH$_2$ molecules

   1. The citric acid cycle

      a. is also called the Krebs cycle (after the German-British researcher Hans Krebs, who worked out much of this pathway in the 1930s),

      b. completes the oxidation of organic molecules, and

      c. generates many NADH and FADH$_2$ molecules.

   2. During the citric acid cycle

      a. the two-carbon group of acetyl CoA is added to a four-carbon compound, forming citrate,

      b. citrate is degraded back to the four-carbon compound,

      c. two CO$_2$ are released, and

      d. 1 ATP, 3 NADH, and 1 FADH$_2$ are produced.

   3. Remember that the citric acid cycle processes two molecules of acetyl CoA for each initial glucose molecule.

   4. Thus, after two turns of the citric acid cycle, the overall yield per glucose molecule is

      a. 2 ATP,

      b. 6 NADH, and

      c. 2 FADH$_2$.

E. 6.10 Most ATP production occurs by oxidative phosphorylation

   1. Oxidative phosphorylation

      a. involves electron transport and chemiosmosis and

      b. requires an adequate supply of oxygen.

   2. Electrons from NADH and FADH$_2$ travel down the electron transport chain to O$_2$.

   3. Oxygen picks up H$^+$ to form water.

   4. Energy released by these redox reactions is used to pump H$^+$ from the mitochondrial matrix into the intermembrane space.

   5. In chemiosmosis, the H$^+$ diffuses back across the inner membrane through **ATP synthase** complexes, driving the synthesis of ATP.

F. 6.11 CONNECTION: Interrupting cellular respiration can have both harmful and beneficial effects

   1. Three categories of cellular poisons obstruct the process of oxidative phosphorylation. These poisons

      a. block the electron transport chain (for example, rotenone, cyanide, and carbon monoxide),

      b. inhibit ATP synthase (for example, the antibiotic oligomycin), or

      c. make the membrane leaky to hydrogen ions (called uncouplers, examples include dinitrophenol).

   2. Brown fat is

      a. a special type of tissue associated with the generation of heat and

      b. more abundant in hibernating mammals and newborn infants.

   3. In brown fat,

      a. the cells are packed full of mitochondria,

      b. the inner mitochondrial membrane contains an uncoupling protein, which allows H$^+$ to flow back down its concentration gradient without generating ATP, and

      c. ongoing oxidation of stored fats generates additional heat.

G. 6.12 Review: Each molecule of glucose yields many molecules of ATP

    1. Recall that the energy payoff of cellular respiration involves

        a. glycolysis,

        b. alteration of pyruvate,

        c. the citric acid cycle, and

        d. oxidative phosphorylation.

    2. The total yield is about 32 ATP molecules per glucose molecule.

    3. This is about 34% of the potential energy of a glucose molecule.

    4. In addition, water and CO_2 are produced.

IV. Fermentation: Anaerobic Harvesting of Energy

  A. 6.13 Fermentation enables cells to produce ATP without oxygen

    1. Fermentation is a way of harvesting chemical energy that does not require oxygen. Fermentation

        a. takes advantage of glycolysis,

        b. produces two ATP molecules per glucose, and

        c. reduces NAD^+ to NADH.

    2. The trick of fermentation is to provide an anaerobic path for recycling NADH back to NAD^+.

    3. Your muscle cells and certain bacteria can oxidize NADH through **lactic acid fermentation**, in which

        a. NADH is oxidized to NAD^+, and

        b. pyruvate is reduced to lactate.

    4. Lactate is carried by the blood to the liver, where it is converted back to pyruvate and oxidized in the mitochondria of liver cells.

    5. The dairy industry uses lactic acid fermentation by bacteria to make cheese and yogurt.

    6. Other types of microbial fermentation turn

        a. soybeans into soy sauce and

        b. cabbage into sauerkraut.

    7. The baking and winemaking industries have used **alcohol fermentation** for thousands of years.

    8. In this process yeasts (single-celled fungi)

        a. oxidize NADH back to NAD^+ and

        b. convert pyruvate to CO_2 and ethanol.

    9. Obligate anaerobes

        a. are poisoned by oxygen, requiring anaerobic conditions, and

        b. live in stagnant ponds and deep soils.

    10. Facultative anaerobes

        a. include yeasts and many bacteria and

        b. can make ATP by fermentation or oxidative phosphorylation.

  B. 6.14 EVOLUTION CONNECTION: Glycolysis evolved early in the history of life on Earth

    1. Glycolysis is the universal energy-harvesting process of life.

    2. The role of glycolysis in fermentation and respiration dates back to

        a. life long before oxygen was present,

        b. when only prokaryotes inhabited the Earth

        c. about 3.5 billion years ago.

3. The ancient history of glycolysis is supported by its
    a. occurrence in all the domains of life and
    b. location within the cell, using pathways that do not involve any membrane-bounded organelles.

V. **Connections Between Metabolic Pathways**
    A. 6.15 Cells use many kinds of organic molecules as fuel for cellular respiration
        1. Although glucose is considered to be the primary source of sugar for respiration and fermentation, ATP is generated using
            a. carbohydrates,
            b. fats, and
            c. proteins.
        2. Fats make excellent cellular fuel because they
            a. contain many hydrogen atoms and thus many energy-rich electrons and
            b. yield more than twice as much ATP per gram than a gram of carbohydrate or protein.
    B. 6.16 Food molecules provide raw materials for biosynthesis
        1. Cells use intermediates from cellular respiration for the biosynthesis of other organic molecules.
        2. Metabolic pathways are often regulated by feedback inhibition in which an accumulation of product suppresses the process that produces the product.

Chapter Guide to Teaching Resources

Cellular Respiration: Aerobic Harvesting of Energy (6.1–6.5)

Student Misconceptions and Concerns

- Students should be cautioned against the assumption that energy is created when it is converted from one form to another. This might be a good time to review the principle of conservation of energy (the first law of thermodynamics addressed in Module 5.10). (6.1–6.5)

- Students often fail to realize that aerobic metabolism is a process generally similar to the burning of wood or the burning of gasoline in an automobile engine. Noting these general similarities can help students comprehend the overall reaction and heat generation associated with these processes. (6.3)

- The advantage of the gradual degradation of glucose may not be obvious to some students. Many analogies exist that reveal the advantages of short and steady steps. Fuel in an automobile is burned slowly to best utilize the energy released from the fuel. A few fireplace logs release gradual heat to keep a room temperature steady. In both situations, excessive use of fuel becomes wasteful, reducing the efficiencies of the systems. (6.5)

Teaching Tips

- You might wish to elaborate on the amount of solar energy striking Earth. Every day Earth is bombarded with solar radiation equal to the energy of 100 million atomic bombs. Of the tiny fraction of light that reaches photosynthetic organisms, only about 1% is converted to chemical energy by photosynthesis. (6.1)

- Energy coupling at the cellular level may be new to many students, but it is a familiar concept when related to the use of money in our society. Students might be discouraged if the only benefit of work was the ability to make purchases from the employer. (We all might soon tire of a fast-food job that only paid its employees in food!) Money permits the coupling of a generation of value (a paycheck, analogous to an energy-releasing reaction) to an energy-consuming reaction (money, which allows us to make purchases in distant locations). This idea of earning and spending is a common concept we all know well. (6.1–6.3)

- During cellular respiration, our cells convert about 34% of our food energy to useful work (Module 6.3). The other 66% of the energy is released as heat. We use this heat to maintain a relatively steady body temperature near 37°C (98–99°F). This is about the same amount of heat generated by a 75-watt incandescent light bulb. If you choose to include a discussion of heat generation from aerobic metabolism, consider the following. (6.3)

  A. Ask your students why they feel warm when it is 30°C (86°F) outside, if their core body temperature is about 37°C (98.6°F). Shouldn't they feel cold? The answer is, our bodies are always producing heat. At these higher temperatures, we are producing more heat than we need to maintain a body temperature around 37°C. Thus, we sweat and behave in ways that helps us get rid of the extra heat from cellular respiration.

  B. Share this calculation with your students. Depending upon a person's size and level of activity, a human might burn 2,000 dietary calories (kilocalories) a day. This is enough energy to raise the temperature of 20 liters of liquid water from 0 to 100°C. This is something to think about the next time you heat water on the stove! (Note: Consider bringing a 2-liter bottle as a visual aid, or ten 2-liter bottles to make the point above. It takes 100 calories to raise 1 liter of water 100°C; it takes much more energy to melt ice or evaporate water as steam.)

- You might share with your students that it takes about 10 million ATP molecules per second to power one active muscle cell. (6.4)

- The use of the word "falling" when discussing the movement of electrons in a redox reaction can be confusing. Consider explaining the use of the term falling, in reference to potential energy of a falling object. (6.5)

Stages of Cellular Respiration (6.6–6.12)

Student Misconceptions and Concerns

- Perhaps more than anywhere else in general biology, students studying aerobic metabolism may fail to see the forest for the trees. Students may focus on the details of each stage of aerobic metabolism and devote little attention to the overall process and products. Consider emphasizing the products and energy yields associated with glycolysis, the citric acid cycle, and oxidative phosphorylation before detailing the specifics of each reaction. (6.6–6.12)

- The location within a cell in which each reaction takes place is often forgotten in the details of the chemical processes, but it is important to emphasize. Consider using Figure 6.12 as a common reference to locate each stage as you discuss the details of cellular respiration. (6.6–6.12)

- Students frequently think that plants have chloroplasts instead of mitochondria. Take care to point out the need for mitochondria in plants when photosynthesis is not efficient or possible (such as during the night). (6.6–6.12)

Teaching Tips

- The production of NADH through glycolysis and the Krebs cycle, as compared to the direct production of ATP, can get confusing for students. Help students understand that NADH molecules have value to be cashed in by the electron transport chain. The NADH can therefore be thought of as casino chips, accumulated along the way to be cashed in at the electron transport cashier. (6.7–6.10)

- As you relate the structure of the inner mitochondrial membrane to its functions, challenge students to explain the adaptive advantage of the many folds of this inner membrane (see Figure 6.6). (These folds greatly increase the surface area available for the associated reactions.) (6.10)

- The authors develop an analogy between the function of the inner mitochondrial membrane and a dam. A reservoir of hydrogen ions is built up between the inner and outer mitochondrial membranes, like a dam holding back water. As the hydrogen ions move down their concentration gradient, they "spin" the ATP synthase, which helps generate ATP. In a dam, water rushing downhill turns giant turbines, which generate electricity. (6.10)

- Module 6.11 explores the many points in cellular respiration where poisons may produce their deadly effects. Like any complex process, such as an engine of a car or the cooperation of athletes on a team, the results depend upon the proper functioning of each part. Poisons can stop a metabolic pathway by disrupting a single step in the process. (6.11)

- Students should be reminded that the ATP yield of up to 32 ATP per glucose molecule is only a potential. The complex chemistry of aerobic metabolism can yield this amount only under ideal conditions, when every substrate and enzyme is immediately available. Such circumstances may occur only rarely in a working cell. (6.12)

Fermentation: Anaerobic Harvesting of Energy (6.13–6.14)

Student Misconceptions and Concerns

- Students may expect that fermentation will produce alcohol and maybe even carbon dioxide. Take the time to clarify the different possible products of fermentation and correct this general misconception. (6.13)

Teaching Tips

- The text notes that some microbes are useful in the dairy industry because they produce lactic acid. However, the impact of acids on milk may not be obvious to many students. Consider a simple demonstration mixing about equal portions of milk (skim or 2%) with some acid (vinegar will work). Notice the accumulation of strands of milk curd (protein) on the side of the container and stirring device. (6.13)

- Dry wines are produced when the yeast cells use up all or most of the sugar available. Sweet wines result when the alcohol accumulates enough to inhibit fermentation before the sugar is depleted. (6.13)

- Exposing fermenting yeast to oxygen will slow or stop the process, because the yeast will switch back to aerobic respiration. When fermentation is rapid, the carbon dioxide produced drives away the oxygen immediately above the wine. However, as fermentation slows down, the wine must be sealed to prevent oxygen exposure and permit the fermentation process to finish. (6.13)

- The widespread occurrence of glycolysis, which takes place in the cytosol and independent of organelles, suggests that this process had an early evolutionary origin. Since atmospheric oxygen was not available in significant amounts during the early stages of Earth's history, and glycolysis does not require oxygen, it is likely that this chemical pathway was used by the prokaryotes in existence at that time. Students focused on the evolution of large, readily apparent structures such as wings and teeth may have never considered the evolution of cellular chemistry. (6.14)

Connections Between Metabolic Pathways (6.15–6.16)

Student Misconceptions and Concerns

- Some students may only view nutrients as sources of calories. As noted in Module 6.16, the monomers of many nutrients are recycled into synthetic pathways of organic molecules. (6.16)

Teaching Tips

- The same mass of fat stores nearly twice as many calories (about 9 kcal per gram) as an equivalent mass of protein or carbohydrates (about 4.5–5 kcal per gram). Fat is therefore an efficient way to store energy in animals and many plants. To store an equivalent amount of energy in the form of carbohydrates or proteins would require about twice the mass, adding a significant burden to the organism's structure. (For example, if you were 20 lbs overweight, you would be nearly 40 lbs overweight if the same energy were stored as carbohydrates or proteins instead of fat). (6.15)

- Figure 6.15 is an important visual synthesis of the diverse fuels that can enter into cellular respiration and the various stages of this process. Figures such as this can serve as a visual anchor to integrate the many aspects of this chapter. (6.15)

- The final modules in this chapter may raise questions about obesity and proper diet. The Center for Disease Control and Prevention website, www.cdc.gov/nccdphp/dnpa, discusses many aspects of nutrition, obesity, and general physical fitness and is a useful reference for teachers and students. (6.15–6.16)

Key Terms

acetyl CoA (acetyl coenzyme A)	electron transport chain	oxidative phosphorylation
	glycolysis	pyruvate oxidation
alcohol fermentation	intermediates	redox reaction
ATP synthase	kilocalorie (kcal)	reduction
chemiosmosis	lactic acid fermentation	substrate-level
citric acid cycle	oxidation	phosphorylation

Word Roots

aero- = air (*aerobic*: using oxygen)

an- = not (*anaerobic*: not using oxygen)

chemi- = chemical (*chemiosmosis*: the production of ATP using the energy of hydrogen ion gradients across membranes to phosphorylate ADP)

de- = without; **-hydro** = water (*dehydrogenase*: an enzyme that removes water when catalyzing a chemical reaction)

glyco- = sweet; **-lysis** = split (*glycolysis*: the multistep chemical breakdown of a molecule of glucose into two molecules of pyruvate)

CHAPTER 7

Photosynthesis: Using Light to Make Food

Chapter Objectives

Opening Essay

Explain how plants can be used as a renewable energy source. Explain why this is better than burning fossil fuels.

An Overview of Photosynthesis

7.1 Define autotrophs, heterotrophs, producers, and photoautotrophs.

7.2 Describe the structure of chloroplasts and their location in a leaf. Identify specifically where most light energy is converted to chemical energy.

7.3 Explain how plants produce oxygen. Describe the experiments that revealed the source of the oxygen produced during photosynthesis.

7.4 Describe the role of redox reactions in photosynthesis and cellular respiration.

7.5 Compare the reactants and products of the light reactions and the Calvin cycle. Explain how photosynthesis relates to these reactions.

The Light Reactions: Converting Solar Energy to Chemical Energy

7.6 Describe the properties and functions of the different photosynthetic pigments.

7.7 Explain how photosystems capture solar energy.

7.8–7.9 Explain how the electron transport chain and chemiosmosis generate ATP, NADPH, and oxygen in the light reactions.

7.9 Compare photophosphorylation and oxidative phosphorylation.

The Calvin Cycle: Reducing CO_2 to Sugar

7.10 Describe the reactants and products of the Calvin cycle. Explain why this cycle is dependent upon the light reactions.

7.11 Compare the mechanisms that C_3, C_4, and CAM plants use to obtain and use carbon dioxide. Note examples of plants that use each of these systems.

Photosynthesis Reviewed and Extended

7.12 Review the overall process of the light reactions and the Calvin cycle, noting the products, reactants, and locations of every major step.

7.13 Describe the greenhouse effect. Explain how deforestation and the use of fossil fuels contribute to global warming.

7.14 Explain how the ozone layer forms, how human activities have damaged it, and the consequences of the destruction of the ozone layer.

Lecture Outline

I. Introduction

A. Plants, algae, and certain prokaryotes
   1. convert light energy to chemical energy and
   2. store the chemical energy in sugar, made from
      a. carbon dioxide and
      b. water.
B. Algae farms can be used to produce
   1. oils for biodiesel or
   2. carbohydrates to generate ethanol.

II. An Overview of Photosynthesis

A. 7.1 Autotrophs are the producers of the biosphere
   1. Autotrophs
      a. make their own food through the process of **photosynthesis**,
      b. sustain themselves, and
      c. do not usually consume organic molecules derived from other organisms.
   2. Photoautotrophs use the energy of light to produce organic molecules.
   3. Chemoautotrophs are prokaryotes that use inorganic chemicals as their energy source.
   4. **Heterotrophs** are consumers that feed on
      a. plants,
      b. animals, or
      c. decompose organic material.
   5. Photosynthesis in plants
      a. takes place in chloroplasts,
      b. converts carbon dioxide and water into organic molecules, and
      c. releases oxygen.
B. 7.2 Photosynthesis occurs in chloroplasts in plant cells
   1. Chloroplasts are the major sites of photosynthesis in green plants.
   2. **Chlorophyll**
      a. is an important light-absorbing pigment in chloroplasts,
      b. is responsible for the green color of plants, and
      c. plays a central role in converting solar energy to chemical energy.
   3. Chloroplasts are concentrated in the cells of the **mesophyll**, the green tissue in the interior of the leaf.
   4. **Stomata** are tiny pores in the leaf that allow
      a. carbon dioxide to enter and
      b. oxygen to exit.
   5. Veins in the leaf deliver water absorbed by roots.
   6. Chloroplasts consist of an envelope of two membranes, which
      a. enclose an inner compartment filled with a thick fluid called **stroma** and
      b. contain a system of interconnected membranous sacs called **thylakoids**.

7. Thylakoids

    a. are often concentrated in stacks called **grana** and

    b. have an internal compartment called the thylakoid space, which has functions analogous to the intermembrane space of a mitochondrion.

    c. Thylakoid membranes also house much of the machinery that converts light energy to chemical energy.

8. Chlorophyll molecules

    a. are built into the thylakoid membrane and

    b. capture light energy.

C. 7.3 SCIENTIFIC DISCOVERY: Scientists traced the process of photosynthesis using isotopes

  1. Scientists have known since the 1800s that plants produce O_2. But does this oxygen come from carbon dioxide or water?

    a. For many years, it was assumed that oxygen was extracted from CO_2 taken into the plant.

    b. However, later research using a heavy isotope of oxygen, ^{18}O, confirmed that oxygen produced by photosynthesis comes from H_2O.

D. 7.4 Photosynthesis is a redox process, as is cellular respiration

  1. Photosynthesis, like respiration, is a redox (oxidation-reduction) process.

    a. CO_2 becomes reduced to sugar as electrons along with hydrogen ions from water are added to it.

    b. Water molecules are oxidized when they lose electrons along with hydrogen ions.

  2. Cellular respiration uses redox reactions to harvest the chemical energy stored in a glucose molecule.

    a. This is accomplished by oxidizing the sugar and reducing O_2 to H_2O.

    b. The electrons lose potential as they travel down the electron transport chain to O_2.

    c. In contrast, the food-producing redox reactions of photosynthesis require energy.

  3. In photosynthesis,

    a. light energy is captured by chlorophyll molecules to boost the energy of electrons,

    b. light energy is converted to chemical energy, and

    c. chemical energy is stored in the chemical bonds of sugars.

E. 7.5 Overview: The two stages of photosynthesis are linked by ATP and NADPH

  1. Photosynthesis occurs in two metabolic stages.

    a. The **light reactions** occur in the thylakoid membranes. In these reactions

      i. water is split, providing a source of electrons and giving off oxygen as a by-product,

      ii. ATP is generated from ADP and a phosphate group, and

      iii. light energy is absorbed by the chlorophyll molecules to drive the transfer of electrons and H^+ from water to the electron acceptor **NADP$^+$**, reducing it to NADPH.

      iv. NADPH produced by the light reactions provides the electrons for reducing carbon in the Calvin cycle.

    b. The second stage is the **Calvin cycle**, which occurs in the stroma of the chloroplast.

      i. The Calvin cycle is a cyclic series of reactions that assembles sugar molecules using CO_2 and the energy-rich products of the light reactions.

      ii. During the Calvin cycle, CO_2 is incorporated into organic compounds in a process called **carbon fixation**.

         iii. After carbon fixation, enzymes of the cycle make sugars by further reducing the carbon compounds.

         iv. The Calvin cycle is often called the dark reactions or light-independent reactions, because none of the steps requires light directly.

III. The Light Reactions: Converting Solar Energy to Chemical Energy

  A. 7.6 Visible radiation absorbed by pigments drives the light reactions

    1. Sunlight contains energy called electromagnetic energy or electromagnetic radiation.

      a. Visible light is only a small part of the **electromagnetic spectrum**, the full range of electromagnetic wavelengths.

      b. Electromagnetic energy travels in waves, and the **wavelength** is the distance between the crests of two adjacent waves.

    2. Light behaves as discrete packets of energy called photons.

      a. A **photon** is a fixed quantity of light energy.

      b. The shorter the wavelength, the greater the energy.

    3. Pigments

      a. absorb light and

      b. are built into the thylakoid membrane.

    4. Plant pigments

      a. absorb some wavelengths of light and

      b. reflect or transmit other wavelengths.

    5. We see the color of the wavelengths that are transmitted. For example, chlorophyll transmits green wavelengths.

    6. Chloroplasts contain several different pigments, which absorb light of different wavelengths.

      a. **Chlorophyll *a*** absorbs blue-violet and red light and reflects green.

      b. Chlorophyll *b* absorbs blue and orange and reflects yellow-green.

      c. Carotenoids

         i. broaden the spectrum of colors that can drive photosynthesis and

         ii. provide photoprotection, absorbing and dissipating excessive light energy that would otherwise damage chlorophyll or interact with oxygen to form reactive oxidative molecules.

  B. 7.7 Photosystems capture solar energy

    1. Pigments in chloroplasts absorb photons (capturing solar power), which

      a. increases the potential energy of the pigment's electrons and

      b. sends the electrons into an unstable state.

      c. These unstable electrons

         i. drop back down to their "ground state," and as they do,

         ii. release their excess energy as heat.

    2. Within a thylakoid membrane, chlorophyll and other pigment molecules

      a. absorb photons and

      b. transfer the energy to other pigment molecules.

    3. In the thylakoid membrane, chlorophyll molecules are organized along with other pigments and proteins into photosystems.

    4. A photosystem consists of a number of light-harvesting complexes surrounding a reaction-center complex.

    5. A light-harvesting complex contains various pigment molecules bound to proteins.

    6. Collectively, the light-harvesting complexes function as a light-gathering antenna.

7. The light energy is passed from molecule to molecule within the photosystem.

    a. Finally, it reaches the reaction center where a primary electron acceptor accepts these electrons and consequently becomes reduced.

    b. This solar-powered transfer of an electron from the reaction-center pigment to the primary electron acceptor is the first step in the transformation of light energy to chemical energy in the light reactions.

8. Two types of photosystems (photosystem I and photosystem II) cooperate in the light reactions.

9. Each type of photosystem has a characteristic reaction center.

    a. Photosystem II, which functions first, is called P680 because its pigment absorbs light with a wavelength of 680 nm.

    b. Photosystem I, which functions second, is called P700 because it absorbs light with a wavelength of 700 nm.

C. 7.8 Two photosystems connected by an electron transport chain generate ATP and NADPH

    1. In the light reactions, light energy is transformed into the chemical energy of ATP and NADPH.

    2. To accomplish this, electrons are

        a. removed from water,

        b. passed from photosystem II to photosystem I, and

        c. accepted by $NADP^+$, reducing it to NADPH.

    3. Between the two photosystems, the electrons

        a. move down an electron transport chain and

        b. provide energy for the synthesis of ATP.

    4. The products of the light reactions are

        a. NADPH,

        b. ATP, and

        c. oxygen.

D. 7.9 Chemiosmosis powers ATP synthesis in the light reactions

    1. Interestingly, chemiosmosis is the mechanism that

        a. is involved in oxidative phosphorylation in mitochondria and

        b. generates ATP in chloroplasts.

    2. ATP is generated because the electron transport chain produces a concentration gradient of hydrogen ions across a membrane.

    3. In **photophosphorylation**, using the initial energy input from light,

        a. the electron transport chain pumps H^+ into the thylakoid space, and

        b. the resulting concentration gradient drives H^+ back through ATP synthase, producing ATP.

    4. How does photophosphorylation compare with oxidative phosphorylation?

        a. Mitochondria use oxidative phosphorylation to transfer chemical energy from food into the chemical energy of ATP.

        b. Chloroplasts use photophosphorylation to transfer light energy into the chemical energy of ATP.

IV. The Calvin Cycle: Reducing CO_2 to Sugar

    A. 7.10 ATP and NADPH power sugar synthesis in the Calvin cycle

        1. The Calvin cycle makes sugar within a chloroplast.

2. To produce sugar, the necessary ingredients are

   a. atmospheric CO_2 and

   b. ATP and NADPH generated by the light reactions.

3. The Calvin cycle uses these three ingredients to produce an energy-rich, three-carbon sugar called glyceraldehyde-3-phosphate (G3P).

4. A plant cell may then use G3P to make glucose and other organic molecules.

5. The steps of the Calvin cycle include

   a. carbon fixation,

   b. reduction,

   c. release of G3P, and

   d. regeneration of the starting molecule ribulose bisphosphate (RuBP).

B. 7.11 EVOLUTION CONNECTION: Other methods of carbon fixation have evolved in hot, dry climates

1. Most plants use CO_2 directly from the air, and carbon fixation occurs when the enzyme rubisco adds CO_2 to RuBP.

2. Such plants are called **C_3 plants** because the first product of carbon fixation is a three-carbon compound, 3-PGA.

3. In hot and dry weather, C_3 plants

   a. close their stomata to reduce water loss but

   b. prevent CO_2 from entering the leaf and O_2 from leaving.

   c. As O_2 builds up in a leaf, rubisco adds O_2 instead of CO_2 to RuBP, and a two-carbon product of this reaction is then broken down in the cell.

   d. This process is called **photorespiration** because it occurs in the light, consumes O_2, and releases CO_2.

   e. But unlike cellular respiration, it uses ATP instead of producing it.

4. **C_4 plants** have evolved a means of

   a. carbon fixation that saves water during photosynthesis while

   b. optimizing the Calvin cycle.

5. C_4 plants are so named because they first fix CO_2 into a four-carbon compound.

6. When the weather is hot and dry, C_4 plants keep their stomata mostly closed, thus conserving water.

7. Another adaptation to hot and dry environments has evolved in the CAM plants, such as pineapples and cacti.

8. **CAM plants** conserve water by opening their stomata and admitting CO_2 only at night.

9. CO_2 is fixed into a four-carbon compound,

   a. which banks CO_2 at night and

   b. releases it to the Calvin cycle during the day.

V. Photosynthesis Reviewed and Extended

A. 7.12 Review: Photosynthesis uses light energy, carbon dioxide, and water to make organic molecules

1. Most of the living world depends on the food-making machinery of photosynthesis.

2. The chloroplast

   a. integrates the two stages of photosynthesis and

   b. makes sugar from CO_2.

3. About half of the carbohydrates made by photosynthesis are consumed as fuel for cellular respiration in the mitochondria of plant cells.

4. Sugars also serve as the starting material for making other organic molecules, such as proteins, lipids, and cellulose.

5. Excess food made by plants is stockpiled as starch in roots, tubers, seeds, and fruits.

B. 7.13 CONNECTION: Photosynthesis may moderate global climate change

   1. The **greenhouse effect** operates on a global scale.

      a. Solar radiation includes visible light that penetrates the Earth's atmosphere and warm's the planet's surface.

      b. Heat radiating from the warmed planet is absorbed by gases in the atmosphere, which then reflects some of the heat back to Earth.

      c. Without the warming of the greenhouse effect, the Earth would be much colder and most life as we know it could not exist.

   2. The gases in the atmosphere that absorb heat radiation are called greenhouse gases. These include

      a. water vapor,

      b. carbon dioxide, and

      c. methane.

   3. Increasing concentrations of greenhouse gases have been linked to **global climate change** (also called global warming), a slow but steady rise in Earth's surface temperature.

   4. Since 1850, the atmospheric concentration of CO_2 has increased by about 40%, mostly due to the combustion of fossil fuels including

      a. coal,

      b. oil, and

      c. gasoline.

   5. The predicted consequences of continued warming include

      a. melting of polar ice,

      b. rising sea levels,

      c. extreme weather patterns,

      d. droughts,

      e. increased extinction rates, and

      f. the spread of tropical disease.

   6. Widespread deforestation has aggravated the global warming problem by reducing an effective CO_2 sink.

   7. Global warming caused by increasing CO_2 levels may be reduced by

      a. limiting deforestation,

      b. reducing fossil fuel consumption, and

      c. growing biofuel crops that remove CO_2 from the atmosphere.

C. 7.14 SCIENTIFIC DISCOVERY: Scientific study of Earth's ozone layer has global significance

   1. Solar radiation converts O_2 high in the atmosphere to ozone (O_3), which shields organisms from damaging UV radiation.

   2. Industrial chemicals called CFCs have caused dangerous thinning of the ozone layer, but international restrictions on CFC use are allowing a slow recovery.

Chapter Guide to Teaching Resources

An Overview of Photosynthesis (7.1–7.5)

Student Misconceptions and Concerns

- Students may not connect the growth in plant mass to the fixation of carbon during the Calvin cycle. It can be difficult for many students to appreciate that molecules in air can contribute significantly to the mass of plants. (7.3)

- Students may understand the overall chemical relationships between photosynthesis and cellular respiration, but many struggle to understand the use of carbon dioxide in the Calvin cycle. Photosynthesis is much more than gas exchange. (7.5)

Teaching Tips

- When introducing the diverse ways that plants impact our lives, consider challenging your students to come up with a list of products made from plants that they come across on a regular basis. The collective lists from your students can be surprisingly long and might help to build up your catalog of examples. (7.1)

- The evolution of chloroplasts from photosynthetic prokaryotes living inside of eukaryotic cells is discussed in Module 4.15. If your students have not already read Chapter 4, consider discussing this theory of endosymbiosis. (7.1)

- Some students might think that the term producers applies to the production of oxygen by plants. In turn, they might think that consumers are organisms that use oxygen (which would include all aerobic organisms). Extra care may be needed to clarify the definitions of these frequently used terms. (7.1)

- The authors note the analogous roles of the thylakoid space and the intermembrane space of a mitochondrion. Students might be encouraged to create a list of the similarities in structure and function of mitochondria and chloroplasts through these related chapters. (7.2)

- The living world contains many examples of adaptations to increase surface area. Some examples are the many folds of the inner mitochondrial membrane; the highly branched surfaces of plant roots, fish gills, and human lungs; and the highly branched system of capillaries in the tissues of our bodies. Consider relating this broad principle to the extensive folding of the thylakoid membranes. (7.2)

- Many students do not realize that glucose is not the direct product of photosynthesis. Although glucose is often shown as a final product of photosynthesis, a three-carbon sugar is directly produced (G3P, as the authors note later in module 7.10). A plant can use G3P to make many types of organic molecules, including glucose. (7.3)

- In our world, energy is frequently converted to a usable form in one place and used in another. For example, electricity is generated by power plants, transferred to our homes, and used to run computers, create light, and help us prepare foods. Consider relating this common energy transfer to the two-stage process of photosynthesis. (7.4–7.5)

- Figure 7.5 is an important visual organizer, which notes the key structures and functions of the two stages of photosynthesis. This figure demonstrates that water and sunlight are used in the thylakoid membranes to generate oxygen, ATP, and NADPH. The second step, in the stroma, reveals the use of carbon dioxide, ATP, and NADPH to ultimately generate carbohydrates. (7.5)

The Light Reactions: Converting Solar Energy to Chemical Energy (7.6–7.9)

Student Misconceptions and Concerns

- The authors note that electromagnetic energy travels through space in waves that are like ripples made by a pebble dropped in a pond. This wave imagery is helpful but can confuse students when energy is also thought of as discrete packets called photons. The dual nature of light, which exhibits the properties of waves and particles, may need to be discussed further, if students are to do more than just accept definitions. (7.6)

- The authors note that sunlight is a type of radiation. Many students think of radiation as a result of radioactive decay, a serious threat to health. The diverse types of radiation and the varying energy associated with each might need to be explained. (7.6)

- Even at the college level, students struggle to understand why we perceive certain colors. The authors discuss the specific absorption and reflection of certain wavelengths of light, noting which colors are absorbed and which are reflected (and thus available for our eyes to detect). Consider spending time to make sure that your students understand how photosynthetic pigments absorb and reflect certain wavelengths. (7.6–7.7)

Teaching Tips

- Consider bringing a prism to class and demonstrating the spectrum of light. Depending on what you have available, it can be a dramatic reinforcement. (7.6)

- The authors discuss a phenomenon that most students have noticed: dark surfaces heat up faster in the sun than do lighter-colored surfaces. This is an opportunity to demonstrate to your students the various depths of scientific explanations and help them appreciate their own educational progress. In elementary school, they might have learned that the sun heats darker surfaces faster than lighter surfaces. In high school, they may have learned about light energy and the fact that dark surfaces absorb more of this energy than lighter surfaces. Now, in college, they are learning that at the atomic level, darker surfaces absorb the energy of more photons, exciting more electrons, which then fall back to a lower state, releasing more heat. (7.7)

- The authors develop a mechanical analogy for the energy levels and movement of electrons in the light reaction. Figure 7.8B equates the height of an electron with its energy state. Thus, electrons captured at high levels carry more energy than electrons in lower positions. Although this figure can be very effective, students might need to be carefully led through the analogy to understand precisely what is represented. (7.8)

- Module 7.9 notes the similarities between oxidative phosphorylation in mitochondria and photophosphorylation in chloroplasts. If your students have not already read or discussed chemiosmosis in mitochondria, consider assigning Modules 6.6 and 6.10 to show the similarities of these processes. (As noted in Module 7.2, the thylakoid space is analogous to the intermembrane space of mitochondria.) (7.9)

The Calvin Cycle: Reducing CO_2 to Sugar (7.10–7.11)

Student Misconceptions and Concerns

- The terms light reactions and dark reactions can lead students to conclude that each set of reactions occurs at different times of the day. However, the Calvin cycle in most plants occurs during daylight, when NADPH and ATP from the light reactions are readily available. (7.10)

Teaching Tips

- Glucose is not the direct product of the Calvin cycle, as might be expected from the general equation for photosynthesis. Instead, as noted in the text, G3P is the main product. Clarify the diverse uses of G3P in the production of many important plant molecules for students. (7.10)

- If you can find examples of C_3, C_4, and CAM plants, consider bringing them to class. Referring to living plants helps students understand these abstract concepts. Nice photographs can serve as a substitute. (7.11)

- Relate the properties of C_3 and C_4 plants to the regions of the country where each is grown. Students might generally understand that crops have specific requirements, but may not specifically relate these physiological differences to their geographic sites of production or specific evolutionary histories. (7.11)

Photosynthesis Reviewed and Extended (7.12–7.14)

Student Misconceptions and Concerns

- Some students do not realize that plant cells also have mitochondria. Instead, they assume that the chloroplasts are sufficient for the plant cell's needs. As noted in the text, nearly 50% of the carbohydrates produced by plant cells are used for cellular respiration (involving mitochondria). (7.12)

- Students often do not fully understand how the burning of fossil fuels contributes to global warming. They might wonder, "How does the burning of fossil fuels differ from the burning of ethanol produced from crops?" Students might not realize that the carbon in fossil fuels was removed from the atmosphere hundreds of millions of years ago, while the carbon in crops was removed much more recently, when the crops were grown. The use of ethanol as an alternative is complicated by the typical reliance upon fossil fuels for ethanol production. (7.13)

- Students may confuse global warming with the breakdown of the ozone layer. Be prepared to explain both phenomena and the impact of human activities. (7.13–7.14)

Teaching Tips

- Challenge students to explain how the energy in beef is ultimately derived from the sun. (7.12)

- The authors note that G3P is also used to produce cellulose, the most abundant organic molecule in a plant and probably on the surface of the Earth! (7.12)

- Some students might better relate the greenhouse effect to what happens inside their closed car on a sunny day. The glass in our automobiles functions like the glass of a greenhouse, trapping heat inside our car. This can be an advantage during the winter but is usually not welcome on a hot summer day! (7.13)

- Consider an analogy between the ozone layer and sunscreen applied to the skin. The thinning of the ozone layer is like putting on less and less sunscreen. In both situations, more harmful UV light penetrates the layers and causes damage. (7.14)

- Frustration can overwhelm concerned students alarmed by the many problems addressed in this chapter. One way to address this is to provide meaningful ways for students to respond to this information (for example, changes in personal choices and voting). The Earth Day Network, www.earthday.net, is just one of many Internet sites devoted to positive action. (7.14)

Key Terms

autotroph	global climate change	photophosphorylation
C₃ plant	grana (singular, granum)	photorespiration
C₄ plant	greenhouse effect	photosynthesis
Calvin cycle	heterotrophs	photosystem
CAM plants	light reactions	stomata (singular, stoma)
carbon fixation	mesophyll	stroma
chlorophyll *a*	NADP⁺	thylakoids
electromagnetic spectrum	photon	wavelength

Word Roots

auto- = self (*autotroph*: an organism that makes its own food, thereby sustaining itself without eating other organisms or their molecules)

chloro- = green; **-phyll** = leaf (*chlorophyll*: a green pigment located within the chloroplasts of plants, algae, and certain prokaryotes)

electro- = electricity; **magnet-** = magnetic (*electromagnetic spectrum*: the entire spectrum of radiation)

meso- = middle (*mesophyll*: the middle layer of tissue inside a leaf)

photo- = light (*photon*: a fixed quantity of light energy)

-synthesis = put together or combine (*photosynthesis*: the process by which autotrophs use light energy to make sugars and other organic food molecules from carbon dioxide and water)

thylaco- = sac or pouch (*thylakoids*: disk-shaped membranous sacs inside a chloroplast)

-troph = food (*autotroph*: an organism that makes its own food, thereby sustaining itself without eating other organisms or their molecules)

CHAPTER 8

The Cellular Basis of Reproduction and Inheritance

Chapter Objectives

Opening Essay

Explain why cancer cells are dangerous and note several strategies of cancer treatment.

Connections Between Cell Division and Reproduction

8.1 Compare the parent-offspring relationship in asexual and sexual reproduction.

8.1 Explain why cell division is essential for prokaryotic and eukaryotic life.

8.2 Explain how daughter prokaryotic chromosomes are separated from each other during binary fission.

The Eukaryotic Cell Cycle and Mitosis

8.3 Compare the structure of prokaryotic and eukaryotic chromosomes.

8.4 Describe the stages of the cell cycle. Identify when DNA is replicated, chromosomes are sorted, and two new cells are formed.

8.5 List the phases of mitosis and describe the events characteristic of each phase. Recognize the phases of mitosis from diagrams and micrographs.

8.6 Compare cytokinesis in animal and plant cells.

8.7–8.8 Explain how anchorage, cell density, and chemical growth factors control cell division.

8.9 Explain how cancerous cells are different from healthy cells. Distinguish between benign and malignant tumors, and explain the strategies behind some common cancer treatments.

8.10 Describe the functions of mitosis.

Meiosis and Crossing Over

8.11 Explain how chromosomes are paired. Distinguish between autosomes and sex chromosomes.

8.12 Distinguish between somatic cells and gametes and between diploid cells and haploid cells.

8.12 Explain why sexual reproduction requires meiosis.

8.13 List the phases of meiosis I and meiosis II and describe the events characteristic of each phase. Recognize the phases of meiosis from diagrams and micrographs.

8.14 Describe the similarities and differences between mitosis and meiosis. Explain how the result of meiosis differs from the result of mitosis.

8.15–8.17 Explain how independent orientation of chromosomes at metaphase I, random fertilization, and crossing over contribute to genetic variation in sexually reproducing organisms.

Alterations of Chromosome Number and Structure

8.18 Explain how and why karyotyping is performed.

8.19 Describe the causes and symptoms of Down syndrome.

8.20 Define nondisjunction, explain how it can occur, and describe what can result.

8.21 Describe the consequences of abnormal numbers of sex chromosomes.

8.22 Explain how new species form from errors in cell division.

8.23 Describe the main types of chromosomal changes. Explain why cancer is not usually inherited.

Lecture Outline

I. Introduction

A. Cancer cells

1. start out as normal body cells,
2. undergo genetic mutations,
3. lose the ability to control the tempo of their own division, and
4. run amok, causing disease.

B. In a healthy body, cell division allows for

1. growth,
2. the replacement of damaged cells, and
3. development from an embryo into an adult.

C. In sexually reproducing organisms, eggs and sperm result from

1. mitosis and
2. meiosis.

II. Cell Division and Reproduction

A. 8.1 Cell division plays many important roles in the lives of organisms

1. Organisms reproduce their own kind, a key characteristic of life.
2. Cell division
   a. is reproduction at the cellular level,
   b. requires the duplication of chromosomes, and
   c. sorts new sets of chromosomes into the resulting pair of daughter cells.
3. Cell division is used
   a. for reproduction of single-celled organisms,
   b. growth of multicellular organisms from a fertilized egg into an adult,
   c. repair and replacement of cells, and
   d. sperm and egg production.
4. Living organisms reproduce by two methods.
   a. **Asexual reproduction**
      i. produces offspring that are identical to the original cell or organism and
      ii. involves inheritance of all genes from one parent.

       b. Sexual reproduction

         i. produces offspring that are similar to the parents, but show variations in traits and

         ii. involves inheritance of unique sets of genes from two parents.

  B. 8.2 Prokaryotes reproduce by binary fission

    1. Prokaryotes (bacteria and archaea) reproduce by **binary fission** ("dividing in half").

    2. The chromosome of a prokaryote is

      a. a singular circular DNA molecule associated with proteins and

      b. much smaller than those of eukaryotes.

    3. Binary fission of a prokaryote occurs in three stages.

      a. duplication of the chromosome and separation of the copies,

      b. continued elongation of the cell and movement of the copies, and

      c. division into two daughter cells.

III. The Eukaryotic Cell Cycle and Mitosis

  A. 8.3 The large, complex chromosomes of eukaryotes duplicate with each cell division

    1. Eukaryotic cells

      a. are more complex and larger than prokaryotic cells,

      b. have more genes, and

      c. store most of their genes on multiple chromosomes within the nucleus.

    2. Eukaryotic chromosomes are composed of **chromatin** consisting of

      a. one long DNA molecule and

      b. proteins that help maintain the chromosome structure and control the activity of its genes.

    3. To prepare for division, the chromatin becomes

      a. highly compact and

      b. visible with a microscope.

    4. Before a eukaryotic cell begins to divide, it duplicates all of its chromosomes, resulting in

      a. two copies called **sister chromatids**

      b. joined together by a narrowed "waist" called the **centromere**.

    5. When a cell divides, the sister chromatids

      a. separate from each other, now called chromosomes, and

      b. sort into separate daughter cells.

  B. 8.4 The cell cycle multiplies cells

    1. The **cell cycle** is an ordered sequence of events that extends

      a. from the time a cell is first formed from a dividing parent cell

      b. until its own division.

    2. The cell cycle consists of two stages, characterized as follows:

      a. Interphase: duplication of cell contents

        i. G_1—growth, increase in cytoplasm

        ii. S—duplication of chromosomes (DNA REPLICATION)

        iii. G_2—growth, preparation for division

      b. Mitotic phase: division

        i. Mitosis—division of the nucleus

        ii. Cytokinesis—division of cytoplasm

C. 8.5 Cell division is a continuum of dynamic changes

    1. Mitosis progresses through a series of stages.

        a. prophase,

        b. prometaphase,

        c. metaphase,

        d. anaphase, and

        e. telophase.

    2. Cytokinesis often overlaps telophase.

    3. A **mitotic spindle** is

        a. required to divide the chromosomes,

        b. composed of microtubules, and

        c. produced by **centrosomes**, structures in the cytoplasm that

            i. organize microtubule arrangement and

            ii. contain a pair of centrioles in animal cells.

    4. Interphase

        a. The cytoplasmic contents double,

        b. two centrosomes form,

        c. chromosomes duplicate in the nucleus during the S phase, and

        d. nucleoli, sites of ribosome assembly, are visible.

    5. Prophase

        a. In the cytoplasm microtubules begin to emerge from centrosomes, forming the spindle.

        b. In the nucleus

            i. chromosomes coil and become compact, and

            ii. nucleoli disappear.

    6. Prometaphase

        a. Spindle microtubules reach chromosomes, where they

            i. attach at kinetochores on the centromeres of sister chromatids and

            ii. move chromosomes to the center of the cell through associated protein "motors."

        b. Other microtubules meet those from the opposite poles.

        c. The nuclear envelope disappears.

    7. Metaphase

        a. The mitotic spindle is fully formed.

        b. Chromosomes align at the cell equator.

        c. Kinetochores of sister chromatids are facing the opposite poles of the spindle.

    8. Anaphase

        a. Sister chromatids separate at the centromeres.

        b. Daughter chromosomes are moved to opposite poles of the cell as

            i. motor proteins move the chromosomes along the spindle microtubules, and

            ii. kinetochore microtubules shorten.

        c. The cell elongates due to lengthening of nonkinetochore microtubules.

    9. Telophase

        a. The cell continues to elongate.

        b. The nuclear envelope forms around chromosomes at each pole, establishing daughter nuclei.

        c. Chromatin uncoils and nucleoli reappear.

        d. The spindle disappears.

10. During **cytokinesis**, the cytoplasm is divided into separate cells.

11. The process of cytokinesis differs in animal and plant cells.

D. 8.6 Cytokinesis differs for plant and animal cells

1. In animal cells, cytokinesis occurs as

a. a **cleavage furrow** forms from a contracting ring of microfilaments, interacting with myosin, and

b. the cleavage furrow deepens to separate the contents into two cells.

2. In plant cells, cytokinesis occurs as

a. a **cell plate** forms in the middle, from vesicles containing cell wall material.

b. The cell plate grows outward to reach the edges, dividing the contents into two cells.

c. Each cell now possesses a plasma membrane and cell wall.

E. 8.7 Anchorage, cell density, and chemical growth factors affect cell division

1. The cells within an organism's body divide and develop at different rates.

2. Cell division is controlled by

a. the presence of essential nutrients,

b. **growth factors**, proteins that stimulate division,

c. **density-dependent inhibition**, in which crowded cells stop dividing, and

d. **anchorage dependence**, the need for cells to be in contact with a solid surface to divide.

F. 8.8 Growth factors signal the cell cycle control system

1. The **cell cycle control system** is a cycling set of molecules in the cell that

a. triggers and

b. coordinates key events in the cell cycle.

2. Checkpoints in the cell cycle can

a. stop an event or

b. signal an event to proceed.

3. There are three major checkpoints in the cell cycle.

a. G_1 checkpoint

i. allows entry into the S phase or

ii. causes the cell to leave the cycle, entering a nondividing G_0 phase.

b. G_2 checkpoint, and

c. M checkpoint.

4. Research on the control of the cell cycle is one of the hottest areas in biology today.

G. 8.9 CONNECTION: Growing out of control, cancer cells produce malignant tumors

1. Cancer currently claims the lives of 20% of the people in the United States and other industrialized nations.

2. Cancer cells escape controls on the cell cycle.

3. Cancer cells

a. divide rapidly, often in the absence of growth factors,

b. spread to other tissues through the circulatory system, and

c. grow without being inhibited by other cells.

4. A **tumor** is an abnormally growing mass of body cells.

a. **Benign tumors** remain at the original site.

b. **Malignant tumors** spread to other locations, called **metastasis**.

5. Cancers are named according to the organ or tissue in which they originate.

a. **Carcinomas** arise in external or internal body coverings.

b. **Sarcomas** arise in supportive and connective tissue.

   c. Leukemias and **lymphomas** arise from blood-forming tissues.
  6. Cancer treatments
   a. Localized tumors can be
    i. removed surgically and/or
    ii. treated with concentrated beams of high-energy radiation.
   b. Chemotherapy is used for metastatic tumors.
 H. 8.10 Review: Mitosis provides for growth, cell replacement, and asexual reproduction
  1. When the cell cycle operates normally, mitosis produces genetically identical cells for
   a. growth,
   b. replacement of damaged and lost cells, and
   c. asexual reproduction.

IV. Meiosis and Crossing Over

 A. 8.11 Chromosomes are matched in homologous pairs
  1. In humans, **somatic cells** have
   a. 23 pairs of homologous chromosomes and
   b. one member of each pair from each parent.
  2. The human **sex chromosomes** X and Y differ in size and genetic composition.
  3. The other 22 pairs of chromosomes are **autosomes** with the same size and genetic composition.
  4. Homologous chromosomes are matched in
   a. length,
   b. centromere position, and
   c. gene locations.
  5. A **locus** (plural, *loci*) is the position of a gene.
  6. Different versions of a gene may be found at the same locus on maternal and paternal chromosomes.
 B. 8.12 Gametes have a single set of chromosomes
  1. An organism's **life cycle** is the sequence of stages leading
   a. from the adults of one generation
   b. to the adults of the next.
  2. Humans and many animals and plants are diploid, with body cells that have
   a. two sets of chromosomes,
   b. one from each parent.
  3. Meiosis is a process that converts diploid nuclei to haploid nuclei.
   a. Diploid cells have two homologous sets of chromosomes.
   b. Haploid cells have one set of chromosomes.
   c. Meiosis occurs in the sex organs, producing **gametes**—sperm and eggs.
  4. Fertilization is the union of sperm and egg.
  5. The **zygote** has a diploid chromosome number, one set from each parent.
  6. All sexual life cycles include an alternation between
   a. a diploid stage and
   b. a haploid stage.
  7. Producing haploid gametes prevents the chromosome number from doubling in every generation.
 C. 8.13 Meiosis reduces the chromosome number from diploid to haploid
  1. Meiosis is a type of cell division that produces haploid gametes in diploid organisms.
  2. Two haploid gametes combine in fertilization to restore the diploid state in the zygote.

3. Meiosis and mitosis are preceded by the duplication of chromosomes. However,
   a. meiosis is followed by two consecutive cell divisions, and
   b. mitosis is followed by only one cell division.
4. Because in meiosis, one duplication of chromosomes is followed by two divisions, each of the four daughter cells produced has a haploid set of chromosomes.
5. **Meiosis I – Prophase I** – events occurring in the nucleus.
   a. Chromosomes coil and become compact.
   b. Homologous chromosomes come together as pairs by **synapsis**.
   c. Each pair, with four chromatids, is called a tetrad.
   d. Nonsister chromatids exchange genetic material by crossing over.
6. **Meiosis I – Metaphase I** – Tetrads align at the cell equator.
7. **Meiosis I – Anaphase I** – Homologous pairs separate and move toward opposite poles of the cell.
8. **Meiosis I – Telophase I**
   a. Duplicated chromosomes have reached the poles.
   b. A nuclear envelope re-forms around chromosomes in some species.
   c. Each nucleus has the haploid number of chromosomes.
9. Meiosis II follows meiosis I without chromosome duplication.
10. Each of the two haploid products enters meiosis II.
11. **Meiosis II – Prophase II**
    a. Chromosomes coil and become compact (if uncoiled after telophase I).
    b. Nuclear envelope, if re-formed, breaks up again.
12. **Meiosis II – Metaphase II** – Duplicated chromosomes align at the cell equator.
13. **Meiosis II – Anaphase II**
    a. Sister chromatids separate, and
    b. chromosomes move toward opposite poles.
14. **Meiosis II – Telophase II**
    a. Chromosomes have reached the poles of the cell.
    b. A nuclear envelope forms around each set of chromosomes.
    c. With cytokinesis, four haploid cells are produced.

D. 8.14 Mitosis and meiosis have important similarities and differences
   1. Mitosis and meiosis both
      a. begin with diploid parent cells that
      b. have chromosomes duplicated during the previous interphase.
   2. However, the end products differ.
      a. Mitosis produces two genetically identical diploid somatic daughter cells.
      b. Meiosis produces four genetically unique haploid gametes.
E. 8.15 Independent orientation of chromosomes in meiosis and random fertilization lead to varied offspring
   1. Genetic variation in gametes results from
      a. independent orientation at metaphase I and
      b. random fertilization.
   2. Independent orientation at metaphase I
      a. Each pair of chromosomes independently aligns at the cell equator.
      b. There is an equal probability of the maternal or paternal chromosome facing a given pole.
      c. The number of combinations for chromosomes packaged into gametes is 2^n where n = haploid number of chromosomes.

3. Random fertilization – The combination of each unique sperm with each unique egg increases genetic variability.

F. 8.16 Homologous chromosomes may carry different versions of genes

    1. Separation of homologous chromosomes during meiosis can lead to genetic differences between gametes.

        a. Homologous chromosomes may have different versions of a gene at the same locus.

        b. One version was inherited from the maternal parent and the other came from the paternal parent.

        c. Since homologues move to opposite poles during anaphase I, gametes will receive either the maternal or paternal version of the gene.

G. 8.17 Crossing over further increases genetic variability

    1. Genetic recombination is the production of new combinations of genes due to crossing over.

    2. Crossing over is an exchange of corresponding segments between separate (nonsister) chromatids on homologous chromosomes.

        a. Nonsister chromatids join at a **chiasma** (plural, *chiasmata*), the site of attachment and crossing over.

        b. Corresponding amounts of genetic material are exchanged between maternal and paternal (nonsister) chromatids.

V. Alterations of Chromosome Number and Structure

    A. 8.18 A karyotype is a photographic inventory of an individual's chromosomes

        1. A **karyotype** is an ordered display of magnified images of an individual's chromosomes arranged in pairs.

        2. Karyotypes

            a. are often produced from dividing cells arrested at metaphase of mitosis and

            b. allow for the observation of

            c. homologous chromosome pairs,

            d. chromosome number, and

            e. chromosome structure.

    B. 8.19 CONNECTION: An extra copy of chromosome 21 causes Down syndrome

        1. Trisomy 21

            a. involves the inheritance of three copies of chromosome 21 and

            b. is the most common human chromosome abnormality.

        2. Trisomy 21, called **Down syndrome**, produces a characteristic set of symptoms, which include:

            a. mental retardation,

            b. characteristic facial features,

            c. short stature,

            d. heart defects,

            e. susceptibility to respiratory infections, leukemia, and Alzheimer's disease, and

            f. shortened life span.

        3. The incidence increases with the age of the mother.

    C. 8.20 Accidents during meiosis can alter chromosome number

        1. Nondisjunction is the failure of chromosomes or chromatids to separate normally during meiosis. This can happen during

            a. meiosis I, if both members of a homologous pair go to one pole or

            b. meiosis II if both sister chromatids go to one pole.

2. Fertilization after nondisjunction yields zygotes with altered numbers of chromosomes.

D. 8.21 CONNECTION: Abnormal numbers of sex chromosomes do not usually affect survival

   1. Sex chromosome abnormalities tend to be less severe, perhaps because of

      a. the small size of the Y chromosome or

      b. X-chromosome inactivation.

   2. Table 8.21 in the textbook lists the most common human sex chromosome abnormalities. In general,

      a. a single Y chromosome is enough to produce "maleness," even in combination with several X chromosomes, and

      b. the absence of a Y chromosome yields "femaleness."

E. 8.22 EVOLUTION CONNECTION: New species can arise from errors in cell division

   1. Errors in mitosis or meiosis may produce polyploid species, with more than two chromosome sets.

   2. The formation of polyploid species is

      a. widely observed in many plant species but

      b. less frequently found in animals.

F. 8.23 CONNECTION: Alterations of chromosome structure can cause birth defects and cancer

   1. Chromosome breakage can lead to rearrangements that can produce

      a. genetic disorders or,

      b. if changes occur in somatic cells, cancer.

   2. These rearrangements may include

      a. a **deletion**, the loss of a chromosome segment,

      b. a **duplication**, the repeat of a chromosome segment,

      c. an **inversion**, the reversal of a chromosome segment, or

      d. a **translocation**, the attachment of a segment to a nonhomologous chromosome that can be reciprocal.

   3. Chronic myelogenous leukemia (CML)

      a. is one of the most common leukemias,

      b. affects cells that give rise to white blood cells (leukocytes), and

      c. results from part of chromosome 22 switching places with a small fragment from a tip of chromosome 9.

Chapter Guide to Teaching Resources

Connections Between Cell Division and Reproduction (8.1–8.2)

Student Misconceptions and Concerns

- As the textbook authors note in Module 8.1, biologists use the term daughter to indicate offspring and not gender. Students with little experience in this terminology can easily become confused. (8.1)

- Some basic familiarity or faint memory of mitosis and meiosis might result in a lack of enthusiasm for these topics in some of your students. Consider beginning such lectures with important topics related to cellular reproduction. For example, cancer cells reproduce uncontrollably, stem cells have the capacity to regenerate lost or damaged tissues, and the study of embryonic stem cells is variously restricted and regulated by government. (8.1–8.2)

Teaching Tips

- Sometimes the most basic questions can challenge students and get them focused on the subject at hand. Consider asking your students why we expect that dogs will produce dogs, cats will produce more cats, and chickens will only produce chickens. Why does like produce like? (8.1)

- The principle that "every cell comes from another cell" is worth thinking through with your class. Students might expect that, like automobiles, computers, and cell phones, parts are constructed and cells are assembled. In our society, few nonliving products are generated only from existing products (try to think of such examples). For example, you do not need a painting to paint or a house to construct a house. Yet, this is a common expectation in biology. Further, students who think through this principle might ask how the first cells formed. They might wonder further whether the same environments that produced these cells are still in existence. The conditions on Earth when life first formed were very different from those we know today. Chapter 15 of the textbook addresses the origin and early evolution of life on Earth. (8.2)

- Consider contrasting the timing of DNA replication and cytokinesis in prokaryotes and eukaryotes. In prokaryotes, addressed in Module 8.2 of the textbook, these processes are overlapping. However, as revealed in the next few modules, these events are separate in eukaryotes. (8.2)

The Eukaryotic Cell Cycle and Mitosis (8.3–8.10)

Student Misconceptions and Concerns

- Students often seem confused by the difference between a DNA molecule and a chromosome. This is especially problematic when discussing DNA replication. (8.3)

- Students are often confused by photographs of chromosomes. Such photographs, such as Figure 8.3B, typically show duplicated chromosomes during some aspect of cell division. It remains unclear to many why (a) chromosome structure is typically different between interphase G_1 and the stages of division and (b) why chromosomes are not photographed during interphase (the stage in which chromosomes are typically first discussed) before the chromosomes duplicate. (8.3)

- Students do not typically know that all cancers are genetically based. Consider making this clear early in your discussions. Challenge your students to explain how certain viruses can lead to cancer. (8.9)

Teaching Tips

- Figure 8.3B is an important point of reference for some basic terminology. Consider referring to it as you distinguish between a DNA molecule and a chromosome, unreplicated and replicated chromosomes, and the nature of sister chromatids. (8.3)

- The authors make an analogy between the precise packaging of DNA into chromosomes and packing a home for a move to another home. Tap into the intuitive advantages of packaging DNA using this or any other analogy of highly packaged materials (perhaps a boxed "desk" that requires some assembly). (8.3)

- The concepts of DNA replication and sister chromatids are often obstacles for many students. If you can find twist ties or other bendable wire, you can demonstrate or have students model the difference between (a) a chromosome before DNA replication and (b) sister chromatids after DNA replication. One piece of wire will represent a chromosome before replication. Two twist ties twisted about each other can represent sister chromatids. We have doubled the DNA, but the molecules remain attached (although not attached in the same way as the wire). You might also want to point out that when sister chromatids are separated, they are considered separate chromosomes. (8.3)

- The textbook authors note in Module 8.4 that each of your students consists of about 10 trillion cells. It is likely that this number is beyond comprehension for most of your students. Consider sharing several simple examples of the enormity of that number to try to make it more meaningful. For example, the U.S. population in 2011 is about 312 million people. To give every one of those people about $32,000, we will need a total of 10 trillion dollars. Here is another example. If we gave you $32,000 every second, it would take 10 years to give you 10 trillion dollars. The U.S. Debt Clock helps relate these large numbers to the U.S. national debt at www.usdebtclock.org. (8.4)

- In G_1, the chromosomes have not duplicated. But by G_2, chromosomes consist of sister chromatids. If you have created a demonstration of sister chromatids, relate DNA replication and sister chromatids to the cell cycle. (8.4)

- Students might keep better track of the sequence of events in a cell cycle by simply memorizing the letters IPPMAT which are the first letters of interphase, prophase, prometaphase, metaphase, anaphase, and telophase. (8.5)

- Many students think of mitosis and cytokinesis as one process. In some situations, mitosis occurs without subsequent cytokinesis. Challenge your students to predict the outcome of mitosis without cytokinesis (multinuclear cells called a syncytium). This occurs in human development during the formation of the placenta. (8.6)

- The authors make an analogy between a drawstring on a hooded sweatshirt and the mechanism of cytokinesis in animal cells. Students seem to appreciate this association. Have your students think of a person tightening the drawstring of sweatpants so tight that they pinch themselves in two, or perhaps nearly so! The analogy is especially good because, like the drawstring just beneath the surface of the sweat pants, the microfilaments are just beneath the surface of the cell's plasma membrane. (8.6)

- Students who closely examine a small abrasion on their skin might notice that the wound tends to heal from the outer edges inward. This space-filling mechanism is a natural example of density-dependant inhibition, which is also seen when cells in a cell culture dish stop dividing when they have formed a complete layer. (8.7)

- The cell cycle control system depicted in Figure 8.8A is like the control device of an automatic washing machine (which uses a turning dial). Each has a control system that triggers and coordinates key events in the cycle. However, unlike a washing machine, the components of the control system of a cell cycle are not all located in one place. (8.8)

- Chemotherapy has some disastrous side effects. The drugs used to fight cancer may attack rapidly dividing cells. Unfortunately for men, the cells that make sperm are also rapidly dividing. In some circumstances, chemotherapy can leave a man infertile (unable to produce viable sperm) but still able to produce an erection. Many other approaches are under consideration to attack cancers. You may wish to explore these as sidelights to your lecture. Good resources include cell biology and development textbooks. (8.9)

- Figure 8.10 visually summarizes key functions of mitosis. It is an important image to introduce mitosis or summarize mitosis after addressing its details. (8.10)

Meiosis and Crossing Over (8.11–8.17)

Student Misconceptions and Concerns

- Some students might conclude that sex chromosomes function only in determining the sex of an individual. As the authors note, sex chromosomes contain genes not involved in sex determination. (8.11)

- Students might not immediately see the need for meiosis in sexual reproduction. Consider an example of what would happen over many generations if gametes were produced by mitosis. The resulting genetic doubling is prevented if each gamete has only half the genetic material of the adult cells. (8.12–8.14)

Teaching Tips

- Students might recall some basic genetics, remembering that for many traits a person receives a separate "signal" from mom and dad. These separate signals for the same trait are carried on the same portion of homologous chromosomes, such as the freckle trait noted in Module 8.11 of the textbook. (8.11)

- Consider helping students through mitosis and meiosis by developing an analogy to pairs of shoes. In this case, any given species has a certain number of pairs of shoes, or homologous chromosomes. (8.12)

- In the shoe analogy, females have 23 pairs of matching shoes, while males have 22 matching pairs and 1 odd pair . . . maybe a sandal and a sneaker! (8.12)

- You might want to get your students thinking by asking them why eggs and sperm are different. (This depends upon the species, but within vertebrates, eggs and sperm are specialized for different tasks. Sperm are adapted to move to an egg and donate a nucleus. Eggs contain a nucleus and most of the cytoplasm of the future zygote. Thus eggs are typically larger, nonmotile, and full of cellular resources to sustain cell division and growth.) (8.12)

- Challenge students to identify which stage of meiosis is most like mitosis. Comparing the specific events of mitosis, meiosis I, and meiosis II to each other allows students to identify essential differences. (8.13)

- How meiosis results in four haploid cells, yet mitosis yields two diploid cells, is often memorized but seldom understood. It can be explained like this. Consider a pair of chromosomes in a cell before any cell divisions. This pair of chromosomes duplicates such that two chromosomes become four (although each pair of sister chromatids are joined at their centromeres). Therefore, mitosis and meiosis each typically begin with four "chromosomes" after replication but before division. Mitosis divides once, producing two cells, each with two chromosomes. Meiosis divides twice, sorting the four chromosomes into four separate cells. (8.14)

- Consider emphasizing a crucial difference between the processes of mitosis and meiosis. In mitosis, sister chromatids separate at metaphase. In meiosis I metaphase, sister chromatids stay together, and homologous pairs of chromosomes separate. Consider sketching a comparison of the alignment of the chromosomes at mitosis metaphase and meiosis metaphase I. Figure 8.14 helps to make this important distinction. You might create a test question in which you ask students to draw several pairs of homologous chromosomes lined up at metaphase in mitosis versus meiosis I. (8.14)

- The possible number of combinations produced by independent orientation of human chromosomes at meiosis metaphase I is 2^{23} or 8,388,608. This number squared is more than 70 trillion. The authors rounded down to 8 million for 2^{23} and squared this, to estimate 64 trillion possible combinations. But more precisely, the number of possible zygotes produced by a single pair of reproducing humans, based solely on independent assortment and random fertilization, is over 70 trillion! (8.15)

- Another way to represent the various combinations produced by independent orientation of chromosomes at meiosis metaphase I continues the shoe analogy. Imagine that you have two pairs of shoes. One pair is black, the other is white. You want to make a new pair of shoes by drawing one shoe from each original pair. Four possible pairs can be made. You can have (1) the left black and left white, (2) the right black and right white, (3) the left black and right white, or (4) the right black and left white. Actually using two pairs of shoes from your students can inject humor and create a concrete example that reduces confusion. For an additional bit of humor, ask the class if 46 students want to contribute their shoes as you try to demonstrate all 8,388,608 combinations! (8.15)

- You might have some fun with the concept of different versions of genes. Playing with the pun "jeans," ask students if all jeans are the same. (Some are stone washed, some have buttons instead of zippers, some have more pockets than others, etc.) These versions of clothing jeans are like different versions of genetic genes, representing options and sources of diversity. (8.16)

- If you wish to continue the shoe analogy, crossing over is somewhat like exchanging the shoelaces in a pair of shoes (although this analogy is quite limited). A point to make is that the shoes (chromosomes) before crossing over are what you inherited . . . either from the sperm or the egg; but, as a result of crossing over, you no longer pass along exactly what you inherited. Instead, you pass along a combination of homologous chromosomes (think of shoes with switched shoelaces). Critiquing this limited analogy may also help students to think through the process of crossing over. (8.17)

- In the shoe analogy, after exchanging shoelaces, we have "recombinant shoes"! (8.17)

- Challenge students to consider the number of unique humans that can be formed by the processes of the independent orientation of chromosomes, random fertilization, and crossing over. Without crossing over, we already calculated over 70 trillion possibilities. But as the text notes in Module 8.17, there are typically one to three crossover events for each human chromosome, and these can occur at many different places along the length of the chromosome. The potential number of combinations far exceeds any number that humans can comprehend, representing the truly unique nature of each human being (an important point that delights many students!). (8.17)

Alterations of Chromosome Number and Structure (8.18–8.23)

Student Misconceptions and Concerns

- Before addressing karyotyping and nondisjunction events, consider reviewing the general structure and terminology associated with replicated chromosomes and the arrangement of chromosomes during metaphase of mitosis, meiosis I, and meiosis II. Figures 8.3B and 8.14 will be particularly helpful. A firm foundation in chromosome basics is necessary to understand the irregularities discussed in Modules 8.19–8.23. (8.18–8.23)

Teaching Tips

- The Human Genome website is a tremendous asset for nearly every discussion related to human genetics. It can be accessed at www.genomics.energy.gov. (8.18–8.23)

- If you have several hundred students or more in your class, it is likely that at least one of your students has a sibling with Down syndrome. The authors note that overall, about one in every 700 babies are born with Down syndrome. (8.19)

- The National Down Syndrome Society has a website at www.ndss.org. It is a wonderful resource. (8.19)

- Students might be confused by the term nondisjunction. But simply put, it is an error in the sorting of chromosomes during mitosis or meiosis. Figure 8.20 illustrates two types of nondisjunction errors in meiosis. (8.20)

- Some syndromes related to human sexuality are not the result of abnormalities in sex chromosome number. Androgen insensitivity syndrome produces sterile males who possess mostly female sex characteristics. People with this condition are genetically male but have bodies that fail to respond to male sex hormones. The National Institute of Health website "Genetics Home Reference" can provide additional details about this and most genetic disorders at http://ghr.nlm.nih.gov. (8.21)

- In general, flowering plants are more likely to form new species through polyploidy than animals, because unlike most animals, many flowering plants can fertilize themselves. (8.22)

- The gray treefrog, which is found over most of the eastern half of the United States, from Florida and Texas to Ontario and Maine, consists of two species: *Hyla chrysoscelis*, which is diploid, and *Hyla versicolor*, which is tetraploid. The two species cannot be distinguished except by the number of chromosomes in their cells. The tetraploid species is thought to have been formed by an error in meiosis, similar to that frequently seen in plants. (8.22)

- Challenge students to create a simple sentence and then modify that sentence to represent (a) a deletion, (b) a duplication, and (c) an inversion as an analogy to these changes to a chromosome. (8.23)

Key Terms

anaphase	benign tumor	cell cycle
anchorage dependence	binary fission	cell cycle control system
asexual reproduction	cancer	cell division
autosome	carcinoma	cell plate

centromere

centrosome

chiasma (plural, chiasmata)

chromatin

chromosome

cleavage furrow

crossing over

cytokinesis

deletion

density-dependent inhibition

diploid cell

Down syndrome

duplication

fertilization

gamete

genetic recombination

growth factor

haploid cell

homologous chromosomes

interphase

inversion

karyotype

leukemia

life cycle

locus (plural, loci)

lymphoma

malignant tumor

meiosis

metaphase

metastasis

mitotic phase (M phase)

mitotic spindle

mitosis

prometaphase

prophase

sarcomas

sex chromosome

sexual reproduction

sister chromatid

somatic cell

telophase

tetrad

translocation

trisomy 21

tumor

zygote

Word Roots

a- = not or without (*asexual reproduction*: the creation of offspring by a single parent, without the participation of sperm and egg)

ana- = up, throughout, again (*anaphase*: the fourth stage of mitosis, beginning when sister chromatids separate from each other and ending when a complete set of daughter chromosomes arrives at each of the two poles of the cell)

auto- = self; **-soma** = body (*autosome*: a chromosome not directly involved in determining the sex of an organism)

bi- = two (*binary fission*: a means of asexual reproduction in which a parent organism, often a single cell, divides into two individuals of about equal size)

centro- = the center; **-mere** = a part (*centromere*: the region of a duplicated chromosome where two sister chromatids are joined and where spindle microtubules attach during mitosis and meiosis); **-soma** = body (*centrosome*: a nonmembranous organelle that functions throughout the cell cycle to organize the cell's microtubules)

chiasm- = marked crosswise (*chiasma*: the X-shaped microscopically visible site where crossing over has occurred between the chromatids of homologous chromosomes during prophase I of meiosis)

chroma- = colored (*chromatin*: DNA and the various associated proteins that form eukaryotic chromosomes); **-soma** = body (*chromosome*: a threadlike, gene-carrying structure composed of chromatin, found in the nucleus of eukaryotic cells)

cyto- = cell; **-kinet** = move (*cytokinesis*: the division of the cytoplasm to form two separate daughter cells)

di- = two (*diploid cell*: in an organism that reproduces sexually, a cell containing two homologous sets of chromosomes, one from each parent)

fertil- = fruitful (*fertilization*: the union of the nucleus of a sperm cell with the nucleus of an egg cell, producing a zygote)

gamet- = a wife or husband (*gamete*: a haploid egg or sperm cell)

haplo- = single (*haploid cell*: in the life cycle of an organism that reproduces sexually, a cell containing a single set of chromosomes)

homo- = like (*homologous chromosomes*: the two chromosomes that make up a matched pair in a diploid cell)

inter- = between (*interphase*: the period in the eukaryotic cell cycle when the cell is not actually dividing)

karyo- = nucleus (*karyotype*: a display of micrographs of the metaphase chromosomes of a cell)

mal- = bad or evil (*malignant tumor*: an abnormal tissue mass that can spread into neighboring tissue and to other parts of the body)

meio- = less (*meiosis*: a form of cell division that yields daughter cells with half as many chromosomes as the parent cell)

meta- = between (*metaphase*: the third mitotic stage, during which all the cell's duplicated chromosomes are aligned in the middle of the cell)

mito- = a thread (*mitosis*: the division of a single nucleus into two genetically identical daughter nuclei)

pro- = before (*prophase*: the first mitotic stage, during which the chromatin condenses to form sister chromatids)

soma- = body (*somatic cell*: any cell in a multicellular organism except a sperm or egg cell, or a cell that develops into a sperm or egg)

telos- = an end (*telophase*: the final stage of mitosis, during which daughter nuclei form)

trans- = across (*translocation*: attachment of a chromosomal fragment to a nonhomologous chromosome)

tri- = three; **soma-** = body (*trisomy*: a chromosomal condition in which a particular cell has an extra copy of one chromosome, instead of the normal two; the cell is said to be trisomic for that chromosome)

CHAPTER 9

Patterns of Inheritance

Chapter Objectives

Opening Essay

Explain how human experiences breeding dog and food crops can provide insights into principles of genetics.

Mendel's Laws

9.1 Describe pangenesis theory and the blending hypothesis. Explain why both ideas are now rejected.

9.2 Explain why Mendel's decision to work with peas was a good choice. Define and distinguish between true-breeding organisms, hybrids, the P generation, the F_1 generation, and the F_2 generation.

9.3 Define and distinguish between the following pairs of terms: homozygous and heterozygous; dominant allele and recessive allele; genotype and phenotype. Also, define a monohybrid cross and a Punnett square.

9.3 Explain how Mendel's law of segregation describes the inheritance of a single characteristic.

9.4 Describe the genetic relationships between homologous chromosomes.

9.5 Explain how Mendel's law of independent assortment applies to a dihybrid cross. Illustrate this law with examples from Labrador retrievers and Mendel's work with peas.

9.6 Explain how a testcross is performed to determine the genotype of an organism.

9.7 Explain how and when the rule of multiplication and the rule of addition can be used to determine the probability of an event. Explain why Mendel was wise to use large sample sizes in his studies.

9.8 Explain how family pedigrees can help determine the inheritance of many human traits.

9.9 Explain how recessive and dominant disorders are inherited. Provide examples of each.

9.10 Compare the health risks, advantages, and disadvantages of the following forms of fetal testing: amniocentesis, chorionic villus sampling, and ultrasound imaging. Describe the ethical dilemmas created by advances in biotechnology discussed in this chapter.

Variations on Mendel's Laws

9.11–9.15 Describe the inheritance patterns of incomplete dominance, multiple alleles, codominance, pleiotropy, and polygenic inheritance. Provide an example of each.

9.13 Explain how the sickle-cell allele can be adaptive.

9.14–9.15 Explain why human skin coloration is not sufficiently explained by polygenic inheritance.

The Chromosomal Basis of Inheritance

9.16 Define the chromosome theory of inheritance. Explain the chromosomal basis of the laws of segregation and independent assortment.

9.17 Explain how linked genes are inherited differently from nonlinked genes.

9.18 Describe T. H. Morgan's studies of crossing over in fruit flies. Explain how crossing over produces new combinations of alleles.

9.19 Explain how Sturtevant created linkage maps.

Sex Chromosomes and Sex-Linked Genes

9.20 Explain how sex is genetically determined in humans and the significance of the *SRY* gene. Compare the sex determination system in humans to those in fruit flies, grasshoppers, birds, and bees.

9.21–9.22 Describe patterns of sex-linked inheritance, noting examples in fruit flies and humans.

9.22 Explain why sex-linked disorders are expressed more frequently in men than in women.

9.23 Explain how the Y chromosome can be used to trace human ancestry.

Lecture Outline

I. Introduction

   A. Dogs are one of man's longest genetic experiments.

      1. Over thousands of years, humans have chosen and mated dogs with specific traits.

      2. The result has been an incredibly diverse array of dogs with distinct

         a. body types and

         b. behavioral traits.

II. Mendel's Laws

   A. 9.1 The science of genetics has ancient roots

      1. Pangenesis, proposed around 400 B.C. by Hippocrates, was an early explanation for inheritance that suggested that

         a. particles called pangenes came from all parts of the organism to be incorporated into eggs or sperm, and

         b. characteristics acquired during the parents' lifetime could be transferred to the offspring.

      2. Aristotle rejected pangenesis and argued that instead of particles, the *potential* to produce the traits was inherited.

      3. The idea that hereditary materials mix in forming offspring, called the blending hypothesis, was

         a. suggested in the 19th century by scientists studying plants but

         b. later rejected because it did not explain how traits that disappear in one generation can reappear in later generations.

B. 9.2 Experimental genetics began in an abbey garden

1. **Heredity** is the transmission of traits from one generation to the next.
2. **Genetics** is the scientific study of heredity.
3. Gregor Mendel
    a. began the field of genetics in the 1860s,
    b. deduced the principles of genetics by breeding garden peas, and
    c. relied upon a background of mathematics, physics, and chemistry.
4. In 1866, Mendel
    a. correctly argued that parents pass on to their offspring discrete "heritable factors" and
    b. stressed that the heritable factors (today called genes), retain their individuality generation after generation.
5. Heritable features that vary among individuals, such as flower color, are called a **character**.
6. Each variant for a character, such as purple or white flowers, is a **trait**.
7. **True-breeding** varieties result when self-fertilization produces offspring all identical to the parent.
8. The offspring of two different varieties are **hybrids**.
9. The cross-fertilization is a hybridization, or genetic **cross**.
10. True-breeding parental plants are the **P generation**.
11. Hybrid offspring are the **F₁ generation**.
12. A cross of F₁ plants produces an **F₂ generation**.

C. 9.3 Mendel's law of segregation describes the inheritance of a single character

1. A cross between two individuals differing in a single character is a **monohybrid cross**.
2. Mendel performed a monohybrid cross between a plant with purple flowers and a plant with white flowers.
    a. The F₁ generation produced all plants with purple flowers.
    b. A cross of F₁ plants with each other produced an F₂ generation with ¾ purple and ¼ white flowers.
3. The all purple F₁ generation did not produce light purple flowers, as predicted by the blending hypothesis.
4. Mendel needed to explain why the
    a. white color seemed to disappear in the F₁ generation and
    b. white color reappeared in one quarter of the F₂ offspring.
5. Mendel observed the same patterns of inheritance for six other pea plant characters.
6. Mendel developed four hypotheses, described below using modern terminology.
    a. **Alleles** are alternative versions of genes that account for variations in inherited characters.
    b. For each characteristic, an organism inherits two alleles, one from each parent. The alleles can be the same or different.
        i. A **homozygous** genotype has identical alleles.
        ii. A **heterozygous** genotype has two different alleles.
    c. If the alleles of an inherited pair differ, then one determines the organism's appearance and is called the **dominant** allele. The other has no noticeable effect on the organism's appearance and is called the **recessive** allele.
        i. The **phenotype** is the appearance or expression of a trait.
        ii. The **genotype** is the genetic makeup of a trait.

       iii. The same phenotype may be determined by more than one genotype.

    d. A sperm or egg carries only one allele for each inherited character because allele pairs separate (segregate) from each other during the production of gametes. This statement is called the **law of segregation**.

  7. Mendel's hypotheses also explain the 3:1 ratio in the F$_2$ generation.

    a. The F$_1$ hybrids all have a *Pp* genotype.

    b. A **Punnett square** shows the four possible combinations of alleles that could occur when these gametes combine.

D. 9.4 Homologous chromosomes bear the alleles for each character

  1. A **locus** (plural, *loci*) is the specific location of a gene along a chromosome.

  2. For a pair of homologous chromosomes, alleles of a gene reside at the same locus.

    a. Homozygous individuals have the same allele on both homologues.

    b. Heterozygous individuals have a different allele on each homologue.

E. 9.5 The law of independent assortment is revealed by tracking two characters at once

  1. A **dihybrid cross** is a mating of parental varieties that differ in two characters.

  2. Mendel performed the following dihybrid cross with the following results:

    a. P generation: round yellow seeds × wrinkled green seeds

    b. F$_1$ generation: all plants with round yellow seeds

    c. F$_2$ generation:

      i. 9/16 had round yellow seeds

      ii. 3/16 had wrinkled yellow seeds

      iii. 3/16 had round green seeds

      iv. 1/16 had wrinkled green seeds

  3. Mendel needed to explain why the F$_2$ offspring

    a. had new nonparental combinations of traits and

    b. a 9:3:3:1 phenotypic ratio.

  4. Mendel

    a. suggested that the inheritance of one character has no effect on the inheritance of another,

    b. suggested that the dihybrid cross is the equivalent to two monohybrid crosses, and

    c. called this the **law of independent assortment**.

  5. Figure 9.5C demonstrates the law of independent assortment as it applies to two characters in Labrador retrievers:

    a. black versus chocolate color,

    b. normal vision versus progressive retinal atrophy.

F. 9.6 Geneticists can use the testcross to determine unknown genotypes

  1. A **testcross** is the mating between an individual of unknown genotype and a homozygous recessive individual.

  2. A testcross can show whether the unknown genotype includes a recessive allele.

  3. Mendel used testcrosses to verify that he had true-breeding genotypes.

  4. The following figure demonstrates how a testcross can be performed to determine the genotype of a Lab with normal eyes.

G. 9.7 Mendel's laws reflect the rules of probability

  1. Using his strong background in mathematics, Mendel knew that the rules of mathematical probability affected

    a. the segregation of allele pairs during gamete formation and

    b. the reforming of pairs at fertilization.

2. The probability scale ranges from 0 to 1. An event that is
    a. certain has a probability of 1 and
    b. certain *not* to occur has a probability of 0.
3. The probability of a specific event is the number of ways that event can occur out of the total possible outcomes.
4. Determining the probability of two independent events uses the **rule of multiplication**, in which the probability is the *product* of the probabilities for each event.
5. The probability that an event can occur in two or more alternative ways is the *sum* of the separate probabilities, called the **rule of addition**.

H. 9.8 CONNECTION: Genetic traits in humans can be tracked through family pedigrees
1. In a simple dominant-recessive inheritance of dominant allele *A* and recessive allele *a*,
    a. a recessive phenotype always results from a homozygous recessive genotype (*aa*), but
    b. a dominant phenotype can result from either
        i. the homozygous dominant genotype (*AA*) or
        ii. a heterozygous genotype (*Aa*).
2. **Wild-type traits**, those prevailing in nature, are not necessarily specified by dominant alleles.
3. The inheritance of human traits follows Mendel's laws.
4. A **pedigree**
    a. shows the inheritance of a trait in a family through multiple generations,
    b. demonstrates dominant or recessive inheritance, and
    c. can also be used to deduce genotypes of family members.

I. 9.9 CONNECTION: Many inherited disorders in humans are controlled by a single gene
1. Inherited human disorders show either
    a. recessive inheritance in which
        i. two recessive alleles are needed to show disease,
        ii. heterozygous parents are carriers of the disease-causing allele, and
        iii. the probability of inheritance increases with **inbreeding**, mating between close relatives.
    b. dominant inheritance in which
        i. one dominant allele is needed to show disease and
        ii. dominant lethal alleles are usually eliminated from the population.
2. The most common fatal genetic disease in the United States is **cystic fibrosis** (CF), resulting in excessive thick mucus secretions. The CF allele is
    a. recessive and
    b. carried by about 1 in 31 Americans.
3. Dominant human disorders include
    a. **achondroplasia**, resulting in dwarfism, and
    b. **Huntington's disease**, a degenerative disorder of the nervous system.

J. 9.10 CONNECTION: New technologies can provide insight into one's genetic legacy
1. New technologies offer ways to obtain genetic information
    a. before conception,
    b. during pregnancy, and
    c. after birth.
2. Genetic testing of parents can identify potential parents who are heterozygous carriers for certain diseases.

3. Several technologies can be used for detecting genetic conditions in a fetus.
   a. **Amniocentesis** extracts samples of amniotic fluid containing fetal cells and permits
      i. karyotyping and
      ii. biochemical tests on cultured fetal cells to detect other conditions, such as Tay-Sachs disease.
   b. **Chorionic villus sampling** removes a sample of chorionic villus tissue from the placenta and permits similar karyotyping and biochemical tests.
4. Blood tests on the mother at 14–20 weeks of pregnancy can help identify fetuses at risk for certain birth defects.
5. Fetal imaging enables a physician to examine a fetus directly for anatomical deformities. The most common procedure is **ultrasound imaging**, using sound waves to produce a picture of the fetus.
6. Newborn screening can detect diseases that can be prevented by special care and precautions.
7. New technologies raise ethical considerations that include
   a. the confidentiality and potential use of results of genetic testing,
   b. time and financial costs, and
   c. determining what, if anything, should be done as a result of the testing.

III. Variations on Mendel's Laws

A. 9.11 Incomplete dominance results in intermediate phenotypes
   1. Mendel's pea crosses always looked like one of the parental varieties, called **complete dominance**.
   2. For some characters, the appearance of F_1 hybrids falls between the phenotypes of the two parental varieties. This is called **incomplete dominance**, in which
      a. neither allele is dominant over the other and
      b. expression of both alleles occurs.
   3. Incomplete dominance does not support the blending hypothesis because the original parental phenotypes reappear in the F_2 generation.
   4. One example of incomplete dominance in humans is hypercholesterolemia, in which
      a. dangerously high levels of cholesterol occur in the blood and
      b. heterozygotes have intermediately high cholesterol levels.
B. 9.12 Many genes have more than two alleles in the population
   1. Although an individual can at most carry two different alleles for a particular gene, more than two alleles often exist in the wider population.
   2. Human ABO blood group phenotypes involve three alleles for a single gene.
   3. The four human blood groups, A, B, AB, and O, result from combinations of these three alleles.
   4. The A and B alleles are both expressed in heterozygous individuals, a condition known as **codominance**.
   5. In codominance,
      a. neither allele is dominant over the other and
      b. expression of both alleles is observed as a distinct phenotype in the heterozygous individual.
      c. AB blood type is an example of codominance.

C. 9.13 A single gene may affect many phenotypic characters

   1. Pleiotropy occurs when one gene influences many characteristics.

   2. Sickle-cell disease is a human example of pleiotropy. This disease

      a. affects the type of hemoglobin produced and the shape of red blood cells and

      b. causes anemia and organ damage.

   3. Sickle-cell and nonsickle alleles are codominant.

   4. Carriers of sickle-cell disease are resistant to malaria.

D. 9.14 A single character may be influenced by many genes

   1. Many characteristics result from **polygenic inheritance**, in which a single phenotypic character results from the additive effects of two or more genes.

   2. Human skin color is an example of polygenic inheritance.

E. 9.15 The environment affects many characters

   1. Many characters result from a combination of heredity and the environment. For example,

      a. skin color is affected by exposure to sunlight,

      b. susceptibility to diseases, such as cancer, has hereditary and environmental components, and

      c. identical twins show some differences.

   2. Only genetic influences are inherited.

IV. The Chromosomal Basis of Inheritance

   A. 9.16 Chromosome behavior accounts for Mendel's laws

      1. The chromosome theory of inheritance states that

         a. genes occupy specific loci (positions) on chromosomes and

         b. chromosomes undergo segregation and independent assortment during meiosis.

      2. Mendel's laws correlate with chromosome separation in meiosis.

         a. The law of segregation depends on separation of homologous chromosomes in anaphase I.

         b. The law of independent assortment depends on alternative orientations of chromosomes in metaphase I.

   B. 9.17 SCIENTIFIC DISCOVERY: Genes on the same chromosome tend to be inherited together

      1. Bateson and Punnett studied plants that did not show a 9:3:3:1 ratio in the F_2 generation. What they found was an example of **linked genes**, which

         a. are located close together on the same chromosome and

         b. tend to be inherited together.

   C. 9.18 SCIENTIFIC DISCOVERY: Crossing over produces new combinations of alleles

      1. Crossing over between homologous chromosomes produces new combinations of alleles in gametes.

      2. Linked alleles can be separated by crossing over, forming recombinant gametes.

      3. The percentage of recombinants is the **recombination frequency**.

   D. 9.19 Geneticists use crossover data to map genes

      1. When examining recombinant frequency, Morgan and his students found that the greater the distance between two genes on a chromosome, the more points there are between them where crossing over can occur.

      2. Recombination frequencies can thus be used to map the relative position of genes on chromosomes.

V. Sex Chromosomes and Sex-Linked Genes

A. 9.20 Chromosomes determine sex in many species

  1. Many animals have a pair of **sex chromosomes**,

    a. designated X and Y,

    b. that determine an individual's sex.

  2. In mammals,

    a. males have XY sex chromosomes,

    b. females have XX sex chromosomes,

    c. the Y chromosome has genes for the development of testes, and

    d. an absence of the Y allows ovaries to develop.

  3. Grasshoppers, roaches, and some other insects have an X-O system, in which

    a. O stands for the absence of a sex chromosome,

    b. females are XX, and

    c. males are XO.

  4. In certain fishes, butterflies, and birds,

    a. the sex chromosomes are Z and W,

    b. males are ZZ, and

    c. females are ZW.

  5. Some organisms lack sex chromosomes altogether.

  6. In bees, sex is determined by chromosome number.

    a. Females are diploid.

    b. Males are haploid.

  7. In some animals, environmental temperature determines the sex.

    a. For some species of reptiles, the temperature at which the eggs are incubated during a specific period of development determines whether the embryo will develop into a male or female.

    b. Global climate change may therefore impact the sex ratio of such species.

B. 9.21 Sex-linked genes exhibit a unique pattern of inheritance

  1. **Sex-linked genes** are located on either of the sex chromosomes.

  2. The X chromosome carries many genes unrelated to sex.

  3. The inheritance of white eye color in the fruit fly illustrates an X-linked recessive trait.

C. 9.22 CONNECTION: Human sex-linked disorders affect mostly males

  1. Most sex-linked human disorders are

    a. due to recessive alleles and

    b. seen mostly in males.

  2. A male receiving a single X-linked recessive allele from his mother will have the disorder.

  3. A female must receive the allele from both parents to be affected.

  4. Recessive and sex-linked human disorders include

    a. **hemophilia**, characterized by excessive bleeding because hemophiliacs lack one or more of the proteins required for blood clotting,

    b. **red-green color blindness**, a malfunction of light-sensitive cells in the eyes, and

    c. **Duchenne muscular dystrophy**, a condition characterized by a progressive weakening of the muscles and loss of coordination.

D. 9.23 EVOLUTION CONNECTION: The Y chromosome provides clues about human male evolution

    1. The Y chromosome provides clues about human male evolution because

        a. Y chromosomes are passed intact from father to son and

        b. mutations in Y chromosomes can reveal data about recent shared ancestry.

Chapter Guide to Teaching Resources

Mendel's Laws (9.1–9.10)

Student Misconceptions and Concerns

- The authors note that Mendel's work was published in 1866, seven years after Darwin published *Origin of Species*. Consider challenging your students to consider whether Mendel's findings supported Darwin's ideas. Some scientists have noted that Darwin often discussed the evolution of traits by matters of degree. Yet, Mendel's selection of pea plant traits typically showed complete dominance, rather than the possibility for such gradual inheritance. (9.2)

- Students using Punnett squares need to be reminded that the calculations are expected statistical probabilities and not absolutes. Just as we would expect that any six playing cards dealt might be half black and half red, we frequently find that this is not true. This might be a good time to show how larger sample sizes increase the likelihood that sampling will reflect expected ratios. (9.3–9.7)

- Students might think that dominant alleles are naturally (a) more common, (b) more likely to be inherited, and (c) better for an organism. The text notes that this is not necessarily true. However, this might need to be emphasized further in lecture. (9.8)

Teaching Tips

- As you begin your lectures on genetics, consider challenging your students to explain why the theories of pangenesis and blending are incorrect. Perhaps just pick one of the two. You might even ask for short responses from everyone at the start of class or as an assignment before the first lectures. In addition to arousing interest in the answers, the responses should reveal the diverse backgrounds of your students entering this discussion and reveal any preexisting confusion on the subject of genetics. (9.1)

- The concept of pangenesis is analogous to the structure of United States representation in Congress. Each congressional district sends a person (pangene) to the U.S. House of Representatives (gamete). There, all parts of the United States (body) are represented. (9.1)

- In this or future lectures addressing evolution, you may mention that pangenesis was a mechanism consistent with Lamarckian evolution. (9.1)

- In Module 9.2, the authors make the analogy between genes and playing cards, noting that each are shuffled but retain their original identity. This analogy may form a very useful reference point for your students and can be used later, as new principles of genetics are discussed. (9.2)

- This early material introduces many definitions that are vital to understanding the later discussions in this chapter. Therefore, students need to be encouraged to master these definitions immediately. This may be a good time for a short quiz to encourage their progress. (9.2–9.3)

- Many students benefit from a little quick practice with a Punnett square. Have them try these crosses for practice: (a) PP × pp and (b) Pp × pp. (9.3)

- For students struggling with basic terminology, an analogy between a genetic trait and a pair of shoes might be helpful. A person might wear a pair of shoes in which both shoes match (homozygous), or less likely, a person might wear shoes that do not match (heterozygous). (9.3)

- Another analogy that might help struggling students is a pair of people trying to make a decision about where to eat tonight. One person wants to eat at a restaurant, the other wants to eat a meal at home. If this "heterozygous" couple eats at home, the dominant allele "wins." (9.3)

- Figure 9.4 can be of great benefit when introducing genetic terminology of genes. For students struggling to think abstractly, such a visual aid may be essential when describing these features in lecture. (9.4)

- Dihybrid crosses may be the most difficult concept in this chapter. Consider spending additional time to make these ideas very clear. As the text indicates, dihybrid crosses are essentially two monohybrid crosses occurring simultaneously. (9.5)

- Consider challenging your students to explain why a testcross of two black Labs of unknown genotypes might not reveal the genotype of each dog. (If both dogs are heterozygous, or homozygous, the results would reveal the genotypes because the offspring would either be three dark and one brown or all dark. But if one black Lab was homozygous and the other heterozygous, we could not determine which Lab has which genotype.) (9.6)

- Many students have trouble with the basic statistics that are necessary for many of these calculations. Give your students some practice. Consider having them work in pairs, each with a pair of dice (for large class sizes, this can be done in laboratories). Let them calculate the odds of rolling three sixes in a row and other possibilities. (9.7)

- Students seem to learn much from Figure 9.8b by analyzing the possible genotypes for the people whose complete genotype is not known. Consider challenging your students to suggest the possible genotypes for these people, perhaps during lecture. (9.8)

- The 2/3 fraction noted in the discussion of carriers of a recessive disorder for deafness often catches students off guard . . . as they are expecting odds of 1/4, 1/2, or 3/4. However, when we eliminate the dd (deaf) possibility, as it would not be a carrier, we have three possible genotypes. Thus, the odds are based out of the remaining three genotypes Dd, dD, and DD. Consider adding this point of clarification to your lecture. (9.9)

- As a simple test of comprehension, ask students to explain why lethal alleles are not eliminated from a population. Several possibilities exist: a) The lethal allele might be recessive, persisting in the population due to the survival of carriers, or b) the lethal allele might be dominant, but is not expressed until after the age of reproduction. (9.9)

- Ask your class a) what the odds are of a person developing Huntington's disease if a parent has this disease (50%) and b) whether they would want this genetic test if they were a person at risk. The Huntington Disease Society website, www.hdsa.org, offers many additional details. It is a good starting point for those who want to explore this disease in more detail. (9.9)

- Medical technology raises many ethical issues. Consider asking your students this practical question. How much routine fetal testing do we want our insurance companies to cover and at what cost for health insurance? Ultrasound, for example, is routinely performed on pregnant women as a normal part of prenatal care. What other tests should be standard? Who should decide? Who should pay? (9.10)

Variations on Mendel's Laws (9.11–9.15)

Student Misconceptions and Concerns

- After reading the preceding modules, students might expect all traits to be governed by a single gene with two alleles, one dominant over the other. Modules 9.11–9.15 describe deviations from simplistic models of inheritance. (9.11–9.15)

- As these variations of Mendel's laws are introduced, students are likely to get confused and become uncertain about the prior definitions. Consider keeping a clear definition of these different patterns of inheritance available for the class to refer to as new patterns are discussed (perhaps as a handout for student reference). (9.11–9.15)

- As your class size increases, the chances increase that at least one student will have a family member with one of the genetic disorders discussed. Some students may find this embarrassing, but others might have a special interest in learning more about these topics, and may even be willing to share some of their family's experiences with the class. (9.11–9.15)

Teaching Tips

- Incomplete dominance is analogous to a compromise or a gray shade. The key concept is that both "sides" have input. Complete dominance is analogous to an authoritarian style, overruling others and insisting on things being a certain way. Although these analogies might seem obvious to instructors, many students new to genetics appreciate them. (9.11)

- Another analogy for cholesterol receptors is fishing poles. The more fishing poles you use at the same time, the more fish you are likely to catch. Heterozygotes for hypercholesterolemia have fewer "fishing poles" for cholesterol. Thus, fewer "fish" are caught and more "fish" remain in the water. (9.11)

- Students can think of blood types as analogous to socks on their feet. You can have socks that match, a sock on one foot but not the other, you can wear two socks that do not match, or you can even go barefoot (type O blood)! Developed further, think of Amber (A) and Blue (B) socks. Type A blood can have an Amber sock with either another Amber sock or a bare foot (or "zero" sock). Blue socks work the same way. One amber and one blue sock represent the AB blood type. Having no socks, as already noted, represents type O. (9.12)

- Consider specifically comparing the principles of codominance (expression of both alleles) and incomplete dominance (expression of one intermediate trait). Students will likely benefit from this direct comparison. (9.12)

- The American Sickle Cell Anemia Association's website, www.ascaa.org, is a good place to find additional details. (9.13)

- Polygenic inheritance makes it possible for children to inherit genes to be taller or shorter than either parent. Similarly, skin tones can be darker or lighter than either parent. The environment also contributes significantly to the final phenotype for both of these traits. (9.14)

- The authors note that polygenic inheritance is the converse of pleiotropy. This is worth noting in lecture as these concepts are discussed. We often remember concepts better when they are contrasted in pairs. (9.14–9.15)

- As the authors are careful to note, although genetics and the environment both contribute to the final phenotypes, only the genetic factors are inherited. This distinction is important to understanding the limitations of Lamarck's mechanisms of evolution. If you will address principles of evolution soon after this chapter, this may be an important distinction to reinforce in lecture. References to tattoos and piercing may also help to distinguish between environmental influences and inheritance. Students with tattoos will not produce children born with tattoos! (9.15)

The Chromosomal Basis of Inheritance (9.16–9.19)

Student Misconceptions and Concerns

- This section of the chapter relies upon a good understanding of the chromosome sorting process of meiosis. If students were not assigned Chapter 8, and meiosis has not otherwise been addressed, it will be difficult for students to understand the chromosomal basis of inheritance or linked genes. (9.16–9.19)

- The nature of linked genes builds upon our natural expectations that items that are closely together are less likely to be separated. Yet, students may find such concepts initially foreign. Whether it is parents holding the hands of children or people and their pets, we generally know that separation is more likely when things are farther apart. (9.18–9.19)

Teaching Tips

- Figure 9.16 requires an understanding of meiosis and the general cell cycle from Chapter 8. Students may need to be reminded that chromosomes are duplicated in the preceding interphase, as indicated in the first step. Furthermore, students may not initially notice that this diagram represents four possible outcomes, not stages of any one meiotic cycle. (9.16)

- Building on the shoe analogy developed in Chapter 8, linked genes are like a shoe and its shoelaces. The two are usually transferred together but can be moved separately under special circumstances. (9.17)

- Crossing over (from Chapter 8) is like randomly editing out a minute of film from two movies and swapping them. Perhaps the fifth minute of *Bambi* is swapped for the fifth minute of *Gone With the Wind*. Clearly, the closer together two frames of film are, the more likely they are to move or remain together. (9.18–9.19)

- Challenge students to explain why Sturtevant and Morgan studied the genetics of fruit flies. As the text notes, their small size, ease of care, and ability to produce several generations in a matter of weeks or months were important factors. (9.18–9.19)

Sex Chromosomes and Sex-Linked Genes (9.20–9.23)

Student Misconceptions and Concerns

- The prior discussion of linked genes addresses a different relationship than the use of the similar term sex-linked genes. Consider emphasizing this distinction for your students. (9.21)

- The likelihood that at least some students in larger classes are color-blind is very high. Some of these students might find this interesting and want to discuss it further. However, others might be embarrassed and not wish to self-identify. (9.22)

Teaching Tips

- As the text notes, in crocodilians and many turtles, sex is not genetically determined. Instead, the incubation temperature of the eggs determines an animal's sex. Students may enjoy researching this unique form of sex determination, often identified as TSD (temperature-dependent sex determination). (9.20)

- An analogy can be drawn between sex-linked genes and the risk of not having a backup copy of a file on your computer. If you only have one copy, and it is damaged, you have to live with the damaged file. Females, who have two X chromosomes, thus have a "backup copy" that can function if one of the sex-linked genes is damaged. (9.21)

- Female hemophiliacs are very rare because both X chromosomes would need to have the recessive trait. Although very unlikely, female hemophiliacs are known. Students may enjoy searching for details of these rare cases. For additional information about hemophilia, consider visiting the website of the National Hemophilia Foundation at www.hemophilia.org. (9.22)

- Hemophilia and other genetic diseases may also result from spontaneous mutations in a family with no known history of the disease. Although rare, this possibility should always be considered when tracing the history of an inherited disease. (9.22)

- Like the Y chromosome, mitochondrial DNA (mtDNA) can be used to trace maternal ancestry (because mitochondria are characteristically inherited from the egg). For a fee, several commercial groups offer to provide information about a person's ancestry based upon genetic samples. Such groups can be found by searching the Internet using the keywords "genetic ancestry." (9.23)

Key Terms

ABO blood groups	codominant	genetics
achondroplasia	complete dominance	genotype
alleles	cross	hemophilia
amniocentesis	cross-fertilization	heredity
carrier	cystic fibrosis (CF)	heterozygous
character	dihybrid cross	homozygous
chorionic villus sampling (CVS)	dominant	Huntington's disease
chromosome theory of inheritance	Duchenne muscular dystrophy	hybrids
	F_1 generation	inbreeding
	F_2 generation	incomplete dominance

law of independent
  assortment
law of segregation
linkage map
linked genes
locus (plural, loci)
monohybrid cross
P generation
pedigree

phenotype
pleiotropy
polygenic inheritance
Punnett square
recessive
recombination frequency
red-green colorblindness
rule of addition
rule of multiplication

self-fertilize
sex chromosome
sex-linked gene
sickle-cell disease
testcross
trait
true-breeding
ultrasound imaging
wild-type traits

Word Roots

-centesis = a puncture (*amniocentesis*: a technique for determining genetic abnormalities in a fetus based on the presence of certain chemicals or defective fetal cells in the amniotic fluid, obtained by aspiration from a needle inserted into the uterus)

co- = together (*codominance*: an inheritance pattern in which a heterozygote expresses the distinct trait of both alleles)

di- = two (*dihybrid cross*: an experimental mating of individuals differing at two genetic loci)

gen- = produce (*genotype*: the genetic makeup of an organism)

hemo- = blood (*hemophilia*: a human genetic disease caused by a sex-linked recessive allele, characterized by excessive bleeding following injury)

hetero- = different (*heterozygous*: having two different alleles for a given gene)

homo- = alike (*homozygous*: having two identical alleles for a given gene)

mono- = one (*monohybrid cross*: an experimental mating of individuals differing at one genetic locus)

pedi- = a child (*pedigree*: a family tree describing the occurrence of heritable characters in parents and offspring across a number of generations)

pheno- = appear (*phenotype*: the expressed traits of an organism)

pleio- = more (*pleiotropy*: the control of multiple phenotypic characteristics by a single gene)

poly- = many; **gene-** = produce (*polygenic inheritance*: the additive effect of two or more gene loci on a single phenotypic character)

re- = again; **com-** = together; **bin-** = two at a time (*recombinant*: an offspring carrying combinations of alleles different from those in either of its parents as a result of independent assortment or crossing over)

CHAPTER 10

Molecular Biology of the Gene

Chapter Objectives

Opening Essay

Explain how a herpesvirus invades a cell and causes disease.

The Structure of the Genetic Material

10.1	Describe the experiments of Griffith, Hershey, and Chase, which supported the idea that DNA was life's genetic material.
10.2–10.3	Compare the structures of DNA and RNA.
10.3	Explain how Chargaff's rules relate to the structure of DNA.

DNA Replication

10.4	Explain how the structure of DNA facilitates its replication.
10.5	Describe the process of DNA replication. Describe the mechanisms that correct errors caused by environmental damage or errors from replication.

The Flow of Genetic Information from DNA to RNA to Protein

10.6	Describe the locations, reactants, and products of transcription and translation.
10.7–10.8	Explain how the "languages" of DNA and RNA are used to produce polypeptides.
10.9	Explain how mRNA is produced using DNA.
10.10	Explain how eukaryotic RNA is processed before leaving the nucleus.
10.11	Relate the structure of tRNA to its functions in the process of translation.
10.12	Describe the structure and function of ribosomes.
10.13	Explain how translation begins.
10.14	Describe the step-by-step process by which amino acids are added to a growing polypeptide chain.
10.15	Diagram the overall process of transcription and translation.
10.16	Describe the major types of mutations, causes of mutations, and potential consequences.

Microbial Genetics

10.17	Compare the lytic and lysogenic reproductive cycles of a phage.
10.18	Compare the structures and reproductive cycles of the mumps virus and a herpesvirus.
10.19	Describe three processes that contribute to the emergence of viral disease and note examples of each.
10.19	Explain why RNA viruses tend to have an unusually high rate of mutation.
10.20	Explain how the AIDS virus enters a host cell and reproduces.

10.21 Describe the structure of viroids and prions and explain how they cause disease.

10.22 Define and compare the processes of transformation, transduction, and conjugation.

10.23 Describe the roles of bacterial F factors. Define a plasmid and explain why R plasmids pose serious human health problems.

Lecture Outline

I. Introduction

A. Viruses infect organisms by
    1. binding to receptors on a host's target cell,
    2. injecting viral genetic material into the cell, and
    3. hijacking the cell's own molecules and organelles to produce new copies of the virus.

B. The host cell is destroyed, and newly replicated viruses are released to continue the infection.

C. Viruses are not generally considered alive because they
    1. are not cellular and
    2. cannot reproduce on their own.

D. Because viruses have much less complex structures than cells, they are relatively easy to study at the molecular level.

E. For this reason, viruses are used to study the functions of DNA.

II. The Structure of the Genetic Material

A. 10.1 SCIENTIFIC DISCOVERY: Experiments showed that DNA is the genetic material
    1. Until the 1940s, the case for proteins serving as the genetic material was stronger than the case for DNA.
        a. Proteins are made from 20 different amino acids.
        b. DNA was known to be made from just four kinds of nucleotides.
    2. Studies of bacteria and viruses
        a. ushered in the field of **molecular biology**, the study of heredity at the molecular level, and
        b. revealed the role of DNA in heredity.
    3. In 1928, Frederick Griffith discovered that a "transforming factor" could be transferred into a bacterial cell. He found that
        a. when he exposed heat-killed pathogenic bacteria to harmless bacteria, some harmless bacteria were converted to disease-causing bacteria and
        b. the disease-causing characteristic was inherited by descendants of the transformed cells.
    4. In 1952, Alfred Hershey and Martha Chase used bacteriophages to show that DNA is the genetic material of T2, a virus that infects the bacterium *Escherichia coli* (*E. coli*).
        a. **Bacteriophages** (or **phages** for short) are viruses that infect bacterial cells.
        b. Phages were labeled with radioactive sulfur to detect proteins or radioactive phosphorus to detect DNA.
        c. Bacteria were infected with either type of labeled phage to determine which substance was injected into cells and which remained outside the infected cell.

d. The sulfur-labeled protein stayed with the phages outside the bacterial cell, while the phosphorus-labeled DNA was detected inside cells.

e. Cells with phosphorus-labeled DNA produced new bacteriophages with radioactivity in DNA but not in protein.

B. 10.2 DNA and RNA are polymers of nucleotides

  1. DNA and RNA are nucleic acids.

  2. One of the two strands of DNA is a DNA **polynucleotide**, a nucleotide polymer (chain).

  3. A **nucleotide** is composed of a

    a. nitrogenous base,

    b. five-carbon sugar, and

    c. phosphate group.

  4. The nucleotides are joined to one another by a **sugar-phosphate backbone**.

  5. Each type of DNA nucleotide has a different nitrogen-containing base:

    a. adenine (A),

    b. cytosine (C),

    c. thymine (T), and

    d. guanine (G).

  6. RNA (ribonucleic acid) is unlike DNA in that it

    a. uses the sugar ribose (instead of deoxyribose in DNA) and

    b. RNA has the nitrogenous base **uracil** (U) instead of thymine.

C. 10.3 SCIENTIFIC DISCOVERY: DNA is a double-stranded helix

  1. In 1952, after the Hershey-Chase experiment demonstrated that the genetic material was most likely DNA, a race was on to

    a. describe the structure of DNA and

    b. explain how the structure and properties of DNA can account for its role in heredity.

  2. In 1953, James D. Watson and Francis Crick deduced the secondary structure of DNA, using

    a. X-ray crystallography data of DNA from the work of Rosalind Franklin and Maurice Wilkins and

    b. Chargaff's observation that in DNA,

      i. the amount of adenine was equal to the amount of thymine and

      ii. the amount of guanine was equal to that of cytosine.

  3. Watson and Crick reported that DNA consisted of two polynucleotide strands wrapped into a **double helix**.

    a. The sugar-phosphate backbone is on the outside.

    b. The nitrogenous bases are perpendicular to the backbone in the interior.

    c. Specific pairs of bases give the helix a uniform shape.

      i. A pairs with T, forming two hydrogen bonds, and

      ii. G pairs with C, forming three hydrogen bonds.

  4. In 1962, the Nobel Prize was awarded to

    a. James D. Watson, Francis Crick, and Maurice Wilkins.

    b. Rosalind Franklin probably would have received the prize as well but for her death from cancer in 1958. Nobel Prizes are never awarded posthumously.

  5. The Watson-Crick model gave new meaning to the words *genes* and *chromosomes*. The genetic information in a chromosome is encoded in the nucleotide sequence of DNA.

III. DNA Replication

A. 10.4 DNA replication depends on specific base pairing

    1. In their description of the structure of DNA, Watson and Crick noted that the structure of DNA suggests a possible copying mechanism.

    2. DNA replication follows a **semiconservative model**.

        a. The two DNA strands separate.

        b. Each strand is used as a pattern to produce a complementary strand, using specific base pairing.

        c. Each new DNA helix has one old strand with one new strand.

B. 10.5 DNA replication proceeds in two directions at many sites simultaneously

    1. DNA replication begins at the origins of replication where

        a. DNA unwinds at the origin to produce a "bubble,"

        b. replication proceeds in both directions from the origin, and

        c. replication ends when products from the bubbles merge with each other.

    2. DNA replication occurs in the 5′ to 3′ direction.

        a. Replication is continuous on the 3′ to 5′ template.

        b. Replication is discontinuous on the 5′ to 3′ template, forming short segments.

    3. Two key proteins are involved in DNA replication.

        a. DNA ligase joins small fragments into a continuous chain.

        b. DNA polymerase

            i. adds nucleotides to a growing chain and

            ii. proofreads and corrects improper base pairings.

    4. DNA polymerases and DNA ligase also repair DNA damaged by harmful radiation and toxic chemicals.

    5. DNA replication ensures that all the somatic cells in a multicellular organism carry the same genetic information.

IV. The Flow of Genetic Information from DNA to RNA to Protein

A. 10.6 The DNA genotype is expressed as proteins, which provide the molecular basis for phenotypic traits

    1. DNA specifies traits by dictating protein synthesis.

    2. The molecular chain of command is from

        a. DNA in the nucleus to RNA and

        b. RNA in the cytoplasm to protein.

    3. Transcription is the synthesis of RNA under the direction of DNA.

    4. Translation is the synthesis of proteins under the direction of RNA.

    5. The connections between genes and proteins

        a. The initial one gene–one enzyme hypothesis was based on studies of inherited metabolic diseases.

        b. The one gene–one enzyme hypothesis was expanded to include all proteins.

        c. Most recently, the one gene–one polypeptide hypothesis recognizes that some proteins are composed of multiple polypeptides.

B. 10.7 Genetic information written in codons is translated into amino acid sequences

    1. The sequence of nucleotides in DNA provides a code for constructing a protein.

        a. Protein construction requires a conversion of a nucleotide sequence to an amino acid sequence.

        b. Transcription rewrites the DNA code into RNA, using the same nucleotide "language."

    c. The flow of information from gene to protein is based on a **triplet code**: The genetic instructions for the amino acid sequence of a polypeptide chain are written in DNA and RNA as a series of nonoverlapping three-base "words" called **codons**.

    d. Translation involves switching from the nucleotide "language" to the amino acid "language."

    e. Each amino acid is specified by a codon.

        i. 64 codons are possible.

        ii. Some amino acids have more than one possible codon.

C. 10.8 The genetic code dictates how codons are translated into amino acids

    1. Characteristics of the **genetic code**

        a. Three nucleotides specify one amino acid.

            i. 61 codons correspond to amino acids.

            ii. AUG codes for methionine and signals the start of transcription.

            iii. 3 "stop" codons signal the end of translation.

    2. The genetic code is

        a. *redundant*, with more than one codon for some amino acids,

        b. *unambiguous* in that any codon for one amino acid does not code for any other amino acid,

        c. *nearly universal*—the genetic code is shared by organisms from the simplest bacteria to the most complex plants and animals, and

        d. *without punctuation* in that codons are adjacent to each other with no gaps in between.

D. 10.9 Transcription produces genetic messages in the form of RNA

    1. Overview of transcription

        a. An RNA molecule is transcribed from a DNA template by a process that resembles the synthesis of a DNA strand during DNA replication.

        b. RNA nucleotides are linked by the transcription enzyme **RNA polymerase**.

        c. Specific sequences of nucleotides along the DNA mark where transcription begins and ends.

        d. The "start transcribe" signal is a nucleotide sequence called a **promoter**.

        e. Transcription begins with *initiation*, as the RNA polymerase attaches to the promoter.

        f. During the second phase, *elongation*, the RNA grows longer.

        g. As the RNA peels away, the DNA strands rejoin.

        h. Finally, in the third phase, *termination*, the RNA polymerase reaches a sequence of bases in the DNA template called a **terminator**, which signals the end of the gene.

        i. The polymerase molecule now detaches from the RNA molecule and the gene.

E. 10.10 Eukaryotic RNA is processed before leaving the nucleus as mRNA

    1. Messenger RNA (mRNA)

        a. encodes amino acid sequences and

        b. conveys genetic messages from DNA to the translation machinery of the cell, which in

            i. prokaryotes occurs in the same place that mRNA is made, but in

            ii. eukaryote, mRNA must exit the nucleus via nuclear pores to enter the cytoplasm.

        c. Eukaryotic mRNA has

            i. **introns**, interrupting sequences that separate

            ii. **exons**, the coding regions.

2. Eukaryotic mRNA undergoes processing before leaving the nucleus.
   a. **RNA splicing** removes introns and joins exons to produce a continuous coding sequence.
   b. A cap and tail of extra nucleotides are added to the ends of the mRNA to
      i. facilitate the export of the mRNA from the nucleus,
      ii. protect the mRNA from attack by cellular enzymes, and
      iii. help ribosomes bind to the mRNA.

F. 10.11 Transfer RNA molecules serve as interpreters during translation
   1. **Transfer RNA (tRNA)** molecules function as a language interpreter,
      a. converting the genetic message of mRNA
      b. into the language of proteins.
   2. Transfer RNA molecules perform this interpreter task by
      a. picking up the appropriate amino acid and
      b. using a special triplet of bases, called an **anticodon**, to recognize the appropriate codons in the mRNA.

G. 10.12 Ribosomes build polypeptides
   1. Translation occurs on the surface of the **ribosome**.
      a. Ribosomes coordinate the functioning of mRNA and tRNA and, ultimately, the synthesis of polypeptides.
      b. Ribosomes have two subunits: small and large.
      c. Each subunit is composed of ribosomal RNAs and proteins.
      d. Ribosomal subunits come together during translation.
      e. Ribosomes have binding sites for mRNA and tRNAs.

H. 10.13 An initiation codon marks the start of an mRNA message
   1. Translation can be divided into the same three phases as transcription:
      a. initiation,
      b. elongation, and
      c. termination.
   2. Initiation brings together
      a. mRNA,
      b. a tRNA bearing the first amino acid, and
      c. the two subunits of a ribosome.
   3. Initiation establishes where translation will begin.
   4. Initiation occurs in two steps.
      a. An mRNA molecule binds to a small ribosomal subunit and the first tRNA binds to mRNA at the **start codon**.
         i. The start codon reads AUG and codes for methionine.
         ii. The first tRNA has the anticodon UAC.
      b. A large ribosomal subunit joins the small subunit, allowing the ribosome to function.
         i. The first tRNA occupies the **P site**, which will hold the growing peptide chain.
         ii. The **A site** is available to receive the next tRNA.

I. 10.14 Elongation adds amino acids to the polypeptide chain until a stop codon terminates translation
   1. Once initiation is complete, amino acids are added one by one to the first amino acid.
   2. Elongation is the addition of amino acids to the polypeptide chain.

3. Each cycle of elongation has three steps.
   a. **Codon recognition**: The anticodon of an incoming tRNA molecule, carrying its amino acid, pairs with the mRNA codon in the A site of the ribosome.
   b. **Peptide bond formation**: The new amino acid is joined to the chain.
   c. **Translocation**: tRNA is released from the P site and the ribosome moves tRNA from the A site into the P site.
4. Elongation continues until the termination stage of translation, when
   a. the ribosome reaches a **stop codon**,
   b. the completed polypeptide is freed from the last tRNA, and
   c. the ribosome splits back into its separate subunits.
J. 10.15 Review: The flow of genetic information in the cell is DNA → RNA → protein
   1. Transcription is the synthesis of RNA from a DNA template. In eukaryotic cells,
      a. transcription occurs in the nucleus and
      b. the mRNA must travel from the nucleus to the cytoplasm.
   2. Translation can be divided into four steps, all of which occur in the cytoplasm:
      a. amino acid attachment,
      b. initiation of polypeptide synthesis,
      c. elongation, and
      d. termination.
K. 10.16 Mutations can change the meaning of genes
   1. A **mutation** is any change in the nucleotide sequence of DNA.
   2. Mutations can involve
      a. large chromosomal regions or
      b. just a single nucleotide pair.
   3. Mutations within a gene can be divided into two general categories.
      a. Base substitutions involve the replacement of one nucleotide with another. Base substitutions may
         i.   have no effect at all, producing a **silent mutation**,
         ii. change the amino acid coding, producing a **missense mutation**, which produces a different amino acid,
         iii. lead to a base substitution that produces an improved protein that enhances the success of the mutant organism and its descendant, or
         iv. change an amino acid into a stop codon, producing a **nonsense mutation**.
      b. Mutations can result in deletions or insertions that may
         i.   alter the **reading frame** (triplet grouping) of the mRNA, so that nucleotides are grouped into different codons,
         ii. lead to significant changes in amino acid sequence downstream of the mutation, and
         iii. produce a nonfunctional polypeptide.
   4. **Mutagenesis** is the production of mutations.
   5. Mutations can be caused by
      a. spontaneous errors that occur during DNA replication or recombination or
      b. **mutagens**, which include
         i. high-energy radiation such as X-rays and ultraviolet light and
         ii. chemicals.

V. The Genetics of Viruses and Bacteria

A. 10.17 Viral DNA may become part of the host chromosome

  1. A virus is essentially "genes in a box," an infectious particle consisting of

    a. a bit of nucleic acid,

    b. wrapped in a protein coat called a **capsid**, and

    c. in some cases, a membrane envelope.

  2. Viruses have two types of reproductive cycles.

    a. In the **lytic cycle**,

      i. viral particles are produced using host cell components,

      ii. the host cell lyses, and

      iii. viruses are released.

    b. **Lysogenic cycle**

      i. Viral DNA is inserted into the host chromosome by recombination.

      ii. Viral DNA is duplicated along with the host chromosome during each cell division.

      iii. The inserted phage DNA is called a **prophage**.

      iv. Most prophage genes are inactive.

      v. Environmental signals can cause a switch to the lytic cycle, causing the viral DNA to be excised from the bacterial chromosome and leading to the death of the host cell.

B. 10.18 CONNECTION: Many viruses cause disease in animals and plants

  1. Viruses can cause disease in animals and plants.

  2. DNA viruses and RNA viruses cause disease in animals.

  3. A typical animal virus has a membranous outer envelope and projecting spikes of glycoprotein.

  4. The envelope helps the virus enter and leave the host cell.

  5. Many animal viruses have RNA rather than DNA as their genetic material. These include viruses that cause the common cold, measles, mumps, polio, and AIDS.

  6. The reproductive cycle of the mumps virus, a typical enveloped RNA virus, has seven major steps:

    a. entry of the protein-coated RNA into the cell,

    b. uncoating—the removal of the protein coat,

    c. RNA synthesis—mRNA synthesis using a viral enzyme,

    d. protein synthesis—mRNA is used to make viral proteins,

    e. new viral genome production—mRNA is used as a template to synthesize new viral genomes,

    f. assembly—the new coat proteins assemble around the new viral RNA, and

    g. exit—the viruses leave the cell by cloaking themselves in the host cell's plasma membrane.

  7. Some animal viruses, such as herpesviruses, reproduce in the cell nucleus.

  8. Most plant viruses are RNA viruses.

    a. To infect a plant, they must get past the outer protective layer of the plant.

    b. Viruses spread from cell to cell through plasmodesmata.

    c. Infection can spread to other plants by insects, herbivores, humans, or farming tools.

  9. There are no cures for most viral diseases of plants or animals.

C. 10.19 EVOLUTION CONNECTION: Emerging viruses threaten human health
   1. Viruses that appear suddenly or are new to medical scientists are called **emerging viruses**. These include the
      a. AIDS virus,
      b. Ebola virus,
      c. West Nile virus, and
      d. SARS virus.
   2. Three processes contribute to the emergence of viral diseases:
      a. mutation—RNA viruses mutate rapidly.
      b. contact between species—viruses from other animals spread to humans.
      c. spread from isolated human populations to larger human populations, often over great distances.
D. 10.20 The AIDS virus makes DNA on an RNA template
   1. **AIDS** (acquired immunodeficiency syndrome) is caused by **HIV** (human immunodeficiency virus).
   2. HIV
      a. is an RNA virus,
      b. has two copies of its RNA genome,
      c. carries molecules of **reverse transcriptase**, which causes reverse transcription, producing DNA from an RNA template.
   3. After HIV RNA is uncoated in the cytoplasm of the host cell,
      a. reverse transcriptase makes one DNA strand from RNA,
      b. reverse transcriptase adds a complementary DNA strand,
      c. double-stranded viral DNA enters the nucleus and integrates into the chromosome, becoming a provirus,
      d. the provirus DNA is used to produce mRNA,
      e. the viral mRNA is translated to produce viral proteins, and
      f. new viral particles are assembled, leave the host cell, and can then infect other cells.
E. 10.21 Viroids and prions are formidable pathogens in plants and animals
   1. Some infectious agents are made only of RNA or protein.
      a. **Viroids** are small, circular RNA molecules that infect plants. Viroids
         i. replicate within host cells without producing proteins and
         ii. interfere with plant growth.
      b. **Prions** are infectious proteins that cause degenerative brain diseases in animals. Prions
         i. appear to be misfolded forms of normal brain proteins,
         ii. which convert normal protein to misfolded form.
F. 10.22 Bacteria can transfer DNA in three ways
   1. Viral reproduction allows researchers to learn more about the mechanisms that regulate DNA replication and gene expression in living cells.
   2. Bacteria are also valuable but for different reasons.
      a. Bacterial DNA is found in a single, closed loop chromosome.
      b. Bacterial cells divide by replication of the bacterial chromosome and then by binary fission.
      c. Because binary fission is an asexual process, bacteria in a colony are genetically identical to the parent cell.

3. Bacteria use three mechanisms to move genes from cell to cell.

    a. **Transformation** is the uptake of DNA from the surrounding environment.

    b. **Transduction** is gene transfer by phages.

    c. **Conjugation** is the transfer of DNA from a donor to a recipient bacterial cell through a cytoplasmic (mating) bridge.

4. Once new DNA gets into a bacterial cell, part of it may then integrate into the recipient's chromosome.

G. 10.23 Bacterial plasmids can serve as carriers for gene transfer

  1. The ability of a donor *E. coli* cell to carry out conjugation is usually due to a specific piece of DNA called the **F factor**.

  2. During conjugation, the F factor is integrated into the bacterium's chromosome.

  3. The donor chromosome starts replicating at the F factor's origin of replication.

  4. The growing copy of the DNA peels off and heads into the recipient cell.

  5. The F factor serves as the leading end of the transferred DNA.

  6. An F factor can also exist as a **plasmid**, a small circular DNA molecule separate from the bacterial chromosome.

    a. Some plasmids, including the F factor, can bring about conjugation and move to another cell in linear form.

    b. The transferred plasmid re-forms a circle in the recipient cell.

  7. **R plasmids**

    a. pose serious problems for human medicine by

    b. carrying genes for enzymes that destroy antibiotics.

Chapter Guide to Teaching Resources

The Structure of the Genetic Material (10.1–10.3)

Student Misconceptions and Concerns

- Understanding bacteriophage replication can be difficult for students with limited knowledge of cell biology or genetics. Therefore, understanding the methods, results, and significance of the Hershey and Chase experiments is even more problematic. Considerable time and attention to these details will be required for many of your students. (10.1)

- If your class has not yet studied Chapter 3, consider assigning module 3.15 on "Nucleic Acids" before addressing the contents of Chapter 10. (10.1–10.3)

- Students often confuse the terms nucleic acids, nucleotides, and bases. It helps to note the hierarchy of relationships: nucleic acids consist of long chains of nucleotides (polynucleotides), while nucleotides include nitrogenous bases. (10.2–10.3)

Teaching Tips

- A phage functions like a needle and syringe, injecting a drug. The needle and syringe are analogous to the protein components of the phage. The drug to be injected is analogous to the phage DNA. (10.1)

- The descriptions of the discovery of DNA's structure are a good time to point out that science is a collaborative effort. Watson, Crick, and Wilkins earned Nobel Prizes due to their historic conclusions based upon the work of many others (including Franklin, Griffith, Hershey, Chase, and Chargaff). (10.1–10.3)

- Consider comparing DNA, RNA, and proteins to a train (polymer). DNA and RNA are like a train of various lengths and combinations of four types of train cars (monomers). Proteins are also "trains" of various lengths but made of a combination of 20 types of train cars. (10.2)

- The authors note that the structure of DNA is analogous to a twisted rope ladder. In class, challenge your students to explain what the parts of the ladder represent. The wooden rungs represent pairs of nitrogenous bases joined by hydrogen bonds. Each rope represents a sugar-phosphate backbone. (10.3)

DNA Replication (10.4–10.5)

Student Misconceptions and Concerns

- The authors note that although the general process of semiconservative DNA replication is relatively simple, it involves complex biochemical gymnastics. The DNA molecule is unwound, each strand is copied simultaneously, the correct bases are inserted, and the product is proofread and corrected. Before discussing these details, be sure that your students understand the overall process, what is accomplished, and why each step is important. (10.4–10.5)

Teaching Tips

- Demonstrate the complementary base pairing within DNA. Present students with the base sequence to one side of a DNA molecule and have them work quickly at their seats to determine the sequence of the complimentary strand. For some students, these sorts of quick practice are necessary to reinforce a concept and break up a lecture. (10.4)

- The semiconservative model of DNA replication is like making a photo from a negative and then a new negative from the photo. In each new negative and photo pair, the new item was made from an old item. (10.4)

- To explain the adaptive advantage of multiple replication sites over a single site of replication, ask the students to imagine copying, by hand, the first ten chapters of your biology textbook. The task would certainly go faster if ten students each copied a different chapter. (10.5)

- There are about 500,000 words in the *Biology: Concepts & Connections* textbook. The accuracy of DNA replication would be like copying every word in this textbook by hand 2,000 times and writing just one word incorrectly, making one error in every 1 billion words. (10.5)

The Flow of Genetic Information from DNA to RNA to Protein (10.6–10.16)

Student Misconceptions and Concerns

- Beginning college students are often intensely focused on writing detailed notes. The risk is that they will miss the overall patterns and the broader significance of the topics discussed. Consider a gradual approach to the subjects of transcription and translation, beginning quite generally and testing comprehension, before venturing into the finer mechanics of each process. (10.6–10.16)

- Consider placing the basic content from Figure 10.6A on the board, noting the sequence, products, and locations of transcription and translation in eukaryotic cells. This reminder can create a quick concept check for students as they learn additional detail. (10.6)

- As students learn about transcription, they might wonder which of the two strands of DNA is read. This uncertainty may add to the confusion about the details of the process, and students might not even think to ask. As noted in Module 10.9, the location of the promoter, a specific binding site for RNA polymerase, determines which strand is read. (10.9)

- Mutations are often discussed as part of evolutionary mechanisms. In this sense, mutations may be considered a part of a creative process. The dual nature of mutations, potentially deadly yet potentially innovative, should be clarified. (10.16)

Teaching Tips

- It has been said that everything about an organism is an interaction between the genome and the environment. You might wish to challenge your students to evaluate the validity of this statement. (10.6)

- The information in DNA is used to direct the production of RNA, which in turn directs the production of proteins. However, in Chapter 3, four different types of biological molecules were noted as significant components of life. Students who think this through might wonder, and you could point out, that DNA does not directly control the production of carbohydrates and lipids. So how does DNA exert its influence over the synthesis of these two chemical groups? The answer is largely by way of enzymes, proteins with the ability to promote the production of carbohydrates and lipids. (10.6)

- The transcription of DNA into RNA is like a reporter who transcribes a political speech. In both situations, the language remains the same, although in the case of the reporter, it changes its form from spoken to written language. (10.7)

- The sequential information in DNA and RNA is analogous to the sequential information in the letters of a sentence. This analogy is also helpful when explaining the impact of insertion or deletion mutations that cause a shift in the reading frame (see Module 10.16). (10.7)

- You may want to note the parallel between the discovery in 1799 of the Rosetta stone, which provided the key that enabled scholars to crack the previously indecipherable hieroglyphic code, and the cracking of the genetic code in 1961. Consider challenging your students to explain what part of the genetic code is similar to the Rosetta stone. This could be a short in-class activity for small groups. (10.8)

- The authors note the universal use of the genetic code in all forms of life. The evolutionary significance of this fundamental, universal language is a reminder of the shared ancestry of all life. The universal genetic code is part of the overwhelming evidence for evolution. (10.8)

- Another advantage to the use of RNA to direct protein synthesis is that the original code (DNA) remains safely within the nucleus, away from the many potentially damaging chemicals in the cytoplasm. This is like making photocopies of important documents for study, keeping the originals safely stored away. (10.9)

- Many analogies can be developed to represent the selective expression of a gene requiring the deletion of introns. Instructors that only assign some modules of a chapter are treating the chapters like sections of exons and introns, portions to be read and portions to be skipped. Alternately, students who highlight a chapter might be thought of as editing the book into exons, portions to be reviewed, and introns, nonhighlighted sections that will not be studied. Both analogies are imperfect, but may still convey the concept of selective reading. (10.10)

- The unique structure of tRNA, with binding sites for an amino acid and its codon, permits the translation of the genetic code. Like an interpreter who speaks two languages, the tRNA molecules match codons to the specified amino acid. (10.11)

- Students might wonder why the details of transcription and translation are important. As the text notes, differences in the composition of prokaryotic and eukaryotic ribosomes form the basis of action for antibiotics. By identifying differences, we can develop drugs that target crucial features of prokaryotic pathogens without harming their eukaryotic hosts. (10.12)

- Ribosomal RNA is transcribed in the nucleolus of eukaryotic cells. The ribosomal subunits are assembled in the nucleus using proteins imported from the cytosol. These subunits are then exported to the cytosol, where they are only assembled into a functional ribosome when they attach to an mRNA molecule. Some of these details are not specifically noted in the text but may be required to fill out your explanations. (10.12–10.13)

- If you use a train analogy for the assembly of monomers into polymers, the DNA and RNA trains are traded in on a three-for-one basis for the polypeptide train during translation. In general, this produces polypeptides that have about one-third as many monomers as the mRNA that coded for them. (10.12–10.15)

- Students might want to think of the A and P sites as stages in an assembly line. The A site is where a new amino acid is brought in, according to the blueprint of the codon on the mRNA. The P site is where the growing product/polypeptide is anchored as it is being built. To help students better remember details of translation, they might think of the letters for the two sites as meaning A for addition, where an amino acid is added, and P for polypeptide, where the growing polypeptide is located. (10.14)

- After translation is addressed, consider asking your students (working singly or in small groups) to list all of the places where base pairing is used (in the construction of a DNA molecule during DNA replication, in transcription, and during translation when the tRNA attaches). (10.15)

- A simple way to demonstrate the effect of a reading frame shift is to have students compare the following three sentences. The first is a simple sentence. However, look what happens when a letter is added (2) or deleted (3). The reading frame, or words, are reformed into nonsense. (10.16)

  (1) The big red pig ate the red rag.
  (2) The big res dpi gat eth ere dra g.
  (3) The big rep iga tet her edr ag.

- The authors have noted elsewhere that "A random mutation is like a random shot in the dark. It is not likely to improve a genome any more than shooting a bullet through the hood of a car is likely to improve engine performance!" (10.16)

Microbial Genetics (10.17–10.23)

Student Misconceptions and Concerns

- Students and many parents with young children expect antibiotics to be used to treat many respiratory infections, even though such infections may result from a virus. Students will benefit from a thorough explanation of why antibiotics are inappropriate for viral infections as well as the rising numbers of antibiotic-resistant bacteria that have evolved as a result of the overuse of antibiotics. (10.17–10.23)

- The success of modern medicine has perhaps led to overconfidence in our ability to treat disease. Students often do not understand that there are few successful treatments for viral infections. Instead, the best defense against viruses is prevention, by reducing the chances of contacting the virus and through the use of vaccines. (10.17–10.23)

- Many misconceptions about AIDS exist. A list of 18 common misconceptions is located at www.gng.org/currents/teachers/hiv101/misconceptions.html. (10.20)

Teaching Tips

- Students (and instructors) might enjoy thinking of a prophage as a smudge mark on the master copy of a class handout. The smudge is replicated every time the original is copied! (10.17)

- As noted in Module 10.18, viruses can spread throughout a plant by moving through plasmodesmata. This is like smoke spreading throughout a building by moving through air ducts. (10.18)

- There is an interesting relationship between the speed at which a virus kills or debilitates a host and the extent to which it spreads from one organism to another. This is something to consider for a class discussion. Compare two viral infections. Infection A multiplies within the host, is spread by the host to other people through casual contact, but does not cause its lethal symptoms until 5–10 years after infection. Virus B kills the host within 1–2 days of infection, is easily transmitted, and causes severe symptoms within hours of contact. Which virus is likely to spread the fastest through the human population on Earth? Which might be considered the most dangerous to humans? (10.19)

- Students might wonder why a person needs to get a new seasonal flu vaccination every year. The annual mutations and variations in flu viruses require the production of a new flu vaccine annually. The Centers for Disease Control and Prevention monitors patterns of flu outbreaks, especially in Asia (where many variations of flu viruses originate). They must predict which strains are most likely to be dangerous in the coming year and then synthesize an appropriate vaccine. (10.19)

- The Centers for Disease Control and Prevention has extensive information about AIDS at www.cdc.gov/hiv. (10.20)

- Students often do not understand the disproportionate distribution of HIV infections and AIDS in our world. Consider an Internet assignment, asking students to identify the regions of the world most affected by HIV-AIDS and then discuss why this uneven distribution of disease exists. (10.20)

- Viroids can cause significant damage to plants. More than 30 million coconut palms in the Philippines have been killed by viroids. (10.21)

- The authors note that the figures in Module 10.22 represent the size of the bacterial chromosome as much smaller than they actually are. They note that a bacterial chromosome is hundreds of times longer than the cell. These chromosomes use extensive folding to fit inside the cell. (10.22)

- You might challenge students to explain why conjugation is sometimes called bacterial sex. Students might note that two organisms cooperate to produce a new, genetically unique bacterium. (10.22)

- The figures in Module 10.23 provide essential imagery for a detailed discussion of bacterial conjugation. The abstract details presented in Module 10.23 are likely new to most of your students. (10.23)

- Module 10.23 notes the possible consequences of widespread use of antibiotics. Consider asking your students to consider the value of widespread use of antibacterial soaps throughout their homes. (10.23)

Key Terms

adenine (A)	lytic cycle	ribosomal RNA (rRNA)
AIDS	messenger RNA (mRNA)	RNA polymerase
anticodon	missense mutations	RNA splicing
bacteriophages	molecular biology	semiconservative model
capsid	mutagens	silent mutation
codon	mutagenesis	start codon
conjugation	mutation	stop codon
cytosine (C)	nonsense mutations	sugar-phosphate backbone
DNA	nucleotides	terminator
deoxyribonucleic acid	P site	thymine (T)
DNA ligase	phages	transcription
DNA polymerase	plasmid	transduction
double helix	polynucleotide	transfer RNA (tRNA)
emerging viruses	prions	transformation
exon	promoter	translation
F factor	prophage	triplet code
genetic code	R plasmids	uracil (U)
guanine (G)	reading frame	viroids
HIV	retrovirus	virus
intron	reverse transcriptase	
lysogenic cycle	ribosomes	

Word Roots

anti- = opposite (*anticodon*: a specific sequence of three nucleotides on a tRNA molecule that is complementary to a particular codon triplet on an mRNA molecule)

capsa- = a box (*capsid*: the protein shell that encloses the viral genome)

exo- = out, outside, without (*exon*: in eukaryotes, the coding portion of a gene)

-genesis = origin, birth (*mutagenesis*: the creation of a mutation)

helic- = a spiral (*double helix*: The form of native DNA, composed of two adjacent polynucleotide strands wound into a spiral shape)

intro- = within (*intron*: a noncoding, intervening sequence within a eukaryotic gene; in eukaryotes, a nonexpressed [noncoding] portion of a gene that is excised from the RNA transcript)

liga- = bound or tied (*DNA ligase*: an enzyme that catalyzes the covalent bonding of adjacent DNA nucleotides)

lyso- = loosen (*lysogenic cycle*: a type of bacteriophage replication cycle in which the viral genome is incorporated into the bacterial host chromosome as a prophage)

lyto- = loosen (*lytic cycle*: a type of viral replication cycle resulting in the release of new viruses by lysis [breaking open] of the host cell)

muta- = change (*mutation*: a change in the nucleotide sequence of DNA); **-gen** = producing (*mutagen*: a physical or chemical agent that causes mutations; *mutagenesis:* the creation of a mutation)

-phage = to eat (*bacteriophage*: a virus that infects bacteria)

poly- = many (*polynucleotide*: a molecule composed of many nucleotide monomers, covalently bonded together)

pro- = before (*promoter*: a sequence of DNA that provides the binding site for RNA polymerase during transcription); **-phage** = to eat (*prophage*: phage DNA that has inserted by genetic recombination into the DNA of a prokaryotic chromosome)

retro- = backward (*retrovirus*: an RNA virus that reproduces by reverse-transcribing its RNA into DNA and then inserting the DNA into a cellular chromosome)

semi- = half (*semiconservative model*: type of DNA replication in which the replicated double helix consists of one old strand, derived or "conserved" from the parent molecule, and one newly made strand)

trans- = across (*transduction*: the transfer of DNA from one cell to another via a bacteriophage; *transformation:* a phenomenon in which external DNA is assimilated by a cell; *translation:* the process in which an amino acid sequence is produced by reading an RNA transcript); **-script** = write (*transcription*: the synthesis of RNA on a DNA template)

virul- = poisonous (*viroid*: a plant pathogen composed of molecules of naked, circular RNA several hundred nucleotides long; *virus:* an infectious agent that requires a host cell for reproduction)

CHAPTER 11

How Genes Are Controlled

Chapter Objectives

Opening Essay

Explain how cloning can be used to help protect endangered species. Describe the risks and limits of cloning animals.

Control of Gene Expression

11.1 Describe and compare the regulatory mechanisms of the *lac* operon, trp operon, and operons using activators.

11.2 Explain how selective gene expression yields a variety of cell types in multicellular eukaryotes.

11.2 Explain how DNA is packaged into chromosomes. Explain how packing influences gene expression.

11.2 Explain how a cat's tortoiseshell coat pattern is formed and why this pattern is only seen in female cats.

11.3 Explain how eukaryotic gene expression is controlled. Compare the eukaryotic gene expression mechanisms to those of prokaryotes.

11.4 Describe the process and significance of alternative DNA splicing.

11.5 Describe the significance of miRNA molecules.

11.6 Explain how mRNA breakdown, initiation of translation, protein activation, and protein breakdown regulate gene expression.

11.7 Explain how the control of gene expression in eukaryotic cells is analogous to the control of water moving through the series of pipes that carry water from a local water supply to a home or business.

11.8 Describe the roles of homeotic genes in development.

11.9 Explain how DNA microarrays can be used to study gene activity and treat disease.

11.10 Explain how a signal transduction pathway triggers a specific response inside a target cell.

11.11 Compare the cell-signaling systems of yeast and animal cells.

Cloning of Plants and Animals

11.12 Describe experiments that demonstrate that differentiated cells retain all of their genes.

11.13 Explain how nuclear transplantation can be used to clone animals.

11.14 Describe some of the practical applications of reproductive cloning.

11.15 Describe the process and goals of therapeutic cloning.

The Genetic Basis of Cancer

11.16 Explain how viruses, proto-oncogenes, and tumor-suppressor genes can each contribute to cancer.

11.17 Describe the main events in the development of colorectal cancer. Explain why the development of most cancers is a slow and gradual process.

11.18 Explain how mutations in *ras* or *p53* proteins can lead to cancer.

11.19 Describe factors that can increase or decrease the risks of developing cancer.

Lecture Outline

I. Introduction

A. Cloning is the creation of an individual by asexual reproduction.

B. The ability to clone an animal from a single cell demonstrates that every adult body cell

    1. contains a complete genome that is

    2. capable of directing the production of all the cell types in an organism.

C. Cloning has been attempted to save endangered species.

D. However, cloning

    1. does not increase genetic diversity and

    2. may trivialize the tragedy of extinction and detract from efforts to preserve natural habitats.

II. Control of Gene Expression

A. 11.1 Proteins interacting with DNA turn prokaryotic genes on or off in response to environmental changes

    1. Gene regulation is the turning on and off of genes.

    2. Gene expression is the overall process of information flow from genes to proteins.

    3. The control of gene expression allows cells to produce specific kinds of proteins when and where they are needed.

    4. Our earlier understanding of gene control came from the study of *E. coli*.

    5. A cluster of genes with related functions, along with the control sequences, is called an **operon**.

    6. With few exceptions, operons only exist in prokaryotes.

    7. When an *E. coli* encounters lactose, all the enzymes needed for its metabolism are made at once using the lactose operon.

    8. The lactose (*lac*) operon includes

        a. three adjacent lactose-utilization genes,

        b. a **promoter** sequence where RNA polymerase binds and initiates transcription of all three lactose genes, and

        c. an **operator** sequence where a **repressor** can bind and block RNA polymerase action.

    9. Regulation of the *lac* operon

        a. A **regulatory gene**, located outside the operon, codes for a repressor protein.

        b. In the absence of lactose, the repressor binds to the operator and prevents RNA polymerase action.

  c. Lactose inactivates the repressor, so

   i. the operator is unblocked,

   ii. RNA polymerase can bind to the promoter, and

   iii. all three genes of the operon are transcribed.

 10. There are two types of repressor-controlled operons.

  a. In the *lac* operon, the repressor is

   i. active when alone and

   ii. inactive when bound to lactose.

  b. In the *trp* bacterial operon, the repressor is

   i. inactive when alone and

   ii. active when bound to the amino acid Tryptophan (Trp).

 11. Another type of operon control involves **activators**, proteins that turn operons on by

  a. binding to DNA and

  b. making it easier for RNA polymerase to bind to the promoter.

 12. Activators help control a wide variety of operons.

B. 11.2 Chromosome structure and chemical modifications can affect gene expression

 1. Differentiation

  a. involves cell specialization, in structure and function, and

  b. is controlled by turning specific sets of genes on or off.

 2. Almost all of the cells in an organism contain an identical genome.

 3. The differences between cell types are

  a. not due to the presence of different genes but instead

  b. due to selective gene expression.

 4. Eukaryotic chromosomes undergo multiple levels of folding and coiling, called DNA packing.

  a. Nucleosomes are formed when DNA is wrapped around **histone** proteins.

   i. This packaging gives a "beads on a string" appearance.

   ii. Each nucleosome bead includes DNA plus eight histones.

   iii. Stretches of DNA, called linkers, join consecutive nucleosomes.

  b. At the next level of packing, the beaded string is wrapped into a tight helical fiber.

  c. This fiber coils further into a thick supercoil.

  d. Looping and folding can further compact the DNA.

 5. DNA packing can prevent gene expression by preventing RNA polymerase and other transcription proteins from contacting the DNA.

 6. Cells seem to use higher levels of packing for long-term inactivation of genes.

 7. Highly compacted chromatin, found in varying regions of interphase chromosomes, is generally not expressed at all.

 8. Chemical modification of DNA bases or histone proteins can result in epigenetic inheritance.

  a. Certain enzymes can add a methyl group to DNA bases, without changing the sequence of the bases.

  b. Individual genes are usually more methylated in cells in which the genes are not expressed. Once methylated, genes usually stay that way through successive cell divisions in an individual.

  c. Removal of the extra methyl groups can turn on some of these genes.

  d. Inheritance of traits transmitted by mechanisms not directly involving the nucleotide sequence is called **epigenetic inheritance**. These modifications can be reversed by processes not yet fully understood.

9. X-chromosome inactivation

    a. In female mammals, one of the two X chromosomes is highly compacted and tran-scriptionally inactive.

    b. Either the maternal or paternal chromosome is randomly inactivated.

    c. Inactivation occurs early in embryonic development, and all cellular descendants have the same inactivated chromosome.

    d. An inactivated X chromosome is called a **Barr body**.

    e. Tortoiseshell fur coloration is due to inactivation of X chromosomes in heterozy-gous female cats.

C. 11.3 Complex assemblies of proteins control eukaryotic transcription

  1. Prokaryotes and eukaryotes employ regulatory proteins (activators and repressors) that

    a. bind to specific segments of DNA and

    b. either promote or block the binding of RNA polymerase, turning the transcription of genes on and off.

  2. In eukaryotes, activator proteins seem to be more important than repressors. Thus, the default state for most genes seems to be off.

  3. A typical plant or animal cell needs to turn on and transcribe only a small percentage of its genes.

  4. Eukaryotic RNA polymerase requires the assistance of proteins called **transcription factors**. Transcription factors include

    a. activator proteins, which bind to DNA sequences called enhancers and initiate gene transcription. The binding of the activators leads to bending of the DNA.

    b. Other transcription factor proteins interact with the bound activators, which then collectively bind as a complex at the gene's promoter.

  5. RNA polymerase then attaches to the promoter and transcription begins.

  6. Silencers are repressor proteins that

    a. may bind to DNA sequences and

    b. inhibit transcription.

  7. Coordinated gene expression in eukaryotes often depends on the association of a specific combination of control elements with every gene of a particular metabolic pathway.

D. 11.4 Eukaryotic RNA may be spliced in more than one way

  1. Alternative RNA splicing

    a. produces different mRNAs from the same transcript,

    b. results in the production of more than one polypeptide from the same gene, and

    c. may be common in humans.

E. 11.5 Small RNAs play multiple roles in controlling gene expression

  1. Only about 1.5% of the human genome codes for proteins. (This is also true of many other multicellular eukaryotes.)

  2. Another small fraction of DNA consists of genes for ribosomal RNA and transfer RNA.

  3. A flood of recent data suggests that a significant amount of the remaining genome is transcribed into functioning but non-protein-coding RNAs, including a variety of small RNAs.

  4. microRNAs (miRNAs) can bind to complementary sequences on mRNA molecules either

    a. degrading the target mRNA or

    b. blocking its translation.

5. RNA interference (RNAi) is the use of miRNA to artificially control gene expression by injecting miRNAs into a cell to turn off a specific gene sequence.

F. 11.6 Later stages of gene expression are also subject to regulation

    1. After mRNA is fully processed and transported to the cytoplasm, gene expression can still be regulated by

        a. breakdown of mRNA,

        b. initiation of translation,

        c. protein activation, and

        d. protein breakdown.

G. 11.7 Review: Multiple mechanisms regulate gene expression in eukaryotes

    1. Multiple control points exist where gene expression in eukaryotes can be

        a. turned on or off or

        b. speeded up, or slowed down.

    2. These control points are like a series of pipes carrying water from your local water supply to a faucet in your home. Valves in this series of pipes are like the control points in gene expression.

    3. These controls points include:

        a. chromosome changes and DNA unpacking,

        b. control of transcription,

        c. control of RNA processing, including the

            i. addition of a cap and tail and

            ii. splicing,

        d. flow through the nuclear envelope,

        e. breakdown of mRNA,

        f. control of translation, and

        g. control after translation, including

            i. cleavage/modification/activation of proteins and

            ii. breakdown of protein.

H. 11.8 Cell signaling and cascades of gene expression direct animal development

    1. Early research on gene expression and embryonic development came from studies of a fruit fly, revealing the control of these key events.

        a. Orientation of the head and tail, top-to-bottom, and side-to-side axes are determined by early genes in the egg that produce proteins and maternal mRNAs.

        b. Segmentation of the body is influenced by cascades of proteins that diffuse through the cell layers.

        c. Adult features develop under the influence of **homeotic genes**, master control genes that determine the anatomy of the parts of the body.

I. 11.9 CONNECTION: DNA microarrays test for the transcription of many genes at once

    1. DNA microarrays help researchers study the expression of large groups of genes.

    2. A DNA microarray

        a. contains DNA sequences arranged on a grid and

        b. is used to test for transcription in the following way:

            i. mRNA from a specific cell type is isolated,

            ii. fluorescent cDNA is produced from the mRNA,

            iii. cDNA is applied to the microarray,

            iv. unbound cDNA is washed off, and

            v. complementary cDNA is detected by fluorescence.

3. DNA microarrays are a potential boon to medical research.
   a. In 2002, a study showed that DNA microarray data can classify different types of leukemia, helping to identify which chemotherapies will be most effective.
   b. Other research suggests that many cancers have a variety of subtypes with different gene expression patterns.
   c. DNA microarrays also reveal general profiles of gene expression over the lifetime of an organism.
J. 11.10 Signal transduction pathways convert messages received at the cell surface to responses within the cell
   1. A **signal transduction pathway** is a series of molecular changes that convert a signal on the target cell's surface to a specific response within the cell.
   2. Signal transduction pathways are crucial to many cellular functions.
K. 11.11 EVOLUTION CONNECTION: Cell-signaling systems appeared early in the evolution of life
   1. In the yeast used to make bread, beer, and wine, mating is controlled by a signal transduction pathway.
   2. These yeast cells identify their mates by chemical signaling.
   3. Yeast have two mating types: **a** and $\tilde{\alpha}$
      a. Each produces a chemical factor that binds to receptors on cells of the opposite mating type.
      b. Binding to receptors triggers growth toward the other cell and fusion.
   4. Cell signaling processes in multicellular organisms are derived from those in unicellular organisms such as bacteria and yeast.

III. Cloning of Plants and Animals
A. 11.12 Plant cloning shows that differentiated cells may retain all of their genetic potential
   1. Most differentiated cells retain a full set of genes, even though only a subset may be expressed. Evidence is available from
      a. plant cloning, in which a root cell can divide to form an adult plant and
      b. salamander limb **regeneration**, in which the cells in the leg stump dedifferentiate, divide, and then redifferentiate, giving rise to a new leg.
B. 11.13 Nuclear transplantation can be used to clone animals
   1. Animal cloning can be achieved using **nuclear transplantation**, in which the nucleus of an egg cell or zygote is replaced with a nucleus from an adult somatic cell.
   2. Using nuclear transplantation to produce new organisms is called **reproductive cloning**. It was first used in mammals in 1997 to produce the sheep Dolly.
   3. Another way to clone uses **embryonic stem (ES) cells** harvested from a blastocyst. This procedure can be used to produce
      a. cell cultures for research or
      b. stem cells for therapeutic treatments.
C. 11.14 CONNECTION: Reproductive cloning has valuable applications, but human reproductive cloning raises ethical issues
   1. Since Dolly's landmark birth in 1997, researchers have cloned many other mammals, including mice, cats, horses, cows, mules, pigs, rabbits, ferrets, and dogs.
   2. Cloned animals can show differences in anatomy and behavior due to
      a. environmental influences and
      b. random phenomena.

3. Reproductive cloning is used to produce animals with desirable traits to
   a. produce better agricultural products,
   b. produce therapeutic agents, and
   c. restock populations of endangered animals.
4. Human reproductive cloning raises many ethical concerns.

D. 11.15 CONNECTION: Therapeutic cloning can produce stem cells with great medical potential
   1. When grown in laboratory culture, stem cells can
      a. divide indefinitely and
      b. give rise to many types of differentiated cells.
   2. **Adult stem cells** can give rise to many, but not all, types of cells.
   3. Embryonic stem cells are considered more promising than adult stem cells for medical applications.
   4. The ultimate aim of therapeutic cloning is to supply cells for the repair of damaged or diseased organs.

IV. The Genetic Basis of Cancer

A. 11.16 Cancer results from mutations in genes that control cell division
   1. Mutations in two types of genes can cause cancer.
      a. Oncogenes
         i. **Proto-oncogenes** are normal genes that promote cell division.
         ii. Mutations to proto-oncogenes create cancer-causing **oncogenes** that often stimulate cell division.
      b. Tumor-suppressor genes
         i. Tumor-suppressor genes normally inhibit cell division or function in the repair of DNA damage.
         ii. Mutations inactivate the genes and allow uncontrolled division to occur.

B. 11.17 Multiple genetic changes underlie the development of cancer
   1. Usually four or more somatic mutations are required to produce a full-fledged cancer cell.
   2. One possible scenario is the stepwise development of colorectal cancer.
      a. An oncogene arises or is activated, resulting in increased cell division in apparently normal cells in the colon lining.
      b. Additional DNA mutations cause the growth of a small benign tumor (polyp) in the colon wall.
      c. Additional mutations lead to a malignant tumor with the potential to metastasize.

C. 11.18 Faulty proteins can interfere with normal signal transduction pathways
   1. Proto-oncogenes and tumor-suppressor genes often code for proteins involved in signal transduction pathways leading to gene expression.
   2. Two main types of signal transduction pathways lead to the synthesis of proteins that influence cell division.
      a. One pathway produces a product that *stimulates* cell division.
         i. In a healthy cell, the product of the *ras* proto-oncogene relays a signal when growth factor binds to a receptor.
         ii. But in a cancerous condition, the product of the *ras* proto-oncogene relays the signal in the absence of a growth factor, leading to uncontrolled growth.
         iii. Mutations in *ras* occur in more than 30% of human cancers.

> **b.** A second pathway produces a product that *inhibits* cell division.
>
>> **i.** The normal product of the *p53* gene is a transcription factor that normally activates genes for factors that inhibit cell division.
>>
>> **ii.** In the absence of functional *p53*, cell division continues because the inhibitory protein is not produced.
>>
>> **iii.** Mutations in *p53* occur in more than 50% of human cancers.

D. 11.19 CONNECTION: Lifestyle choices can reduce the risk of cancer

1. After heart disease, cancer is the second-leading cause of death in most industrialized nations.
2. Cancer can run in families if an individual inherits an oncogene or a mutant allele of a tumor-suppressor gene that makes cancer one step closer.
3. But most cancers cannot be associated with an inherited mutation.
4. **Carcinogens** are cancer-causing agents that alter DNA.
5. Most mutagens (substances that promote mutations) are carcinogens.
6. Two of the most potent carcinogens (mutagens) are
   a. X-rays and
   b. ultraviolet radiation in sunlight.
7. The one substance known to cause more cases and types of cancer is tobacco.
   a. More people die of lung cancer than any other form of cancer.
   b. Although most tobacco-related cancers come from smoking, passive inhalation of second-hand smoke is also a risk.
   c. Tobacco use, sometimes in combination with alcohol consumption, causes cancers in addition to lung cancer.
8. Healthy lifestyles that reduce the risks of cancer include
   a. avoiding carcinogens, including the sun and tobacco products,
   b. exercising adequately,
   c. regular medical checks for common types of cancer, and
   d. a healthy, high-fiber, low-fat diet, including plenty of fruits and vegetables.

Chapter Guide to Teaching Resources

Control of Gene Expression (11.1–11.11)

Student Misconceptions and Concerns

- The broad concept of selective reading of the genetic code associated with differentiation and types of cellular activity can be missed when concentrating on the extensive details of regulation. Analogies, noted below in the teaching tips, can help students relate this overall selective process to their own experiences. Students already understand the selective reading of relevant chapters in textbooks and the selective referencing of software manuals to get answers to different questions. These experiences are similar in many ways to the broad processes of gene regulation. (11.1–11.11)

- The many levels of gene regulation in eukaryotic cells can be confusing and frustrating. The water pipe analogy depicted in Figure 11.7 can be a helpful reference to organize the potential sites of regulation. (11.1–11.11)

Teaching Tips

- The lactose operon is turned on by removing the repressor . . . a sort of double negative. Students might enjoy various analogies to other situations, including the familiar refrain "When the cat's away, the mice will play." Like a cat watching mice, if a mom keeps her kids away from cookies, but somebody occupies her attention, kids can sneak by and snatch some cookies. Thus, the person occupying Mom's attention functions most like lactose binding to the repressor. (11.1)

- A key advantage of an operon system is the ability to turn off or on a set of genes with a single "switch." You can demonstrate this relationship in your classroom by turning off or on a set of lights with a single switch. (11.1)

- The control of gene expression is analogous to buying a book about how to build bird-houses and reading only the plans needed to build one particular model. Although the book contains directions to build many different birdhouses, you read and follow only the directions for the particular birdhouse you choose to build. The pages and directions for the other birdhouses remain intact. When cells differentiate, they read, or express, only the genes that are needed in that particular cell type. (11.1–11.2)

- Just as boxes of things that you rarely use are packed into a closet, attic, or basement, chromatin that is not expressed is highly compacted and stored deeply packed away. (11.2)

- Just as a folded map is difficult to read, DNA packaging tends to prevent gene reading or expression. (11.2)

- Students might wonder why a patch of color is all the same on a cat's skin if every cell has an equal chance of being one of the two color forms. The answer is that X chromosome inactivation occurs early in development. Thus, the patch of one color represents the progeny of one embryonic cell after X chromosome inactivation. (11.2)

- The authors note that the selective unpackaging of chromosomes is the "coarse adjustment" of eukaryotic gene expression. The initiation of RNA synthesis is the fine-tuning of the regulation. If you have recently asked your students to use microscopes in the lab, you might relate these degrees of adjustment to the coarse and fine control knobs of a microscope. (11.3)

- Alternative RNA splicing is like remixing music to produce a new song or re-editing a movie for a different effect. (11.4)

- Recent references in older books and outdated websites may characterize DNA that does not code for rRNA, tRNA, or mRNA as junk DNA. The relatively recent discovery of miRNA and its significant roles in gene regulation reveals the danger of concluding that the absence of evidence is evidence of absence! (11.5)

- Describing the discovery of miRNAs and their potential in research and medicine help to illustrate the promise of gene regulation research. Students early in their science careers may appreciate knowing about scientific fields with great potential as they consider the direction of their developing careers. (11.5)

- The authors develop an analogy between the regulation of transcription and the series of water pipes that carry water from a local water supply, perhaps a reservoir, to a faucet. At various points, valves control the flow of water. Similarly, the expression of genes is controlled at many points along the process. Figure 11.7 illustrates the flow of genetic information from a chromosome—a reservoir of genetic information—to an active protein that has been made in the cell's cytoplasm. The multiple mechanisms that control gene expression are analogous to the control valves in water pipes. In the figure, a possible control knob indicates each gene expression "valve." In the figure, the larger size of the transcription control knob highlights its crucial role. (11.6–11.7)

- Homeotic genes are often called master control genes. The relationship between homeotic genes and structural genes is like the relationship between a construction supervisor and the workers. Major rearrangements can result from a few simple changes in the directions for construction. (11.8)

- There is much promise in the use of DNA microarrays to refine cancer therapies. In the past, a diagnosis of cancer was met with general treatments that benefited only a small fraction of the patients. Physicians were left to wonder why some people with breast cancer or lung cancer responded to therapy while others did not. DNA microarrays allow us to identify differences within each type of cancer (breast, lung, prostate, etc.). Consider sharing this important source of hope. It is likely that some of your students will soon have a family member facing these battles. (11.9)

- The authors note that signal transduction pathways were addressed in Module 8.8 and will again be addressed as these pathways are involved in controlling hormone functions in animals in Chapter 26 and in plants in Chapter 33. If your course does not include these other chapters, consider investing some of these aspects into the Chapter 11 materials. (11.10)

- The action of an extracellular signal reaching a cell's surface in a signal transduction pathway is like pushing the doorbell at a home. The signal is converted to another form (pushing a button rings a bell), and activities change within the house as someone comes to answer the door. (11.10–11.11)

- Some of the stages of a signal transduction pathway can be compared to a human reaction. Consider someone calling your name. (1) Reception—The sound waves of someone's voice hitting and changing the shape of your eardrum. (2) Transduction— Your ear converts sound waves to nerve impulses and sends a signal to your brain that your name has been called. (3) Response—You look around to see who is calling. (11.10–11.11)

- As Francois Jacob suggested, evolution works as a tinkerer and not like an engineer. New forms evolve by remodeling old forms. As the text notes, cell signaling mechanisms likely evolved first in ancient prokaryotes and then became adapted for new functions in their multicellular descendants. Examples of remodeling might be a subject you may want to explore in additional detail as an important lesson in evolution. (11.11)

Cloning of Plants and Animals (11.12–11.15)

Student Misconceptions and Concerns

- Students often fail to see the similarities between identical twins and cloning. Each process produces multiple individuals with identical nuclear genetic material. (11.12–11.15)

- Students often assume that clones will appear and act identically. This misunderstanding provides an opportunity to discuss the important influence of the environment in shaping the final phenotype. (11.12–11.15)

Teaching Tips

- The basic question asked in Module 11.12 is whether a cell becomes differentiated by selectively reading the genome or by retaining only the needed sections. In your course, you are unlikely to assign the entire *Concepts* textbook. Instead, you will likely ask your students to selectively read chapters in the book. Students could remove all of the pages that they do not need, leaving only those assigned. Alternately, students could keep their textbooks intact, reading only the assigned and relevant passages. These latter students, with intact textbooks, behave like cells undergoing differentiation. (11.12)

- An even more remarkable aspect of salamander limb regeneration is that only the missing limb segments are regenerated. If an arm is amputated at the elbow, only the forearm, wrist, and hand are regenerated. Somehow, the cells can detect what is missing and replace only those parts! (11.12)

- The researchers who cloned Dolly the sheep from a mammary gland cell named Dolly after the celebrity country singer Dolly Parton. (11.13)

- Preimplantation genetic diagnosis (PGD) is a genetic screening technique that removes one or two cells from an embryo at about the 6 to 10 cell stage. The cells that are removed are genetically analyzed while the remaining embryonic cell mass retains the potential to develop. This technique permits embryos to be genetically screened before implanting them into a woman. However, PGD has another potential use. Researchers can use PGD to obtain embryonic stem cells without destroying a human embryo. This procedure might be more acceptable than methods that destroy the embryo to obtain embryonic stem cells. (11.13–11.15)

- Students might not immediately understand why reproductive cloning is necessary to transmit specific traits in farm animals. They may fail to realize that unlike cloning, sexual reproduction mixes the genetic material and may not produce offspring with the desired trait(s). (11.14)

- The transplantation of pig or other nonhuman tissues into humans (called xenotransplantation) risks the introduction of pig (or other animal) viruses into humans. This viral DNA might not otherwise have the capacity for transmission to humans. (11.14)

- The recent political restrictions on the use of federal funds to study stem cells illustrate the influence of society on the directions of science. As time permits, consider opportunities to discuss or investigate this and other ways that science and society interact. (11.15)

The Genetic Basis of Cancer (11.16–11.19)

Student Misconceptions and Concerns

- Students typically have little background knowledge of cancer at the cellular level. Consider creating your own pre-test to inquire about your students' entering knowledge of cancer. For example, ask students if all cancers are genetic (yes, all cancers are based upon genetic errors and are the main subject of this chapter). In addition, ask students if exposure to a virus can lead to cancer. (Answer: yes, as noted in Module 11.16). (11.16)

- Many students do not appreciate the increased risk of skin cancer associated with the use of tanning beds, which is still popular with many college-age populations. (11.19)

Teaching Tips

- Tumor-suppressor genes function like the repressor in the *E. coli* lactose operon. The *lac* operon is expressed, and cancers appear when their respective repressors do not function. (11.16)

- The production of a vaccine (Gardasil) against a virus known to contribute to cervical cancer has helped students become aware of the risks of HPV exposure. The website of the National Cancer Institute describes the risks of HPV infection at www.cancer.gov/cancertopics/factsheet/Risk/HPV. (11.16)

- Exposure to carcinogens early in life carries greater risks than the same exposure later in life. This is because damage in early life has more time to accumulate additional changes, potentially leading to disease. (11.17)

- Mutations in the *ras* or *p53* genes are like having car problems in which the gas pedal over accelerates or the brakes on the car fail to function. In either situation, an accident is more likely to occur. (11.18)

- Students may not realize the possible consequences of testing positive for a predisposition to cancer. Health insurance companies could use that information to deny insurance to people who are more likely to get ill. Furthermore, people may feel obliged or be obligated to share this information with a potential mate or employer. (11.19)

- Nearly one in five deaths in the United States results from the use of tobacco. Additional information on the risks of tobacco can be found at the website for the American Cancer Society at www.cancer.org. (11.19)

Key Terms

activator	gene regulation	regeneration
adult stem cell	gene expression	regulatory gene
alternative RNA splicing	histone	repressor
Barr body	homeotic gene	reproductive cloning
carcinogen	microRNAs (miRNAs)	RNA interference (RNAi)
clone	nuclear transplantation	signal transduction pathway
differentiation	nucleosome	silencer
DNA microarray	oncogene	therapeutic cloning
embryonic stem cell	operator	transcription factor
(ES cell)	operon	tumor-suppressor gene
enhancer	promoter	X chromosome inactivation
epigenetic inheritance	proto-oncogene	

Word Roots

carcino- = cancer; **-gen** = produce (*carcinogen*: any chemical or environmental factor, such as high-energy radiation, that causes cancer)

homeo- = similar (*homeotic gene*: a master control gene that determines the identity of a body structure in a developing organism)

nucle- = nucleus (*nuclear transplantation*: a technique in which the nucleus of one cell is placed into another cell); **-some** = body (*nucleosome*: the bead-like unit of DNA packaging in a eukaryotic cell, consisting of DNA wound around a protein core)

onco- = tumor (*oncogene*: a cancer-causing gene)

pro- = before (*promoter*: a specific nucleotide sequence in DNA that serves as the binding site for RNA polymerase and the place where transcription begins)

proto- = first, original; **onco-** = tumor (*proto-oncogene*: a normal gene that can be converted to a cancer-causing gene)

trans- = across (*signal transduction pathway*: a series of molecular changes that converts a signal on a target cell's surface to a specific response inside the cell; *transcription factor*: in the eukaryotic cell, a protein that functions in initiating or regulating transcription)

CHAPTER 12

DNA Technology and Genomics

Chapter Objectives

Opening Essay

Explain why DNA technology is important.

Gene Cloning

12.1 Explain how plasmids are used in gene cloning.

12.2 Explain how restriction enzymes are used to "cut and paste" DNA into plasmids.

12.3 Explain how plasmids, phages, and BACs are used to construct genomic libraries.

12.4 Explain how a cDNA library is constructed and how it is different from genomic libraries constructed using plasmids or phages.

12.5 Explain how a nucleic acid probe can be used to identify a specific gene.

Genetically Modified Organisms

12.6 Explain how different organisms are used to mass-produce proteins of human interest.

12.7 Explain how DNA technology has helped to produce insulin, growth hormone, and vaccines.

12.8 Explain how genetically modified (GM) organisms are transforming agriculture.

12.9 Describe the risks posed by the creation and culturing of GM organisms and the safeguards that have been developed to minimize these risks.

12.10 Describe the benefits and risks of gene therapy in humans. Discuss the ethical issues that these techniques present.

DNA Profiling

12.11 Describe the basic steps of DNA profiling.

12.12 Explain how PCR is used to amplify DNA sequences.

12.13 Explain how gel electrophoresis is used to sort DNA and proteins.

12.14 Explain how short tandem repeats are used in DNA profiling.

12.15 Describe the diverse applications of DNA profiling.

12.16 Explain how restriction fragment analysis is used to detect differences in DNA sequences.

Genomics

12.17 Explain why it is important to sequence the genomes of humans and other organisms.

12.18 Describe the structure and possible functions of the noncoding sections of the human genome. Give the current estimate of the total number of human genes. Explain how the complexity of the human organism can result from so few genes.

12.19 Explain how the human genome was mapped.

12.20 Compare the fields of genomics and proteomics.

12.21 Describe the significance of genomics to the study of evolutionary relationships and our understanding of the special characteristics of humans.

Lecture Outline

I. Introduction

A. DNA technology

1. has rapidly revolutionized the field of forensics,
2. permits the use of gene cloning to produce medical and industrial products,
3. allows for the development of genetically modified organisms for agriculture,
4. permits the investigation of historical questions about human family and evolutionary relationships, and
5. is invaluable in many areas of biological research.

II. Gene Cloning

A. 12.1 Genes can be cloned in recombinant plasmids

1. **Biotechnology** is the manipulation of organisms or their components to make useful products.
2. For thousands of years, humans have
   - **a.** used microbes to make wine and cheese and
   - **b.** selectively bred stock, dogs, and other animals.
3. **DNA technology** is the set of modern techniques used to study and manipulate genetic material.
4. **Genetic engineering** involves manipulating genes for practical purposes.
   - **a.** **Gene cloning** leads to the production of multiple, identical copies of a gene-carrying piece of DNA.
   - **b.** **Recombinant DNA** is formed by joining nucleotide sequences from two different sources.
     - **i.** One source contains the gene that will be cloned.
     - **ii.** Another source is a gene carrier called a **vector**.
     - **iii.** **Plasmids** (small, circular DNA molecules independent of the bacterial chromosome) are often used as vectors.
5. Steps in cloning a gene
   - **a.** Plasmid DNA is isolated.
   - **b.** DNA containing the gene of interest is isolated.
   - **c.** Plasmid DNA is treated with a restriction enzyme that cuts in one place, opening the circle.

d. DNA with the target gene is treated with the same enzyme and many fragments are produced.

e. Plasmid and target DNA are mixed and associate with each other.

f. Recombinant DNA molecules are produced when **DNA ligase** joins plasmid and target segments together.

g. The recombinant plasmid containing the target gene is taken up by a bacterial cell.

h. The bacterial cell reproduces to form a **clone**, a group of genetically identical cells descended from a single ancestral cell.

B. 12.2 Enzymes are used to "cut and paste" DNA

　1. Restriction enzymes cut DNA at specific sequences.

　　a. Each enzyme binds to DNA at a different **restriction site**.

　　b. Many restriction enzymes make staggered cuts that produce **restriction fragments** with single-stranded ends called "sticky ends."

　　c. Fragments with complementary sticky ends can associate with each other, forming recombinant DNA.

　2. DNA ligase joins DNA fragments together.

C. 12.3 Cloned genes can be stored in genomic libraries

　1. A **genomic library** is a collection of all of the cloned DNA fragments from a target genome.

　2. Genomic libraries can be constructed with different types of vectors:

　　a. plasmid library: genomic DNA is carried by plasmids,

　　b. bacteriophage (phage) library: genomic DNA is incorporated into bacteriophage DNA,

　　c. bacterial artificial chromosome (BAC) library: specialized plasmids that can carry large DNA sequences.

D. 12.4 Reverse transcriptase can help make genes for cloning

　1. Complementary DNA (cDNA) can be used to clone eukaryotic genes.

　　a. In this process, mRNA from a specific cell type is the template.

　　b. Reverse transcriptase produces a DNA strand from mRNA.

　　c. DNA polymerase produces the second DNA strand.

　2. Advantages of cloning with cDNA include the ability to

　　a. study genes responsible for specialized characteristics of a particular cell type and

　　b. obtain gene sequences

　　　i. that are smaller in size,

　　　ii. easier to handle, and

　　　iii. do not have introns.

E. 12.5 Nucleic acid probes identify clones carrying specific genes

　1. Nucleic acid probes bind very selectively to cloned DNA.

　　a. Probes can be DNA or RNA sequences complementary to a portion of the gene of interest.

　　b. A probe binds to a gene of interest by base pairing.

　　c. Probes are labeled with a radioactive isotope or fluorescent tag for detection.

　2. One way to screen a gene library is as follows:

　　a. Bacterial clones are transferred to filter paper.

　　b. Cells are broken apart and the DNA is separated into single strands.

　　c. A probe solution is added and any bacterial colonies carrying the gene of interest will be tagged on the filter paper.

　　d. The clone carrying the gene of interest is grown for further study.

III. Genetically Modified Organisms

A. 12.6 Recombinant cells and organisms can mass-produce gene products

    1. Recombinant cells and organisms constructed by DNA technologies are used to manufacture many useful products, chiefly proteins.

    2. Bacteria are often the best organisms for manufacturing a protein product because bacteria

        a. have plasmids and phages available for use as gene-cloning vectors,

        b. can be grown rapidly and cheaply,

        c. can be engineered to produce large amounts of a particular protein, and

        d. often secrete the proteins directly into their growth medium.

    3. Yeast cells

        a. are eukaryotes,

        b. have long been used to make bread and beer,

        c. can take up foreign DNA and integrate it into their genomes,

        d. have plasmids that can be used as gene vectors, and

        e. are often better than bacteria at synthesizing and secreting eukaryotic proteins.

    4. Mammalian cells must be used to produce proteins with chains of sugars. Examples include

        a. human erythropoietin (EPO), which stimulates the production of red blood cells,

        b. factor VIII to treat hemophilia, and

        c. tissue plasminogen activator (TPA) used to treat heart attacks and strokes.

    5. Pharmaceutical researchers are currently exploring the mass production of gene products by

        a. whole animals or

        b. plants.

    6. Recombinant animals

        a. are difficult and costly to produce and

        b. must be cloned to produce more animals with the same traits.

B. 12.7 CONNECTION: DNA technology has changed the pharmaceutical industry and medicine

    1. Products of DNA technology are already in use.

        a. Therapeutic hormones produced by DNA technology include

            i. insulin to treat diabetes and

            ii. human growth hormone to treat dwarfism.

        b. DNA technology is used to

            i. test for inherited diseases,

            ii. detect infectious agents such as HIV, and

            iii. produce **vaccines**, harmless variants (mutants) or derivatives of a pathogen that stimulate the immune system.

C. 12.8 CONNECTION: Genetically modified organisms are transforming agriculture

    1. **Genetically modified (GM)** organisms contain one or more genes introduced by artificial means.

    2. **Transgenic organisms** contain at least one gene from another species.

    3. The most common vector used to introduce new genes into plant cells is

        a. a plasmid from the soil bacterium *Agrobacterium tumefaciens* and

        b. called the **Ti plasmid**.

4. GM plants are being produced that

   a. are more resistant to herbicides and pests and

   b. provide nutrients that help address malnutrition.

5. GM animals are being produced with improved nutritional or other qualities.

D. 12.9 Genetically modified organisms raise concerns about human and environmental health

   1. Scientists use safety measures to guard against production and release of new pathogens.

   2. Concerns related to GM organisms include the potential

      a. introduction of allergens into the food supply and

      b. spread of genes to closely related organisms.

   3. Regulatory agencies are trying to address the

      a. safety of GM products,

      b. labeling of GM produced foods, and

      c. safe use of biotechnology.

E. 12.10 CONNECTION: Gene therapy may someday help treat a variety of diseases

   1. Gene therapy aims to treat a disease by supplying a functional allele.

   2. One possible procedure is the following:

      a. Clone the functional allele and insert it in a retroviral vector.

      b. Use the virus to deliver the gene to an affected cell type from the patient, such as a bone marrow cell.

      c. Viral DNA and the functional allele will insert into the patient's chromosome.

      d. Return the cells to the patient for growth and division.

   3. Gene therapy is an

      a. alteration of an afflicted individual's genes and

      b. attempt to treat disease.

   4. Gene therapy may be best used to treat disorders traceable to a single defective gene.

   5. The first successful human gene therapy trial in 2000

      a. tried to treat ten children with SCID (severe combined immune deficiency),

      b. helped nine of these patients, but

      c. caused leukemia in three of the patients, and

      d. resulted in one death.

   6. The use of gene therapy raises many questions.

      a. How can we build in gene control mechanisms that make appropriate amounts of the product at the right time and place?

      b. How can gene insertion be performed without harming other cell functions?

      c. Will gene therapy lead to efforts to control the genetic makeup of human populations?

      d. Should we try to eliminate genetic defects in our children and descendants when genetic variety is a necessary ingredient for the survival of a species?

IV. DNA Profiling

  A. 12.11 The analysis of genetic markers can produce a DNA profile

   1. DNA profiling is the analysis of DNA fragments to determine whether they come from the same individual. DNA profiling

      a. compares genetic markers from noncoding regions that show variation between individuals and

      b. involves amplifying (copying) of markers for analysis.

B. 12.12 The PCR method is used to amplify DNA sequences

   1. Polymerase chain reaction (PCR) is a method of amplifying a specific segment of a DNA molecule.

   2. PCR relies upon a pair of **primers** that are

      a. short,

      b. chemically synthesized, single-stranded DNA molecules, and

      c. complementary to sequences at each end of the target sequence.

   3. PCR

      a. is a three-step cycle that

      b. doubles the amount of DNA in each turn of the cycle.

   4. The advantages of PCR include

      a. the ability to amplify DNA from a small sample,

      b. obtaining results rapidly, and

      c. a reaction that is highly sensitive, copying only the target sequence.

C. 12.13 Gel electrophoresis sorts DNA molecules by size

   1. Gel electrophoresis can be used to separate DNA molecules based on size as follows:

      a. A DNA sample is placed at one end of a porous gel.

      b. Current is applied and DNA molecules move from the negative electrode toward the positive electrode.

      c. Shorter DNA fragments move through the gel matrix more quickly and travel farther through the gel.

      d. DNA fragments appear as bands, visualized through staining or detecting radioactivity or fluorescence.

      e. Each band is a collection of DNA molecules of the same length.

D. 12.14 STR analysis is commonly used for DNA profiling

   1. Repetitive DNA consists of nucleotide sequences that are present in multiple copies in the genome.

   2. Short tandem repeats (STRs) are short nucleotide sequences that are repeated in tandem,

      a. composed of different numbers of repeating units in individuals and

      b. used in DNA profiling.

   3. STR analysis

      a. compares the lengths of STR sequences at specific sites in the genome and

      b. typically analyzes 13 different STR sites.

E. 12.15 CONNECTION: DNA profiling has provided evidence in many forensic investigations

   1. DNA profiling is used to

      a. determine guilt or innocence in a crime,

      b. settle questions of paternity,

      c. identify victims of accidents, and

      d. probe the origin of nonhuman materials.

F. 12.16 RFLPs can be used to detect differences in DNA sequences

   1. A **single nucleotide polymorphism (SNP)** is a variation at a single-base-pair within a genome.

   2. Restriction fragment length polymorphism (RFLP) is a change in the length of restriction fragments due to a SNP that alters a restriction site.

3. RFLP analysis involves

    a. producing DNA fragments by restriction enzymes and

    b. sorting these fragments by gel electrophoresis.

V. Genomics

A. 12.17 Genomics is the scientific study of whole genomes

    1. Genomics is the study of an organism's complete set of genes and their interactions.

        a. Initial studies focused on prokaryotic genomes.

        b. Many eukaryotic genomes have since been investigated.

    2. Genomics allows another way to examine evolutionary relationships.

        a. Genomic studies showed a 96% similarity in DNA sequences between chimpanzees and humans.

        b. Functions of human disease-causing genes have been determined by comparing human genes to similar genes in yeast.

B. 12.18 CONNECTION: The Human Genome Project revealed that most of the human genome does not consist of genes

    1. The goals of the **Human Genome Project (HGP)** include

        a. determining the nucleotide sequence of all DNA in the human genome and

        b. identifying the location and sequence of every human gene.

    2. Results of the Human Genome Project indicate that

        a. humans have about 20,000 genes in 3.2 billion nucleotide pairs,

        b. only 1.5% of the DNA codes for proteins, tRNAs, or rRNAs, and

        c. the remaining 98.5% of the DNA is noncoding DNA including

            i. **telomeres**, stretches of noncoding DNA at the ends of chromosomes, and

            ii. **transposable elements**, DNA segments that can move or be copied from one location to another within or between chromosomes.

C. 12.19 The whole-genome shotgun method of sequencing a genome can provide a wealth of data quickly

    1. The Human Genome Project proceeded through three stages that provided progressively more detailed views of the human genome.

        a. A low-resolution *linkage map* was developed using RFLP analysis of 5,000 genetic markers.

        b. A *physical map* was constructed from nucleotide distances between the linkage-map markers.

        c. DNA sequences for the mapped fragments were determined.

    2. The **whole-genome shotgun method**

        a. was used in 1992 by molecular biologist J. Craig Venter, who

        b. used restriction enzymes to produce fragments that were cloned and sequenced in just one stage and

        c. ran high-performance computer analyses to assemble the sequence by aligning overlapping regions.

    3. Today, this whole-genome shotgun approach is the method of choice for genomic researchers because it is

        a. relatively fast and

        b. inexpensive.

    4. However, limitations of the whole-genome shotgun method suggest that a hybrid approach using the genome shotgunning and physical maps may prove to be the most useful.

D. 12.20 Proteomics is the scientific study of the full set of proteins encoded by a genome

    1. Proteomics

        a. is the study of the full protein sets encoded by genomes and

        b. investigates protein functions and interactions.

    2. The human proteome includes about 100,000 proteins.

    3. Genomics and proteomics are helping biologists study life from an increasingly holistic approach.

E. 12.21 EVOLUTION CONNECTION: Genomes hold clues to human evolution

    1. Human and chimp genomes differ by

        a. 1.2% in single-base substitutions and

        b. 2.7% in insertions and deletions of larger DNA sequences.

    2. Genes showing rapid evolution in humans include

        a. genes for defense against malaria and tuberculosis,

        b. a gene regulating brain size, and

        c. the *FOXP2* gene involved with speech and vocalization.

    3. Neanderthals

        a. were close human relatives,

        b. were a separate species,

        c. also had the *FOXP2* gene,

        d. may have had pale skin and red hair, and

        e. were lactose intolerant.

Chapter Guide to Teaching Resources

Gene Cloning (12.1–12.5)

Student Misconceptions and Concerns

- Student comprehension of restriction enzymes, nucleic acid probes, and many other aspects of recombinant DNA techniques depends upon a comfortable understanding of basic molecular genetics. Consider addressing Chapter 12 after an exam that covers the content in Chapters 10 and 11. (12.1–12.5)

- Students might bring some awareness and/or concerns about biotechnology to the classroom, for example, in their reactions to the controversies regarding genetically modified (GM) foods. This experience can be used to generate class interest and to highlight the importance of good information when making judgments. Consider starting class with a headline addressing one of these issues. The recent process of FDA approval for genetically engineered salmon raised for food might be particularly useful and relevant. (12.1–12.5)

Teaching Tips

- Figure 12.1B is a synthesis of the techniques discussed in further detail in Modules 12.2–12.5. Figure 12.1 is therefore an important integrative piece that lays the foundation of most of the biotechnology discussion. Repeatedly referring to this figure in class helps students relate the text to your lecture. (12.1)

- The general genetic engineering challenge discussed in Module 12.1 begins with the need to insert a gene of choice into a plasmid. This process is very similar to film or video editing. What do we need to do to insert a minute of one film into another? We will need techniques to a) cut and remove the minute of film to be inserted, b) a way to cut the new film apart, and c) a way to insert the new minute. In general, this is also like removing one boxcar from one train, and transferring the boxcar to another train. Students can become confused by the details of gene cloning through misunderstanding this basic editing relationship. (12.1)

- The authors note the origin of the name restriction enzymes. In nature, these enzymes protect bacterial cells against foreign DNA. Thus, these enzymes "restrict" the invasion of foreign genetic material. (12.2)

- A genomic library of the sentence you are now reading would be all of the sentence fragments that made up the sentence. One could string together all of the words of this first sentence, without spaces between letters, and then conduct a word processing edit, placing a space between any place where the letter "e" is followed by the letter "n." The resulting fragments of this original sentence would look like this and would be similar to a genomic library.

  -Age nomiclibraryofthese nte nceyouare nowreadingwouldbeallofthese nte ncefragme ntsthatmadeupthese nte nce. (12.2–12.3)

- A cDNA library is a way to learn what portion of the genome is active at any given time in a cell's life. In a very general way, it is like looking at the list of books checked out at a school library (assuming that the checked-out books are being used). (12.4)

- Reverse transcriptase is introduced in Module 10.20, where HIV is discussed. Even if students were not assigned this chapter, Module 10.20 provides a meaningful background for the natural and significant roles of this enzyme. (12.4)

- Some Internet search programs rely upon a methodology similar in one way to the use of a nucleic acid probe. For example, if you want to find the lyrics to a particular song, but do not know the song title or artist, you might search the Internet using a unique phrase from the song. The search engine will scan millions of web pages to identify those sites containing that particular phrase. However, unlike a nucleic acid probe, you would search for the song by using a few of the lyrics. A nucleic acid probe search uses a sequence *complementary* to the desired sequence. (12.5)

Genetically Modified Organisms (12.6–12.10)

Student Misconceptions and Concerns

- The genetic engineering of organisms can be controversial, creating various degrees of social unease and resistance. Yet, many debates about scientific issues are confused by misinformation. This provides an opportunity for you to assign students to take a position on such issues and support their arguments with accurate research. Students might debate whether a food or drug made from GM/transgenic organisms should be labeled as such, or discuss the risks and advantages of producing GM organisms. (12.6–12.10)

- The fact that the technologies described in this chapter can be used to swap genes between prokaryotes and eukaryotes reveals the fundamental similarities in genetic mechanisms shared by all forms of life. This very strong evidence of common descent is evidence of evolution that may be missed by your students. (12.6–12.10)

Teaching Tips

- As noted in Module 12.6, DNA technology is primarily used to produce proteins. Challenge your students to explain why lipids and carbohydrates are not typically produced by these processes. (12.6)

- Annual flu vaccinations are a common way to prevent diseases that cannot be easily treated. However, students might not understand why many people receive the vaccine every year. A new annual vaccine is necessary because the flu viruses keep evolving, another lesson in evolution that may be missed by your students. (12.7)

- Roundup Ready Corn, a product of the agricultural biotechnology corporation Monsanto, is resistant to the herbicide Roundup. The general strategy for farmers is to spray fields of Roundup Ready corn with the herbicide Roundup, killing weeds but not the corn. A search of the Internet will quickly reveal the controversy associated with this and other genetically modified organisms (GMO), which can encourage interesting discussions and promote critical thinking skills. Module 12.9 discusses some of the issues related to the concerns over the use of GM organisms. (12.8–12.9)

- In 2008, the Genetic Information Nondiscrimination Act (GINA) was signed into law.

  The following link to a related U.S. government web site characterizes the effect of the act as follows. GINA "…prohibits U.S. insurance companies and employers from discriminating on the basis of information derived from genetic tests." The web site can be found at www.ornl.gov/sci/techresources/Human_Genome/elsi/legislat.shtml. (12.10)

- As gene therapy technology expands, our ability to modify the genome in human embryos through *in vitro* fertilization permits genetic modification at the earliest stages of life. Future generations of humans, like our crops today, may include those with and without a genetically modified ancestry. The benefits and challenges of these technologies raise issues many students have never considered. Our students, and the generations soon to follow, will face the potential of directed human evolution. (12.10)

DNA Profiling (12.11–12.16)

Student Misconceptions and Concerns

- Television programs might lead some students to expect DNA profiling to be quick and easy. Ask students to consider why DNA profiling actually takes many days or weeks to complete. (12.11–12.16)

- Students might expect DNA profiling for criminal investigations to involve an analysis of the entire human genome. Consider explaining why such an analysis is unrealistic and unnecessary. Modules 12.12–12.16 describe methods used to describe specific portions of the genome of particular interest. (12.12–12.16)

Teaching Tips

- Figure 12.11 describes the general steps of DNA profiling. This overview is a useful reference to employ while the details of each step are discussed. (12.11)

- In PCR, the product becomes another master copy. Imagine that while you are photocopying, every copy is used as a master at another copy machine. This would require many copy machines. However, it would be very productive! (12.12)

- Separating ink using paper chromatography is a simple experiment that approximates some of what occurs in gel electrophoresis. Consider doing this as a class demonstration while addressing electrophoresis. Cut a large piece of filter paper into a rectangle or square. Use markers to color large dots about 2 cm away from one the edge of the paper. Separate the dots from each other by 3–4 cm. Place the paper on edge, dots down, into a beaker containing about 1 cm of ethanol or isopropyl alcohol (50% or higher will do). The dots should not be in contact with the pool of alcohol in the bottom of the beaker. As the alcohol is drawn up the filter paper by capillary action, the alcohol will dissolve the ink dots. As the alcohol continues up the paper, the ink follows. Not all of the ink components move at the same speed, based upon their size and chemical properties. If you begin the process at the start of class, you should have some degree of separation by the end of a 50-minute period. Experiment with the technique a day or two before class to fine-tune the demonstration. (Save and air-dry these samples for your class.) Consider using brown, green, and black markers, because these colors are often made by color combinations. (12.13)

- In most legal cases, the probability of two people having identical DNA profiles can be one in 10 billion or more. However, eyewitness testimony has been a standard part of the justice system. If you want to make the point about the unreliability of eyewitnesses in a trial, compared to techniques such as genetic profiling, consider this exercise. Arrange for a person who is not well known to the class to run into your classroom, take something you have placed near you (perhaps a bag, stack of papers, or box), and leave quickly. You need to take care that no one in the class is so alarmed as to do something dangerous. Once the "thief" is gone, tell the class that this was planned and do not speak. Have them each write a description of the person, including height, hair color, clothing, facial hair, behavior, etc. Many students will be accurate, but some will likely get details wrong. This is also an effective exercise to demonstrate the need for large sample sizes and accurate recording devices for good scientific technique. (12.14)

- Although the statistical odds of a DNA-profiling match can exceed one in 10 billion, the odds of a mistake in the collecting and testing procedures can be much greater. This is an important distinction. An error as simple as mislabeling a sample can confuse the results. Unfortunately, the odds of human error will vary and are difficult to determine. (12.15)

- Here is another way to explain restriction fragment analysis. Consider these two words, equilibrium and equalibrium. Imagine that a mutation produced the spelling error of the second word. If we used a "restriction enzyme" that splits these words between u and i, how will the fragments compare in size and number? (12.16)

equilibrium = equ ilibri um (three fragments of three, six, and two letters)
equalibrium = equalibri um (two fragments of nine and two letters)

Genomics (12.17–12.21)

Student Misconceptions and Concerns

- The similarities in genotypes and phenotypes among members of a human family are expected and understood by most students. Yet many students have a difficult time extrapolating this knowledge and applying it to the phylogenetic relationships of other groups. The use of genomics to test phylogenetic relationships is an enormously powerful tool for modern systematics and genomics provides significant support of the other types of evidence for evolution. (12.17–12.21)

- Students might assume that the term junk DNA implies that these noncoding regions of DNA are useless. This might be a good time to note the old saying, absence of evidence is not evidence of absence. Our current inability to understand the role(s) of noncoding DNA does not mean that these regions have no significance. (12.18)

- Students might know that humans have 23 pairs of chromosomes. Consider asking them how many different types of chromosomes are found in humans. Some will not have realized that there are 24 types, 22 autosomes plus X and Y sex chromosomes. (12.18)

Teaching Tips

- The first targets of genomics were prokaryotic pathogenic organisms. Consider asking your students in class to suggest why this was a good choice. Students may note that the genomes of these organisms are smaller than eukaryotes and that many of these organisms are of great medical significance. (12.17)

- The main U.S. Department of Energy Office website in support of the Human Genome Project is found at www.ornl.gov/sci/techresources/Human_Genome/home.shtml. (12.18)

- The website for the National Center for Biotechnology Information is www.ncbi.nlm.nih.gov. The center, established in 1988, serves as a national resource for biomedical information related to genomic data. (12.18)

- The authors note that there are 3.2 billion nucleotide pairs in the human genome. There are about 3.2 billion seconds in 101.4 years. This simple reference can add meaning to the significance of these large numbers. (21.8)

- Challenge students to explain why a complete understanding of an organism's genome and proteomes is still not enough to understand the full biology of an organism. Ask them to consider the role of the environment in development and physiology. (One striking example of the influence of the environment is that the sex of some reptiles is determined not by the inheritance of certain chromosomes, but by incubation temperature.) (12.18–12.20)

- Students may enter your course with little appreciation of the scientific questions that remain unanswered. Struggling with the details of what we now know can overwhelm our students, leaving little room to wonder about what is not yet understood. The surprises and questions noted in Modules 12.18–12.21 reveal broad challenges that await the work of our next generation of scientists. Emphasize the many opportunities that exist to resolve unanswered questions, here and throughout your course, as an invitation to future adventures for students. (12.18–12.21)

Key Terms

biotechnology	gene therapy	polymerase chain reaction
clone	genetic engineering	(PCR)
complementary DNA	genetically modified	primers
(cDNA)	(GM) organism	proteomics
DNA ligase	genomic library	recombinant DNA
DNA profiling	genomics	repetitive DNA
DNA technology	Human Genome Project	restriction enzyme
forensics	(HGP)	restriction fragment length
gel electrophoresis	nucleic acid probe	polymorphism (RFLP)
gene cloning	plasmid	restriction fragments

restriction site STR analysis vector

reverse transcriptase telomeres whole-genome shotgun

short tandem repeat Ti plasmid method

(STR) transgenic organism

single nucleotide transposable element

polymorphism (SNP) vaccine

Word Roots

bio- = life; **-tech-** = skill or art (*biotechnology*: the manipulation of organisms or their components to make useful products)

electro- = electricity (*gel electrophoresis*: a technique for separating and purifying macromolecules, including DNA, by using an electrical charge to stimulate their migration through a gel-based matrix)

gen- = produce (*genetic engineering*: the direct manipulation of genes for practical purposes)

liga- = bound, tied (*DNA ligase*: an enzyme that catalyzes the covalent bonding of adjacent DNA nucleotides in DNA replication)

poly- = many (*polymerase chain reaction*: a technique used to obtain many copies of a DNA molecule or part of a DNA molecule, involving use of the enzyme DNA polymerase)

proteo- = proteins (*proteomics*: the study of whole sets of proteins and their interactions)

telos- = an end (*telomere*: the repetitive DNA at each end of a eukaryotic chromosome)

trans- = across (*transgenic organism*: an organism that contains genes from a different species)

CHAPTER 13

How Populations Evolve

Chapter Objectives

Opening Essay

Describe three adaptations that help blue-footed boobies survive.

Darwin's Theory of Evolution

13.1   Briefly summarize the history of evolutionary thought by characterizing the views of early Lamarck, Darwin, and Greek philosophers.

13.1   Explain how Darwin's voyage on the Beagle influenced his thinking.

13.1   Describe the ideas and events that led to Darwin's 1859 publication of *The Origin of Species*.

13.2   Explain how the work of Thomas Malthus and the process of artificial selection influenced Darwin's development of the idea of natural selection.

13.2   Describe Darwin's observations and inferences in developing the concept of natural selection.

13.2   Explain why individuals cannot evolve and why evolution does not lead to perfectly adapted organisms.

13.3   Describe two examples of natural selection known to occur in nature. Note two key points about how natural selection works.

13.4   Explain how fossils form, noting examples of each process.

13.4   Explain how the fossil record provides some of the strongest evidence of evolution.

13.5   Explain how biogeography, comparative anatomy, and molecular biology support evolution.

13.6   Explain how evolutionary trees are constructed and used to represent ancestral relationships.

The Evolution of Populations

13.7   Define the gene pool, a population, and microevolution.

13.8   Explain how mutation and sexual reproduction produce genetic variation.

13.8   Explain why prokaryotes can evolve more quickly than eukaryotes.

13.9   Describe the five conditions required for the Hardy-Weinberg equilibrium.

13.9–13.10   Explain the significance of the Hardy-Weinberg equilibrium to natural populations and to public health science.

Mechanisms of Microevolution

13.11   Define genetic drift and gene flow. Explain how the bottleneck effect and the founder effect influence microevolution.

13.11   Explain how genetic bottlenecks threaten the survival of certain species.

13.12 Explain why natural selection is the only mechanism that consistently leads to adaptive evolution.

13.13 Distinguish between stabilizing selection, directional selection, and disruptive selection. Describe an example of each.

13.14 Define and compare intrasexual selection and intersexual selection.

13.15 Explain how antibiotic resistance has evolved.

13.16 Explain how genetic variation is maintained in populations.

13.17 Explain why natural selection cannot produce perfection.

Lecture Outline

I. Introduction

A. The blue-footed booby has adaptations that make it suited to its environment. These include

1. webbed feet,
2. streamlined shape that minimizes friction when it dives, and
3. a large tail that serves as a brake.

II. Darwin's Theory of Evolution

A. 13.1 A sea voyage helped Darwin frame his theory of evolution

1. A five-year voyage around the world helped Darwin make observations that would lead to his theory of **evolution**, the idea that Earth's many species are descendants of ancestral species that were different from those living today.

2. Some early Greek philosophers suggested that life might change gradually over time.
   a. However, the Greek philosopher Aristotle viewed species as perfect and unchanging.
   b. Judeo-Christian culture reinforced this idea with a literal interpretation of the biblical book Genesis.

3. **Fossils** are the imprints or remains of organisms that lived in the past.

4. In the century prior to Darwin, fossils suggested that species had indeed changed over time.

5. In the early 1800s, Jean Baptiste Lamarck suggested that life on Earth evolves, but by a different mechanism than that proposed by Darwin.

6. Lamarck proposed that
   a. organisms evolve by the use and disuse of body parts and
   b. these acquired characteristics are passed on to offspring.

7. During Darwin's round-the-world voyage he was influenced by Lyell's *Principles of Geology,* suggesting that natural forces
   a. gradually changed Earth and
   b. are still operating today.

8. Darwin came to realize that
   a. the Earth was very old and
   b. over time, present day species have arisen from ancestral species by natural processes.

9. During his voyage, Darwin
   a. collected thousands of plants and animals and
   b. noted their characteristics that made them well suited to diverse environments.

10. In 1859, Darwin published *On the Origin of Species by Means of Natural Selection,*

    a. presenting a strong, logical explanation of *descent with modification,* evolution by the mechanism of natural selection, and

    b. noting that as organisms spread into various habitats over millions of years, they accumulated diverse **adaptations** that fit them to specific ways of life in these new environments.

B. 13.2 Darwin proposed natural selection as the mechanism of evolution

  1. Darwin devoted much of *The Origin of Species* to exploring adaptations of organisms to their environment.

  2. Darwin discussed many examples of **artificial** selection, in which humans have modified species through selection and breeding.

  3. Darwin recognized the connection between

    a. natural selection and

    b. the capacity of organisms to overreproduce.

  4. Darwin had read an essay written in 1798 by the economist Thomas Malthus, who argued that human suffering was the consequence of human populations increasing faster than essential resources.

  5. Darwin observed that organisms

    a. vary in many traits and

    b. produce more offspring than the environment can support.

  6. Darwin reasoned that

    a. organisms with traits that increase their chance of surviving and reproducing in their environment tend to leave more offspring than others and

    b. organisms with this unequal reproduction will lead to the accumulation of favorable traits in a population over generations.

  7. There are three key points about evolution by natural selection that clarify this process.

    a. Individuals do not evolve: populations evolve.

    b. Natural selection can amplify or diminish only heritable traits. Acquired characteristics cannot be passed on to offspring.

    c. Evolution is not goal directed and does not lead to perfection. Favorable traits vary as environments change.

C. 13.3 Scientists can observe natural selection in action

  1. Camouflage adaptations in insects that evolved in different environments are examples of the results of natural selection.

  2. Biologists have documented natural selection in action in thousands of scientific studies.

  3. Rosemary and Peter Grant have worked on Darwin's finches in the Galápagos for over 30 years. They found that

    a. in wet years, small seeds are more abundant and small beaks are favored, but

    b. in dry years, large strong beaks are favored because large seeds remain.

  4. Another example of natural selection in action is the evolution of pesticide resistance in insects.

    a. A relatively small amount of a new pesticide may kill 99% of the insect pests, but subsequent sprayings are less effective.

    b. Those insects that initially survived were fortunate enough to carry alleles that somehow enable them to resist the pesticide.

  c. When these resistant insects reproduce, the percentage of the population resistant to the pesticide increases.

 5. These examples of evolutionary adaptation highlight two important points about natural selection.

  a. Natural selection is more of an editing process than a creative mechanism.

  b. Natural selection is contingent on time and place, favoring those characteristics in a population that fit the current, local environment.

D. 13.4 The study of fossils provides strong evidence for evolution

 1. Darwin's ideas about evolution also relied on the **fossil record**, the sequence in which fossils appear within **strata** (layers) of sedimentary rocks.

 2. Paleontologists, scientists who study fossils, have found many types of fossils.

 3. The fossil record shows that organisms have evolved in a historical sequence.

  a. The oldest known fossils, extending back about 3.5 billion years ago, are prokaryotes.

  b. The oldest eukaryotic fossils are about a billion years younger.

  c. Another billion years passed before we find fossils of multicellular eukaryotic life.

 4. Many fossils link early extinct species with species living today.

  a. A series of fossils traces the gradual modification of jaws and teeth in the evolution of mammals from a reptilian ancestor.

  b. A series of fossils documents the evolution of whales from a group of land mammals.

E. 13.5 Many types of scientific evidence support the evolutionary view of life

 1. Biogeography, the geographic distribution of species, suggested to Darwin that organisms evolve from common ancestors.

 2. Darwin noted that Galápagos animals resembled species on the South American mainland more than they resembled animals on islands that were similar but much more distant.

 3. Comparative anatomy

  a. is the comparison of body structures in different species,

  b. was extensively cited by Darwin, and

  c. illustrates that evolution is a remodeling process.

  d. Homology is the similarity in characteristics that result from common ancestry.

  e. Homologous structures have different functions but are structurally similar because of common ancestry.

 4. Comparative embryology

  a. is the comparison of early stages of development among different organisms and

  b. reveals homologies not visible in adult organisms.

  c. For example, all vertebrate embryos have, at some point in their development,

   i. tail posterior to the anus and

   ii. pharyngeal throat pouches.

  d. Vestigial structures are remnants of features that served important functions in an organism's ancestors.

 5. Advances in **molecular biology** reveal evolutionary relationships by comparing DNA and amino acid sequences between different organisms. These studies indicate that

  a. all life-forms are related,

  b. all life shares a common DNA code for the proteins found in living cells, and

  c. humans and bacteria share homologous genes that have been inherited from a very distant common ancestor.

F. 13.6 Homologies indicate patterns of descent that can be shown on an evolutionary tree

    1. Darwin was the first to represent the history of life as a tree,

        a. with multiple branchings from a common ancestral trunk

        b. to the descendant species at the tips of the twigs.

    2. Today, biologists

        a. represent these patterns of descent with an **evolutionary tree**, but

        b. often turn the trees sideways.

    3. Homologous structures can be used to determine the branching sequence of an evolutionary tree. These homologies can include

        a. anatomical structure and/or

        b. molecular structure.

        c. Figure 13.6 illustrates an example of an evolutionary tree.

III. The Evolution of Populations

  A. 13.7 Evolution occurs within populations

    1. A **population** is

        a. a group of individuals of the same species and

        b. living in the same place at the same time.

    2. Populations may be isolated from one another (with little interbreeding).

    3. Individuals within populations may interbreed.

    4. We can measure evolution as a change in heritable traits in a population over generations.

    5. A **gene pool** is the total collection of genes in a population at any one time.

    6. **Microevolution** is a change in the relative frequencies of alleles in a gene pool over time.

    7. **Population genetics** studies how populations change genetically over time.

    8. The **modern synthesis** connects Darwin's theory with population genetics.

  B. 13.8 Mutation and sexual reproduction produce the genetic variation that makes evolution possible

    1. Organisms typically show individual variation.

    2. However, in *The Origin of Species*, Darwin could not explain

        a. the cause of variation among individuals or

        b. how variations were passed from parents to offspring.

    3. **Mutations** are

        a. changes in the nucleotide sequence of DNA and

        b. the ultimate source of new alleles.

    4. On rare occasions, mutant alleles improve the adaptation of an individual to its environment.

        a. This kind of effect is more likely when the environment is changing such that mutations that were once disadvantageous are favorable under new conditions.

        b. The evolution of DDT-resistant houseflies is such an example.

    5. Chromosomal duplication is an important source of genetic variation.

        a. If a gene is duplicated, the new copy can undergo mutation without affecting the function of the original copy.

        b. For example, an early ancestor of mammals had a single gene for an olfactory receptor. That gene has been duplicated many times, and mice now have 1,300 different olfactory receptor genes.

6. Sexual reproduction shuffles alleles to produce new combinations in three ways.

   a. Homologous chromosomes sort independently as they separate during anaphase I of meiosis.

   b. During prophase I of meiosis, pairs of homologous chromosomes cross over and exchange genes.

   c. Further variation arises when sperm randomly unite with eggs in fertilization.

C. 13.9 The Hardy-Weinberg equation can test whether a population is evolving

   1. Sexual reproduction alone does not lead to evolutionary change in a population.

      a. Although alleles are shuffled, the frequency of alleles and genotypes in the population does not change.

      b. Similarly, if you shuffle a deck of cards, you will deal out different hands, but the cards and suits in the deck do not change.

   2. The **Hardy-Weinberg principle** states that

      a. within a sexually reproducing, diploid population,

      b. allele and genotype frequencies will remain in equilibrium,

      c. unless outside forces act to change those frequencies.

   3. For a population to remain in Hardy-Weinberg equilibrium for a specific trait, it must satisfy five conditions. There must be

      a. a very large population,

      b. no gene flow between populations,

      c. no mutations,

      d. random mating, and

      e. no natural selection.

   4. Imagine that there are two alleles in a blue-footed booby population, W and w.

      a. Uppercase W is a dominant allele for a nonwebbed booby foot.

      b. Lowercase w is a recessive allele for a webbed booby foot.

   5. Consider the gene pool of a population of 500 boobies.

      a. 320 (64%) are homozygous dominant (WW).

      b. 160 (32%) are heterozygous (Ww).

      c. 20 (4%) are homozygous recessive (ww).

      d. $p = 80\%$ of alleles in the booby population are W.

      e. $q = 20\%$ of alleles in the booby population are w.

   6. The frequency of all three genotypes must be 100% or 1.0.

      a. $p^2 + 2pq + q^2 = 100\% = 1.0$

      b. homozygous dominant (p^2) + heterozygous ($2pq$) + homozygous recessive (q^2) = 100%

   7. What about the next generation of boobies?

      a. The probability that a booby sperm or egg carries $W = 0.8$ or 80%.

      b. The probability that a sperm or egg carries $w = 0.2$ or 20%.

      c. The genotype frequencies will remain constant generation after generation unless something acts to change the gene pool.

   8. How could the Hardy-Weinberg equilibrium be disrupted?

      a. Small populations could increase the chances that allele frequencies will fluctuate by chance.

      b. Individuals moving in or out of populations add or remove alleles.

      c. Mutations can change or delete alleles.

d. Preferential mating can change the frequencies of homozygous and heterozygous genotypes.

e. Unequal survival and reproductive success of individuals (natural selection) can alter allele frequencies.

D. 13.10 CONNECTION: The Hardy-Weinberg equation is useful in public health science

    1. Public health scientists use the Hardy-Weinberg equation to estimate frequencies of disease-causing alleles in the human population.

    2. One out of 10,000 babies born in the United States has phenylketonuria (PKU), an inherited inability to break down the amino acid phenylalanine.

    3. Individuals with PKU must strictly limit the intake of foods with phenylalanine.

    4. PKU is a recessive allele.

    5. The frequency of individuals born with PKU corresponds to the q^2 term in the Hardy-Weinberg equation and would equal 0.0001.

        a. The value of q is 0.01.

        b. The frequency of the dominant allele would equal $1 - q$, or 0.99.

        c. The frequency of carriers

            i. $= 2pq$

            ii. $= 2 \times 0.99 \times 0.01 = 0.0198 = 1.98\%$ of the U.S. population.

[handwritten margin notes: "B/C ITS RECESSIVE" with arrow pointing to item 4; "DETERMINE DOMINANT ALLELE" with arrow pointing to item b]

IV. Mechanisms of Microevolution

A. 13.11 Natural selection, genetic drift, and gene flow can cause microevolution

    1. If the five conditions for the Hardy-Weinberg equilibrium are not met in a population, the population's gene pool may change. However,

        a. mutations are rare and random and have little effect on the gene pool, and

        b. nonrandom mating may change genotype frequencies but usually has little impact on allele frequencies.

    2. The three main causes of evolutionary change are

        a. natural selection,

        b. genetic drift, and

        c. gene flow.

    3. 1—**Natural selection**

        a. If individuals differ in their survival and reproductive success, natural selection will alter allele frequencies.

        b. Consider the imaginary booby population. Webbed boobies (*ww*) might

            i. be more successful at swimming,

            ii. capture more fish,

            iii. produce more offspring, and

            iv. increase the frequency of the *w* allele in the gene pool.

    4. 2—**Genetic drift**

        a. **Genetic drift** is a change in the gene pool of a population due to chance.

        b. In a small population, chance events may lead to the loss of genetic diversity.

        c. The **bottleneck effect** leads to a loss of genetic diversity when a population is greatly reduced.

            i. For example, the greater prairie chicken once numbered in the millions, but was reduced to about 50 birds in Illinois by 1993.

            ii. A survey comparing the DNA of the surviving chickens with DNA extracted from museum specimens dating back to the 1930s showed a loss of 30% of the alleles.

    d. Genetic drift also results from the **founder effect**, when a few individuals colonize a new habitat.
        i. A small group cannot adequately represent the genetic diversity in the ancestral population.
        ii. The frequency of alleles will therefore be different between the old and new populations.
  5. 3—Gene flow
    a. is the movement of individuals or gametes/spores between populations and
    b. can alter allele frequencies in a population.
    c. To counteract the lack of genetic diversity in the remaining Illinois greater prairie chickens,
        i. researchers added 271 birds from neighboring states to the Illinois populations, which
        ii. successfully introduced new alleles.

B. 13.12 Natural selection is the only mechanism that consistently leads to adaptive evolution
  1. Genetic drift, gene flow, and mutations could each result in microevolution, but only by chance could these events improve a population's fit to its environment.
  2. Natural selection is a blend of
    a. chance and
    b. sorting.
  3. Because of this sorting, only natural selection consistently leads to adaptive evolution.
  4. An individual's **relative fitness** is the contribution it makes to the gene pool of the next generation relative to the contribution of other individuals.
  5. The fittest individuals are those that
    a. produce the largest number of viable, fertile offspring and
    b. pass on the most genes to the next generation.

C. 13.13 Natural selection can alter variation in a population in three ways
  1. Natural selection can affect the distribution of phenotypes in a population.
    a. Stabilizing selection favors intermediate phenotypes, acting against extreme phenotypes.
    b. Directional selection acts against individuals at *one* of the phenotypic extremes.
    c. Disruptive selection favors individuals at *both* extremes of the phenotypic range.

D. 13.14 Sexual selection may lead to phenotypic differences between males and females
  1. Sexual selection
    a. is a form of natural selection
    b. in which individuals with certain characteristics are more likely than other individuals to obtain mates.
  2. In many animal species, males and females show distinctly different appearances, called **sexual dimorphism**.
  3. *Intrasexual selection* (within the same sex) involves competition for mates, usually by males.
  4. In *intersexual selection* (between sexes) or *mate choice*, individuals of one sex (usually females)
    a. are choosy in picking their mates and
    b. often select flashy or colorful mates.

E. 13.15 EVOLUTION CONNECTION: The evolution of antibiotic resistance in bacteria is a serious public health concern
  1. The excessive use of antibiotics is leading to the evolution of antibiotic-resistant bacteria.
  2. As a result, natural selection is favoring bacteria that are naturally resistant to antibiotics.
    a. Natural selection for antibiotic resistance is particularly strong in hospitals.
    b. Methicillin-resistant (MRSA) bacteria can cause "flesh-eating disease" and potentially fatal infections.
F. 13.16 Diploidy and balancing selection preserve genetic variation
  1. What prevents natural selection from eliminating unfavorable genotypes?
    a. In diploid organisms, recessive alleles are usually not subject to natural selection in heterozygotes.
    b. **Balancing selection** maintains stable frequencies of two or more phenotypes in a population.
      i. In **heterozygote advantage**, heterozygotes have greater reproductive success than homozygotes.
      ii. **Frequency-dependent selection** is a type of balancing selection that maintains two different phenotypes in a population.
G. 13.17 Natural selection cannot fashion perfect organisms
  1. The evolution of organisms is constrained.
    a. *Selection can act only on existing variations*. New, advantageous alleles do not arise on demand.
    b. *Evolution is limited by historical constraints*. Evolution co-opts existing structures and adapts them to new situations.
    c. *Adaptations are often compromises*. The same structure often performs many functions.
    d. *Chance, natural selection, and the environment interact*. Environments often change unpredictably.

Chapter Guide to Teaching Resources

Darwin's Theory of Evolution (13.1–13.6)

Student Misconceptions and Concerns

- Students often think that Charles Darwin was the first to suggest that life evolves: the early contributions by Greek philosophers such as Anaximander and the work of Jean Baptiste de Lamarck are unappreciated. Consider emphasizing these earlier contributions. (13.1)

- Students often misunderstand the basic process of evolution and instead express a Lamarckian point of view. Organisms do not evolve structures because of want or need. Instead, evolution is a passive process in which the environment favors certain traits that exist within a population. Adaptations evolve in populations. Organisms do not actively or willingly evolve. (13.1–13.6)

- Students often think of evolution as a process that improves. As the text notes, an adaptation in one context might be a handicap in another context. Reptiles are not "better" animals than fish. Neither could survive long in the other's environment. Instead, the adaptations found in reptiles allow them to survive in a terrestrial environment, as those of fish allow them to survive in an aquatic one. (13.2–13.3)

- Students must understand that the environment does the selecting (editing) in natural selection. Species do not evolve because of need. Biological diversity exists, and the environment selects. Evolution is not deliberate, it is reactive. As teachers, we must be careful in how we express evolution to best reflect this process. For example, the statement "Birds evolved wings" may make it sound as if birds did something deliberately. "Wings evolved in birds" is more accurate, in that something happened to birds through a process. This use of the passive voice in our descriptions of evolution better reflects the nature of evolution. (13.3)

- Students might expect that every living organism will leave fossils and that we should be able to find them. Furthermore, they might falsely conclude that the absence of evidence is evidence of absence. Understanding the rare circumstances under which fossils form (the scientific study of fossil formation is referred to as taphonomy), the geological processes that distort and destroy layers (for example, earthquakes and glaciers), and the long odds against the discovery of fossils helps students understand why the fossil record is limited. (13.4)

- Students who struggle with the concept of evolution may also bring personal objections to the classroom. Modules 13.4 and 13.5, on the evidence of evolution, permits a demonstration of the scientific method, in which confidence in our conclusions increases based on multiple, independent lines of evidence. Science requires evidence and cannot rely upon faith or supernatural explanations. (13.4–13.5)

- Students might become confused by some scientific debates. Evolution can be considered on three levels, sometimes referred to as (a) fact, (b) course, and (c) mechanism: (a) Does evolution occur? (b) Who gave rise to whom? and (c) Is natural selection the only mechanism of evolution that produces adaptations? Students who listen to scientific debates about the course of evolution might think that that fact of evolution is under attack. Doubts about ancestry can be misconstrued as doubts about evolution itself. Make sure students understand these distinctions. (13.6)

Teaching Tips

- Consider beginning your unit on evolution by asking each student to explain how a particular adaptation evolved. The evolution of flight in birds is a good example. Reviewing these student explanations can provide great insight into the misconceptions that students may bring to the class. (13.1)

- Many resources related to Charles Darwin are available on the Internet. The following are only a few examples:

  www.ucmp.berkeley.edu/history/evolution.html and **www.natcenscied.org** are extensive sites rich with details and references.

  www.literature.org/authors/darwin-charles/ includes the texts of *The Voyage of the Beagle*, *The Origin of Species* first and sixth editions, and *The Descent of Man*.

  http://williamcalvin.com/bookshelf/down_hse.htm includes details of Charles Darwin's home.

  www.talkorigins.org is an extensive usenet newsgroup devoted to the discussion and debate of biological and physical origins. (13.1)

- Students may be asked to consider this question: Can individuals evolve? Sometimes such simple questions require complex answers. Might Lamarck have answered this question differently from Darwin? Module 13.2 addresses this question. (13.2)

- An analogy can be made between the specialized functions of finch beaks and the many types of screwdrivers (or pliers) that exist today. Each type of screwdriver (Phillips, flathead, hex, etc.) represents a specialization for a particular job. (13.3)

- Beginning college students are likely to have scant or uneven knowledge of the subject of fossils. Describe several ways that a fossil's age can be determined (for example, radiometric dating, association with other fossils of known age in the same layer, correlation to other strata of known ages). These methods demonstrate the importance of independent lines of evidence and consistency. (13.4)

- Any sort of a fossil makes a nice visual aid. Of course, the larger the fossil, the better. Many shops in natural history museums carry large and common fossils that can be purchased for less than $50.00. Crinoid stems from the Midwest or marine shells from Montana can make the point that life and ecosystems change over time. (13.4)

- The sequence, but not the absolute age, of layers is revealed by the stratifications in sedimentary rocks. This is like peeling the layers of wallpaper from the walls of a very old house that has been inhabited by many owners. By the sequence, we can tell which layers are older, but not the absolute ages of each layer. (13.4)

- Another popular example of biogeography is the distribution of lungfish in Australia, southern South America, and southern Africa. At one time, these three continents were united as Gondwanaland. (13.5)

- One striking example of evolutionary remodeling is the shell of turtles, which is primarily made from modified ribs and vertebrae. If you find an old turtle shell and soak it in water, the shell may fall apart, leaving isolated ribs and vertebrae that make interesting visual aids. (13.5)

- You can have some fun with this analogy to molecular evidence for evolution. As teachers, we have to be keenly aware of cheating. Certainly, if two students turned in written assignments that differed by just a few words, we would conclude that they had a "common heritage" or that one was derived from the other. (13.5)

- Students often fail to fully understand all of the information and meaning communicated in cladograms. Consider spending extra time to help students understand how shared traits imply an evolutionary sequence. (13.6)

The Evolution of Populations (13.7–13.10)

Student Misconceptions and Concerns

- Students often suggest that individuals evolve. As this chapter section clarifies, populations are the smallest units that can evolve. Individuals do not have genetic diversity from which to select. However, individuals can change during their lifetime in response to the environment. Muscles can grow larger through use. But these individual changes are not passed on to the next generation (after all, boys have been circumcised for thousands of years, but are still born with a foreskin). (13.7–13.10)

- Another misperception is that evolution results from need. Challenge your students to explain how need and want cannot drive evolution (because neither need nor want can generate genetic variation!). (13.7–13.10)

- Challenge your students to explain how extinction is predicted by an understanding of natural selection. (Genetic diversity is generated by random processes, but the variety generated may not be sufficient for the survival of a population or species, leading to its extinction.) (13.7–13.10)

- Students may think of mutations in a positive sense, as if they come as needed. Yet, mutations in key genes are the cause of cancer and other diseases. It is rare that a mutation leads to a change that increases the chances for survival. However, these rare events can become significant if given enough time. This is an opportunity to emphasize an important related point: given a long enough span of time, even rare events will occur, and can be expected to do so. (13.8)

- Extending the point just made, our comprehension of time and what constitutes a rare event are on a different scale than most evolutionary change. Ask your students if they think it would be rare for something to happen one time every one thousand years. Then ask how many times that event will occur in one million years (answer: one thousand times!). What is rare to us may be relatively frequent in geological history. (13.8)

Teaching Tips

- Try to find good local examples of populations. If you are near a seashore, the many invertebrate populations (starfish, sea urchin, and kelp) might be ideal. Further inland, you might find somewhat isolated populations of fish and continuous and clumped populations of squirrels, separated by vast fields of corn, wheat, or soybeans! Bring the subject home with local examples. (13.7)

- A single bacterium can divide by fission as quickly as every 20 minutes. Given unlimited resources (a mostly unlikely assumption), after 36 hours, there would be enough bacteria to cover Earth's surface 1 foot deep. Natural selection is premised on overpopulation and the expected death of most of these bacteria. (13.8)

- It might be interesting to discuss with students whether the Internet would have helped Mendel and Darwin. Is the Internet facilitating scientific communication? Has this technology created new problems in the process? (13.8)

- No doubt about it, the Hardy-Weinberg equation is problematic for some students. Students should create a quick reference key to the definitions of the elements. Consider some practice problems varying the value of p and q. Much of the remainder of the chapter builds upon deviations from a Hardy-Weinberg equilibrium. (13.9–13.10)

- Heterozygotes can form in two ways, the recessive from mom and the dominant from dad or the reverse. This should serve to remind students that the $2pq$ portion of the equation represents the heterozygotes. (13.9–13.10)

- Another example that can be used for Hardy-Weinberg practice is cystic fibrosis. Cystic fibrosis strikes one out of every 3,300 Caucasian children. It results from the homozygous recessive condition. Thus, q^2 would equal 1/3,300 = 0.000303 and the square root of 0.000303 = 0.0174. The frequency of carriers = $2pq$ = 2 × .0174 × .9826 = 0.0342 = 3.42%, about one in every 29 Caucasian adults. To bring the point home to your class, divide the number of Caucasian students in your class by 29 to estimate the number of students who are likely carriers. (13.10)

Mechanisms of Microevolution (13.11–13.17)

Student Misconceptions and Concerns

- The concept of a genetic bottleneck contributing to a loss of diversity can be difficult for some students to understand. Without an appreciation for population genetics, students might think that a recovery in terms of sheer numbers is all that is needed. Yet the loss of genetic diversity might ultimately doom a population that is later faced with widespread disease. (13.11)

- Students may be misled by the phrase "survival of the fittest." Fitness requires survival. Saying "survival of the fittest" may be interpreted as "survival of the survivors," misrepresenting the process of natural selection. (13.12)

- Students may think that organisms steadily improve until they are perfectly adapted. However, a species may change only to keep up with environmental changes. Coevolution of two or more species, such as between a parasite and its host, are ongoing changes in response to each other. (13.12, 13.17)

Teaching Tips

- To demonstrate the concept of genetic drift, consider a demonstration with several colored beans (different kinds of dried beans are cheap and easy to find in grocery stores). Fill a bottle with ten beans of five different colors. Then remove ten beans as a population sample. It is very likely that the sample will not adequately represent the diversity of the original bean collection. In fact, it is common for not all colors to be represented. As an alternative, draw eight cards out of a shuffled deck of 52 cards. Are all four suits represented? Are they represented equally? (13.11)

- Sampling error, a cause of genetic drift, can be difficult for some students to understand, but the following exercise may help. Have students work in pairs to flip a coin ten times. For each pair, list the number of heads on the board as just a long list of numbers (no need to keep track of heads and tails). This can be done quickly, as long as you have been sure to bring enough pennies. Now analyze the results. There should be considerable variation from the expected five. Now determine the average of all the groups and the collective sample size. By pooling the results, and increasing the sample size, the means should be closer to five. (13.11)

- The loss of genetic diversity in a population due to bottlenecks is a significant problem in conservation. When a species is reduced to relatively few individuals, and then is brought back to abundance by extraordinary efforts, the species is not fully recovered. The lost genetic diversity may be a prerequisite for the long-term survival of the species. Consider challenging your students to identify modern endangered species not mentioned in the textbook that might suffer from a genetic bottleneck. (13.11)

- The following thought exercise might help students understand founder effect "bias." Ask them to imagine that all the students present in today's class are the only survivors of some global catastrophe. Would your class adequately represent the biological diversity of the current human population? (13.11)

- Challenge your students to explain why evolution applies primarily but not exclusively to individuals who reproduce. Like people who vote, reproduction contributes to change. However, like nonvoters who influence opinions of voters, organisms that do not reproduce can still influence the actions of those who do reproduce. (13.12)

- Students will better understand each type of selection if they can think of their own examples. Consider a short homework assignment or small in-class group work to suggest other examples beyond those that are in the text. (13.13)

- Students are often surprised to learn that overweight human newborns can be as unhealthy as underweight newborns. Thus, stabilizing selection favors human birth weights clustered narrowly around a mean weight. (13.13)

- Challenge your students to distinguish between natural selection, sexual selection, and artificial selection. One criterion for comparison is the nature of the selective environment. In natural selection, the interaction is between the organism and its immediate environment. In sexual selection, competition occurs within a species for access to mates. In artificial selection, humans are an important component of the environment, favoring traits of human interest. (13.14)

- Module 13.15 can be used to remind students why an understanding of evolution is necessary for modern human medicine. Without the explanatory power of evolution, we would not understand why our once-powerful antibiotics are increasingly ineffective. The failure to properly understand evolution can result in the deaths of many people. (13.15)

- If your students have not already studied basic characteristics of inheritance in Chapter 9, they may struggle with the information in Module 13.16. Knowledge of dominant and recessive traits and homozygous and heterozygous conditions serves as background for this aspect of evolutionary biology. (13.16)

- Some predator-prey relationships result in frequency-dependent selection. In some birds that feed on molluscs, birds consume the most abundant mollusc color. As the frequency shifts, the birds may preferentially consume a different color pattern. (13.16)

- Studying Module 13.17 provides a good opportunity to remind your students that most species that have ever lived are now extinct. Species do not have a mechanism to obtain what they need to survive. Instead, preexisting variation from preceding generations and new variations that emerge from mutation and genetic recombination provide the raw materials for survival. No amount of need can influence the variety upon which selection must act. It is, therefore, quite possible that the variety in any generation may be insufficient for survival, particularly during periods of relatively fast environmental change. (13.17)

Key Terms

artificial selection	founder effect	molecular biology
balancing selection	frequency-dependent selection	natural selection
biogeography	gene flow	paleontologist
bottleneck effect	gene pool	population
directional selection	genetic drift	relative fitness
disruptive selection	Hardy-Weinberg principle	sexual dimorphism
evolution	heterozygote advantage	sexual selection
evolutionary tree	homologous structures	stabilizing selection
fossil record	homology	strata
fossils	microevolution	vestigial structures

Word Roots

bio- = life; **geo-** = the Earth (*biogeography*: the study of the past and present distribution of organisms)

homo- = like, resembling (*homologous structures*: structures in different species that are similar because of common ancestry; *homology*: similarity in characteristics resulting from a shared ancestry)

micro- = small (*microevolution*: a change in a population's gene pool over generations)

muta- = change (*mutation*: a change in the nucleotide sequence of an organism's DNA)

paleo- = ancient (*paleontologist*: a scientist who studies fossils)

vestigi- = trace (*vestigial organs*: a structure of marginal or no importance to an organism that is the historical remnant of structures that had important functions in ancestors)

CHAPTER 14

The Origin of Species

Chapter Objectives

Opening Essay

Explain how the absence of mammals on the Galápagos has influenced the evolution of Galápagos cormorants.

Defining Species

14.1 Distinguish between microevolution and speciation.

14.2 Compare the definitions, advantages, and disadvantages of the different species concepts.

14.3 Describe five types of prezygotic barriers and three types of postzygotic barriers that prevent populations of closely related species from interbreeding.

Mechanisms of Speciation

14.4 Explain how geologic processes can fragment populations and lead to speciation.

14.5 Explain how reproductive barriers might evolve in isolated populations of organisms. Refer to studies of laboratory-raised fruit flies and monkey flowers.

14.6 Explain how sympatric speciation can occur, noting examples in plants and animals.

14.7 Explain why polyploidy is important to modern agriculture. Explain how modern wheat evolved.

14.8 Describe the circumstances that led to the adaptive radiation of the Galápagos finches.

14.9 Describe the discoveries made by Peter and Rosemary Grant in their work with Galápagos finches.

14.10 Explain how hybrid zones are useful in the study of reproductive isolation.

14.11 Compare the gradual model and the punctuated equilibrium model of evolution. Explain how each model applies to the fossil record.

Lecture Outline

I. Introduction

    A. Many species of cormorants around the world can fly.

    B. Cormorants on the Galápagos Islands cannot fly.

    C. How did these flightless cormorants get to the Galápagos Islands?

    D. Why are these flightless cormorants found nowhere else in the world?

    E. An ancestral cormorant species is thought to have flown from the Americas to the Galápagos Islands more than 3 million years ago.

F. Terrestrial mammals could not make the trip over the wide distance, and no predatory mammals naturally occur on these islands today.

G. Without predators, the environment of these cormorants favored birds with smaller wings, perhaps channeling resources to the production of offspring.

II. Defining Species

A. 14.1 The origin of species is the source of biological diversity

  1. Microevolution is the change in the gene pool of a population from one generation to the next.

  2. Speciation is the process by which one species splits into two or more species.

    a. Every time speciation occurs, the diversity of life increases.

    b. The many millions of species on Earth have all arisen from an ancestral life form that lived around 3.5 billion years ago.

B. 14.2 There are several ways to define a species

  1. The word species is from the Latin for "kind" or "appearance."

  2. Although the basic idea of species as distinct life-forms seems intuitive, devising a more formal definition is not easy and raises questions.

    a. How similar are members of the same species?

    b. What keeps one species distinct from others?

  3. The **biological species concept** defines a species as

    a. a group of populations,

    b. whose members have the potential to interbreed in nature, and

    c. produce fertile offspring.

    d. Therefore, members of a species are similar because they reproduce with each other.

  4. Reproductive isolation

    a. prevents members of different species from mating with each other,

    b. prevents gene flow between species, and

    c. maintains separate species.

    d. Therefore, species are distinct from each other because they do not share the same gene pool.

  5. The biological species concept can be problematic.

    a. Some pairs of clearly distinct species occasionally interbreed and produce **hybrids**.

      i. For example, grizzly bears and polar bears may interbreed and produce hybrids called grolar bears.

      ii. Melting sea ice may bring these two bear species together more frequently and produce more hybrids in the wild.

    b. Reproductive isolation cannot usually be determined for extinct organisms known only from fossils.

    c. Reproductive isolation does not apply to prokaryotes or other organisms that reproduce only asexually.

    d. Therefore, alternate species concepts can be useful.

  6. The **morphological species concept**

    a. classifies organisms based on observable physical traits and

    b. can be applied to

      i. asexual organisms and

      ii. fossils.

      iii. However, there is some subjectivity in deciding which traits to use.

7. The **ecological species concept**
   a. defines a species by its ecological role or niche and
   b. focuses on unique adaptations to particular roles in a biological community.
   c. For example, two species may be similar in appearance but distinguishable based on
      i. what they eat or
      ii. where they live.
8. The **phylogenetic species concept**
   a. defines a species as the smallest group of individuals that shares a common ancestor and thus
   b. forms one branch of the tree of life.
   c. Biologists trace the phylogenetic history of a species by comparing its
      i. morphology or
      ii. DNA.
   d. However, defining the amount of difference required to distinguish separate species is a problem.

C. 14.3 Reproductive barriers keep species separate
   1. Reproductive barriers
      a. serve to isolate the gene pools of species and
      b. prevent interbreeding.
   2. Depending on whether they function *before* or *after* zygotes form, reproductive barriers are categorized as
      a. prezygotic or
      b. postzygotic.
   3. Five types of **prezygotic barriers** prevent mating or fertilization between species.
      a. In *habitat isolation*, two species live in the same general area but not in the same kind of place.
      b. In *temporal isolation*, two species breed at different times (seasons, times of day, years).
      c. In *behavioral isolation*, there is little or no mate recognition between females and males of different species.
      d. In *mechanical isolation*, female and male sex organs are not compatible.
      e. In *gametic isolation*, female and male gametes are not compatible.
   4. Three types of **postzygotic barriers** operate after hybrid zygotes have formed.
      a. In *reduced hybrid viability*, most hybrid offspring do not survive.
      b. In *reduced hybrid fertility*, hybrid offspring are vigorous but sterile.
      c. In *hybrid breakdown*,
         i. the first-generation hybrids are viable and fertile but
         ii. the offspring of the hybrids are feeble or sterile.

III. Mechanisms of Speciation

A. 14.4 In allopatric speciation, geographic isolation leads to speciation
   1. In **allopatric speciation**, populations of the same species are geographically separated, isolating their gene pools.
   2. Isolated populations will no longer share changes in allele frequencies caused by
      a. natural selection,
      b. genetic drift, and/or
      c. mutation.

3. Gene flow between populations is initially prevented by a geographic barrier. For example

    a. the Grand Canyon and Colorado River separate two species of antelope squirrels, and

    b. the Isthmus of Panama separates 15 pairs of snapping shrimp.

B. 14.5 Reproductive barriers can evolve as populations diverge

  1. How do reproductive barriers arise?

  2. Experiments have demonstrated that reproductive barriers can evolve as a by-product of changes in populations as they adapt to different environments.

  3. These studies have included

    a. laboratory studies of fruit flies and

    b. field studies of monkey flowers and their pollinators.

C. 14.6 Sympatric speciation takes place without geographic isolation

  1. **Sympatric speciation** occurs when a new species arises within the same geographic area as a parent species.

    a. How can reproductive isolation develop when members of sympatric populations remain in contact with each other?

  2. Gene flow between populations may be reduced by

    a. polyploidy,

    b. habitat differentiation, or

    c. sexual selection.

  3. Many plant species have evolved by **polyploidy** in which cells have more than two complete sets of chromosomes.

  4. This sort of sympatric speciation can result from polyploidy

    a. within a species or

    b. between two species.

D. 14.7 EVOLUTION CONNECTION: Most plant species trace their origin to polyploid speciation

  1. Plant biologists estimate that 80% of all living plant species are descendants of ancestors that formed by polyploid speciation.

  2. Hybridization between two species accounts for most of these species.

  3. Polyploid plants include

    a. cotton,

    b. oats,

    c. potatoes,

    d. bananas,

    e. peanuts,

    f. barley,

    g. plums,

    h. apples,

    i. sugarcane,

    j. coffee, and

    k. bread wheat.

  4. Wheat

    a. has been domesticated for at least 10,000 years and

    b. is the most widely cultivated plant in the world.

5. Bread wheat, *Triticum aestivum*, is

    a. a polyploid with 42 chromosomes and

    b. the result of hybridization and polyploidy.

E. 14.8 Isolated islands are often showcases of speciation

  1. Most of the species on Earth are thought to have originated by allopatric speciation.

  2. Isolated island chains offer some of the best evidence of this type of speciation.

  3. Multiple speciation events are more likely to occur in island chains that have

    a. physically diverse habitats,

    b. islands far enough apart to permit populations to evolve in isolation, and

    c. islands close enough to each other to allow occasional dispersions between them.

  4. The evolution of many diverse species from a common ancestor is **adaptive radiation**.

  5. The Galápagos Archipelago

    a. is located about 900 km (560 miles) west of Ecuador,

    b. is one of the world's great showcases of adaptive radiation,

    c. was formed naked from underwater volcanoes,

    d. was colonized gradually from other islands and the South America mainland, and

    e. has many species of plants and animals found nowhere else in the world.

  6. The Galápagos islands currently have 14 species of closely related finches, called Darwin's finches, because Darwin collected them during his around-the-world voyage on the *Beagle*.

  7. These finches

    a. share many finchlike traits,

    b. differ in their feeding habits and their beaks, specialized for what they eat, and

    c. arose through adaptive radiation.

F. 14.9 SCIENTIFIC DISCOVERY: A long-term field study documents evolution in Darwin's finches

  1. Peter and Rosemary Grant have worked

    a. for more than three decades,

    b. on medium ground finches, and

    c. on tiny, isolated, uninhabited Daphne Major in the Galápagos Islands.

  2. Medium ground finches and cactus finches occasionally interbreed. Hybrids

    a. have intermediate bill sizes,

    b. survive well during wet years, when there are plenty of soft, small seeds around,

    c. are outcompeted by both parental types during dry years, and

    d. can introduce more genetic variation on which natural selection acts.

G. 14.10 Hybrid zones provide opportunities to study reproductive isolation

  1. What happens when separated populations of closely related species come back into contact with each other?

  2. Biologists try to answer such questions by studying **hybrid zones**, regions in which members of different species meet and mate to produce at least some hybrid offspring.

  3. Over time in hybrid zones

    a. reinforcement may strengthen barriers to reproduction, such as occurs in flycatchers, or

    b. fusion may reverse the speciation process as gene flow between species increases, as may be occurring among the cichlid species in Lake Victoria.

  4. In stable hybrid zones, a limited number of hybrid offspring continue to be produced.

H. 14.11 Speciation can occur rapidly or slowly

    1. There are two models for the tempo of speciation.

        a. The **punctuated equilibria** model draws on the fossil record, where species

            i. change most as they arise from an ancestral species and then

            ii. experience relatively little change for the rest of their existence.

        b. Other species appear to have evolved more gradually.

    2. What is the total length of time between speciation events (between formation of a species and subsequent divergence of that species)?

        a. In a survey of 84 groups of plants and animals, the time ranged from 4,000 to 40 million years.

        b. Overall, the time between speciation events averaged 6.5 million years.

Chapter Guide to Teaching Resources

Defining Species (14.1–14.3)

Student Misconceptions and Concerns

- Students might not realize that evolutionary change includes both (a) linear events, in which a species changes over time, and (b) branching events, which produce new species and diversity. Some students simply expect that whenever new species evolve, they replace their ancestors. (14.1)

- Students might have never considered how species are naturally kept separate and unique. Instead, students may consider species as fixed entities, especially the species to which they belong. To help ease students into the topic, consider pointing out that species do not reflect an even spectrum of diversity. Instead, there are many groups of clearly related organisms (owls, grasses, sharks, beetles, butterflies, trees, mushrooms, and bacteria, for example). Ask students to consider why such groupings exist. Could such groupings represent shared ancestry? (14.2–14.3)

Teaching Tips

- Challenge your students to explain why the field of paleontology has largely been concerned with macroevolution. The broader perspective of evolutionary change studied by paleontologists rarely permits an examination of change within a species. (14.1)

- Before lecturing about species concepts, consider a short writing assignment. Have students work individually or in small groups, without the benefit of books, to define a species. (14.2)

- Identify or have your students find several commonly recognized and related species of plants or animals in your area and find out what reproductive barriers keep these species from interbreeding. Local examples always help to bring a point home. (14.3)

Mechanisms of Speciation (14.4–14.11)

Student Misconceptions and Concerns

- Students must understand that species do not evolve because of need. Biological diversity exists and the environment selects. Evolution is not deliberate; it is reactive. Species do not deliberately change. There is no plan. As teachers, we must take care that our descriptions of evolution accurately reflect its process. The use of the passive voice in descriptions of evolution is one way of doing this. (14.4–14.11)

- Most of us are unable to comprehend the vast lengths of time considered by geologists. Exercises and examples can increase this comprehension. Consider the number of seconds in a year ($60 \times 60 \times 24 \times 365.25 = 31,557,600$) or how much money you could spend each day if you spent \$1 million a year (\$1,000,000/365 = \$2,739.73/day). (14.4–14.11)

- Students also need to be reminded that 1 billion is 1,000 million. Many students (and some politicians) easily confuse million and billion without realizing the scale of the error. (14.4–14.11)

- The concept of rarity is likely to be misunderstood when applied to geologic time. Events such as major floods, earthquakes, or asteroid impacts, which might be so rare as to occur every 1,000 years, are actually common in geological terms. Students might not realize that 1,000 such events would be expected to occur over a million years. (14.11)

Teaching Tips

- The isolation of a few individuals from a parent population may result from a catastrophic weather or geological event. Ask your students to think back to news footage of torrential rains, massive debris rocketing down a river, and the struggles of animals to haul themselves onto these rafts. Better yet, show them a short news clip of such events. Dramatic weather and geological events may be rare in our lifetimes but are frequent enough to play a role in speciation. (14.4)

- When discussing Module 14.5, consider referring back to Figure 14.3A. Challenge students to explain how each of the prezygotic barriers might impact the evolution of a new species. (14.5)

- The Silvery Salamander, *Ambystoma platineum*, is a triploid, all-female species living in parts of the U.S. Midwest. It is believed to have formed by the hybridization of two related species thousands of years ago. It is an unusual example of sympatric speciation in animals. A good starting point for learning more about this species is www.inhs.uiuc.edu/cbd/herpdist/species/am_platine.html. (14.6)

- The abundance of polyploid plants used for food facilitates further study for student assignments. Perhaps small groups or individuals can select a polyploid crop and describe its evolutionary history and/or its current method of reproduction. (14.7)

- An analogy might be made between the specialized functions of finch beaks and the many types of screwdrivers (or pliers) that exist today. Each type of screwdriver (Phillips, flathead, hex, etc.) represents a specialization for a particular job or a generalist approach, useful in a variety of applications. (14.8)

- Numerous examples of adaptive radiations exist in the Hawaiian Islands. Hawaiian honeycreepers (birds), fruit flies, and species of the plant genera *Cyrtandra* and *Geranium* are excellent examples for additional illustration. (14.8)

- The work of the Grants with Darwin's finches helps to explain to students that the concept of "better" in evolution is relative. As the environment changes, organisms must respond or suffer the consequences. In these circumstances, organisms are reacting, not improving. (14.9)

- Students might wish to debate whether two cichlid species that fuse into one were previously separate species. If each species retained the natural ability to hybridize with each other, and did so extensively as the environment changed, were they separate species? Such difficult distinctions test our definitions and reveal some of the challenges of biology. (14.10)

- Have your students think of analogous examples of punctuated equilibrium in our culture. One such example is the switch from vinyl records to compact discs, with the brief transitional form of cassette tapes (which students currently entering college may barely remember). Between the years 1900 and 2000, there were both long periods of stasis (vinyl records) and a relatively short period of transition to CDs and now to digital music files (who knows how long they will last?). Similarly, high-definition television is a new technology replacing more than 50 years' worth of older technology. Debating the validity of analogies can itself be instructive as students articulate the biological principles and compare them to the analogies. (14.11)

Key Terms

adaptive radiation	hybrid zone	postzygotic barrier
allopatric speciation	hybrids	prezygotic barrier
biological species concept	morphological species concept	punctuated equilibria
		reproductive isolation
ecological species concept	phylogenetic species concept	speciation
	polyploid	sympatric speciation

Word Roots

allo- = other; **-patri** = father (*allopatric speciation*: the formation of new species in populations that are geographically isolated from one another)

post- = after; **zygo-** = fertilized cell (*postzygotic barrier*: any of several reproductive barriers that prevent hybrid zygotes produced by two different species from developing into viable, fertile adults)

pre- = before; **zygo-** = fertilized cell (*prezygotic barrier*: any of several reproductive barriers that impede mating between species or hinder fertilization if mating between two species is attempted)

sym- = together; **-patri** = father (*sympatric speciation*: the formation of new species in populations that live in the same geographic area)

CHAPTER 15

Tracing Evolutionary History

Chapter Objectives

Opening Essay

Compare the structure of the wings of pterosaurs, birds, and bats. Explain how the wings are based upon a remodeling from a shared ancestral pattern.

Early Earth and the Origin of Life

15.1 Describe the conditions on the surface of the early Earth. Describe the evidence that life on Earth existed at least 3.5 billion years ago.

15.1 Describe the four stages that might have produced the first cells on Earth.

15.2 Describe the experiments of Stanley Miller and others in understanding how life might have first evolved on Earth.

15.3 Describe the significance of protocells and ribozymes in the origin of the first cells.

Major Events in the History of Life

15.4 Describe the key events in the history of life on Earth.

15.5 Explain how radiometric dating and the relative position of a fossil within rock strata are used to determine the age of rocks.

15.6 Briefly describe the history of life on Earth, noting the major eras, their time range, and which types of life were most abundant. Describe the key events that serve to divide these eras.

Mechanisms of Macroevolution

15.7 Describe how Earth's continents have changed over the past 250 million years. Explain the consequences of these changes for life on Earth.

15.8 Explain how volcanoes and earthquakes result from plate tectonics.

15.9 Describe the causes, frequency, and consequences of mass extinctions over the last 500 million years.

15.10 Explain how and why adaptive radiations occur.

15.11 Explain how genes that program development function in the evolution of life.

15.11 Define and describe examples of paedomorphosis.

15.12 Define exaptation and describe two examples in birds.

15.13 Explain why evolutionary trends do not reflect "directions" or "goals."

Phylogeny and the Tree of Life

15.14 Distinguish between homologous and analogous structures and provide examples of each. Describe the process of convergent evolution.

15.15 Describe the goals of systematics. List the progressively broader categories of classification used in systematics in order, from most specific to most general.

15.16 Define the terms clade, monophyletic groups, shared derived characters, shared ancestral characters, ingroup, outgroup, phylogenetic trees, and parsimony.

15.17 Explain how molecular biology is used as a tool in systematics. Describe examples used to study panda and human evolution. Explain why some studies use DNA coding for ribosomal RNA (rRNA) and other studies use mitochondrial DNA (mtDNA).

15.18 Explain how molecular clocks are used to track evolutionary time. Describe the limits of this process.

15.19 Explain why a diagram of the tree of life is difficult to construct.

Lecture Outline

I. Introduction

A. Different types of wings evolved from the same ancestral tetrapod limb.

1. Pterosaur wings consist of a membrane primarily supported by one greatly elongated finger.
2. Bird wings consist of feathers supported by an elongated forearm and modified wrist and hand bones.
3. Bat wings consist of a membrane supported by arm bones and four very elongated fingers.

II. Early Earth and the Origin of Life

A. 15.1 Conditions on early Earth made the origin of life possible

1. The Earth formed about 4.6 billion years ago.
2. As the Earth cooled and the bombardment slowed about 3.9 billion years ago, the conditions on the planet were extremely different from those today.
   a. The first atmosphere was probably thick with
      i. water vapor and
      ii. various compounds released by volcanic eruptions, including nitrogen and its oxides, carbon dioxide, methane, ammonia, hydrogen, and hydrogen sulfide.
   b. Lightning, volcanic activity, and ultraviolet radiation were much more intense than today.
3. The earliest evidence for life on Earth
   a. comes from 3.5 billion year old fossils of **stromatolites**,
   b. built by ancient photosynthetic prokaryotes still alive today.
4. Because these 3.5 billion year old prokaryotes used photosynthesis, it suggests that life first evolved earlier, perhaps as much as 3.9 billion years ago.
5. The first life may have evolved through four stages.
   a. The abiotic (nonliving) synthesis of small organic molecules, such as amino acids and nitrogenous bases.
   b. The joining of these small molecules into polymers, such as proteins and nucleic acids.
   c. The packaging of these molecules into "protocells," droplets with membranes that maintained an internal chemistry different from that of their surroundings.
   d. The origin of self-replicating molecules that eventually made inheritance possible.

B. 15.2 SCIENTIFIC DISCOVERY: Experiments show that the abiotic synthesis of organic molecules is possible

1. In the 1920s, two scientists, the Russian A. I. Oparin and the British J. B. S. Haldane, independently proposed that organic molecules could have formed on the early Earth.

2. Our modern atmosphere is rich in O_2, which oxidizes and disrupts chemical bonds.

3. The early Earth likely had a reducing atmosphere.

4. In 1953, graduate student Stanley Miller, working under Harold Urey, tested the Oparin-Haldane hypothesis.

    a. Miller set up an airtight apparatus with gases circulating past an electrical discharge, to simulate conditions on the early Earth.

    b. He also set up a control with no electrical discharge.

5. After a week, Miller's setup produced abundant amino acids and other organic molecules.

    a. Similar experiments used other atmospheres and other energy sources, with similar results.

    b. Stage 1, abiotic synthesis of organic molecules, was demonstrated to be possible by the Miller-Urey experiments.

C. 15.2 SCIENTIFIC DISCOVERY: Experiments show that the abiotic synthesis of organic molecules is possible

1. Other hypotheses about the origins of life include

    a. deep sea environments near submerged volcanoes or hydrothermal vents or

    b. meteorites as sources of amino acids and other key organic molecules.

D. 15.3 Stages in the origin of the first cells probably included the formation of polymers, protocells, and self-replicating RNA

1. **Stage 2: The joining of monomers into polymers**

    a. Hot sand, clay, or rock may have helped monomers combine to form polymers.

    b. Waves may have splashed organic molecules onto fresh lava or other hot rocks and then rinsed polypeptides and other polymers back into the sea.

2. **Stage 3: Packaging of polymers into protocells**

    a. Small membrane-bounded sacs or vesicles form when lipids are mixed with water.

    b. These abiotically created vesicles are able to grow and divide (reproduce).

3. **Stage 4: The origin of self-replicating molecules**

    a. Today's cells transfer genetic information from DNA to RNA to protein assembly. However, RNA molecules can assemble spontaneously from RNA monomers.

    b. RNA monomers in the presence of RNA molecules form new RNA molecules complementary to parts of the starting RNA.

    c. Some RNA molecules, called **ribozymes**, can carry out enzyme-like functions.

III. Major Events in the History of Life

A. 15.4 The origins of single-celled and multicelled organisms and the colonization of land were key events in life's history

1. **Macroevolution** is the broad pattern of changes in life on Earth.

2. The entire 4.6 billion years of Earth's history can be broken into three eons of geologic time.

    a. The Archaean and Proterozoic eons lasted about 4 billion years.

    b. The Phanerozoic eon includes the last half billion years.

3. Prokaryotes lived alone on Earth for 1.5 billion years, from 3.5 to 2 billion years ago.
   a. During this time, prokaryotes transformed the atmosphere.
   b. Prokaryotic photosynthesis produced oxygen that enriched the water and atmosphere of Earth.
   c. Anaerobic and aerobic cellular respiration allowed prokaryotes to flourish.
4. The oldest fossils of eukaryotes are about 2.1 billion years old.
5. The common ancestor of all multicellular eukaryotes lived about 1.5 billion years ago.
6. The oldest fossils of multicellular eukaryotes are about 1.2 billion years old.
7. The first multicellular plants and fungi began to colonize land about 500 million years ago.
8. Humans diverged from other primates about 6 to 7 million years ago.
9. Our species, *Homo sapiens*, originated about 195,000 years ago.
10. If the Earth's history were compressed into an hour, humans appeared less than 0.2 seconds ago!

B. 15.5 The actual ages of rocks and fossils mark geologic time
   1. **Radiometric dating** measures the decay of radioactive isotopes.
   2. The rate of decay is expressed as a half-life, the time required for 50% of an isotope in a sample to decay.
   3. There are many different isotopes that can be used to date fossils. These isotopes have different half-lives, ranging from thousands to hundreds of millions of years.
   4. The age of a fossil can also be inferred from the ages of rock layers above and below the strata in which a fossil is found.

C. 15.6 The fossil record documents the history of life
   1. The **geologic record** is based on the sequence and age of fossils in the rock strata.
   2. The most recent Phanerozoic eon
      a. includes the past 542 million years and
      b. is divided into three eras
         i. Paleozoic,
         ii. Mesozoic, and
         iii. Cenozoic.
   3. The boundaries between eras are marked by mass extinctions.

IV. Mechanisms of Macroevolution

A. 15.7 Continental drift has played a major role in macroevolution
   1. According to the theory of **plate tectonics**,
      a. the Earth's crust is divided into giant, irregularly shaped plates that
      b. essentially float on the underlying mantle.
   2. In a process called continental drift, movements in the mantle cause the plates to move.
   3. Since the origin of multicellular life roughly 1.5 billion years ago, there have been three occasions in which the landmasses of Earth came together to form a supercontinent.
   4. About 250 million years ago
      a. plate movements brought all the landmasses together and
      b. the supercontinent of **Pangaea** was formed.
   5. During the Mesozoic era,
      a. Pangaea started to break apart,
      b. the physical environment and climate changed dramatically,

    c. Australia became isolated, and

    d. biological diversity was reshaped.

  6. Continental drift explains the distribution of lungfishes.

    a. Fossils of lungfishes are found on every continent except Antarctica.

    b. Today, living lungfishes are found in

      i. South America,

      ii. Africa, and

      iii. Australia.

    c. This evidence suggests that lungfishes evolved when Pangaea was still intact.

B. 15.8 CONNECTION: Plate tectonics may imperil human life

  1. Volcanoes and earthquakes result from the movements of crustal plates.

    a. The boundaries of plates are hotspots of volcanic and earthquake activity.

    b. An undersea earthquake caused the 2004 tsunami, when a fault in the Indian Ocean ruptured.

C. 15.9 During mass extinctions, large numbers of species are lost

  1. Extinction is inevitable in a changing world.

  2. The fossil record shows that the vast majority of species that have ever lived are now extinct.

  3. Over the last 500 million years,

    a. five mass extinctions have occurred, and

    b. in each event, more than 50% of the Earth's species went extinct.

  4. The Permian mass extinction

    a. occurred about 251 million years ago,

    b. defines the boundary between the Paleozoic and Mesozoic eras,

    c. claimed 96% of marine animal species,

    d. took a tremendous toll on terrestrial life, and

    e. was likely caused by enormous volcanic eruptions.

  5. The Cretaceous mass extinction

    a. caused the extinction of all the dinosaurs except birds and

    b. was likely caused by a large asteroid that struck the Earth, blocking light and disrupting the global climate.

  6. Mass extinctions affect biological diversity profoundly.

  7. It took 100 million years for the number of marine families to recover after Permian mass extinction.

  8. Is a sixth extinction under way?

    a. The current extinction rate is 100–1,000 times the normal background rate.

    b. It may take life on Earth millions of years to recover.

D. 15.10 Adaptive radiations have increased the diversity of life

  1. Adaptive radiations are periods of evolutionary change that

    a. occur when many new species evolve from a common ancestor that colonizes a new, unexploited area and

    b. often follow extinction events.

  2. Radiations may result from the evolution of new adaptations such as

    a. wings in pterosaurs, birds, bats, and insects and

    b. adaptations for life on land in plants, insects, and tetrapods.

E. 15.11 Genes that control development play a major role in evolution
1. The fossil record can tell us
   a. *what* the great events in the history of life have been and
   b. *when* they occurred.
2. Continental drift, mass extinctions, and adaptive radiation provide a big-picture view of *how* those changes came about.
3. We are now increasingly able to understand the basic biological mechanisms that underlie the changes seen in the fossil record.
4. The field of **evo-devo**
   a. addresses the interface of evolutionary biology and developmental biology and
   b. examines how slight genetic changes can produce major morphological differences.
5. Genes that program development control the
   a. rate,
   b. timing, and
   c. spatial pattern of change in an organism's form as it develops.
6. Many dramatic evolutionary transformations are the result of a change in the rate or timing of developmental events.
7. **Paedomorphosis**
   a. is the retention in the adult of body structures that were juvenile features in an ancestral species and
   b. occurs in the axolotl salamander in which sexually mature adults retain gills and other larval features.
8. Slight changes in the relative growth of different body parts can change an adult form substantially.
9. Skulls of humans and chimpanzees are
   a. more similar as fetuses but
   b. quite different as adults due to different rates of growth.
10. **Homeotic genes**
    a. are called master control genes and
    b. determine basic features, such as where pairs of wings or legs develop on a fruit fly.
11. Profound alterations in body form can result from
    a. changes in homeotic genes or
    b. how or where homeotic genes are expressed.
12. Duplication of developmental genes can also be important in the formation of new morphological features.
    a. A fruit fly has a single cluster of homeotic genes.
    b. A mouse has four clusters of homeotic genes.
    c. Two duplications of these gene clusters occurred in the evolution of vertebrates from invertebrates.
13. In the threespine stickleback fish, those fish that live
    a. in the ocean have bony plates and a large set of pelvic spines but
    b. in lakes have reduced or absent bony plates and pelvic spines, resulting from a change in the expression of a developmental gene in the pelvic region.

F. 15.12 Evolutionary novelties may arise in several ways
1. In most cases, complex structures evolve by increments from simpler versions with the same basic functions.

2. In the evolution of an eye or any other complex structure, behavior, or biochemical pathway, each step must
   a. bring a selective advantage to the organism possessing it and
   b. increase the organism's fitness.
3. Mollusc eyes evolved from an ancestral patch of photoreceptor cells through a series of incremental modifications that were adaptive at each stage.
4. A range of complexity can be seen in the eyes of living molluscs.
5. Cephalopod eyes are as complex as vertebrate eyes, but arose separately.
6. In other cases, evolutionary novelties result from the gradual adaptation of existing structures to new functions.
7. Such structures that evolve in one context but become co-opted for another function are often called *exaptations*.
8. Examples of exaptations include
   a. feathers that may have first functioned for insulation and later were co-opted for flight and
   b. flippers of penguins that first functioned for flight and were co-opted for underwater swimming.

G. 15.13 EVOLUTION CONNECTION: Evolutionary trends do not mean that evolution is goal directed
1. The fossil record seems to reveal trends in the evolution of many species, but identifying trends can be problematic.
2. The evolution of horses reveals a potential misunderstanding.
   a. If we select only certain species in this family tree, it appears that there was a general trend toward the reduction in the number of toes, larger size, and teeth modified for grazing.
   b. However, if we consider all of the known members of this family tree, this apparent trend vanishes.
3. Branching evolution can lead to genuine trends.
4. The species selection model of long-term trends compares species to individuals.
   a. Speciation is their birth,
   b. extinction their death, and
   c. new species that diversify from them are their offspring.
   d. Unequal survival of species and unequal generation of new species play a role in macroevolution similar to the role of unequal reproduction in microevolution.
5. Evolutionary trends can also result directly from natural selection. For example,
   a. when horse ancestors invaded the grasslands that spread during the mid-Cenozoic,
   b. there was strong selection for grazers that could escape predators by running fast.
6. Whatever its cause, it is important to recognize that an evolutionary trend does not imply that evolution is goal directed.
7. Evolution is the result of interactions between organisms and the current environment.

V. Phylogeny and the Tree of Life

A. 15.14 Phylogenies based on homologies reflect evolutionary history
1. **Phylogeny** is the evolutionary history of a species or group of species.
2. Phylogeny can be inferred from
   a. the fossil record,
   b. morphological homologies, and
   c. molecular homologies.

3. Homologies are similarities due to shared ancestry, evolving from the same structure in a common ancestor.
4. Generally, organisms that share similar morphologies are closely related.
   a. However, some similarities are due to similar adaptations favored by a common environment, a process called **convergent evolution**.
   b. A similarity due to convergent evolution is called **analogy**.

B. 15.15 Systematics connects classification with evolutionary history
1. **Systematics** is a discipline of biology that focuses on
   a. classifying organisms and
   b. determining their evolutionary relationships.
2. Carolus Linnaeus introduced **taxonomy**, a system of naming and classifying species.
3. Biologists assign each species a two-part scientific name, or **binomial**, consisting of
   a. a **genus** and
   b. a unique part for each species within the genus.
4. Genera are grouped into progressively larger categories.
5. Each taxonomic unit is a **taxon**.
6. Biologists traditionally use a **phylogenetic tree** to depict hypothesis about the evolutionary history of species.
   a. The branching diagrams reflect the hierarchical classification of groups nested within more inclusive groups.
   b. Phylogenetic trees indicate the probable evolutionary relationships among groups and patterns of descent.

C. 15.16 Shared characters are used to construct phylogenetic trees
1. **Cladistics**
   a. is the most widely used method in systematics and
   b. groups organisms into **clades**.
2. Each clade is a **monophyletic** group of species that
   a. includes an ancestral species and
   b. all of its descendants.
3. Cladistics is based on the Darwinian concept that organisms share characteristics with their ancestors and differ from them. Thus, there are two main types of characters.
   a. Shared ancestral characters group organisms into clades.
   b. Shared derived characters distinguish clades and form the branching points in the tree of life.
4. An important step in cladistics is the comparison of the
   a. **ingroup** (the taxa whose phylogeny is being investigated) and
   b. **outgroup** (a taxon that diverged before the lineage leading to the members of the ingroup),
   c. to identify the derived characters that define the branch points in the phylogeny of the ingroup.
5. As an example, consider
   a. a frog representing the outgroup and
   b. four other tetrapods representing the ingroup.
6. The presence or absence of traits is indicated as
   a. 1 if the trait is present or
   b. 0 if the trait is absent.
   c. In our example, the phylogenetic tree is constructed from a series of branch points, represented by the emergence of a lineage with a new set of derived traits.

    d. When constructing a phylogenetic tree, scientists use **parsimony**, looking for the simplest explanation for observed phenomena.

  7. Systematists use many kinds of evidence. However, even the best tree represents only the most likely hypothesis.

  8. The phylogenetic tree of reptiles shows that crocodilians are the closest *living* relatives of birds.

    a. They share numerous features, including

      i. four-chambered hearts,

      ii. "singing" to defend territories, and

      iii. parental care of eggs within nests.

    b. These traits were likely present in the common ancestor of birds, crocodiles, and dinosaurs.

D. 15.17 An organism's evolutionary history is documented in its genome

  1. **Molecular systematics** uses DNA and other molecules to infer relatedness.

    a. Scientists have sequenced more than 110 billion bases of DNA from thousands of species.

    b. This enormous database has fueled a boom in the study of phylogeny and clarified many evolutionary relationships.

  2. The more recently two species have branched from a common ancestor, the more similar their DNA sequences should be.

  3. The longer two species have been on separate evolutionary paths, the more their DNA should have diverged.

  4. Different genes evolve at different rates.

    a. DNA coding for ribosomal RNA (rRNA)

      i. changes slowly and

      ii. is useful for investigating relationships between taxa that diverged hundreds of millions of years ago.

    b. In contrast, DNA in mitochondria (mtDNA)

      i. evolves rapidly and

      ii. is more useful to investigate more recent evolutionary events.

  5. Remarkable commonality of molecular biology demonstrates that all living organisms share many biochemical and developmental pathways and provides overwhelming support of evolution.

    a. The genomes of humans and chimpanzees are amazingly similar.

    b. About 99% of the genes of humans and mice are detectably homologous.

    c. About 50% of human genes are homologous with those of yeast.

E. 15.18 Molecular clocks help track evolutionary time

  1. **Molecular clocks**

    a. rely on genes that have a reliable average rate of change,

    b. can be calibrated in real time by graphing the number of nucleotide differences against the dates of evolutionary branch points known from the fossil record,

    c. are used to estimate dates of divergences without a good fossil record, and

    d. have been used to date the origin of HIV infection in humans.

F. 15.19 Constructing the tree of life is a work in progress

  1. Molecular systematics and cladistics are remodeling some trees.

  2. Biologists currently recognize a **three-domain system** consisting of

    a. two domains of prokaryotes: Bacteria and Archaea, and

    b. one domain of eukaryotes called Eukarya including

       i. fungi,

       ii. plants, and

       iii. animals.

3. Molecular and cellular evidence indicates that

    a. Bacteria and Archaea diverged very early in the evolutionary history of life, and

    b. Archaea are more closely related to eukaryotes than to bacteria.

4. Comparisons of complete genomes from all three domains show that

    a. there have been substantial interchanges of genes between organisms in different domains and

    b. these took place through **horizontal gene transfer**, a process in which genes are transferred from one genome to another through mechanisms such as plasmid exchange and viral infection.

5. Some biologists suggest that the early history of life may be best represented by a ring, from which the three domains emerge.

Chapter Guide to Teaching Resources

Early Earth and the Origin of Life (15.1–15.3)

Student Misconceptions and Concerns

- Students might not have considered that cells today are not created from scratch. Unlike baking a cake or constructing an automobile, where components are assembled to create something new, the reproduction of cells does not currently involve anything other than cells. (15.1–15.3)

- Some students might think that scientists have answers for all of life's questions. Other students might rely upon supernatural explanations when faced with scientific uncertainty. The material in this chapter provides a good opportunity to further distinguish between the process of science and other ways of knowing. (15.1–15.3)

- Most of us are unable to comprehend the vast lengths of time considered by geologists. Exercises and examples can increase this comprehension. Consider a) the number of seconds in a year $= 60 \times 60 \times 24 \times 365.25 = 31{,}557{,}600$, or b) that you would live your 1 billionth second of life at age 31 and 8 months of age, or c) how much money you could spend each day if you spent $1 million dollars a year ($1{,}000{,}000/365 = $2{,}739.73$/day). (15.1–15.3)

- Students may need to be reminded that one billion is 1,000 million. Many students (and some politicians) easily confuse million and billion without realizing the scale of the error. Challenge students to translate either of the examples above to illustrate one billion. (For example, one billion seconds equals about 31.7 years. If you were to spend one billion dollars in a year, you would need to spend $2,739,730 each day of that year! (15.1–15.3)

Teaching Tips

- Students who have studied cell theory might wonder how the first cells formed. Furthermore, they might wonder if spontaneous generation of cells could occur today. Module 15.1 describes how conditions on the surface of Earth when life first formed were dramatically different from today. Furthermore, if new life were evolving on Earth today, it would face competition from the vast amount of life already present. (15.1)

- Consider pointing out the logic of the theory of spontaneous generation, given the state of scientific knowledge during that period in history. Piles of manure and rotting flesh left in the open would apparently produce flies out of nowhere. At that time, so little was understood about eggs, sperm, and fertilization that spontaneous generation was a logical conclusion. (15.1)

- The four-stage hypothesis for the origin of life is a little like a recipe for building cells from the bottom up. If your students do not remember details about biological molecules and basic cell structure, you may need to review them before addressing these stages. (15.1)

- At some point in the presentation of the four-stage hypothesis for the origin of life, students should be encouraged to consider at what point "life" exists. Are self-replicating, RNA-based, membrane-bound structures alive? Discussing the evolution of the first cells helps clarify definitions of life. (15.1)

- Some scientists distinguish between biological evolution and chemical evolution. Biological evolution addresses changes in life once it existed on Earth. Chemical evolution includes the origin of the first forms of life. The word evolution, if strictly defined as a change over time, also applies to changes in the universe. (15.2)

- The experiments and hypotheses discussed in Module 15.2 demonstrate the tentative nature of science. As evidence is collected, old hypotheses are tested and new hypotheses arise. (15.2)

- The inherent property of bipolar molecules such as phospholipids to naturally form double membranes or micelles is worth discussing with your class. Because of these properties, membranes heal naturally as the hydrophobic phospholipid tails and polar heads align together. (15.3)

- As you discuss the conditions on early Earth and the pathways through which life might have first evolved, you might challenge your class to identify a set of defining traits for something to be considered alive. What are the essential properties of life? (15.3)

Major Events in the History of Life (15.4–15.6)

Student Misconceptions and Concerns

- Comprehending the length of time of the major phases of life's history is problematic for most students. Even the mass extinction of most dinosaurs 65 million years ago took place far beyond any period in recorded human history (65 million years ago is about 27,000 times the period of time since the life of Aristotle). Consider noting, as a reference point, that multicellular animal life, as we know it today, has existed for only about 13% of Earth's history (0.6 of 4.6 billion years). The period during which only prokaryotic life existed on earth was more than twice as long as the amount of time multicellular life has existed. Other proportional comparisons can help to put these periods in perspective. (15.4)

- Table 15.6 includes a timeline of the entire history of Earth, with a large section focused on the most recent 13% of Earth's history. Students might not notice that this enlarged section is an expansion of this proportionately small, but significant, period. Furthermore, the bottom of the enlarged portion is not scaled to the top portion. These clarifications may be needed for proper appreciation of this table. Coupling Table 15.6 and Figure 15.4 may also help clarify this information. (15.6)

Teaching Tips

- The evolution from prokaryotes to eukaryotes and single-celled life to multicellular life represent major leaps and dramatic change. Consider pointing out to students that extensive amounts of time did pass between each of these dramatic transitions. This is consistent with the gradual evolution of life on Earth. (15.4)

- Assigning students, individually or in small groups, to create timelines using the dates in Table 15.6 can help them appreciate the proportional relationship of these periods. (15.4–15.6)

- With a half-life of 5,730 years, carbon-14 is an inappropriate measure of large periods of time, such as the dinosaur bones that are 100 million years old. This is like trying to measure the distance across a state with a tape measure. (15.5)

- The sequence of layers, but not their absolute age, is revealed by the stratifications in sedimentary rocks. Imagine peeling the layers of wallpaper from the walls of a very old house that has been inhabited by many owners. We can tell which layers are older than others, but not the exact age of each. (15.5–15.6)

- Students might not appreciate the difficulty of finding fossils of early life. Early life forms were likely microscopic and lacked hard parts such as shells and bone. Furthermore, over time, heat, pressure, friction, and erosion may destroy what fossils were formed or render them difficult to detect. (15.6)

Mechanisms of Macroevolution (15.7–15.13)

Student Misconceptions and Concerns

- Student backgrounds in earth sciences may be uneven based upon their specific high school and college coursework. An emphasis on chemistry, physics, and biology may leave large gaps in basic content regarding geology and Earth's history. (15.7–15.13)

- The slow speed at which life can evolve in response to human damage of natural systems may not be appreciated by our students. As noted in Module 15.9, it may take 5 to 10 million years for the planet to recover from the ongoing human-induced loss of biological diversity. (15.9)

Teaching Tips

- Consider this analogy to help students understand the biological consequences of speciation as continents drifted apart. As your students left high school and entered the workforce or continued their education, their high school social groups lost contact and drifted apart. Your students, in their new circumstances, adapted and changed in different ways, separate from the members of their old social groups. A note of caution: This analogy to individual social changes is not an example of biological evolution, which occurs over generations. (15.7)

- The mid-Atlantic ridge can be easily seen via satellite in Google maps. (15.8)

- The consequences of an asteroid impact, large or small, reveal the role of random events in evolution. Like throwing a dart at a spinning globe, where the asteroid hits and what continents and forms of life are most affected can change greatly if the impact occurs even a few hours earlier or later. An asteroid delayed by 12 hours, in what might be a journey of millions or billions of years, will land on the opposite side of the Earth! (15.9)

- Students might not realize that entire categories of animals have come and gone. The once-abundant Trilobites and nonavian dinosaurs are now extinct. Birds and mammals are relatively recent additions. Such examples of macroevolution are apparent in the fossil record. (15.9)

- Many business models reveal analogies to adaptive radiations. Personal computers of all types and sizes represent a type of technological radiation. The Internet is an ongoing radiation that has changed the way we communicate with each other and make purchases. Many other analogies can be developed as they relate to culture and commercialism. Challenge your students to suggest their own. (15.10)

- Students may not be familiar enough with salamander life histories to appreciate the similarity of a larval salamander to the axolotl form. By analogy, students might be asked to imagine what would result if a caterpillar reproduced and never developed into a winged adult butterfly. The caterpillar stage can then be related to the early larval form of salamanders. Furthermore, students might wonder why paedomorphosis occurs in salamanders but not frogs or butterflies. (15.11)

- Clear examples of evolutionary remodeling include the many variations of the pattern of bones in the vertebrate forelimb. Bat wings, bird wings, penguin flippers, the arms of apes, and the digging forelimbs of moles all show how the ancestral pattern evolved in response to various selective pressures. Descent with modification is a powerful explanation of such diversity. (15.12)

- Another way to think about evolutionary remodeling is to make an analogy to remodeling a home. A remodeled home retains many of the "ancestral" traits . . . perhaps the same plumbing and electrical system. However, the place where there was once a wall might now be an opening into an enlarged family room or a window to the outside. Evolution can work like the TV show *This Old House*! (15.12)

- When discussing exaptations, have students consider the many new uses for common household items if they were to have them in a survival situation, stranded on an island, or lost in the woods. A handkerchief, a screwdriver, and a pair of pliers might take on new functions in this different context. (15.12)

- Consider challenging your students to explain why the evolution of a group is not driven in any particular direction, or directed towards any ideal form or function. As a hint, you can ask them to describe the mechanisms by which variety arises in a species. (15.13)

Phylogeny and the Tree of Life (15.14–15.19)

Student Misconceptions and Concerns

- Homologous and analogous relationships can be confusing for students. Simple explanations and concrete examples can serve as guides to understanding each process. Homologous relationships reflect modifications of one form for many functions. Analogous relationships reflect modifications of many forms for one function. (15.14)

- Students can be frustrated by the changing state of systematics. Some comfort can be offered by noting that this is true about many active areas of science. For example, scientists continue to learn more and revise advice regarding the causes, treatment, and prevention of heart disease and cancer. (15.15)

- Students might express concern over the need to learn scientific names, when common names already seem sufficient. Depending upon where you live, find some examples of common organisms with more than one common name. Fishermen are famous for the various names they assign to the same species, depending upon the geographic region where they fish. Have your students imagine the problems of using common names when communicating with someone in another language. Clearly, there are advantages to scientific names! (15.15)

- Students may struggle with many aspects of phylogenetic trees, including: (a) Students may not realize that each node/branch can be rotated to rearrange the groups without changing the nature of the relationships. For example, in Figure 15.16A, the position of the beaver and kangaroo can be reversed without changing any relationships represented in the phylogenetic tree. (b) The length of each branch is not meaningful and is not intended to be proportional to time. (c) The spacing between groups is not meaningful and does not denote the degree of divergence between them. Whether the tree is compressed or expanded in size, the information communicated in it remains the same. (15.16)

Teaching Tips

- The National Center for Science Education is an organization working to support the teaching of evolution and defend it against sectarian attack. Its website, http://ncse.com, contains a great deal of useful information. (15.14–15.19)

- Our hierarchical classification system is analogous to sorting mail first by zip code, then by street, house number, and finally individual name. Such a system of classification based upon hierarchical categories is also common in the military and many other places in our lives. (15.14)

- Although Linnaeus recognized a hierarchical structure in the natural world, he had no natural explanation for the occurrence of such groups. One might wonder why all life does not blend evenly from one form to another. One of Darwin's greatest insights was to understand that these clusters reflect similarities due to shared ancestry, i.e., life itself is grouped into family trees. Furthermore, Darwin proposed a natural mechanism for the formation of new species and the generation of this diversity. (15.15)

- Emphasize to students that phylogenetic trees are tentative hypotheses. As new data are collected, the hypotheses are modified or rejected outright. (15.16)

- Genetic relationships provide one strong line of evidence for the ancestral relationships of life. Fossils, anatomy, embryology, and biogeography can also be used to test these same relationships. Remind students that scientists prefer to use multiple lines of evidence to test hypotheses such as phylogenies. (15.17–15.18)

- Molecular clocks reveal the usefulness of corroborative data, since they can be made more precise through calibration against the fossil record or other evidence. This is not much different from the accuracy of a watch set to a time standard every week, every year, or every ten years. (15.18)

- The authors reference Modules 10.22 and 10.23 for information on horizontal gene transfer. If this module was not previously addressed, consider covering it in your final discussion of the early evolution of life. (15.19)

- For some students, the discussion of the ambiguous relationships of early life and the three domains can be unsettling. Students who expect clear answers and sharp definitions from science may be uncomfortable with such ambiguity. (15.19)

Key Terms

analogy	ingroup	phylogenetic trees
binomial	kingdoms	phylogeny
clades	macroevolution	plate tectonics
cladistics	molecular clock	radiometric dating
classes	molecular systematics	ribozyme
convergent evolution	monophyletic	shared ancestral characters
domains	orders	shared derived characters
"evo-devo"	outgroup	stromatolite
family	paedomorphosis	systematics
genus (plural, genera)	Pangaea	taxon
geologic record	parsimony	taxonomy
horizontal gene transfer	phyla (singular, phylum)	three-domain system

Word Roots

analog- = proportion (*analogy*: a similarity between two species that is due to convergent evolution rather than to descent from a common ancestor with the same trait)

bi- = two; **nom-** = name (*binomial*: a two-part Latinized name of a species)

clado- = branch (*clade*: a group of species that includes an ancestral species and all its descendants)

macro- = large (*macroevolution*: evolutionary change on a grand scale, encompassing the origin of new taxonomic groups, evolutionary trends, adaptive radiation, and mass extinction)

mono- = one (*monophyletic*: a taxon derived from a single ancestral species that gave rise to no species in any other taxa)

paedo- = child; **morph-** = form (*paedomorphosis*: the retention in an adult organism of the juvenile features of its evolutionary ancestors)

parsi- = few (*parsimony*: the quest for the simplest explanation for observed phenomena)

phylo- = tribe (*phylum*: the taxonomic category above class); **-geny** = origin (*phylogeny*: the evolutionary history of a species or group of species)

stromato- = something spread out; **-lite** = a stone (*stromatolite*: layered rocks that result from the activities of prokaryotes that bind thin films of sediment together)

CHAPTER 16

Microbial Life: Prokaryotes and Protists

Chapter Objectives

Opening Essay

Explain why a coral reef is dependent upon the protists and prokaryotes that also inhabit this ecosystem.

Prokaryotes

16.1 Describe the diverse roles and abundance of prokaryotic life.

16.2 Compare the different shapes, cell walls, and projections of prokaryotes.

16.3 Explain how bacteria can evolve quickly and how bacteria can survive stressful environments.

16.4 Describe the nutritional diversity of prokaryotes.

16.5 Explain why biofilms are unique and potentially dangerous to human health.

16.6 Explain how prokaryotes are employed to address the needs of human society.

16.7 Compare the three domains of life based upon differences in cellular and biochemical traits. Explain why biologists consider Archaea to be more closely related to Eukarya than to Bacteria.

16.8 Describe the diverse types of Archaea living in extreme and more moderate environments.

16.9 Distinguish between the subgroups of the domain Bacteria, noting the particular structure, special features, and habitats of each group.

16.10 Describe some of the diseases associated with bacteria. Distinguish between exotoxins and endotoxins, noting examples of each.

16.11 Describe the four parts of Koch's postulates. Explain why this method is used and how it relates to our new understanding of the cause of most peptic ulcers.

16.12 Describe the recent U.S. attacks using bacteria and the effectiveness of anthrax as a weapon.

Protists

16.13 Describe the basic types of protists. Explain why biologists currently think that they represent many clades.

16.14 Explain how primary endosymbiosis and secondary endosymbiosis led to further cellular diversity.

16.15 Describe and distinguish between the chromalveolate groups, noting characteristics and examples of each.

16.16 Explain how cultured algae may be used as renewable fuels and the current challenges that remain.

16.17–16.20 Describe and distinguish between the Rhizaria, Excavata, Unikonta, and Archaeplastida groups.

16.20 Describe the life cycle of *Ulva*, noting each form in the alternation of generations and how each is produced.

16.21 Describe the protist ancestors of animals, plants, and fungi. Explain how each ancestral protist group is similar to its most likely descendants.

Lecture Outline

I. Introduction

    A. The abundant life of a coral reef depends upon microbes.

        1. Photosynthesis by protists and prokaryotes feed all of the animals.

        2. Prokaryotes convert dead organic material into fertilizer.

        3. Protists that reside in the cells of corals use photosynthesis to produce sugars that nourish their hosts.

    B. Prokaryotes and protists are essential to the health of every ecosystem, including the human body.

II. Prokaryotes

    A. 16.1 Prokaryotes are diverse and widespread

        1. Prokaryotic cells are smaller than eukaryotic cells.

            a. Prokaryotes range from 1–5 µm in diameter.

            b. Eukaryotes range from 10–100 µm in diameter.

        2. The collective biomass of prokaryotes is at least 10 times that of all eukaryotes.

        3. Prokaryotes live in habitats

            a. too cold,

            b. too hot,

            c. too salty,

            d. too acidic, and

            e. too alkaline for eukaryotes to survive.

        4. Some bacteria are **pathogens**, causing disease. But most bacteria on our bodies are benign or beneficial.

        5. Several hundred species of bacteria live in and on our bodies,

            a. decomposing dead skin cells,

            b. supplying essential vitamins, and

            c. guarding against pathogenic organisms.

        6. Prokaryotes in soil decompose dead organisms, sustaining chemical cycles.

    B. 16.2 External features contribute to the success of prokaryotes

        1. Prokaryotic cells have three common cell shapes.

            a. **Cocci** are spherical prokaryotic cells. They sometimes occur in chains that are called streptococci.

            b. **Bacilli** are rod-shaped prokaryotes. Bacilli may also be threadlike, or filamentous.

            c. Spiral prokaryotes are like a corkscrew.

                i.   Short and rigid prokaryotes are called *spirilla*.

                ii. Longer, more flexible cells are called *spirochetes*.

        2. Nearly all prokaryotes have a cell wall. Cell walls

            a. provide physical protection and

            b. prevent the cell from bursting in a hypotonic environment.

3. When stained with **Gram stain**, cell walls of bacteria are either
  a. Gram-positive, with simpler cell walls containing **peptidoglycan**, or
  b. Gram-negative, with less peptidoglycan and are more complex and more likely to cause disease.
4. The cell wall of many prokaryotes is covered by a capsule, a sticky layer of polysaccharides or protein.
5. The capsule
  a. enables prokaryotes to adhere to their substrate or to other individuals in a colony and
  b. shields pathogenic prokaryotes from attacks by a host's immune system.
6. Some prokaryotes have external structures that extend beyond the cell wall.
  a. Flagella help prokaryotes move in their environment.
  b. Hairlike projections called **fimbriae** enable prokaryotes to stick to their substrate or each other.

C. 16.3 Populations of prokaryotes can adapt rapidly to changes in the environment
1. Prokaryote population growth
  a. occurs by binary fission,
  b. can rapidly produce a new generation within hours, and
  c. can generate a great deal of genetic variation
    i. by spontaneous mutations,
    ii. increasing the likelihood that some members of the population will survive changes in the environment.
2. The genome of a prokaryote typically
  a. has about one-thousandth as much DNA as a eukaryotic genome and
  b. is one long, circular chromosome packed into a distinct region of the cell.
3. Many prokaryotes also have additional small, circular DNA molecules called plasmids, which replicate independently of the chromosome.
4. Some prokaryotes form specialized cells called **endospores** that remain dormant through harsh conditions.
5. Endospores can survive extreme heat or cold.

D. 16.4 Prokaryotes have unparalleled nutritional diversity
1. Prokaryotes exhibit much more nutritional diversity than eukaryotes.
2. Two sources of energy are used.
  a. *Phototrophs* capture energy from sunlight.
  b. *Chemotrophs* harness the energy stored in chemicals.
3. Two sources of carbon are used by prokaryotes.
  a. **Autotrophs** obtain carbon atoms from carbon dioxide.
  b. **Heterotrophs** obtain their carbon atoms from the organic compounds present in other organisms.
4. The terms that describe how prokaryotes obtain energy and carbon are combined to describe their modes of nutrition.
  a. **Photoautotrophs** obtain energy from sunlight and use carbon dioxide for carbon.
  b. **Photoheterotrophs** obtain energy from sunlight but get their carbon atoms from organic molecules.
  c. **Chemoautotrophs** harvest energy from inorganic chemicals and use carbon dioxide for carbon.
  d. **Chemoheterotrophs** acquire energy and carbon from organic molecules.

E. 16.5 CONNECTION: Biofilms are complex associations of microbes

    1. Biofilms

        a. are complex associations of one or several species of prokaryotes and

        b. may also include protists and fungi.

    2. Prokaryotes attach to surfaces and form biofilm communities that

        a. are difficult to eradicate and

        b. may cause medical and environmental problems.

    3. Biofilms are large and complex "cities" of microbes that

        a. communicate by chemical signals,

        b. coordinate a division of labor and defense against invaders, and

        c. use channels to distribute nutrients and collect wastes.

    4. Biofilms that form in the environment can be difficult to eradicate.

    5. Biofilms

        a. clog and corrode pipes,

        b. gum up filters and drains, and

        c. Coat the hulls of ships.

F. 16.6 CONNECTION: Prokaryotes help clean up the environment

    1. Prokaryotes are useful for cleaning up contaminants in the environment because prokaryotes

        a. have great nutritional diversity,

        b. are quickly adaptable, and

        c. can form biofilms.

    2. Bioremediation is the use of organisms to remove pollutants from

        a. soil,

        b. air, or

        c. water.

    3. Prokaryotic decomposers are the mainstays of sewage treatment facilities.

        a. Raw sewage is first passed through a series of screens and shredders.

        b. Solid matter then settles out from the liquid waste, forming sludge.

        c. Sludge is gradually added to a culture of anaerobic prokaryotes, including bacteria and archaea.

        d. The microbes decompose the organic matter into material that can be placed in a landfill or used as fertilizer.

    4. Liquid wastes are treated separately from the sludge.

        a. Liquid wastes are sprayed onto a thick bed of rocks.

        b. Biofilms of aerobic bacteria and fungi growing on the rocks remove much of the dissolved organic material.

        c. Fluid draining from the rocks is sterilized and then released, usually into a river or ocean.

    5. Bioremediation is becoming an important tool for cleaning up toxic chemicals released into the soil and water by industrial processes.

    6. Environmental engineers change the natural environment to accelerate the activity of naturally occurring prokaryotes capable of metabolizing pollutants.

G. 16.7 Bacteria and archaea are the two main branches of prokaryotic evolution

    1. New studies of representative genomes of prokaryotes and eukaryotes strongly support the three-domain view of life.

a. Prokaryotes are now classified into two domains:

    i. Bacteria and

    ii. Archaea.

b. Archaea have at least as much in common with eukaryotes as they do with bacteria.

H. 16.8 Archaea thrive in extreme environments—and in other habitats

    1. Archaeal inhabitants of extreme environments have unusual proteins and other molecular adaptations that enable them to metabolize and reproduce effectively.

        a. Extreme halophiles thrive in very salty places.

        b. Extreme thermophiles thrive in

            i. very hot water, such as geysers, and

            ii. acid pools.

    2. Methanogens

        a. live in anaerobic environments,

        b. give off methane as a waste product from

            i. the digestive tracts of cattle and deer and

            ii. decomposing materials in landfills.

I. 16.9 Bacteria include a diverse assemblage of prokaryotes.

    1. The domain Bacteria is currently divided into five groups, based on comparisons of genetic sequences.

        a. Proteobacteria

            i. are all gram negative,

            ii. share a particular rRNA sequence, and

            iii. represent all four modes of nutrition.

            iv. *Thiomargarita namibiensis* is a type of proteobacteria that

                (I) is a giant among prokaryotes, typically ranging up to 100–300 microns in diameter,

                (II) uses H_2S to generate organic molecules from CO_2, and

                (III) produces sulfur wastes.

            v. Proteobacteria also include *Rhizobium* species that

                (I) live symbiotically in root nodules of legumes and

                (II) convert atmospheric nitrogen gas into a form usable by their legume host.

                (III) Symbiosis is a close association between organisms of two or more species.

                (IV) *Rhizobium* is an endosymbiont, living within another species.

        b. Gram-positive bacteria

            i. rival proteobacteria in diversity and

            ii. include the actinomycetes common in soil.

            iii. *Streptomyces* is often cultured by pharmaceutical companies as a source of many antibiotics.

        c. Cyanobacteria

            i. Cyanobacteria are the only group of prokaryotes with plantlike, oxygen-generating photosynthesis.

            ii. Some species, such as *Anabaena*, have specialized cells that fix nitrogen.

        d. Chlamydias

            i. Chlamydias live inside eukaryotic host cells.

            ii. *Chlamydia trachomatis*

                (I) is a common cause of blindness in developing countries and

                (II) is the most common sexually transmitted disease in the United States.

  e. Spirochetes are

   i. helical bacteria and

   ii. notorious pathogens, causing

    (I) syphilis and

    (II) Lyme disease.

J. 16.10 CONNECTION: Some bacteria cause disease

 1. All organisms are almost constantly exposed to pathogenic bacteria.

 2. Most bacteria that cause illness do so by producing a poison.

  a. Exotoxins are proteins that bacterial cells secrete into their environment.

  b. Endotoxins are components of the outer membrane of gram-negative bacteria.

K. 16.11 SCIENTIFIC DISCOVERY: Koch's postulates are used to prove that a bacterium causes a disease

 1. Koch's postulates are four essential conditions used to establish that a certain bacterium is the cause of a disease. They are

  a. find the bacterium in every case of the disease,

  b. isolate bacteria from a person who has the disease and grow it in pure culture,

  c. show that the cultured bacteria cause the disease when transferred to a healthy subject, and

  d. isolate the bacteria from the experimentally infected subject.

 2. Koch's postulates were used to demonstrate that the bacterium *Helicobacter pylori* is the cause of most peptic ulcers.

 3. The 2005 Nobel Prize in Medicine was awarded to Barry Marshall and Robin Warren for this discovery.

L. 16.12 CONNECTION: Bacteria can be used as biological weapons

 1. Bacteria that cause anthrax and the plague can be used as biological weapons.

  a. *Bacillus anthracis* killed five people in the United States in 2001.

  b. Yersinia pestis bacteria

   i. are typically carried by rodents and transmitted by fleas, causing the plague and

   ii. can cause a pneumonic form of plague if inhaled.

 2. *Clostridium botulinum* produces the exotoxin botulinum, the deadliest poison on earth.

 3. Botulinum blocks transmission of nerve signals and prevents muscle contraction.

III. Protists

A. 16.13 Protists are an extremely diverse assortment of eukaryotes

 1. Protists

  a. are a diverse collection of mostly unicellular eukaryotes,

  b. may constitute multiple kingdoms within the Eukarya, and

  c. refer to eukaryotes that are not:

   i. plants,

   ii. animals, or

   ii. fungi.

 2. Protists obtain their nutrition in many ways. Protists include

  a. autotrophs, called **algae**, producing their food by photosynthesis,

  b. heterotrophs, called **protozoans**, eating bacteria and other protists,

  c. heterotrophs, called **parasites**, deriving their nutrition from a living host, and

  d. mixotrophs, using photosynthesis and heterotrophy.

3. Protists are found in many habitats including

   a. anywhere there is moisture and

   b. the bodies of host organisms.

4. Recent molecular and cellular studies indicate that nutritional modes used to categorize protists do not reflect natural clades.

5. Protist phylogeny remains unclear.

6. One hypothesis, used here, proposes five monophyletic supergroups.

B. 16.14 EVOLUTION CONNECTION: Secondary endosymbiosis is the key to much of protist diversity

   1. The endosymbiont theory explains the origin of mitochondria and chloroplasts.

      a. Eukaryotic cells evolved when prokaryotes established residence within other, larger prokaryotes.

      b. This theory is supported by present-day mitochondria and chloroplasts that

         i. have structural and molecular similarities to prokaryotic cells and

         ii. replicate and use their own DNA, separate from the nuclear DNA of the cell.

   2. Secondary endosymbiosis is

      a. the process in which an autotrophic eukaryotic protist became endosymbiotic in a heterotrophic eukaryotic protist and

      b. key to protist diversity.

C. 16.15 Chromalveolates represent the range of protist diversity.

   1. Chromalveolates include

      a. diatoms, unicellular algae with a glass cell wall containing silica,

      b. dinoflagellates, unicellular autotrophs, heterotrophs, and mixotrophs that are common components of marine plankton,

      c. brown algae, large, multicellular autotrophs,

      d. water molds, unicellular heterotrophs,

      e. ciliates, unicellular heterotrophs and mixotrophs that use cilia to move and feed, and

      f. a group including parasites, such as *Plasmodium*, which causes malaria.

D. 16.16 CONNECTION: Can algae provide a renewable source of energy?

   1. Fossil fuels

      a. are the organic remains of organisms that lived hundreds of millions of years ago and

      b. primarily consist of

         i. diatoms and

         ii. primitive plants.

   2. Lipid droplets in diatoms and other algae may serve as a renewable source of energy.

   3. If unicellular algae could be grown on a large scale, this oil could be harvested and processed into biodiesel.

   4. Numerous technical hurdles remain before industrial-scale production of biofuel from algae becomes a reality.

E. 16.17 Rhizarians include a variety of amoebas

   1. The two largest groups of Rhizaria are among the organisms referred to as **amoebas**.

   2. Amoebas move and feed by means of **pseudopodia**, temporary extensions of the cell.

   3. Foraminiferans

      a. are found in the oceans and in fresh water,

      b. have porous shells, called tests, composed of calcium carbonate, and

      c. have pseudopodia that function in feeding and locomotion.

4. Radiolarians

    a. are mostly marine and

    b. produce a mineralized internal skeleton made of silica.

F. 16.18 Some excavates have modified mitochondria

    1. Excavata has recently been proposed as a clade on the basis of molecular and morphological similarities.

    2. The name refers to an "excavated" feeding groove possessed by some members of the group.

    3. Excavates

        a. have modified mitochondria that lack functional electron transport chains and

        b. use anaerobic pathways such as glycolysis to extract energy.

    4. Excavates include

        a. heterotrophic termite endosymbionts,

        b. autotrophic species,

        c. mixotrophs such as *Euglena,*

        d. the common waterborne parasite *Giardia intestinalis,*

        e. the parasite *Trichomonas vaginalis*, which causes 5 million new infections each year of human reproductive tracts, and

        f. the parasite *Trypanosoma*, which causes sleeping sickness in humans.

G. 16.19 Unikonts include protists that are closely related to fungi and animals

    1. Unikonta is a controversial grouping joining

        a. amoebozoans and

        b. a group that includes animals and fungi, addressed at the end of this unit on Protists.

    2. Amoebozoans have lobe-shaped pseudopodia and include

        a. many species of free-living amoebas,

        b. some parasitic amoebas, and

        c. slime molds.

    3. Plasmodial slime molds

        a. are common where there is moist, decaying organic matter and

        b. consist of a single, multinucleate mass of cytoplasm undivided by plasma membranes, called a **plasmodium**.

    4. Cellular slime molds

        a. are common on rotting logs and decaying organic matter and

        b. usually exist as solitary amoeboid cells, but when food is scarce, amoeboid cells

            i. swarm together, forming a slug-like aggregate that wanders around for a short time and then

            ii. Form a stock supporting an asexual reproductive structure that produces spores.

H. 16.20 Archaeplastids include red algae, green algae, and land plants

    1. Archaeplastids include

        a. red algae,

        b. green algae, and

        c. land plants.

    2. Red algae

        a. are mostly multicellular,

        b. contribute to the structure of coral reefs, and

        c. are commercially valuable.

    3. Green algae may be unicellular, colonial, or multicellular.

    a. *Volvox* is a colonial green algae, and

    b. *Chlamydomonas* is a unicellular alga propelled by two flagella.

  4. *Ulva*, or sea lettuce, is

    a. a multicellular green alga with

    b. a complex life cycle that includes an **alternation of generations** that consists of

      i. a multicellular diploid ($2n$) form, the **sporophyte**, that alternates with

      ii. a multicellular haploid ($1n$) form, the **gametophyte**.

I. 16.21 EVOLUTION CONNECTION: Multicellularity evolved several times in eukaryotes

  1. The origin of the eukaryotic cell led to an evolutionary radiation of new forms of life.

  2. Unicellular protists are much more diverse in form than simpler prokaryotes.

  3. Multicellular organisms (seaweeds, plants, animals, and most fungi) are fundamentally different from unicellular organisms.

    a. A multicellular organism has various specialized cells that perform different functions and are interdependent.

    b. All of life's activities occur within a single cell in unicellular organisms.

  4. Multicellular organisms have evolved from three different lineages:

    a. brown algae evolved from chromalveolates,

    b. fungi and animals evolved from unikonts, and

    c. red algae and green algae evolved from achaeplastids.

  5. One hypothesis states that two separate unikont lineages led to fungi and animals, diverging more than 1 billion years ago.

  6. A combination of morphological and molecular evidence suggests that choanoflagellates are the closest living protist relative of animals.

Chapter Guide to Teaching Resources

Prokaryotes (16.1–16.12)

Student Misconceptions and Concerns

- Students might think of evolution as a progression, with eukaryotes somehow fundamentally "better" than prokaryotes. However, as the authors note, a world of eukaryotes cannot exist without prokaryotes. Further, prokaryotes can survive without eukaryotes. (16.1–16.21)

- Many students struggle with concepts of size and volume. For example, they may not realize that a cube twice as wide as another has a volume eight times greater. The text notes that the diameter of eukaryotic cells is about ten times greater than the diameter of prokaryotic cells. Thus, the volume of eukaryotic cells can be nearly 1,000 times greater than prokaryotic cells. (16.1)

- Students may think that hand washing and the use of soap, especially antibacterial soap, leaves the washed parts free of bacteria. The tremendous numbers of bacteria that typically remain and routinely reside on and within our bodies are little appreciated. (16.1–16.10)

- Students often have difficulty grasping geological timescales. Many students do not intuitively understand that a billion is a thousand times greater than a million. Exercises and examples such as the following may help students comprehend such large numbers: (16.1–16.10)

a. If an earthquake occurs or a volcano erupts once every 1,000 years, how often will one or the other take place over a million years? (Answer: 1,000 times.) Note that what is rare to us becomes common in geological terms.

b. Have students calculate the age of a human when he or she reaches the one-billionth second of life (if we begin counting at birth, the answer is 31.688 years). Then have them calculate how long it takes to live 1,000,000 seconds. (Answer: about 11.6 days.)

- Students might immediately expect that all symbiotic relationships benefit both members. Consider noting that parasitism is a type of symbiotic relationship in which one member is harmed. (16.9)

Teaching Tips

- Much of this chapter describes the traits and habits of single-celled prokaryotes and single-celled eukaryotes. Students might benefit by developing a series of tables that allow them to quickly review the properties of various groups, organized by size, shape, cell wall structure, surface modifications, and/or mode of nutrition. (16.1–16.12)

- Students might easily be led to believe that we have already documented the diversity of life on Earth. However, by most estimates, we have identified fewer than 10% of the suspected species of eukaryotes. The ongoing discovery of new prokaryotes humbles microbiologists working today. The diversity of prokaryotic life may very well be beyond human determination. (16.1–16.12)

- Consider making some sort of timeline to scale in a hallway, long laboratory, or the side of the lecture hall, marking it proportionally as follows: (16.1)

  0.0%: Earth forms. (4.6 billion years ago)
  13%: Earth's crust solidifies. (4 billion years ago)
  15–25%: The first life appears. (3.5–3.9 billion years ago)
  41%: Photosynthetic prokaryotes start producing an oxygen-rich atmosphere. (2.7 billion years ago)
  54%: The first eukaryotes appear. (2.1 billion years ago)
  67%: The first multicellular eukaryotes appear. (1.5 billion years ago)
  89%: Plants first invade land. (500 million years ago)
  99.9%: Human and ape ancestries diverge! (6–7 million years ago)

- Remind students that the term "bacteria" is not equivalent to the term "prokaryotes." A discussion of the domains Archaea and Bacteria will help with this distinction. (16.1)

- Some modeling clay (oil-based clay never dries out) and toothpicks can be used to make some quick and easy visual aids to demonstrate the various shapes of these bacteria for lecture. The construction of these diverse shapes can also make for a quick lab activity. (16.2)

- Module 16.2 provides a broad spectrum of bacterial form and function. If you are selectively assigning chapters, consider this module of high importance. (16.2)

- The exponential growth of bacteria is like the growth represented in the correct answer to the classic math question "Would you rather have a million dollars or start out with just a penny for the first day of the month, but have your pay doubled every remaining day of that month?" Choosing the doubling amount pays off at about $10 million after just one month! (16.3)

- Students may need help thinking through why short generation times and large numbers of offspring permit rapid evolution. The authors address this important aspect of evolution in

Module 16.3. However, students may need additional clarity and examples to better understand the speed of evolutionary change permitted in bacteria as compared to long-lived organisms such as whales, elephants, and humans. (16.3)

- Consider asking students to examine the four modes of nutrition presented in Figure 16.4. Then, predict which of the four modes of nutrition are typically used by A) plants, B) animals, and C) fungi. Unusual exceptions to these patterns are also an opportunity for some critical thinking. (16.4)

- Chemoautotrophs permit ecosystems that do not rely upon sunlight for a source of metabolic energy (though Earth would quickly freeze solid without the sun!). Students may have been taught that all ecosystems are based upon photosynthesis. Chemoautotrophs are an exception. (16.4)

- Some aspects of the complex structure and organization of biofilms are similar to eukaryotic tissues and organs. Challenge students to identify analogous components of biofilms and eukaryotic tissues and organs. (16.5)

- The ecological impact of prokaryotes is directly relevant to students' lives, and can be of great interest to them. Consider a short Internet assignment in which each student must locate a recent article or website that addresses one aspect of this topic. (For example, exotoxins, endotoxins, bioremediation, etc.) They can then write a short summary or e-mail the website address to you for your inspection. (16.6–16.12)

- Students might enjoy an assignment to determine where and to what extent bioremediation is being used to help address the devastating results of the 2010 BP oil spill in the Gulf of Mexico. (16.6)

- The website http://water.usgs.gov/wid/html/bioremed.html is a good source for information on bioremediation. (16.6)

- Students may enter your class equating the terms *bacteria* and *prokaryotes*. Module 16.7 is a good distinction between the Bacteria and the Archaea. (16.7)

- The relatively new distinction between the prokaryote groups Bacteria and Archaea helps to illustrate the tentative nature of science. You might wish to point out to your students that science textbooks and our understanding of biological diversity are subject to change. (16.7)

- A Google Image search using the key words "Yellowstone hot springs color" will quickly identify photographic resources revealing extremophile diversity. (16.8)

- Students interested in global warming might research the estimated impact of methanogens in the digestive tract of herbivores raised by humans. (16.8)

- As the text in Module 16.9 notes, *Chlamydia* is the most common sexually transmitted disease in the United States. A rich and reliable source of information on chlamydia can be found at www.cdc.gov/std/Chlamydia/STDFact-Chlamydia.htm. (16.9)

- The many aspects of bacterial toxins often provoke student interest and can provide a rich opportunity for further student investigation. Consider having students prepare short reports on a toxin of their choice as a required or extra credit assignment. (16.10 and 16.12)

- Module 16.11 describing the steps of Koch's postulates and their utility today invites a discussion of scientific philosophy. Consider discussing with your class the use of the word *proof*. In particular, you might mention that science is never certain, although evidence can lead to conclusions reached with the highest levels of confidence.

- Students may not know that Botox injections used to reduce facial wrinkles use small injections of botulinum to paralyze facial muscles. The toxin is also used therapeutically for other muscular conditions. (16.12)

Protists (16.13–16.21)

Student Misconceptions and Concerns

- Students might think of protists as "simple" organisms in comparison to our own complex multicellular bodies. However, as the authors note, within a single cell, protists must carry out all the basic functions performed by the set of specialized cells that collectively form the bodies of plants and animals. (16.13)

- Students often mistakenly think that chloroplasts are a substitute for mitochondria in plant cells. They might think that cells either have mitochondria or they have chloroplasts. You might challenge this thinking by asking how plant cells generate ATP at night. (16.14)

- Students may think that fossil fuels largely consist of decayed animals such as dinosaurs. However, as the authors note, diatoms and primitive plants are thought to be responsible for most fossil fuels. (16.16)

Teaching Tips

- The reconsideration of the classification of protists further illustrates the tentative nature of science, in which no information is considered final. You may point out that new molecular tools have allowed us to understand new levels of diversity and required reconsiderations of classification schemes. (16.13)

- The evidence that mitochondria and chloroplasts evolved from free-living prokaryotes is further supported by the small prokaryote size of these organelles in eukaryotes. Mitochondria and chloroplasts are therefore helpful in comparing the general size of eukaryotic and prokaryotic cells. You might think of these organelles as built-in comparisons. (16.14)

- The endosymbiont theory for the origin of mitochondria and chloroplasts is also discussed in detail in Module 4.15. Consider assigning this module in addition to Chapter 16. (16.14)

- Figure 16.14 is especially useful for distinguishing between primary and secondary endosymbiosis and explaining the origin of some protist diversity. (16.14)

- Students can be encouraged to create their own table of traits, resembling Table 16.7 in organization, to distinguish between the groups addressed in Modules 16.15 and 16.17–16.20. Alternately, you might create such a table to be completed by students while they study these modules. Beginning science students often need help learning how to organize information gained through reading and note taking. (16.15 and 16.17–16.20)

- The great diversity of protists presents an opportunity for students to report on different types of protists and enhance their knowledge. For example, students can sketch their protist and identify reliable Web resources for additional details and clarity. You might collect and edit these Web references to serve as an aid for your entire class. These short exercises in content ownership allow students to develop a greater depth of understanding and increase interaction with the subject. (16.15 and 16.17–16.20)

- This is a very exciting time for new scientists entering the field of renewable fuels. Module 16.16 is an opportunity to illustrate to your students how they can still get in on the "ground floor" of these emerging energy fields. Sometimes instructors need to help students imagine a place for them in the future of science. (16.16)

- The evolution of multicellularity requires the subdivision of labor in ways similar to modern human societies. Providing structure, acquiring and processing food, and facilitating movement are specialized functions of cells as well as members of society. (16.21)

- Figure 16.21 presents one potential scenario to account for the diversity of eukaryotes. It is a very helpful organizer for the textbook and discussions of these groups. (16.21)

Key Terms

alga (plural, algae)	dinoflagellates	peptidoglycan
alternation of generations	endospore	photoautotroph
amoebas	endotoxin	photoheterotroph
amoebozoan	Excavata	plasmodial slime mold
Archaea	exotoxin	plasmodium
autotroph	extreme halophile	proteobacteria
bacillus (plural, bacilli)	extreme thermophile	protist
Bacteria	fimbriae	protozoan (plural, protozoa)
biofilm	foraminiferans	pseudopodium (plural,
bioremediation	gametophyte	pseudopodia)
brown algae	Gram stain	radiolarians
cellular slime molds	Gram-positive bacteria	red algae
chemoautotroph	green algae	Rhizaria
chemoheterotroph	heterotroph	secondary endosymbiosis
chlamydias	kelp	spirochetes
ciliates	methanogens	sporophyte
coccus (plural, cocci)	mixotrophs	symbiosis
cyanobacteria	parasite	Unikonta
diatoms	pathogen	water molds

Word Roots

auto- = self; **-troph** = food (*autotroph*: an organism that makes its own food)

chemo- = chemical; **auto-** = self; **-troph** = food (*chemoautotroph*: an organism that obtains both energy and carbon from inorganic chemicals, making its own organic compounds from CO_2 without using light energy); **hetero-** = different (*chemoheterotroph*: an organism that obtains both energy and carbon from organic molecules)

cyan- = dark blue (*cyanobacteria*: Photoautotrophic prokaryotes with plantlike, oxygen-generating photosynthesis. These bacteria are sometimes called blue-green algae.)

endo- = inner, within (*endospore*: a thick-coated protective cell produced within a bacterial cell that can become dormant to survive harsh environmental conditions; *endotoxin*: a poisonous component of the outer membrane of gram-negative bacteria, released only when the bacteria die)

exo- = outside (*exotoxin*: a poisonous protein secreted by certain bacteria)

-gen = produce (*methanogen*: Archaea that produce methane as a metabolic waste product)

halo- = salt; **-philos** = loving (*extreme halophile*: a microorganism that lives in a highly saline environment)

hetero- = different (*chemoheterotroph*: an organism that obtains both energy and carbon from organic molecules)

photo- = light; **auto-** = self; **-troph** = food, nourish (*photoautotroph*: an organism that obtains energy from sunlight and carbon from CO_2)

-phyte = plant (*gametophyte*: the multicellular haploid form in the life cycle of organisms undergoing alternation of generations)

pseudo- = false; **-podium** = foot (*pseudopodium* [plural, *pseudopodia*]: a temporary extension of an amoeboid cell that functions in moving and feeding)

sym- = with, together; **-bios** = life (*symbiosis*: a close association between organisms of two or more species)

thermo- = heat; **-philos** = loving (*extreme thermophile*: a microorganism that thrives in a hot environment)

CHAPTER **17**

The Evolution of Plant and Fungal Diversity

Chapter Objectives

Opening Essay

Explain why some plants have adaptations to entrap and digest animals.

Plant Evolution and Diversity

17.1–17.2   Describe the key plant adaptations to life on land.
17.2   Compare the bryophytes, seedless vascular plants, gymnosperms, and angiosperms.

Alternation of Generations and Plant Life Cycles

17.3   Describe the alternation of generations life cycle. Explain why it appears that this cycle has evolved independently in algae and land plants.
17.4–17.5   Describe the key events of the moss and fern life cycles.
17.6   Explain how coal is formed. Explain why coal, oil, and natural gas are called fossil fuels.
17.7   Describe the stages of the gymnosperm life cycle.
17.8   Describe the parts of a flower and explain their functions.
17.9   Describe the stages of the angiosperm life cycle.
17.10   List the angiosperm adaptations that promote seed dispersal.
17.11   Describe the significance of angiosperms to humans.
17.12   Explain how flowers are adapted to attract pollinators.
17.13   Describe the human impact on plant diversity. Explain the significance of this loss for humanity.

Fungi

17.14   Describe the main traits of fungi and their ecological roles.
17.15   Describe the generalized life cycle of a fungus. Explain how molds and yeast reproduce.
17.16   Distinguish between the five groups of fungi.
17.17   Compare the life cycles of zygomycetes, ascomycetes, and basidiomycetes.
17.18   Explain how parasitic fungi harm plants and animals.
17.19   Describe the positive ecological roles of fungi.
17.20   Describe the practical uses of fungi.
17.21   Describe the structure and characteristics of lichens.

Lecture Outline

I. Introduction

A. The Venus flytrap has adaptations to
   1. capture and
   2. digest insects.

B. More than 600 species of plants
   1. are carnivores and
   2. typically live where soil nutrients, including nitrogen levels, are poor.

C. Carnivorous plants absorb and use nutrients, including nitrogen, from animals.

II. Plant Evolution and Diversity

A. 17.1 Plants have adaptations for life on land

1. More than 500 million years ago, the algal ancestors of plants may have carpeted moist fringes of lakes and coastal salt marshes.

2. Plants and green algae called **charophytes**
   a. are thought to have evolved from a common ancestor,
   b. have complex multicellular bodies, and
   c. are photosynthetic eukaryotes.

3. Life on land offered many opportunities for plant adaptations that took advantage of
   a. unlimited sunlight,
   b. abundant CO_2 and
   c. initially, few pathogens or herbivores.

4. But life on land had disadvantages too. On land, plants must
   a. maintain moisture inside their cells, to keep from drying out,
   b. support their body in a nonbuoyant medium,
   c. reproduce and disperse offspring without water, and
   d. obtain resources from soil and air.

5. Unlike land plants, algae
   a. generally have no rigid tissues,
   b. are supported by surrounding water,
   c. obtain CO_2 and minerals directly from the water surrounding the entire algal body,
   d. receive light and perform photosynthesis over most of their body,
   e. use flagellated sperm that swim to fertilize an egg, and
   f. disperse offspring by water.

6. Land plants maintain moisture in their cells using
   a. a waxy cuticle and
   b. cells that regulate the opening and closing of stomata.

7. Land plants obtain
   a. water and minerals from roots in the soil and
   b. CO_2 from the air and sunlight through leaves.

8. Growth-producing regions of cell division, called **apical meristems**, are found near the tips of stems and roots.

9. In many land plants, water and minerals move up from roots to stems and leaves using **vascular tissues**.

10. **Xylem**
   a. consists of dead cells and
   b. conveys water and minerals.

11. **Phloem**
    a. consists of living cells and
    b. conveys sugars.
12. Many land plants support their body against the pull of gravity using **lignin**.
13. The absence of lignified cell walls in mosses and other plants that lack vascular tissue limits their height.
14. In all plants, the
    a. gametes and embryos must be kept moist,
    b. fertilized egg (zygote) develops into an embryo while attached to and nourished by the parent plant, and
    c. life cycle involves an alternation of a
        i. haploid generation, which produces eggs and sperm, and
        ii. diploid generation, which produces spores within protective structures called **sporangia**.
15. Pines and flowering plants have **pollen grains**, structures that contain the sperm-producing cells.

B. 17.2 Plant diversity reflects the evolutionary history of the plant kingdom
   1. Four key adaptations for life on land distinguish the main lineages of the plant kingdom.
       a. Dependent embryos are present in all plants.
       b. Lignified vascular tissues mark a lineage that gave rise to most living plants.
       c. Seeds are found in a lineage that includes all living gymnosperms and angiosperms.
       d. Flowers mark the angiosperm lineage.
   2. Early diversification of plants gave rise to seedless, nonvascular plants called **bryophytes**, including
       a. mosses,
       b. liverworts, and
       c. hornworts.
   3. These plants resemble other plants in having apical meristems and embryos retained on the parent plant, but they lack
       a. true roots,
       b. leaves, and
       c. lignified cell walls.
   4. About 425 million years ago, vascular plants evolved with lignin-hardened vascular tissues.
   5. The **seedless vascular plants** include
       a. lycophytes (including club mosses) and
       b. pterophytes (ferns and their relatives).
   6. The first vascular plants with seeds evolved about 360 million years ago.
   7. A **seed** consists of an embryo packaged with a food supply within a protective covering.
   8. Vascular plants with seeds include
       a. **gymnosperms** (including ginkgo, cycad, and conifer species) and
       b. **angiosperms** (such as flowering trees and grasses).
   9. **Gymnosperms**
       a. have naked seeds that are not produced in special chambers and
       b. include ginkgo, cycad, and conifer species.

10. Angiosperms

    a. are flowering plants and

    b. include flowering trees and grasses.

III. Alternation of Generations and Plant Life Cycles

A. 17.3 Haploid and diploid generations alternate in plant life cycles

    1. Plants have an **alternation of generations** in which the haploid and diploid stages are distinct, multicellular bodies.

        a. The haploid **gametophyte** produces gametes (eggs or sperm) by mitosis.

        b. Fertilization results in a diploid zygote.

        c. The zygote develops into the diploid **sporophyte**, which produces haploid spores by meiosis.

        d. Spores grow into gametophytes.

B. 17.4 The life cycle of a moss is dominated by the gametophyte

    1. Gametophytes make up a bed of moss.

        a. Gametes develop in male and female gametangia.

        b. Sperm swim through water to the egg in the female gametangium.

    2. The zygote

        a. develops within the gametangium into a mature sporophyte,

        b. which remains attached to the gametophyte.

    3. Meiosis occurs in sporangia at the tips of the sporophyte stalks.

    4. Haploid spores are released from the sporangium and develop into gametophyte plants.

C. 17.5 Ferns, like most plants, have a life cycle dominated by the sporophyte

    1. Fern gametophytes are small and inconspicuous.

    2. Gametophytes produce flagellated sperm that swim to the egg and fertilize it to produce a zygote.

    3. The zygote initially develops within the female gametangia but eventually develops into an independent sporophyte.

    4. Sporangia develop on the underside of the leaves of the sporophyte.

    5. Within the sporangia, cells undergo meiosis to produce haploid spores.

    6. Spores are released and develop into gametophytes.

D. 17.6 Seedless vascular plants dominated vast "coal forests"

    1. Two groups of seedless plants formed vast ancient forests in low-lying wetlands during the Carboniferous period (360–299 million years ago):

        a. lycophytes (such as club mosses) and

        b. pterophytes (such as ferns).

    2. When these plants died, they formed peat deposits that eventually formed coal.

    3. Coal, oil, and natural gas are **fossil fuels**.

        a. Oil and natural gas formed from marine organisms.

        b. Coal formed from seedless plants.

    4. Burning fossil fuels releases CO_2 and other greenhouse gases into the atmosphere, which are now causing a warming climate.

    5. As temperatures dropped during the late Carboniferous,

        a. glaciers formed,

        b. the climate turned drier,

        c. the vast swamps and forests began to disappear, and

        d. wind-dispersed pollen and protective seeds gave seed plants a competitive advantage.

E. 17.7 A pine tree is a sporophyte with gametophytes in its cones
1. A pine tree is a sporophyte.
2. Tiny gametophytes grow in sporophyte cones.
3. The **ovule** is a key adaptation, a protective device for all the female stages in the life cycle, as well as the site of
    a. **pollination**,
    b. fertilization, and
    c. embryonic development.
4. A sperm from a pollen grain fertilizes an egg in the female gametophyte.
5. The zygote develops into a sporophyte embryo.
6. The ovule becomes the seed with
    a. stored food and
    b. a protective **seed coat**.
7. The seed is a key adaptation for life on land and a major factor in the success of seed plants.
F. 17.8 The flower is the centerpiece of angiosperm reproduction
1. Flowers house separate male and female sporangia and gametophytes.
2. Flowers are the sites of
    a. pollination and
    b. fertilization.
3. Flowers usually consist of
    a. **sepals**, which enclose the flower before it opens,
    b. **petals**, which attract animal pollinators,
    c. **stamens**, which include a filament and **anther**, a sac at the top of each filament that contains male sporangia and releases pollen, and
    d. **carpels**, the female reproductive structure that produce eggs.
4. Ovules develop into seeds.
5. Ovaries mature into fruit.
G. 17.9 The angiosperm plant is a sporophyte with gametophytes in its flowers
1. Key events in a typical angiosperm life cycle
    a. Meiosis in the anthers produces haploid spores that form the male gametophyte (pollen grains).
    b. Meiosis in the ovule produces a haploid spore that forms the few cells of the female gametophyte, one of which becomes the egg.
    c. Pollination occurs when a pollen grain lands on the stigma. A pollen tube grows from the pollen grain to the ovule.
    d. The tube carries a sperm that fertilizes the egg to form a zygote.
    e. Each ovule develops into a seed, consisting of
        i.   an embryo (a new sporophyte) surrounded by a food supply and
        ii. a seed coat derived from the integuments.
    f. While the seeds develop, the ovary's wall thickens, forming the fruit that encloses the seeds.
    g. When conditions are favorable, a seed germinates.
H. 17.10 The structure of a fruit reflects its function in seed dispersal
1. **Fruits** are
    a. ripened ovaries of flowers and
    b. adaptations that disperse seeds.

2. Seed dispersal mechanisms include relying on

    a. wind,

    b. hitching a ride on animals, or

    c. fleshy, edible fruits that attract animals, which then deposit the seed in a supply of natural fertilizer at some distance from the parent plant.

I. 17.11 CONNECTION: Angiosperms sustain us—and add spice to our diets

    1. Most human food is provided by the fruits and seeds of angiosperms.

        a. Corn, rice, wheat, and other grains are dry fruits.

        b. Apples, cherries, tomatoes, and squash are fleshy fruits.

        c. Spices such as nutmeg, cinnamon, cumin, cloves, ginger, and licorice are also angiosperm fruits.

J. 17.12 EVOLUTION CONNECTION: Pollination by animals has influenced angiosperm evolution

    1. About 90% of angiosperms use animals to transfer their pollen.

        a. Birds are usually attracted by colorful flowers, but not scent.

        b. Most beetles are attracted by fruity odors, but are indifferent to color.

        c. Night-flying bats and moths are usually attracted by large, highly scented flowers.

        d. Wind-pollinated flowers typically produce large amounts of pollen.

K. 17.13 CONNECTION: Plant diversity is vital to the future of the world's food supply

    1. Early hunter-gatherer humans made use of any edible plant species available at the time.

    2. Modern agriculture has narrowed the pool of food plant diversity by creating a select few genotypes.

    3. Most of the world's population is now fed by varieties of

        a. rice,

        b. wheat,

        c. corn, and

        d. soybeans.

        e. Agriculture has changed the landscape.

    4. As plant biodiversity is lost through extinction and habitat destruction, we lose

        a. potential crop species and

        b. valuable genes.

IV. Diversity of Fungi

    A. 17.14 Fungi absorb food after digesting it outside their bodies

        1. Fungi

            a. are absorptive heterotrophic eukaryotes,

            b. secrete powerful enzymes to digest their food externally, and

            c. acquire their nutrients by **absorption**.

        2. Most fungi consist of a mass of threadlike **hyphae** making up a **mycelium**.

        3. Hyphal cells

            a. are separated by cross-walls with pores large enough for ribosomes, mitochondria, and nuclei to cross,

            b. are sometimes multinucleate without cross-walls, and

            c. have a huge surface area to secrete digestive enzymes and absorb food.

        4. Fungal hyphae

            a. are surrounded by a cell wall made of **chitin** instead of cellulose.

5. Some fungi
   a. are **parasites** and
   b. obtain their nutrients at the expense of living plants or animals.
6. **Mycorrhizae** (plural)
   a. represent a symbiotic relationship between fungi and plant root cells and
   b. are present in nearly all vascular plants.
7. Mycorrhizal fungi absorb phosphorus and other essential materials from the soil and make them available to the plant.
8. Sugars produced by the plant through photosynthesis nourish the mycorrhizal fungi.

B. 17.15 Fungi produce spores in both asexual and sexual life cycles
   1. Fungi produce huge numbers of asexual spores, each of which can germinate to form a new fungus.
   2. In many fungi, sexual fusion of haploid hyphae leads to a **heterokaryotic stage**, in which cells contain two genetically distinct haploid nuclei.
      a. Hours or centuries may pass before parental nuclei fuse to form a short-lived diploid phase.
      b. Zygotes undergo meiosis to produce haploid spores.
   3. In asexual reproduction, spore-producing structures arise from haploid mycelia that have undergone neither a heterokaryotic stage or meiosis.
   4. Many fungi that reproduce sexually can also produce spores asexually.
   5. **Molds** are any rapidly growing fungus that reproduces asexually by producing spores.
   6. **Yeasts** are single-celled fungi that reproduce asexually by cell division or budding.

C. 17.16 Fungi are classified into five groups
   1. There are over 100,000 described fungi species.
   2. Suspected but as yet undescribed species may number as many as 1.5 million.
   3. Sexual reproductive structures are often used to classify fungi.
   4. Fungi and animals may have diverged
      a. from a flagellated unikont ancestor
      b. more than 1 billion years ago.
   5. **Chytrids** are the
      a. only fungi with flagellated spores and
      b. earliest lineage of fungi.
   6. Chytrid fungi are
      a. common in lakes, ponds, and soil and
      b. linked to the widespread decline of amphibian species.
   7. **Zygomycetes**, or **zygote fungi**
      a. are characterized by their protective zygosporangium, where zygotes produce haploid spores by meiosis.
      b. This diverse group includes fast-growing molds that attack
         i. bread
         ii. peaches,
         iii. strawberries,
         iv. sweet potatoes, and
         v. some animals.
   8. **Glomeromycetes**
      a. form a distinct type of mycorrhizae, in which hyphae that invade plant roots branch into treelike structures known as arbuscules.
      b. About 90% of all plants have symbiotic partnerships with glomeromycetes.

9. **Ascomycetes**, or **sac fungi**
   a. form saclike structures called **asci**, which produce spores in sexual reproduction,
   b. live in marine, freshwater, and terrestrial habitats, and
   c. range in size from unicellular years to elaborate morels and cup fungi.
   d. Some ascomycetes live with green algae or cyanobacteria in symbiotic associations called lichens.
10. **Basidiomycetes**, or **club fungi**
    a. include common mushrooms, puffballs, and shelf fungi, and
    b. are named for their club-shaped, spore-producing structure called a basidium.
11. These fungi include
    a. important forest decomposers and
    b. particularly destructive plant parasites called rusts and smuts.

D. 17.17 Fungal groups differ in their life cycles and reproductive structures
   1. The life cycle of a black bread mold is typical of zygomycetes.
   2. Hyphae reproduce asexually by producing spores in sporangia at the tips of upright hyphae.
   3. When food is depleted, the fungus reproduces sexually.
      a. Mycelia of different mating types join and produce a zygosporangium, a cell containing multiple nuclei from two parents.
      b. The zygosporangium develops into a thick-walled structure that can tolerate dry, harsh conditions.
      c. When conditions are favorable, the parental nuclei fuse to form diploid zygotes, which undergo meiosis producing haploid spores.
   4. The life cycle of a mushroom is typical of basidiomycetes.
   5. The heterokaryotic stage
      a. begins when mycelia of two different mating types fuse,
      b. forming a heterokaryotic mycelium,
      c. which grows and produces the mushroom.
   6. In the club-shaped cells called basidia, which line the gills of the mushroom, the haploid nuclei fuse, forming diploid nuclei.
   7. Each diploid nucleus produces haploid spores by meiosis.
   8. A mushroom can release as many as a billion spores.
   9. If spores land on moist matter that can serve as food, they germinate and grown into haploid mycelia.

E. 17.18 CONNECTION: Parasitic fungi harm plants and animals
   1. Of the 100,000 known species of fungi, about 30% are either parasites or pathogens in or on plants.
   2. About 80% of plant diseases are caused by fungi.
      a. Between 10 and 50% of the world's fruit harvest is lost each year to fungal attack.
      b. A variety of fungi, including smuts and rusts, infect grain crops.
   3. Only about 50 species of fungi are parasitic on animals.
   4. The general term for a fungal infection is **mycosis**.
   5. Skin mycoses include
      a. ringworm, named because it appears as circular red areas on the skin,
      b. athlete's foot, also caused by the ringworm fungus,
      c. vaginal yeast infections, and
      d. deadly lung diseases.

F. 17.19 CONNECTION: Fungi have enormous ecological benefits
  1. Fungi
    a. supply essential nutrients to plants through symbiotic mycorrhyizae and
    b. are essential decomposers in ecosystems, breaking down decomposing leaves, logs, and feces and dead animals.
  2. Fungi may also be used to digest petroleum products to clean up oil spills, such as the 2010 BP spill in the Gulf of Mexico.
G. 17.20 CONNECTION: Fungi have many practical uses
  1. Fungi have many practical uses for humans.
    a. We eat mushrooms and cheeses modified by fungi.
    b. Yeasts produce alcohol and cause bread to rise.
    c. Some fungi provide antibiotics that are used to treat bacterial disease.
    d. Fungi figure prominently in molecular biology and in biotechnology. Yeasts, for example, are often used to study molecular genetics of eukaryotes.
    e. Fungi may play a major role in the future production of biofuels from plants.
H. 17.21 Lichens are symbiotic associations of fungi and photosynthetic organisms
  1. Lichens consist of algae or cyanobacteria within a mass of fungal hyphae.
    a. Many lichen associations are mutualistic.
    b. The fungus receives food from its photosynthetic partner.
    c. The fungal mycelium helps the alga absorb and retain water and minerals.
  2. Lichens are important pioneers on new land, where they help to form soil.
  3. Lichens are sensitive to air pollution, because they obtain minerals from the air.

Chapter Guide to Teaching Resources

Plant Evolution and Diversity (17.1–17.2)

Student Misconceptions and Concerns

- Students often mistakenly conceive of evolution as a deliberate and directed process, in which organisms somehow acquire adaptations out of want or need. This chapter provides good examples of how evolution actually occurs. During the period when plants first moved onto land, the demands of a terrestrial environment selected among the diversity already existing within the various marginal plant species. For example, plants that produced structures that provided some physical support outside of water had an advantage over those without such structures. Plants did not evolve adaptations to address the needs of living on land. Instead, terrestrial adaptations in existing aquatic plants conveyed advantages in this new environment and were therefore favored. (17.1–17.2)

- The text identifies charophytes as the algal group most closely related to plants. Students might misinterpret this to mean that modern charophytes were the direct ancestors of plants. Instead, modern charophytes and plants share a common ancestor, but each has been evolving since the lineages diverged. This same confusion occurs when considering the evolutionary history of humans and chimps. Humans and chimps share a common ancestor. Modern humans did not evolve from modern chimps. Although such distinctions may be clear to us as instructors, beginning students with little experience can easily be confused. (17.1–17.2)

Teaching Tips

- Assign your students to work in small groups and list the demands of living on land versus in water. Having them consider the challenges that plants faced when they moved onto land prepares them for the discussion of the resulting adaptations in Chapter 17. (17.1)

- Water lilies and whales are two aquatic organisms that evolved from recent terrestrial ancestors. Students might contemplate the changes in these organisms as they returned to the aquatic environment from which their ancestors emerged. (17.1)

- Point out to your students that in an aquatic environment, resources such as nutrients and water are accessible to the entire plant. However, structural adaptations such as roots and shoots have evolved in plants that live on land, where such resources are less accessible. (17.1)

- Consider an analogy between vascular systems in plants and a major interstate highway, with traffic running in opposite directions. Highways, like vascular tissues, permit the widespread distribution of concentrated resources. (17.1)

- Have your students discuss the specific advantages of similar adaptations in the reproductive systems of plants and mammals. What are the advantages to keeping the developing embryos with the parent? (One example: The embryonic environment can be carefully regulated by the parent and the parent can better protect the young from damage, disease, or predation.) (17.1)

- Consider an analogy between a chicken egg and the first seeds to evolve, although the parallels are limited: each consists of a developing embryo enclosed in a water-resistant packet, along with a store of food. (17.2)

- The support provided by many tightly packed mosses is analogous to the collective support of the many fibers of plush carpeting. Each fiber of carpet and each individual moss plant might easily collapse without the support of its neighbor. (17.2)

Alternation of Generations and Plant Life Cycles (17.3–17.13)

Student Misconceptions and Concerns

- Students can easily confuse the animal and plant reproductive cycles. However, the unique features of alternation of generations in plants (and certain algae) make analogies and parallels challenging and potentially confusing when referencing animal life cycles. One possible relevant exercise would be to compare the timing of mitosis and meiosis in plant and animal life cycles. (17.3–17.5)

- Students often confuse global warming with the destruction of the ozone layer. This might be a good time to discuss or clarify global warming. The carbon removed from the air during the Carboniferous period has been locked up in coal (and other fossil fuels) for about 300 million years. By burning fossil fuels, we are reintroducing carbon that has been out of circulation for a significant time. Thus, there is a net gain in global carbon dioxide, which may act like glass in a car to reflect back heat (or glass in a greenhouse). Note that burning ethanol derived from corn does not directly contribute to global warming by adding sequestered carbon dioxide to the atmosphere. This is because the carbon in the ethanol was removed from the air only a year or two ago, instead of hundreds of millions of years ago (although the use of fossil fuels to raise corn and produce ethanol does contribute to global warming). (17.6)

Teaching Tips

- The authors describe four key adaptations for life on land in Module 17.2. The following modules (17.3–17.13) describe how these adaptations distinguish the main lineages of the plant kingdom. This is consistent with good lecture advice: Tell them what you are going to tell them, tell them, then tell them what you told them (summarize). (17.3–17.13)

- Students might wonder if humans and other animals do not also qualify as having alternation of generations. Although we do have haploid gametes, the haploid stage does not include multicellular individuals. (17.3–17.5)

- Depending upon where your course is taught, coal may be an important part of the economy. The geology of these coal deposits helps us interpret the rich history of life on Earth. If you live in a coal region, consider devoting additional time to explaining how coal was deposited, why it is an important source of energy, and how the use of fossil fuels contributes to global warming. (17.6)

- As the authors note, much time can pass between pollination, fertilization, and the production of seeds in pine trees. This entire process may take two years. This lengthy period of time, the alternation of generations, and other specific details of the gymnosperm life cycle can create confusion. Students with little experience in plant biology may need considerable support in fitting all of these details into the life cycle. (17.7)

- As Francois Jacob suggested, evolution works as a tinkerer and not like an engineer. New forms evolve by remodeling old forms. As the text notes, gymnosperm cones are modified shoots and angiosperm flowers represent the remodeling of leaves. These examples of remodeling might be a subject you may want to explore in additional detail as an important lesson in evolution. (17.7–17.8)

- Floral shops frequently discard magnificent flowers that are just beyond their peak. Teachers can obtain free discards by contacting local floral shops and noting their educational needs. Having a variety of flowers on hand can brighten up any discussion of angiosperms. (17.8–17.9)

- Before lecturing on the examples of angiosperm and animal cooperation, let your students try to name as many as they can. This may be assigned as an in-class activity in small groups or students may compile lists individually that can be brought into class or e-mailed to the instructor. (17.9–17.13)

- The symbiotic relationships between angiosperms and animals are extensive. Challenge students to list all of the ways that plant reproduction benefits from animals (examples include the role of nectar in attracting pollinators, seed dispersal in fruit, and hitchhiker strategies such as that revealed in Figure 17.10B). Not all animals benefit from these relationships. (17.10–17.12)

- You might have your class spend a minute just listing the plant-derived materials in your classroom. These will include cotton cloth, wood for pencils, paper in many forms, etc. In addition, have students try to imagine how they could spend an entire day without encountering plants or plant products. (17.11–17.13)

- The tremendous volume of pollen released into the air is apparent to anyone suffering from allergies. You might wish to have your students find the pollen counts for your area, which is commonly provided as part of weather reports. It might be interesting to track the pollen counts as you go through the semester. (17.12)

- Referencing local examples of monoculture replacing a more diverse native ecosystem can help reinforce the content of Module 17.13. Encouraging students to look around your community and note where old-growth forest has been replaced with a single fast-growing species, or where native prairies have given way to vast fields of corn, wheat, or soybeans, will bring home the loss of plant diversity as modeled in their own backyard. (17.13)

Fungi (17.14–17.21)

Student Misconceptions and Concerns

- The diverse ecological and medical roles of fungi are often underappreciated by students. Consider quizzing your students on the ecological importance of fungi and the medical and ecological significance of fungi to humans before assigning or lecturing on these topics. Such assessments can generate increased student interest and help you evaluate their background knowledge. (17.14–17.21)

- Students often view fungi as some type of plant. However, many differences between them exist (for example, fungi are not photosynthetic and have cell walls made of chitin instead of cellulose). Emphasize these basic differences early in your lectures to clearly distinguish fungi as a separate group. (17.14–17.21)

Teaching Tips

- The physical relationship between a fungus and its hyphae is generally analogous to a fire hydrant and the underground water pipes. Only the fire hydrant emerges above the surface of the ground. (17.14)

- Ask your students to distinguish between fungi and animals. Both are multicellular heterotrophs lacking cellulose. Students will have to dig a little to discover that fungi have cell walls primarily composed of chitin. You might further challenge them to identify animals that also absorb their nutrients directly from their environments (for example, tapeworms). (17.14)

- The heterokaryotic stage is like the merger of two kingdoms in which both kings continue to rule. (17.15)

- As the authors note, chytrid fungi are suspected in the worldwide decline of many amphibian species. The following resources are entry points into the extensive information available about that significant threat to amphibian biodiversity. (17.16)

The Australian government maintains a chytrid fact sheet at www.environment.gov.au/biodiversity/invasive/publications/c-disease/pubs/c-disease.pdf. The Centers for Disease Control describe the origin of the chytrid fungus at www.cdc.gov/ncidod/EID/vol10no12/03-0804.htm. www.jcu.edu.au/school/phtm/PHTM/frogs/ampdis.htm is a website devoted to updates on amphibian disease.

- The mechanism of natural selection depends in part on the overproduction of offspring. As noted in Module 17.17, a single mushroom can release as many as one billion spores. In addition to facilitating reproduction, such overproduction also increases the likelihood of dispersal. (17.17)

- Students often mistakenly conceive of evolution as a deliberate and directed process. Like the elm trees described in Module 17.18, American chestnut trees were nearly driven to extinction because they did not possess adaptations that would have helped them survive the blight fungus. If evolution results from need, why then would the chestnuts or elm trees suffer? (For details on the chestnut blight, see the website of the American Phytopathological Society at www.apsnet.org/online/feature/chestnut/.) (17.18)

- Module 17.18 describes a variety of examples of fungal disease, noting that 80% of plant diseases are from fungi. Further, human diseases include athlete's foot, ringworm, and vaginal yeast infections. If certain fungal infections are particularly problematic in your region, consider emphasizing them in your lecture. (17.18)

- Students are unlikely to appreciate the roles that fungi play in natural environments, or in causing human diseases, or the benefits of fungi to human society, including bioremediation and the production of drugs, alcoholic beverages, baked goods, or fuel. To increase student interest, consider starting your lectures on fungi by noting the many effects of fungi on human life. Also, consider outside of class student assignments to investigate specific roles of fungi that may be of particular interest to students with medical, agricultural, environmental, or industrial majors. (17.18–17.20)

- Wonderful coverage of lichens can be found at the aptly named www.lichen.com/! (17.21)

Key Terms

absorption	glomeromycete	sac fungus
alternation of generations	gymnosperm	seed
angiosperm	heterokaryotic stage	seed coat
anther	hyphae	seedless vascular plants
apical meristem	imperfect fungus	sepal
ascomycete	lichen	sporangium
basidiomycete	lignin	spore
bryophyte	mold	sporophyte
carpel	mycelium (plural, mycelia)	stamen
chitin	mycorrhiza (plural,	vascular plant
chytrid	mycorrhizae)	vascular tissue
embryophyte	ovary	xylem
fossil fuel	parasite	yeast
fruit	petal	zygomycete
fungus (plural, fungi)	phloem	zygote fungus
gametangium	pollen grain	
gametophyte	pollination	

Word Roots

angio- = vessel; **-sperm** = seed (*angiosperm*: a flowering plant, which forms seeds inside a protective chamber called an ovary)

anth- = a flower (*anther*: a sac located at the top of a flower's stamen in which pollen grains develop)

apic- = the tip; **meristo-** = divided (*apical meristem*: a region of cell division at the tip of a plant root or in the terminal or axillary bud of a shoot)

asco- = sac; **-myco-** = fungus (*ascomycete*: a type of fungus that produces spores in sac-like structures called asci)

basidio- = club; **-myco-** = fungus (*basidiomycete*: a type of fungus that produces spores in club-like structures, called basidia)

bryo- = moss; **-phyto** = plant (*bryophytes*: one of a group of nonvascular plants, including mosses, liverworts, and hornworts, that lack xylem and phloem)

carp- = a fruit (*carpel*: the female part of a flower, consisting of a stalk with an ovary at the base and a stigma, which traps pollen, at the tip)

gamet- = a wife or husband; **-angio** = vessel (*gametangium*: a reproductive organ that houses and protects the gametes of a plant); **-phyto** = plant (*gametophyte*: the multicellular haploid form in organisms undergoing alternation of generations, which mitotically produces haploid gametes that unite and grow into the sporophyte generation)

glomer- = a ball; **myco-** = fungus (*glomeromycete*: member of a group of fungi characterized by a distinct branching form of mycorrhizae called arbuscules)

gymno- = naked; **-sperm** = seed (*gymnosperm*: a vascular plant that bears "naked" seeds not enclosed in an ovary)

hetero- = different; **-karyo** = nucleus (*heterokaryotic stage*: a fungal life cycle stage that contains two genetically different nuclei in the same cell)

lign- = wood (*lignin*: a chemical that hardens the cell walls of plants)

myco- = fungus; **rhizo-** = root (*mycorrhiza*: a close association of plant roots and fungi that is beneficial to both partners)

phloe- = the bark of a tree (*phloem*: the portion of a plant's vascular system, made up of sieve-tube members, that conveys phloem sap throughout a plant)

-phyto = a plant (*sporophyte*: the multicellular diploid form in organisms undergoing alternation of generations; it results from the union of gametes and meiotically produces haploid spores that grow into the gametophyte generation)

sporo- = a seed (*sporangium*: a structure in fungi and plants in which meiosis occurs and haploid spores develop; *spore*: in plants and algae, a haploid cell that can develop into a multicellular individual without fusing with another cell)

stam- = standing upright (*stamen*: the pollen-producing male reproductive part of a flower, consisting of a filament and an anther)

vascula- = a little vessel (*vascular tissue*: plant tissue consisting of cells joined into tubes that transport water and nutrients throughout the plant body)

xyl- = wood (*xylem*: the tube-shaped, nonliving portion of the vascular system in plants that provides support and conveys xylem sap from the roots to the rest of the plant)

zygo- = fertilized cell; **-myco-** = fungus (*zygomycete*: a type of fungus that produces spores during sexual reproduction)

CHAPTER 18

The Evolution of Invertebrate Diversity

Chapter Objectives

Opening Essay

Describe the predatory and defensive strategies of the blue-ringed octopus.

Animal Evolution and Diversity

18.1 Describe the defining characteristics of animals.

18.1 Describe the general animal life cycle and the basic animal body plan.

18.2 Describe the Cambrian "explosion" of animal diversity and two hypotheses that have been advanced to explain its occurrence.

18.3 Explain how a hydrostatic skeleton helps an animal keep its shape and move.

18.4 Characterize the nine animal phyla discussed in this chapter in terms of the following traits: (a) presence or absence of true tissues, (b) no symmetry, radial symmetry, or bilateral symmetry, (c) no coelom, a pseudocoelom, or a true coelom, and (d) protostomes or deuterostomes.

Invertebrate Diversity

18.5–18.14 Describe the characteristics of and distinguish between each of the following phyla: Porifera, Cnidaria, Platyhelminthes, Nematoda, Mollusca, Annelida, Arthropoda, Echinodermata, and Chordata. Note several examples of each phylum.

18.10 Define segmentation, explain its functions, and note the animal phyla where it occurs.

18.11–18.12 Compare the characteristics of the four major arthropod lineages. Give examples of each.

18.12 Describe the common characteristics of insects. Describe the process and significance of complete metamorphosis.

Animal Phylogeny and Diversity Revisited

18.15 Compare the phylogenetic relationships in Figures 18.4 and 18.15, noting similarities and differences.

18.16 Explain what we have learned about the evolution of life from the study of "evo-devo."

Lecture Outline

I. Introduction

    A. Most octopuses rely on nonaggressive defense mechanisms such as camouflage.

    B. The blue-ringed octopus is an exception, with

        1. a toxin 10,000 times more lethal than cyanide and

        2. sapphire-blue circles that proclaim its identity.

II. Animal Evolution and Diversity

    A. 18.1 What is an animal?

        1. Animals are

          a. eukaryotic,

          b. multicellular heterotrophs, and

          c. have cells that lack cell walls.

        2. Animals also use **ingestion**, the eating of food.

        3. Fungi absorb nutrients after digesting food outside their body.

        4. Most adult animals are diploid and reproduce sexually.

          a. The eggs and sperm

            i. are produced by meiosis,

            ii. are the only haploid cells, and

            iii. fuse during fertilization to form a zygote.

          b. The zygote divides by mitosis to form a hollow ball of cells called a **blastula**.

          c. One side of the blastula folds in and cells become rearranged to form a **gastrula** that establishes three embryonic layers.

            i. **Endoderm** forms a lining of the future digestive tract.

            ii. **Ectoderm** forms an outer layer that will give rise to the skin and nervous system.

            iii. **Mesoderm** forms a middle layer that will give rise to muscles and most internal organs.

        5. After the gastrula stage, many animals develop directly into adults.

        6. Other animals, such as the sea star, develop into one or more larval stages.

          a. A **larva** is an immature individual that looks different from the adult animal.

          b. A larva undergoes a major change in body form, called **metamorphosis**, and becomes a reproductively mature adult.

        7. Clusters of master control homeotic genes control transformation of the zygote into an adult animal.

    B. 18.2 Animal diversification began more than half a billion years ago

        1. The oldest generally accepted animal fossils that have been found are 575–550 million years old.

        2. Animal diversification appears to have accelerated rapidly from 535–525 million years ago, during the Cambrian period, known as the Cambrian explosion.

        3. The most celebrated source of Cambrian fossils is the Burgess Shale containing a cornucopia of perfectly preserved animal fossils.

        4. The Cambrian explosion may have been caused by

          a. increasingly complex predator-prey relationships or

          b. an increase in atmospheric oxygen.

        5. Much of the diversity in body form among the animal phyla is associated with variations in where and when homeotic genes are expressed within developing embryos.

6. Of the 35 or so animal phyla, all but one are invertebrates, named because they lack vertebra.

C. 18.3 Animals can be characterized by basic features of their "body plan"

1. Animal body plans vary in
   a. symmetry,
   b. presence of true tissues,
   c. number of embryonic layers,
   d. presence of a body cavity and
   e. details of their embryonic development.

2. Symmetry
   a. Animals that have **radial symmetry** have a top and bottom but lack back and front or right and left sides. An imaginary slice through the central axis divides them into mirror images.
   b. Animals with **bilateral symmetry** have mirror-image right and left sides and a
      i. distinct head, or **anterior** end,
      ii. tail, or **posterior** end,
      iii. back, or **dorsal**, surface, and
      iv. bottom, or **ventral**, surface.

3. Tissues
   a. Tissues are collections of specialized cells that perform special functions.
   b. Sponges are the only animals that lack true tissues.

4. Embryonic layers
   a. Some animals have only ectoderm and endoderm.
   b. Most animals have
      i. ectoderm,
      ii. mesoderm, and
      iii. endoderm.

5. Animals with three embryonic layers may have a **body cavity**, a fluid-filled space between the digestive tract and outer body wall that
   a. cushions internal organs,
   b. enables them to grow and move independently of the body wall.
   c. In soft-bodied animals, fluid in the body cavity forms a **hydrostatic skeleton**.
   d. A **true coelom** is completely lined by tissues derived from mesoderm.
   e. A **pseudocoelom** is a body cavity that is not completely lined by tissues derived from mesoderm.

6. Animals with three tissue layers can be separated into two groups based on details of their embryonic development. For example, the opening formed during gastrulation develops into the
   a. mouth in **protostomes** and
   b. anus in **deuterostomes**.

D. 18.4 The body plans of animals can be used to build phylogenetic trees

1. Because animals diversified so rapidly on the scale of geologic time, it is difficult to sort out the evolutionary relationships among phyla using the fossil record.

2. One diagram of evolutionary relationships uses morphology to construct a phylogenetic tree. This tree distinguishes between
   a. sponges and **eumetazoans** (animals with true tissues),
   b. animals with radial or bilateral symmetry (**bilaterians**), and
   c. protostomes and deuterostomes.

3. All phylogenetic trees are hypotheses for the key events in the evolutionary history of animals.

4. Researchers are increasingly adding molecular comparisons to the construction of these trees.

III. Invertebrate Diversity

A. 18.5 Sponges have a relatively simple, porous body
   1. **Sponges** (phylum Porifera) are simple, sedentary animals without true tissues.
   2. Water enters through pores in the body wall into a central cavity, and then flows out through a larger opening.
   3. The body of a sponge consists of two layers of cells separated by a gelatinous region.
      a. The inner layer of flagellated **choanocytes** filters food and engulfs it by phagocytosis.
      b. **Amoebocytes** wander through the middle body region and produce skeletal fibers composed of
         i. flexible protein and
         ii. mineralized particles called spicules.
   4. Sponges are **suspension feeders**, filtering food particles from water passed through food-trapping equipment.
      a. To grow by 100 g, a sponge must filter roughly 1,000 kg of water.
      b. Choanocytes trap food particles in mucus on the membranous collars that surround their flagella.
   5. Adult sponges are **sessile** and cannot escape from predators. They deter pathogens, parasites, and predators by producing
      a. defensive toxins and
      b. antibiotics.

B. 18.6 Cnidarians are radial animals with tentacles and stinging cells
   1. **Cnidarians** (phylum Cnidaria)
      a. are characterized by radial symmetry and
      b. have only two tissue layers:
         i. an outer epidermis,
         ii. an inner cell layer lining the digestive cavity, and
         iii. a jelly-filled middle region may have scattered amoeboid cells.
   2. Cnidarians exhibit two kinds of radially symmetrical body forms.
      a. The most sedentary **polyp** body is cylindrical with tentacles projecting from one end.
      b. The more mobile **medusa** form is exemplified by a marine jelly.
   3. Cnidarians are carnivores that use their tentacles to capture prey and to push prey into their mouths.
      a. The mouth leads to the **gastrovascular cavity**, which functions in digestion and circulation and as a hydrostatic skeleton.
      b. **Cnidocytes** are unique stinging cells that capture prey and function in defense.

C. 18.7 Flatworms are the simplest bilateral animals
   1. The vast majority of animal species belong to the clade Bilateria, consisting of animals with bilateral symmetry.
   2. **Flatworms** (phylum Platyhelminthes) are the simplest bilaterians.
   3. Flatworms live in marine, freshwater, and damp terrestrial habitats.
   4. Some are parasitic and others are free-living.

5. There are three major groups of flatworms.

    a. Free-living flatworms (planarians) have

       i. heads with light-sensitive eyespots,

       ii. flaps to detect chemicals,

       iii. dense clusters of nerve cells that form a simple brain and a pair of nerve cords that runs the length of the body, and

       iv. a branched gastrovascular cavity with a single opening.

    b. Flukes are parasitic flatworms with

       i. complex life cycles and

       ii. suckers to attach to their hosts.

    c. Tapeworms

       i. are parasitic,

       ii. inhabit the digestive tracts of vertebrates,

       iii. consist of a ribbonlike body with repeated units,

       iv. have an anterior *scolex* armed with hooks and suckers that grasp the host,

       v. have no mouth, and simply absorb nutrients across their body surface.

       vi. The units at the posterior end of tapeworms are full of ripe eggs that pass out of the host's body.

D. 18.8 Nematodes have a pseudocoelom and a complete digestive tract

    1. Nematodes or roundworms (phylum Nematoda) are abundant and diverse, with an estimated 500,000 species. Nematodes have

    a. bilateral symmetry,

    b. three tissue layers,

    c. a nonliving cuticle covering the body that prevents them from drying out,

    d. a pseudocoelom body cavity that functions to distribute nutrients and as a hydroskeleton, and

    e. a **complete digestive tract** with a mouth and anus.

    2. Although about 25,000 species of nematodes have been named, estimates of the total number of species range as high as 500,000.

    3. Humans host at least 50 species of parasitic nematodes.

E. 18.9 Diverse molluscs are variations on a common body plan

    1. Molluscs (phylum Mollusca) have

    a. a muscular **foot** that functions in locomotion,

    b. a **visceral mass** containing most of the internal organs,

    c. a **mantle**, which may secrete a shell that encloses the visceral mass, and

    d. a true coelom and a circulatory system that pumps blood throughout the body.

    e. Many molluscs feed with a rasping **radula**, used to scrape up food.

    f. The life cycle of many marine molluscs includes a ciliated larva called a trochophore.

    2. Gastropods are the largest group of molluscs and include the snails and slugs. Gastropods are

    a. found in fresh water, salt water, and terrestrial environments,

    b. the only molluscs that live on land, using the mantle cavity as a lung, and

    c. often protected by a single, spiral shell.

    d. Slugs have lost their mantle and shell and have long colorful projections that function as gills.

3. **Bivalves**
   a. include clams, oysters, mussels, and scallops and
   b. have shells divided into two halves that are hinged together.
   c. Most bivalves are sedentary suspension feeders, attached to the substrate by strong threads.
4. **Cephalopods**
   a. include squids, octopuses, and nautilus,
   b. are fast, agile predators,
   c. have large brains and sophisticated sense organs, including complex image-focusing eyes, and
   d. a shell that is large in a nautilus, small and internal in a squid, or missing in an octopus.
   e. Squid are fast, streamlined predators that use a muscular siphon for jet propulsion.
   f. Octopuses live on the seafloor, where they creep about as active predators.
F. 18.10 Annelids are segmented worms
   1. **Annelids** (phylum Annelida) have
      a. **segmentation**, the subdivision of the body along its length into a series of repeated parts,
      b. a true coelom that functions as a hydrostatic skeleton,
      c. a nervous system that includes a simple brain and ventral nerve cord, and
      d. a **closed circulatory system** in which blood remains enclosed in vessels throughout the body.
      e. Many invertebrates, such as molluscs and arthropods, have an **open circulatory system** in which blood is pumped through vessels into open body cavities.
   2. Annelids are found in damp soil, the sea, and most freshwater habitats.
   3. The three groups of annelids are
      a. earthworms and their relatives,
      b. polychaetes, and
      c. leeches.
   4. Earthworms ingest soil and extract nutrients, aerating soil and improving its texture.
   5. **Polychaetes** are the largest group of annelids.
      a. Each polychaete segment has a pair of fleshy appendages with stiff bristles or chaetae.
      b. Polychaetes search for prey on the seafloor or live in tubes and filter food particles.
   6. Most **leeches** are free-living carnivores, but some suck blood.
      a. Blood-sucking leeches use razor-like jaws, secrete an anesthetic and an anticoagulant, and suck up to 10 times their own weight in blood.
G. 18.11 Arthropods are segmented animals with jointed appendages and an exoskeleton
   1. There are over a million species of **arthropods** (phylum Arthropoda), including crayfish, lobsters, crabs, barnacles, spiders, ticks, and insects.
   2. The diversity and success of arthropods are due to their
      a. segmentation,
      b. a hard exoskeleton, and
      c. jointed appendages, for which the phylum is named.
   3. Arthropods have
      a. an open circulatory system and
      b. an **exoskeleton**, an external skeleton that protects the animal but must be shed in the process of **molting** to permit growth.

    c. The body of most arthropods includes a head, thorax, and abdomen, although these segments may be fused.

  4. Living arthropods represent four major lineages.

    a. Chelicerates include **horseshoe crabs** and **arachnids**, such as spiders, scorpions, mites, and ticks.

      i. Most are terrestrial.

      ii. Scorpions are nocturnal hunters.

      iii. Spiders are a diverse group that typically hunt insects or trap them in webs of silk that they spin from specialized glands on their abdomen.

    b. Millipedes and centipedes are identified by the number of jointed legs per body segment.

      i. Millipedes are herbivores that have two pairs of short legs per body segment.

      ii. Centipedes are carnivores that have one pair of legs per body segment.

    c. Crustaceans are nearly all aquatic. They include crabs, shrimp, and barnacles, which feed with jointed appendages.

    d. Insects are the fourth lineage of arthropods, addressed next.

H. 18.12 EVOLUTION CONNECTION: Insects are the most successful group of animals

  1. 70% of all identified animal species are **insects**.

    a. There may be as many as 30 million insect species.

  2. The body of an insect typically includes

    a. a head,

    b. thorax,

    c. abdomen,

    d. three sets of legs, and

    e. wings (with few exceptions).

  3. The extraordinary success of insects is due to

    a. body segmentation,

    b. an exoskeleton,

    c. jointed appendages,

    d. flight,

    e. a waterproof cuticle, and

    f. a complex life cycle with short generations and large numbers of offspring.

  4. Insect life cycles often include **metamorphosis**, during which the animal takes on different body forms as it develops from larva to adult.

    a. More than 80% of insect species undergo **complete metamorphosis** in which a free-living larva transforms from a pupa into an adult.

    b. Other insect species undergo **incomplete metamorphosis** in which the transition from larva to adult is achieved through multiple molts, but without forming a pupa.

  5. Modular body plan

    a. The adult body parts of insects are formed by the fusion of embryonic segments identical to each other.

    b. The insect body plan is essentially modular in that each embryonic segment develops independently.

    c. Homeotic genes act to modify the structure of insect segments and their appendages.

  6. Insect mouthparts are adapted for various types of feeding, such as

    a. chewing (grasshoppers),

    b. biting and tearing prey (mantids),

  c. lapping up fluids (houseflies), and

  d. piercing and sucking fluids of plants (aphids) and animals (mosquitoes).

 7. Insects have three pairs of legs, which are adapted for

  a. walking,

  b. jumping,

  c. grasping prey,

  d. digging in soil, or

  e. paddling on water.

 8. Wings

  a. Most adult insects have one or two pairs of wings, allowing dispersal and escape from predators.

  b. Because wings are extensions of the cuticle, insects have acquired flight without sacrificing any legs.

 9. Protective color patterns

  a. Many insects have protective color patterns and disguises, including modifications to antennae, wings, and bodies.

I. 18.13 Echinoderms have spiny skin, an endoskeleton, and a water vascular system for movement

 1. Echinoderms (phylum Echinodermata) are

  a. a diverse group including sea stars, sand dollars, and sea urchins,

  b. slow-moving or sessile,

  c. all marine,

  d. radially symmetrical, and

  e. deuterostomes (along with the chordates).

 2. Echinoderms have

  a. an **endoskeleton** of hard calcareous plates under a thin skin,

  b. a **water vascular system** based on a network of water-filled canals that branch into extensions called tube feet, and

  c. the ability to regenerate lost arms.

J. 18.14 Our own phylum, Chordata, is distinguished by four features

 1. Chordates (phylum Chordata) are defined by

  a. a **dorsal**, **hollow nerve cord**,

  b. a flexible, supportive **notochord**,

  c. pharyngeal slits, and

  d. a muscular **post-anal tail**.

 2. The simplest chordates are tunicates and lancelets, which

  a. do not have a backbone and

  b. use their pharyngeal slits for suspension feeding.

  c. Adult **tunicates** are stationary and attached, while the tunicate larva is a tadpole-like organism.

  d. Lancelets are small, bladelike chordates that live in marine sands.

IV. Animal Phylogeny and Diversity Revisited

 A. 18.15 An animal phylogenetic tree is a work in progress

  1. Biologists used evidence from the fossil record, morphology, and embryology to make hypotheses about the evolutionary history of animal groups.

  2. Recently, scientists have accumulated molecular data such as DNA sequences that shed new light on these phylogenetic relationships.

3. Figure 18.15 presents a slightly revised tree based on this new molecular data.

B. 18.16 EVOLUTION CONNECTION: The genes that build animal bodies are ancient

    1. Genes responsible for building animal bodies are shared by virtually every member of the animal kingdom.

    2. These ancient genes are the master control genes called homeotic genes.

    3. Changes in the regulation of homeotic gene expression have been significant factors in the evolution of animal diversity.

Chapter Guide to Teaching Resources

Animal Evolution and Diversity (18.1–18.4)

Student Misconceptions and Concerns

- When considering animals in general, students are typically biased towards vertebrate examples. As a thought exercise, start your first lecture on animal diversity by asking students to write down the name of the very first type of animal that comes to their minds, without giving it any thought. Depending upon your class size, either tabulate their responses quickly or have students raise their hands to indicate the type of animal they chose. In general, fewer than 5% (often fewer than 1%) of my students have thought of an invertebrate. This exercise makes the point that what we tend to think of, when we think of animals, is vertebrates. Many of us have had a dog, cat, or other vertebrate for a pet. Yet, more than 95% of all known species of animals are invertebrates. Students must expand their understanding of what it means to be an animal. The content in Chapter 18 should facilitate that understanding. (18.1–18.4)

- Students often struggle to conceptualize the basic needs of invertebrates and may find it challenging to think of the similarities between, for example, an earthworm and a dog, or a tick and a cat. The common features of animals addressed at the start of Chapter 18 can be expanded to include the needs for oxygen, nourishing food, a tolerable environment, and a suitable habitat to reproduce, which apply to animals representing all of the major phyla. Illustrating these common demands can help students build the intellectual foundations that can be so difficult to fully establish. (18.1–18.4)

Teaching Tips

- Depending upon what chapters you have addressed in your course up to this point, you might begin your lectures on animals by asking your class to compare the features of plants, fungi, and animals. You may want to present a table listing the following characteristics, and ask the class to identify the condition for each kingdom: eukaryotic or prokaryotic cells, single or multicellular organisms, presence of cell walls, and use of photosynthesis. (18.1)

- You might wish to share the now somewhat-famous quote of Lewis Wolpert, who in 1986 said, "It is not birth, marriage, or death, but gastrulation, which is truly the most important time in your life." The development and arrangement of the basic embryonic layers (ectoderm / skin and nervous systems, mesoderm / muscle and bone, and endoderm / digestive tract) establishes the basic body plan. (18.1–18.4)

- Your students might enjoy discussing whether or not they are larvae and if they can be said to go through metamorphosis. (The answer to both questions is "no".) (18.1–18.4)

- The website of the University of California at Berkeley's Museum of Paleontology is an excellent resource for evolution and the history of life, including the portion that specifically addresses the Cambrian period: www.ucmp.berkeley.edu/cambrian/camb.html. (18.2)

- Before addressing the subject of animal symmetry, you might wish to have your students speculate about the adaptive advantages of radial versus bilateral symmetry found in animals. This sort of comparison raises an opportunity to make some larger points about biology. There is no "one" best animal. Each form, each adaptation, and each body plan has advantages and disadvantages. The value of adaptations is relative to the organism's environment and most adaptations represent a compromise. (18.3–18.4)

Invertebrate Diversity (18.5–18.14)

Student Misconceptions and Concerns

- Students typically expect that an animal will have a head. The subject of a head might have already been introduced when discussing body plans. As you proceed through the animal phyla, have students consider how sponges and cnidarians meet their basic needs without the benefit of a well-defined head. (18.5–18.6)

- As students survey the major animal phyla, they might perceive the diversity of animals as spread somewhat evenly across the nine major phyla of invertebrates. Yet, two-thirds of all known species of life (and at least 80% all described animal species) are arthropods. Although sources disagree on the number of living species that have been described, there is widespread agreement that the number of undescribed species is many times more than the number of described species. By examining the number of described species, some amazing proportions emerge. You might consider this exercise to make the point. Determine how many students represent 1% of the class. Then have the entire class stand. Tell the students that collectively, they represent all of the animal species known to exist today. Have 5% of the class sit, representing the proportion of known animal species that are vertebrates. Next, have 15% of the class sit, representing all of the remaining types of animals *except* arthropods. At this point, everyone standing (80% of the class) represents the proportion of known animal species that are arthropods (a conservative fraction). Finally, have 50% of the entire class sit, leaving 30% standing. Have the class guess what group of animals is represented now (clearly some subgroup of arthropods). This final 30% represents the known number of species of beetles! (The numbers used are rounded. Even higher percentages for beetles and invertebrates may be more accurate. The point of this exercise is the relative proportions rather than precise percentages.) (18.5–18.14)

Teaching Tips

- Imagine a country cabin in the winter with a roaring fire in a fireplace. The windows are partially opened to permit air to rush into the house to feed the fire. This flow of air through the windows, through the home, to the fireplace, and then out the chimney is analogous to the flow of water through a sponge. Side note: Many sponges, especially commercial bath sponges, have outer body walls that are highly folded. Simpler vase sponges, with straighter walls, are good examples to show students when discussing this basic water flow pattern. (18.5)

- Students may find it challenging to understand why sponges are animals. It might be helpful to return to the distinctions between animals, plants, and fungi when introducing sponges. (18.5)

- Just about any glass bottle with a narrow neck makes a good model of the cnidarian body plan. The narrowed neck of the body represents the constricted region of a cnidarian that regulates what enters and leaves the gastrovascular cavity. Additional note: The name "gastrovascular" represents the dual function of the cavity. It must serve as the site of digestion and the method of delivery of the nutrients. The cavity extends, like a primitive circulatory system, throughout the body, and is thus vascular in nature. (18.6)

- If students have been stung by a jellyfish, it was a toxin produced by the cnidocytes that caused a reaction. (Nematocysts are the firing part of a cnidocyte cell. The toxin is delivered by the firing of the nematocysts. A new cnidocyte must take the place of one that has fired its nematocyst, since cnidocytes cannot "reload.") (18.6)

- The gastrovascular cavity of cnidarians and flatworms is the functional equivalent of two systems in our bodies. Ask students to explain how nutrients consumed at a meal nourish the cells in our toes. Nutrients absorbed by our gut are transported throughout our body by the circulatory system. Extensions of the gastrovascular cavity permit nutrient distribution in these cnidarians and flatworms. (18.6–18.7)

- A planarian, indicated in Figure 18.7A, ingests food in the middle of its body. Challenge students to think of other animals that have a mouth located far from the head. The discussion that will follow this challenge is likely to touch on the defining features of a head, invoking a critical analysis of animal body plans and providing an important exercise for this chapter. (18.7)

- The undercooking of meat contributes to the spread of parasitic diseases. If you addressed the denaturation of proteins in Chapter 3, here is a chance to reinforce the points about the effects of heat. Proteins denature and discolor when heated (pink meat turns brown). This same process denatures proteins in parasites and kills them (although some parasites can survive relatively high temperatures). If any portion of a steak is still pink, the meat has not been cooked enough to denature the meat or parasitic proteins. Trichinosis is acquired by eating pork that has not been cooked enough to denature all the proteins (and kill the parasites). The details of just about any parasitic infection of humans will get the attention of your students . . . and likely cause them to start scratching! (18.8)

- When we eat clams, we usually eat strips of the muscular foot. If the clams are mushy and/or contain sand, the serving may also include portions of the intestines. (18.9)

- A simple demonstration of the bivalve body plan can be obtained by purchasing smoked oysters in a grocery store. Each smoked oyster (ready to be consumed) is the soft body removed from the paired shells. For an enjoyable demonstration, discuss the anatomy of a specimen and then enjoy it for lunch. (18.9)

- When discussing cephalopods, the subject of animal intelligence may be noted. Defining and identifying animal intelligence is not a simple task. Consider discussing the correlation of intelligence and predation. Why might these two traits be linked? What other characteristics, such as sophistication of communication, correlate with intelligence? (18.10)

- Annelids (and nematodes, Module 18.8) have the advantage of a digestive tract with openings at both ends. This permits the efficiency of a digestive tract specialized for a one-way flow of ingested materials and enjoying the same advantages as an assembly line, but in reverse, serving in fact as a sort of "disassembly" line. These worms (and all animals with a mouth separate from the anus) "disassemble" food as it moves through the digestive tract. (18.8, 18.10)

- As noted in Module 18.10, leeches remain an important tool in modern medicine. Consider presenting some examples of the latest use of leeches in medicine to the class, or asking your students to research and discuss them. Such short asides will often liven up your class. (18.10)

- Conceptually, and very generally speaking, the exoskeleton of an arthropod is like the hard outside of an M&M. The exoskeleton prevents physical damage to the internal organs and protects them against desiccation. The outside of an M&M prevents damage to the chocolate and keeps the chocolate from melting or drying out. (18.11–18.12)

- Many students assume that all insects possess six legs and two pairs of wings. As common examples of variation on this theme, challenge students to consider beetles (in which the outer wings, called elytra, are hardened) and flies (in which one pair of wings is reduced to a pair of structures called halteres). (18.12)

- Beetles have a long history in human culture, where they have been used in textiles, ornamentation, and jewelry. A quick image search of the Internet will reveal many examples. In particular, note the significance for scarab beetles in ancient Egypt. (18.12)

- The life history of dung beetles is a fun and amusing insect story for lecture, revealing the important role of these animals in recycling animal waste. Details of their interesting life cycle can be obtained from many resources, including those resulting from an Internet search for "dung beetle life history." (18.12)

- The bodies of adult echinoderms reveal degrees of radial symmetry, which may cause students to wonder why echinoderms are not grouped with cnidarians. As discussed in Module 18.13, the bilateral symmetry of embryonic echinoderms demonstrates the acquisition of radial symmetry from a bilaterally symmetrical ancestor. Thus, echinoderms are more closely associated with other bilaterally symmetrical organisms. (18.13)

- Radial symmetry, such as that seen in many adult echinoderms, permits an organism to respond well in any direction. You cannot sneak up "behind their back." This ability is especially adaptive in sedentary or relatively sedentary organisms, such as sea urchins, sea stars, and cnidarians. Ask your students if these same advantages also occur in radially symmetrical plants. (18.13)

- If you can obtain a model or image of a one-month-old human embryo, you can demonstrate our four main chordate characteristics. A figure of a human embryo, comparing human and dog embryos of similar stages, was prepared by Charles Darwin and included in the first chapter of his book *The Descent of Man*. This image can be viewed at http://darwin-online.org.uk/converted/published/1871_Descent_F937/1871_Descent_F937.1_fig02.jpg. (18.14)

Animal Phylogeny and Diversity Revisited (18.15–18.16)

Student Misconceptions and Concerns

- Students may be surprised to learn that scientists do not agree on the interrelationships of animal phyla, as they are often unaware that areas of debate still exist in science in general. Whenever possible, note areas of uncertainty in science to demonstrate the ongoing possibilities for research and the need for future scientists to enter the profession. Figure 18.15 also reveals the advantages of fresh perspectives! (18.15–18.16)

Teaching Tips

- Module 18.15 compares the phylogenetic relationships depicted in Figures 18.4 and 18.15, based upon different uses of evidence. Although we all expect such debate as a natural part of science, this discussion helps students understand the ongoing and tentative nature of science. Scientific knowledge advances through the refining, rethinking, and retesting of what we know. (18.15)

- Successful scientific concepts are reinforced by multiple, independent lines of evidence. Just as in a criminal trial, a defendant is more likely to lose as the lines of incriminating evidence accumulate. Molecular data has now joined morphology, biogeography, the fossil record, and embryology to provide an additional independent test. This independent confirmation of previous hypotheses, and the revision of some as noted in Module 18.15, increases our confidence in the results. (18.15)

- The previous edition of *Concepts* included a discussion with Dr. Sean Carroll in Module 18.16. As Dr. Carroll noted, "old genes learn new tricks." Elsewhere, in more obvious examples, we see the wing of a penguin remodeled as a fin, ribs in a turtle remodeled into a shell, and hair in a whale remodeled into baleen for feeding. As Francois Jacob noted, evolution works more like a tinkerer than an engineer. (18.16)

Key Terms

amoebocytes	echinoderm	millipede
annelid	ectoderm	mollusc
anterior	endoderm	molting
arachnid	endoskeleton	nematode
arthropod	eumetazoan	notochord
bilateral symmetry	exoskeleton	open circulatory system
bilaterian	flatworm	pharyngeal slit
bivalve	flukes	polychaete
blastula	foot	polyp
body cavity	free-living flatworm	post-anal tail
centipede	gastropod	posterior
cephalopod	gastrovascular cavity	protostome
chelicerate	gastrula	pseudocoelom
choanocytes	horseshoe crab	radial symmetry
circulatory system	hydrostatic skeleton	radula
closed circulatory system	incomplete metamorphosis	segmentation
cnidarian	ingestion	sessile
cnidocyte	invertebrate	sponge
complete digestive tract	lancelet	suspension feeder
complete metamorphosis	larva (plural, larvae)	tapeworm
crustacean	leeches	true coelom
cuticle	mantle	tunicate
deuterostome	medusa	ventral
dorsal	mesoderm	visceral mass
dorsal, hollow nerve cord	metamorphosis	water vascular system

Word Roots

arachn- = spider (*arachnid*: a member of the arthropod group that includes scorpions, spiders, ticks, and mites)

arthro- = jointed; **-pod** = foot (*arthropod*: segmented coelomates with exoskeletons and jointed appendages)

bi- = two (*bivalve*: a member of the group of molluscs with two paired shells, including clams, mussels, scallops, and oysters); **later-** = side (*bilateral symmetry*: an arrangement of body parts such that an organism has mirror-image right and left sides; *bilaterian*: the branch of eumetazoans possessing bilateral symmetry)

blast- = bud, sprout (*blastula*: a hollow ball of cells that forms the early embryo in animal development)

cephal- = head; **-pod** = foot (*cephalopod*: a member of a group of molluscs, including squids and octopuses, whose body appears to be its head)

cheli- = a claw (*chelicerate*: a group of arthropods, including horseshoe crabs, scorpions, ticks, and spiders, with clawlike feeding appendages)

choano- = a funnel; **-cyte** = cell (*choanocyte*: a flagellated feeding cell with a collar-like ring for trapping food particles found in sponges)

cnido- = a nettle (*cnidarian*: a phylum of invertebrates named for stinging cells called cnidocytes found in their bodies); **-cyte** = cell (*cnidocytes*: unique cells that function in defense and prey capture in cnidarians)

cuti- = the skin (*cuticle*: the exoskeleton of an arthropod)

deutero- = second (*deuterostome*: one of two lines of coelomates characterized by radial, indeterminate cleavage, formation of the coelom from outpockets of mesoderm, and development of the anus from the blastopore)

echino- = spiny; **-derm** = skin (*echinoderm*: sessile or slow-moving animals with a thin skin that covers an exoskeleton; the group includes sea stars, sea urchins, brittle stars, crinoids, sea cucumbers, and sea daisies)

ecto- = outside; **-derm** = skin (*ectoderm*: the outermost of the three primary germ layers in animal embryos)

endo- = within (*endoderm*: the innermost of the three primary germ layers in animal embryos; *endoskeleton*: a hard skeleton located within the soft tissues of an animal)

eu- = true (*eumetazoan*: a group of organisms that have true tissues)

exo- = outside (*exoskeleton*: a hard external skeleton that protects an animal and provides points of attachment for muscles)

gastro- = stomach (*gastrula*: the developmental stage in animals that follows the blastula stage); **-vascula** = a little vessel (*gastrovascular cavity*: the central digestive compartment, usually with a single opening that functions as both mouth and anus)

hydro- = water; **-static** = lack of movement (*hydrostatic skeleton*: a skeletal system composed of fluid held under pressure in a closed body compartment)

in- = into; **-gest** = carried (*ingestion*: the act of eating; the first main stage of food processing)

in- = without (*invertebrate*: an animal that lacks a backbone)

koilos- = a hollow (*coelom*: a true animal body cavity that is completely lined by mesoderm)

meso- = middle; **-derm** = skin (*mesoderm*: the middle primary germ layer of an early embryo)

meta- = boundary, turning point; **-morph** = form (*metamorphosis*: the resurgence of development in an animal larva that transforms it into a sexually mature adult)

nemato- = a thread (*nematode*: a phylum of invertebrates including roundworms)

post- = after (*post-anal tail*: a structure in vertebrates found behind the anus; *posterior*: toward the rear of an organism)

proto- = first; **-stoma** = mouth (*protostomes*: a member of one of two distinct evolutionary lines of coelomates characterized by spiral, determinate cleavage, formation of the coelom as splits in solid masses of mesoderm, and development of the mouth from the blastopore)

pseudo- = false (*pseudocoelom*: a body cavity that is not completely lined by mesoderm)

radia- = a spoke, ray (*radial symmetry*: characterizing a body shaped like a pie or barrel, lacking a left and right side, but having a top and bottom)

tunic- = a covering (*tunicates*: one of a group of invertebrate chordates)

CHAPTER 19

The Evolution of Vertebrate Diversity

Chapter Objectives

Opening Essay

Describe the difficulties of classifying the duck-billed platypus.

Vertebrate Evolution and Diversity

19.1 Describe the key derived traits of the chordates and the chordate subgroups.

19.2–19.8 Describe the characteristics of and distinguish between each of the following vertebrate groups: hagfishes, lampreys, chondrichthyans, ray-finned fishes, lobe-finned fishes, amphibians, reptiles, birds, and mammals.

19.4 Describe the transitional species that occupy the range between fishes and amphibians in evolutionary history.

19.8 Distinguish between monotremes, marsupials, and placental mammals. Provide examples of each.

Primate Diversity

19.9 Compare the three main groups of living primates. List their characteristics and describe their evolutionary relationships.

19.10 Distinguish between monkeys and apes. Compare the different groups of apes to each other and to humans.

Hominin Evolution

19.11 Describe the evidence that suggests that hominins did not evolve in a straight line leading directly to our species.

19.12 Describe the evidence that suggests when upright posture and large brains first evolved in humans.

19.13 Describe the evolution of larger brain size in hominins.

19.14 Describe the relationships between Neanderthals and modern humans. Describe the evidence that suggests that all modern humans share a common ancestor that lived 160,000–200,000 years ago.

19.15 Describe the unusual characteristics of the newly discovered *Homo floresiensis*.

19.16 Describe the adaptive advantages of darker skin in humans living near the equator but lighter skin in humans living in northern latitudes.

19.17 Explain why the total number of animal species alive today remains an estimate.

Lecture Outline

I. Introduction

A. The duck-billed platypus is a strange animal and hard to classify. It has

   1. a furry body,

   2. bill and webbed feet that look like a duck, and

   3. mammary glands that produce milk for its young.

   4. In addition, it lays eggs!

II. Vertebrate Evolution and Diversity

A. 19.1 Derived characters define the major clades of chordates

   1. Biologists have developed hypotheses for the evolution of chordate groups using

     a. anatomical,

     b. molecular, and

     c. fossil evidence.

   2. Figure 19.1

     a. illustrates a current view of the major clades of chordates and

     b. lists some of the derived characters that define the clades.

B. 19.2 Hagfishes and lampreys lack hinged jaws

   1. Hagfishes and lampreys

     a. are craniates,

     b. have a notochord, but

     c. lack hinged jaws and paired fins.

   2. Lampreys but not hagfishes have rudimentary vertebral structures. Thus,

     a. lampreys are vertebrates but

     b. hagfishes are not vertebrates.

   3. Hagfishes are deep-sea scavengers that produce slime as an antipredator defense.

   4. Lamprey adults are parasites that penetrate the sides of fishes with their rasping tongues.

   5. Larval lampreys

     a. resemble lancelets and

     b. are suspension feeders that live in freshwater streams, where they feed, buried in sediment.

C. 19.3 Jawed vertebrates with gills and paired fins include sharks, ray-finned fishes, and lobe-finned fishes

   1. Jawed vertebrates

     a. appeared in the fossil record about 470 million years ago and

     b. quickly diversified using their paired fins and tail to chase a wide variety of prey.

   2. Jaws may have evolved by modifications of skeletal supports of the anterior pharyngeal (gill) slits.

   3. The remaining gill slits remained as sites of gas exchange.

   4. Three lineages of jawed fishes with gills and paired fins that are commonly called fishes:

     a. chrondrichthyans—sharks and rays,

     b. ray-finned fishes—tuna, trout, and goldfish, and

     c. lobe-finned fishes—coelacanths and lungfishes.

5. **Chondrichthyans** have
   a. a flexible skeleton made of cartilage,
   b. electrosensors on their heads, and
   c. a **lateral line system** that helps them locate prey.
   d. Most sharks are fast-swimming predators, with sharp vision and a keen sense of smell.
   e. Most rays are adapted for life on the bottom, with dorsoventrally flattened bodies and eyes on the top of their heads.
6. Ray-finned fishes have
   a. an internal skeleton reinforced with a hard matrix of calcium phosphate,
   b. flattened scales covered with mucus,
   c. an **operculum** that covers a chamber of gills, and
   d. a buoyant **swim bladder** (derived from an ancestral lung).
7. With more than 27,000 species, ray-finned fishes are the most diverse group of vertebrates.
8. Lobe-fins have muscular pelvic and pectoral fins that are supported by rod-shaped bones.
9. Today, three lineages of lobe-fins survive:
   a. coelacanths, living deep in the oceans, were once thought to be extinct,
   b. lungfishes, which can gulp air into lungs, inhabit stagnant waters in the Southern Hemisphere, and
   c. tetrapods, adapted to life on land, include terrestrial vertebrates.
D. 19.4 EVOLUTION CONNECTION: New fossil discoveries are filling in the gaps of tetrapod evolution
   1. During the late Devonian, a line of lobe-finned fishes gave rise to **tetrapods**, jawed vertebrates with limbs and feet that can support weight on land.
   2. Adapting to life on land was a key event in vertebrate history.
   3. All subsequent groups are descendants of these early land-dwellers.
   4. Like plants, vertebrates faced obstacles on land in regard to
      a. gas exchange,
      b. water conservation,
      c. structural support,
      d. a means of locomotion,
      e. adapting sensory organs that worked well in water but not on land, and
      f. reproduction.
E. 19.5 Amphibians are tetrapods—vertebrates with two pairs of limbs
   1. **Amphibians**
      a. include salamanders, frogs, and caecilians,
      b. use their moist skins to supplement their lungs for gas exchange,
      c. often have poison glands in their skins,
      d. usually return to standing water to reproduce,
      e. undergo metamorphosis from a larval stage to the adult form, and
      f. were the first tetrapods able to move on land.
F. 19.6 Reptiles are amniotes—tetrapods with a terrestrially adapted egg
   1. Reptiles (including birds) and mammals are **amniotes**.
   2. The major derived character of this clade is an **amniotic egg** with four internal membranes.
      a. The amnion is a fluid-filled sac surrounding the embryo.

  b. The yolk sac contains a rich store of nutrients for the developing embryo.

  c. The allantois also helps dispose of metabolic waste.

  d. The chorion (and allantois) enable the embryo to obtain oxygen from the air and dispose of carbon dioxide.

 3. Reptiles

  a. include lizards, snakes, turtles, crocodilians, birds, and extinct dinosaurs,

  b. have a skin covered with scales and waterproofed with keratin,

  c. obtain most of their oxygen using lungs, and

  d. are ectothermic, absorbing external heat rather than generating much of their own.

G. 19.7 Birds are feathered reptiles with adaptations for flight

 1. Most **birds** can fly, and nearly every part of their bodies reflect adaptations that enhance flight.

  a. The forelimbs have been remodeled as feather-covered wings that act as airfoils.

  b. Large flight muscles anchored to a central ridge along the breastbone provide power.

  c. Many features help reduce weight for flight:

   i. Present-day birds lack teeth.

   ii. The tail is supported by only a few small vertebrae.

   iii. Feathers have hollow shafts.

   iv. Their bones have a honeycombed structure that makes them strong but light.

 2. Flight is very costly, and present-day birds have a high rate of metabolism.

 3. Unlike other living reptiles, birds are endothermic, using heat generated by metabolism to maintain a warm, steady body temperature.

 4. Birds have relatively large brains and display complex behaviors. They have

  a. acute senses,

  b. fine muscle control, and

  c. excellent eyesight.

 5. Birds evolved from a lineage of small, two-legged dinosaurs called theropods.

  a. *Archaeopteryx* is the oldest, most primitive known bird (150 million years old), with feathered wings.

  b. It resembled a small bipedal dinosaur, with teeth, wing claws, and a long tail with many vertebrae.

H. 19.8 Mammals are amniotes that have hair and produce milk

 1. Mammals are endothermic amniotes with

  a. hair, which insulates their bodies, and

  b. mammary glands, which produce milk.

 2. Mammals have efficient respiratory and circulatory systems that support their high rate of metabolism.

 3. Mammalian teeth are differentiated for many kinds of diets.

 4. Monotremes are egg-laying mammals. Living monotremes include

  a. the duck-billed platypus and

  b. echidnas.

 5. Unlike monotremes, the embryos of marsupials and eutherians are nurtured by a **placenta**, in which nutrients from the mother's blood diffuse into the embryo's blood.

 6. Marsupials have a brief gestation and give birth to tiny, embryonic offspring that complete development while attached to the mother's nipples.

7. **Eutherians** are mammals that bear fully developed live young. They are commonly called **placental mammals** because their placentas are more complex than those of marsupials.

8. The first true mammals arose 200 million years ago and were probably small, nocturnal insectivores.

   a. Monotremes are the oldest lineage of mammals.

   b. Marsupials diverged from eutherians (placental mammals) about 180 million years ago.

   c. Mammals underwent an adaptive radiation following the Cretaceous extinction of dinosaurs, giving rise to large terrestrial carnivores and herbivores, bats, and aquatic whales and porpoises.

III. Primate Diversity

A. 19.9 The human story begins with our primate heritage

1. The mammalian order Primates includes the lemurs, tarsiers, monkeys, and apes.

   a. Primates probably arose as small arboreal mammals before 65 million years ago, when dinosaurs still dominated the planet.

2. Many primate characters are arboreal adaptations.

   a. Shoulder and hip joints allow climbing and brachiation.

   b. Grasping hands and feet are highly mobile and flexible.

   c. Sensitive hands and feet aid in manipulation.

   d. A short snout and forward-pointing eyes enhance depth perception.

3. A phylogenetic tree shows that all primates are divided into three groups:

   a. lemurs, lorises, and pottos,

   b. tarsiers, and

   c. **anthropoids**, including monkeys and apes with a fully **opposable thumb**, in which the tip of all four fingers can touch the thumb.

4. Monkeys do not constitute a monophyletic group.

   a. Old World monkeys (Africa and Asia)

      i. probably evolved first,

      ii. lacked a prehensile tail, and

      iii. have nostrils that open downward.

   b. New World monkeys have

      i. a prehensile tail and

      ii. nostrils that are wide open and farther apart.

B. 19.10 Humans and four other groups of apes are classified as anthropoids

1. In addition to monkeys, the anthropoid group includes apes: gibbons, orangutans, gorillas, chimpanzees (and bonobos), and humans.

2. Apes

   a. lack a tail and

   b. have relatively long arms and short legs,

   c. have relatively larger brains with respect to size, and

   d. more flexible behavior.

3. Gorillas, chimpanzees, and humans have a high degree of social organization.

4. Nonhuman apes

   a. live only in Africa and Southeast Asia, in tropical rain forests and

   b. have a smaller geographic range than monkeys.

5. Gibbons are

    a. monogamous and

    b. the only fully arboreal apes.

6. Orangutans are

    a. shy,

    b. solitary, and

    c. live in rain-forest trees and the forest floor.

7. Gorillas are

    a. the largest of the apes and

    b. fully terrestrial.

8. Chimpanzees make and use tools.

9. Humans and chimpanzees

    a. are closely related,

    b. share 99% of their genes, and

    c. diverged from a common ancestor between 5 and 7 million years ago.

IV. Hominin Evolution

A. 19.11 The hominin branch of the primate tree includes species that coexisted

    1. Paleoanthropology is the study of human origins and evolution, the brief history since the divergence of human and chimpanzee lineages.

    2. Paleoanthropologists have unearthed

        a. about 20 species of extinct hominins, species that are more closely related to humans than to chimpanzees, and

        b. thousands of hominin fossils.

    3. Figure 19.11 presents some of the known hominins.

    4. The oldest hominin yet discovered, *Sahelanthropus tchadensis*, lived about 7 to 6 million years ago.

    5. The fossil record suggests that hominin diversity increased dramatically between 4 to 2 million years ago.

B. 19.12 Australopiths were bipedal and had small brains

    1. Unlike chimpanzees, humans

        a. walk upright and

        b. have larger brains.

    2. Bipedalism arose millions of years before larger brain size. Evidence of bipedalism includes

        a. 3.6-million-year-old upright-walking homin footprints and

        b. fossil skeletons.

C. 19.13 Larger brains mark the evolution of *Homo*

    1. Australopiths had such small brains (400–450 cc) that they were too small to be members of *Homo*.

    2. *Homo habilis* (2.4–1.6 million years ago) had a brain size of 510–690 cc. Their fossils are found with stone tools.

    3. *Homo ergaster* (1.9–1.6 million years ago) had a brain size ranging from 750–850 cc. Their

        a. fossils are found with more sophisticated stone tools and

        b. long, slender legs were adapted for long-distance walking.

    4. *Homo sapiens* has a brain size of around 1300 cc.

5. *Homo erectus*

      a. had a brain volume of around 940 cc and

      b. was the first hominin to leave Africa.

  6. The oldest known fossils of hominins outside of Africa are about 1.8 million years old.

  7. *Homo neanderthalensis*, commonly called Neanderthals

      a. lived in Europe from about 350,000 to 28,000 years ago when they went extinct,

      b. had brains as large as modern humans, and

      c. hunted big game with tools made of stone and wood.

  8. How are Neanderthals related to modern humans?

      a. An analysis of mtDNA isolated from Neanderthal bones suggests that they were a distinct species from modern humans.

      b. The last common ancestor between humans and Neanderthals lived about 500,000 years ago.

D. 19.14 From origins in Africa, *Homo sapiens* spread around the world

  1. Analysis of mtDNA and Y chromosomes suggest that all living humans

      a. inherited their mtDNA from a woman who lived 160,000–200,000 years ago and

      b. diverged from a common African ancestor.

  2. Our species emerged from Africa in one or more waves, migrating to Asia 50,000–60,000 years ago and then to Europe, Southeast Asia, and Australia.

  3. The capacity for creativity and symbolic thought may have spurred human evolution.

E. 19.15 Who were the "hobbits"?

  1. Fossils of small hominins named *Homo floresiensis* that were found in Indonesia are controversial. The 2004 discovery of the nearly complete skeleton was of a hominin that

      a. was about 1 meter tall,

      b. had a chimp-sized brain, and

      c. had a skull that displayed some humanlike traits.

  2. Scientists are trying to determine their relationship to other hominins.

F. 19.16 EVOLUTION CONNECTION: Human skin color reflects adaptations to varying amounts of sunlight

  1. Human skin color varies geographically, likely as a result of natural selection.

  2. Natural selection may have selected for the competing abilities of skin to

      a. block UV radiation, which degrades folate, and

      b. absorb UV radiation to synthesize vitamin D.

      c. Folate is vital for fetal development and spermatogenesis.

      d. Vitamin D is essential for proper bone development.

G. 19.17 CONNECTION: Our knowledge of animal diversity is far from complete

  1. Thousands of new species of organisms are discovered each year.

  2. The pace of discovery has recently increased due to

      a. better access to remote areas and

      b. new mapping technologies.

Chapter Guide to Teaching Resources

Vertebrate Evolution and Diversity (19.1–19.8)

Student Misconceptions and Concerns

- The classification of chordates has undergone some major changes with the rearrangement of vertebrate groups. Birds are now commonly classified as reptiles, an association likely not seen previously in older K–12 textbooks. Students may be surprised by this association. Better classification tools and the attempt to classify organisms only into monophyletic groups have required these reconsiderations. (19.1–19.8)

- Students might think of vertebrate groups as sharply defined, lacking appreciation for the transitional organisms that illuminate aspects of the rich evolutionary history of vertebrates. Recent discoveries such as the 375 million-year-old fossil fish *Tiktaalik* reveal important traits that are intermediate between ancient fishes and modern amphibians. Discussion of this important transitional species, as well as similar species such as *Archaeopteryx* and modern monotremes, will reveal the blurry boundary lines between our classifications of vertebrate groups. (19.1–19.8)

Teaching Tips

- Figure 19.1 facilitates a discussion of modern classification using cladistics. Each group is defined by a set of shared derived traits. Many students may not have encountered this system or such diagrams in their studies preceding college. Depending upon your previous course content, additional time may be needed to clarify this system. (19.1)

- Lampreys possess vertebrae, but hagfishes do not (Figure 19.2). Thus, only lampreys are now classified as vertebrates, a distinction that may not have been made in textbooks used by students before they arrived at college. (19.2)

- As the authors note in Module 19.2, "eel-skin" wallets and purses are typically made from the skin of hagfish. It is possible that one or more of your students has such an item. (19.2)

- The movement of lampreys from Lake Ontario to the other Great Lakes was historically limited by Niagara Falls. However, the creation of canals (about 180 years ago) to bypass the falls created a channel for lamprey invasion. Lampreys are just one example of the tremendous problem of invasive (exotic) species. (19.2)

- The wide, flat bodies of rays provide an obvious exception to the general rule that cartilaginous fishes have streamlined bodies. Their ventral mouths and flattened form are well adapted to a life on the ocean bottom. (19.3)

- Of all of the vertebrate clades alive today, ray-finned fishes are the most abundant. As noted in Module 19.3, more than 27,000 species of ray-finned fishes have been identified. (19.3)

- Sharks, unlike bony fishes, do not have swim bladders. To lift off the bottom, they swim using their stiff pectoral fins and tail for uplift (along with some buoyant materials in their body). (19.3)

- The menacing perception of sharks may be due in part to their particular method of maneuvering in water. Shark fins do not rotate to brake their forward movements. Cruising sharks that swim near an object of interest are not necessarily out to intimidate their prey (although it may have this effect). They may simply be curious, but unable to remain motionless while they investigate their environment. (19.3)

- The transition to a life on land required some major changes. You might ask your students to discuss the challenges of moving from an aquatic to terrestrial lifestyle. These include adaptations to breathing air, additional skeletal support to account for the loss of the support and buoyancy provided by water, loss of a lateral line system, adaptations to hearing in air, mechanisms to reduce water loss through the skin, etc. Reptiles were the first group to be independent of standing water. (19.4–19.6)

- The way amphibians and reptiles move on land reveals the ancestral derivation of their anatomy. As an alligator swings its body from side to side, moving its legs forward, the lateral undulations of its vertebral column resemble those of a fish. In contrast, the movements of a dolphin in water reveal its more recent terrestrial ancestry. It moves its vertebral column vertically so that its back undulates in the same direction, just like a land mammal such as a horse. (19.4–19.6, 19.8)

- Our knowledge about the basic development of vertebrates was significantly advanced by the early study of amphibian embryos. With clear outer layers, the detailed anatomy of many developing amphibians may be observed without disturbing the organism (see Figure 19.5D). Furthermore, their size permitted the identification of basic systems without requiring magnification. (19.5)

- Adult salamanders are the only adult tetrapods that can completely regenerate a lost limb. Although some reptiles can regenerate portions of their tails, no other tetrapod can replace part or all of a limb. Even more amazingly, salamanders that suffer the partial loss of a limb regenerate only the missing sections. Research into the mechanisms of regeneration inform our understanding of limb development and bring hope that medical science may one day be able to achieve the same thing in humans. (19.5)

- One of the most widely studied laboratory amphibians over the past 200 years has been the axolotl, a Mexican salamander that retains juvenile characteristics, including gills that persist into the adult state. These animals do not normally undergo metamorphosis, reproducing instead in their strictly aquatic form. Many images of these neotenic/paedomorphic axolotls can be found by performing a simple Internet image search for "axolotl." (19.5)

- Reptiles diversified in the Mesozoic in much the same way that mammals have diversified today. To make this point, choose some well-known dinosaurs and compare their habitats to modern mammals that live in a similar ecological niche. (Triceratops was a grazer, much like a modern bison; a duck-billed hadrosaur shares much the same diet as a hippopotamus today; Tyrannosaurus rex may have been an aggressive hunter like a modern tiger.) (19.6)

- The intermediate nature of *Archaeopteryx* can be demonstrated to your students. Have your students compare an *Archaeopteryx* fossil to the skeleton of a modern chicken. Good photographs of both organisms can be sufficient. Have them note both the shared and unique characteristics of the two organisms. (19.7)

- In the last few years, the debate about the evolution of birds has been punctuated by exciting new fossil discoveries from China. Your students should be able to find images and details about these recent discoveries on the Internet. (19.7)

- Feathers perform several functions, typically in the same bird. They insulate, they provide species-specific coloration for identification by members of the same species, and they form aerodynamic surfaces. As you list these diverse functions, note that they did not arise simultaneously. Fossil evidence now reveals that feathers first evolved as identifying traits or as an important source of insulation, long before they played any role in flight. (19.7)

- The distribution of marsupials on Earth is a fine example of biogeography. The geographic isolation of Australia has allowed them to evolve independently of much of eutherian evolution, resulting in greater diversification of marsupials. As suggested for the dinosaurs, students can be encouraged to draw parallels between the lifestyles of Australian marsupials and eutherian mammals that occupy similar ecological niches elsewhere in the world. (19.8)

- Mammals and birds, with their endothermic physiology, require very efficient respiratory and circulatory systems to support high levels of metabolic activity. A bird or mammal the same size as a lizard requires about ten times as many calories per day. (19.8)

Primate Diversity (19.9–19.10)

Student Misconceptions and Concerns

- Students who otherwise seem comfortable with evolution applied to other groups may become uncomfortable when evolution is applied to humans and our nearest relatives. Some students may not accept that humans are animals. Be prepared for these reactions. (19.9–19.10)

- Some students raise objections about evolution because they believe it is incompatible with their religious philosophy. Some students see humans as an exception to biological rules. How you handle these philosophical objections depends upon the greater context of your course in the curriculum and the specific political and social circumstances of your institution. Reminding students about the rules and philosophy of science may help to clarify the particular perspective of biology. (19.9–19.10)

Teaching Tips

- Students will need to be reminded that modern apes and humans share ancestry and are not direct relatives of each other. This basic observation may need to be repeated to remind students that evolution is not necessarily a process of replacement, but a branching family tree united by common descent. (19.9)

- Students may struggle to distinguish between primates, anthropoids, and monkeys. The basic relationships between these groups are illustrated in the phylogenetic tree in Figure 19.9B. (19.9)

- Students are often unaware that there is a second type of chimp, the bonobo, which resembles human beings even more closely in certain particulars—such as the use of sex for social bonding rather than procreation! An excellent source of information about this underappreciated species can be found at http://bonobo.org. (19.10)

- Your students may enjoy trying to identify traits unique to humans. To what degree are tool-making and symbolic language specifically human traits? What traits are found only in humans? (19.10)

Hominin Evolution (19.11–19.17)

Student Misconceptions and Concerns

- Students are likely to believe that human evolution resembled the popular "march of progress" image, which depicts a series of apes giving way to increasingly modern-looking and upright humans in a linear progression. Such images are common and can be found easily by searching "human evolution" on a Google image search. As suggested by Figure 19.11, the human family tree has many branches, with multiple species existing simultaneously for long periods (more than a million years). Furthermore, representing the diversity of hominin evolution as a narrow progression from past to present is misleading. It would be the equivalent of depicting any one student's family history as a direct lineage of grandparent to parent to student, ignoring all siblings and cousins. (19.11)

- Students and biologists in general often expect evolutionary intermediates to have characteristics that are an average of ancestors and descendants. They may expect intermediate forms to have intermediate traits. The concept of mosaic evolution, in which intermediates demonstrate a mixture of primitive and derived traits, more accurately depicts the history of life. As discussed in Module 19.12, human ancestors did not walk partially upright with mid-sized brains. Instead, upright posture evolved before larger brains, revealing a "mosaic" of traits. (19.11–19.17)

- Students may continue to struggle with false Lamarckian concepts of evolution. They should be reminded that organisms do not acquire characteristics because of want or need. Instead, naturally occurring genetic variations are selected for or against depending on a population's interactions with its environment. Many students need to be reminded about the process of natural selection wherever it applies. (19.11–19.17)

Teaching Tips

- Figure 19.11 is an excellent way to introduce the history of human evolution. The vertical bars represent the known history of each species based upon the discovery of fossils. However, the relationships between the species are not represented because of uncertainty. The ongoing efforts to clarify human ancestral relationships provide a case study of the process of science, which involves forming tentative hypotheses that are refined as more evidence and insight are added. (19.11)

- There are many excellent Internet sites addressing aspects of human evolution. The Leakey Foundation website lists a variety of them at www.leakeyfoundation.org/resources/. (19.11–19.16)

- Multiple independent lines of evidence supporting the idea that upright body posture evolved before larger brains are discussed in Module 19.12, again providing an example of the process of science in action, where confidence in the validity of a theory grows as the quality and number of lines of evidence supporting it increase. (19.12)

- Students may wonder if people living today with large brains are indeed more intelligent than their smaller-brained colleagues. Although this relationship may generally be true between species, there is no clear evidence that it is valid within a species. (19.13)

- Students may wish to debate whether we are more intelligent than our cave-dwelling ancestors. What is the distinction between knowledge and intelligence? If your course permits it, these could be some interesting discussions. (19.13)

- Excavations of Neanderthal habitation sites have revealed fascinating details of their existence. Student research into these artifacts can stimulate interest and enjoyable conversations. Considering asking your students to identify one artifact of Neanderthal culture that reveals something about the way they lived. A Google search of "Neanderthal culture artifact" will be a good start. (19.14)

- Module 19.14 notes that the oldest known fossils of modern humans have been dated to about 160,000–200,000 years ago. Appreciating the relative youthfulness of our species can be difficult. Consider this short activity. Have students calculate the percentage of time that our species has existed (generously at 200,000 years) compared to the age of the Earth (4.6 billion years) and compared to the approximate age of multicellular animal life (about 600 million years). Your strongest students might enjoy this final calculation. If the entire history of Earth represents one calendar year, what fraction of that year represents the period of modern human existence? The answers would be as follows: Our species has existed for 1/23,000th of Earth's history = 0.0000434 = 0.00434%; our species has existed for 1/3000th of the time that multicellular animal life has existed, 0.0333%. If the 4.6 billion-year history of Earth represented one calendar year, our species has been present for the last 23 minutes of that year. ($0.0000434 \times 365.25 \times 24 \times 60 = 22.83$ minutes.) (19.14)

- The recent research on the fossils of *Homo floresiensis* and surrounding questions and controversy make this species particularly interesting for additional study by your students. They may enjoy reporting new insights and discoveries that have emerged since the publication of this edition of *Concepts*. (19.15)

- Consider discussing the relationship between skin pigmentation and thickness of hair. As the amount of hair decreased in hominins, might this have exposed the skin to greater solar radiation and thus selected more strongly for variations in pigmentation? (19.16)

- Some students might wonder if we are discovering new animal species in part because they continue to form. Consider noting to your class that the evolution of new species of vertebrates likely occurs over a period of thousands of years. (19.17)

Key Terms

amniote	hominins	placental mammal
amniotic egg	lateral line system	ray-finned fish
amphibian	lobe-fins	reptile
anthropoid	mammal	swim bladder
birds	marsupial	tetrapod
chondrichthyan	monotreme	vertebra (plural, vertebrae)
craniate	operculum	vertebral column
ectothermic	opposable thumb	vertebrate
endothermic	paleoanthropology	
eutherian	placenta	

Word Roots

amphi- = both; **-bio** = life (*amphibian*: a type of vertebrate that inhabits both aquatic and terrestrial habitats)

anthro- = human; **-oid** = likeness (*anthropoid*: a member of the primate group including apes and monkeys, all of which resemble humans in certain characteristics)

australo- = southern; **-pithekos** = ape (*australopith*: one of the first hominins)

chondr- = cartilaginous; **-ichthy** = fish (*chondrichthyan*: the group of fish that have cartilaginous skeletons, including sharks and rays)

chord- = a string (*chordates*: the group of organisms that possess a notochord and other characteristics at some point in their lives)

crani- = the skull (*craniate*: a chordate with a head)

ecto- = outside; **-therm** = heat (*ectotherm*: an animal that warms itself mainly by absorbing heat from its surroundings)

endo- = inner; **-therm** = heat (*endotherm*: an animal that derives most of its body heat from its own metabolism)

eu- = good (*eutherian*: one of the mammals whose young complete their embryonic development within the uterus, joined to the mother by the placenta)

homin- = man (*hominin*: species that are more closely related to humans than to chimpanzees)

later- = side (*lateral line system*: a row of sensory organs along each side of a fish's body that is sensitive to changes in water pressure)

marsupi- = a bag, pouch (*marsupial*: a mammal, such as a koala, kangaroo, or opossum, whose young complete their embryonic development inside a maternal pouch called the marsupium)

mono- = one (*monotreme*: an egg-laying mammal, such as the duck-billed platypus)

opercul- = a covering, lid (*operculum*: a protective flap that covers the gills of fishes)

paleo- = ancient; **anthrop-** = man; **-ology** = the science of (*paleoanthropology*: the study of human origins and evolution)

tetra- = four; **-podi** = foot (*tetrapod*: a vertebrate with two pairs of limbs, such as a mammal, amphibian, or reptile)

CHAPTER 20

Unifying Concepts of Animal Structure and Function

Chapter Objectives

Opening Essay

Explain how geckos are able to walk on walls and ceilings.

Structure and Function in Animal Tissues

20.1   Describe the levels of organization in an animal's body.

20.2   Explain how size and shape can influence the structure of an animal.

20.3–20.7   Define a tissue, describe the four main types of animal tissue, and note their structures and functions.

Organs and Organ Systems

20.8   Explain how the structure of organs is based on the cooperative interactions of tissues.

20.9   Explain how artificial tissues are created and used.

20.10   Describe the general structures and functions of the 12 major vertebrate organ systems.

20.11   Compare and contrast X-ray, CT, MRI, and PET imaging technologies. Explain how each technology works and its advantages and disadvantages.

20.12   Relate the structure of skin to its functions.

External Exchange and Internal Regulation

20.13   Describe the systems that help an animal exchange materials with its environment. Describe examples of adaptations to increase the surface-to-volume ratio.

20.14   Define the concept of homeostasis and illustrate it with examples.

20.15   Explain how negative feedback is used to regulate internal body temperature.

Lecture Outline

I. Introduction

   A. How can geckos climb walls and stick to the ceiling?

      1. The surfaces of gecko toes are covered by millions of microscopic hairs.

      2. Each hair has a slight molecular attraction that helps it stick to the surface.

      3. This adhesive relationship is an example of the correlation between structure and function.

II. Structure and Function in Animal Tissues

A. 20.1 Structure fits function at all levels of organization in the animal body

  1. Anatomy is the study of structure.

  2. Physiology is the study of function.

  3. Animals consist of a hierarchy of levels or organization.

   a. Tissues are an integrated group of similar cells that perform a common function.

   b. Organs perform a specific task and consist of two or more tissues.

   c. Organ systems consist of multiple organs that together perform a vital body function.

B. 20.2 EVOLUTION CONNECTION: An animal's form reflects natural selection

  1. The body plan or design of an organism

   a. reflects the relationship between form and function,

   b. results from natural selection, and

   c. does not imply a process of conscious invention.

  2. Streamlined and tapered bodies

   a. increase swimming speeds and

   b. have similarly evolved in fish, sharks, and aquatic birds and mammals, representing convergent evolution.

C. 20.3 Tissues are groups of cells with a common structure and function

  1. Tissues

   a. are an integrated group of similar cells that perform a common function and

   b. combine to form organs.

  2. Animals have four main categories of tissues:

   a. epithelial tissue,

   b. connective tissue,

   c. muscle tissue, and

   d. nervous tissue.

D. 20.4 Epithelial tissue covers the body and lines its organs and cavities

  1. Epithelial tissues, or epithelia, are sheets of closely packed cells that

   a. cover body surfaces and

   b. line internal organs and cavities.

  2. Epithelial cells come in three shapes:

   a. squamous—like a fried egg,

   b. cuboidal—as tall as they are wide, and

   c. columnar—taller than they are wide.

  3. Epithelial tissues are named according to the

   a. number of cell layers they have and

   b. shape of the cells on their apical surface.

  4. Connective tissue can be grouped into six major types.

   a. Loose connective tissue

    i. is the most widespread,

    ii. consists of ropelike collagen and elastic fibers that are strong and resilient, and

    iii. helps to join skin to underlying tissues.

   b. Fibrous connective tissue

    i. has densely packed collagen fibers and

    ii. forms tendons that attach muscle to bone.

   c. Adipose tissue stores fat in large, closely packed cells held in a matrix of fibers.

       d. Cartilage

          i. is a strong and flexible skeletal material and

          ii. commonly surrounds the ends of bones.

       e. Bone

          i. has a matrix of collagen fibers

          ii. embedded in a hard mineral substance containing calcium, magnesium, and phosphate.

       f. Blood transports substances throughout the body.

  E. 20.6 Muscle tissue functions in movement

    1. Muscle tissue is the most abundant tissue in most animals.

    2. There are three types of vertebrate muscle tissue:

       a. Skeletal muscle causes voluntary movements.

       b. Cardiac muscle pumps blood.

       c. Smooth muscle moves walls of internal organs, such as the intestines.

  F. 20.7 Nervous tissue forms a communication network

    1. Nervous tissue

       a. senses stimuli and

       b. rapidly transmits information.

    2. Neurons carry signals by conducting electrical impulses.

    3. Other cells in nervous tissue

       a. insulate axons,

       b. nourish neurons, and

       c. regulate the fluid around neurons.

III. Organs and Organ Systems

  A. 20.8 Organs are made up of tissues

    1. Each tissue performs specific functions.

    2. The heart has

       a. extensive muscle that generate contractions,

       b. epithelial tissues that line the heart chambers,

       c. connective tissues that make the heart elastic, and

       d. neurons which regulate contractions.

    3. The small intestine

       a. is lined by a columnar epithelium,

       b. includes connective tissues that contain blood vessels, and

       c. has two layers of smooth muscle that help propel food.

    4. The inner surface of the small intestine has many fingerlike projections that increase the surface area for absorption.

  B. 20.9 CONNECTION: Bioengineers are learning to produce tissues and organs for transplants

    1. Bioengineering is seeking ways to repair or replace damaged tissues and organs.

    2. New tissues and organs are being grown using a patient's own cells.

    3. These techniques

       a. remove the risk of tissue rejection and

       b. may someday reduce the shortage of organs available for transplants.

  C. 20.10 Organ systems work together to perform life's functions

    1. Each organ system

       a. typically consists of many organs,

    b. has one or more functions, and

    c. works with other organ systems to create a functional organism.

  2. The **skeletal** and **muscular systems** support and move the body.

  3. The **digestive** and **respiratory systems** obtain food and oxygen.

  4. The **circulatory system** transports these materials.

  5. The **urinary system** disposes of wastes.

  6. The **integumentary system** covers the body.

  7. The **lymphatic** and **immune systems** protect the body from infection.

  8. The **nervous** and **endocrine systems** control and coordinate body functions.

  9. The **reproductive system** produces offspring.

D. 20.11 CONNECTION: New imaging technology reveals the inner body

  1. New technologies

    a. are used in medical diagnosis and research and

    b. allow physicians to examine organ systems without surgery.

  2. X-rays help create images of hard structures such as bones and teeth.

  3. Magnetic resonance imaging (MRI)

    a. takes advantage of the behavior of the hydrogen atoms in water molecules and

    b. provides three-dimensional images of very small structures.

  4. A newer X-ray technology called computed tomography (CT)

    a. produces high-resolution images of cross sections of the body and

    b. can detect small differences between normal and abnormal tissues in many organs.

  5. Positron-emission tomography (PET) helps identify metabolic processes at specific body locations.

  6. CT and PET images can be combined for an even more informative image.

E. 20.12 The integumentary system protects the body

  1. The skin consists of two layers:

    a. The epidermis

      i. is a stratified squamous epithelium and

      ii. forms the surface of the skin.

    b. The dermis

      i. forms a deeper skin layer and

      ii. is composed of dense connective tissue with many resilient elastic fibers and strong collagen fibers.

      iii. The dermis contains hair follicles, oil and sweat glands, muscle cells, nerves, sensory receptors, and blood vessels.

  2. Skin has many functions.

    a. The epidermis

      i. resists physical damage,

      ii. decreases water loss, and

      iii. prevents penetration by microbes.

    b. The dermis

      i. collects sensory information,

      ii. synthesizes vitamin D, and

      iii. helps regulate body temperature.

  3. Exposure of the skin to ultraviolet light

    a. causes skin cells to release melanin, which contributes to a visible tan, and

    b. damages DNA of skin cells and can lead to

      i. premature aging of the skin,

ii. cataracts, and

iii. skin cancers.

4. Hair

 a. is an important component of the integumentary system of mammals,

 b. helps to insulate their bodies, and

 c. consists of a shaft of keratin-filled dead cells.

5. Oil glands release oils that

 a. are associated with hair follicles,

 b. lubricate hair,

 c. condition surrounding skin, and

 d. inhibit the growth of bacteria.

IV. External Exchange and Internal Regulation

 A. 20.13 Structural adaptations enhance exchange with the environment

 1. Every organism is an open system which must exchange matter and energy with its surroundings.

 2. Cells in small and flat animals can exchange materials directly with the environment.

 3. However, as organisms increase in size, the surface area

 a. is too small for the corresponding volume and

 b. too far away from the deepest cells of the body.

 c. In these organisms, evolutionary adaptations

 i. consist of extensively branched or folded surfaces that increase the area of these surfaces and

 ii. provide for sufficient environmental exchange.

 4. The respiratory system exchanges gases between the external environment and blood.

 5. The digestive system acquires food and eliminates wastes.

 6. The excretory system eliminates metabolic waste.

 7. The circulatory system

 a. distributes gases, nutrients, and wastes throughout the body and

 b. exchanges materials between blood and body cells through the **interstitial fluid** that bathes body cells.

 8. **Homeostasis** is the active maintenance of a steady state within the body.

 a. External environmental conditions may fluctuate wildly.

 b. Homeostatic mechanisms regulate internal conditions.

 9. Control systems

 a. detect change and

 b. direct responses.

 10. **Negative-feedback** mechanisms

 a. keep internal variables steady and

 b. permit only small fluctuations around set points.

Chapter Guide to Teaching Resources

Structure and Function in Animal Tissues (20.1–20.7)

Student Misconceptions and Concerns

- Students often find it challenging to gain a proper understanding of the evolution of form and function relationships. Such relationships appear to have been "constructed" to meet a purpose, a consequence of deliberate planning and design. Ask students to explain why we have lungs, and they will typically answer something along the line of "because we need to breathe," or "because we need oxygen." Need, however, does not cause evolution. Natural selection involves editing rather than creating diversity. A better answer might be "Because lung-like structures conveyed an advantage in gas exchange in our ancestors." (20.1–20.7)

- Relationships between form and function are found all around us. For some of us, noticing the connections is easy. However, many students have spent little time considering why any particular structure has its characteristic shape. Practice with examples helps to build a better understanding of these important relationships. (20.1–20.7)

- As noted in Module 20.2, the use of the term "design" in biology does not imply conscious invention. Instead, the term identifies the arrangement of the parts and their interrelated functions. Natural selection is not a deliberate process. (20.2)

Teaching Tips

- When you discuss form and function relationships, ask students to consider their own teeth as an example. Ask them to use their tongues to feel their teeth and relate the shape of the teeth to the human diet. Incisors and canines slice, while molars are more effective at crushing. (20.1)

- Students often fail to consider the significance of body size. Consider asking your students to think about the impact of being small. Have they ever had difficulty emerging from a swimming pool because of the adhesive properties of water? Of course not—and yet, small insects that land on a pond's surface may find these forces to be lethal, preventing them from breaking away from the water's surface! Ask students if they are ever unable to leave their homes because of high winds, which make it impossible for them to walk around outside. The movements of small insects are often hampered by winds that would do little more than toss around our hair! Many campers know that mosquitoes and flies are less of a nuisance on days when there is a good breeze. (20.2)

- Extracellular substances, such as collagen fibers, are the source of the main functional properties of many connective tissues such as tendons, ligaments, cartilage, and bone. (20.3)

- Simple squamous cells have a shape that is generally similar to a fried egg: flattened, with a bump in the middle representing the nucleus or yolk. (20.4)

- Students might misunderstand how the cilia lining our respiratory passages work. Cilia do not "filter" the air like a comb. Instead, cilia are covered by a layer of mucus. Dust particles adhere to sticky mucus, which is then swept up the respiratory tract by the cilia. If students clear their throats, they will identify the fate of this mucus. We swallow after clearing our throats! (20.4)

- The elastic cartilage in the human ear is a wonderful example of a form and function relationship. Elastic fibers are abundant in the extracellular matrix, increasing the flexibility of elastic cartilage. Have students bend their own ears to feel the effects. (20.5)

- Muscle cells are only able to contract. None can actively relengthen. Challenge your students to explain how muscle cells return to their extended length. (Answer: Opposing muscles or other forces, such as gravity, act in opposition to relengthen muscle cells when they relax.) (20.6)

- Students might enjoy this simple observation when discussing neurons. As we consider the structure and functions of neurons, we are using our own neurons to think about them. Our neurons become self-aware! (20.7)

Organs and Organ Systems (20.8–20.12)

Student Misconceptions and Concerns

- Students often find it challenging to gain a proper understanding of the evolution of form and function relationships. Such relationships appear to have been "constructed" to meet a purpose, a consequence of deliberate planning and design. Ask students to explain why we have lungs, and they will typically answer something along the line of "because we need to breathe," or "because we need oxygen." Need, however, does not cause evolution. Natural selection involves editing rather than creating diversity. A better answer might be "Because lung-like structures conveyed an advantage in gas exchange in our ancestors." (20.8–20.12)

- Relationships between form and function are found all around us. For some of us, noticing the connections is easy. However, many students have spent little time considering why any particular structure has its characteristic shape. Practice with examples helps to build a better understanding of these important relationships. (20.8–20.12)

Teaching Tips

- Sponges are well adapted to maximize surface area exposed to water. Like the small intestine with its many villi, the highly porous structure of sponges dramatically increases the area available for water filtering. (20.8)

- As noted in Module 20.9, researchers often use cells derived from newborns' foreskin. Students may not realize that this is actually the excess tissue removed during circumcision of newborn baby boys. Such tissues are widely available as a by-product of this procedure. (20.9)

- To help them appreciate the functional integration of the major systems of the body, have students pick any system and discuss its relationship to the other body systems. As a start, you might begin with the circulatory system. As each successive system is covered, you can create a concept map noting the nature of each interrelationship. (20.10)

- Module 20.11 provides an excellent opportunity to discuss the impact of technology on science and medicine. New ways of viewing, detecting, and monitoring our bodies invite additional avenues of inquiry. (20.11)

- The stratified squamous epithelium on most outside surfaces of our body resists abrasions in part because it is keratinized. However, the nonkeratinized epithelial tissue that lines our body cavities, such as the mouth, pharynx, esophagus, and anus, is also resistant to abrasion as a result of its mucus coatings, which provide friction-reducing lubrication. Students may not realize that the same type of tissue performs similar functions in very different parts of the body. (20.12)

- Students might have noticed that their skin wrinkles when soaked in water. Some students may have noticed that their hands wrinkle even faster in soapy water. Skin absorbs water through osmosis (just as a freshwater fish gains water). The wrinkling occurs because the skin can expand only in certain areas, creating puckers. Oils on our skin reduce the influx of water. Therefore, soapy water, which washes away these oils, speeds up the movement of water into our keratinized skin. (20.12)

External Exchange and Internal Regulation (20.13–20.15)

Student Misconceptions and Concerns

- It can be difficult for students to think of their own bodies in terms of simple surfaces and tubes. Perceiving the digestive tract as one continuous tube, in which food passes through but never technically enters the body, is one such challenge. Illustrate these fundamental principles first using less complex animals (such as earthworms) as examples. Then apply these principles to humans as a final test of comprehension. (20.13)

- If students have not previously studied the diversity of animals, consider giving a brief overview of the basic animal body plans before explaining how the fundamental principles of form and function generally apply to the animal kingdom. (20.13–20.15)

- The concept of homeostasis may be new to many students who have never considered how organisms maintain their structure and physiology. Analogies to other systems that engage in self-regulation (noted in the text and the following) can help. (20.14–20.15)

Teaching Tips

- Large organisms must transport and exchange material throughout their entire structure, including their inner core. This principle applies equally to natural organisms, such as a whale or a redwood tree, and to collective "organisms," such as the United States. The U.S. railway and highway networks are analogous to animal transport and exchange systems. They move essential products from their point of entry (ocean ports) into the country's interior, where they can be warehoused or sold. As a result of this system, people who live in the Midwest have access to the same goods as those who live in New York or San Francisco. (20.13)

- Organisms and individual cells need sufficient surface exchange and transport systems to support their surface to volume ratios. Cell size is limited, in part, by the ability of a cell to exchange materials efficiently with its surface. Thus, adaptations that increase surface area can permit cells to reach larger sizes. (20.13)

- The heat generated by aerobic metabolism is analogous to the heat generated by the engine of an automobile. In both cases, the heat is a by-product of the process. In the winter, this excess heat helps keep the body and an automobile warm. In the summer, both the body and the automobile's engine must work to keep from overheating. (20.14)

- Ask students to explain how blood vessel constriction near the body's surface, shivering, and a general increase in metabolism help a person to keep warm in a cold environment. (20.14)

- Have students list the many factors that affect heat gain and loss during periods of physical activity to demonstrate how much our homeostatic mechanisms must work to maintain a steady body temperature. These factors include (a) the person's physical condition, (b) the level of physical activity, (c) the age of the person (younger people tend to have higher metabolic rates), (d) the person's level of hydration (which in turn affects the amount of sweating and evaporative cooling), (e) the external level of humidity (higher levels decrease evaporative cooling), (f) the intensity of the wind (greater intensity promotes evaporative cooling), (g) the intensity of sunlight, and (h) the color of the person's clothing (which affects the amount of light energy the body absorbs). (20.14)

- Challenge your students to think of other examples of negative feedback in their environments, including the filling of a toilet tank with water after flushing. Students from diverse disciplines may think of many new examples. (20.15)

Key Terms

adipose tissue	homeostasis	organ
anatomy	immune system	organ system
blood	integumentary system	physiology
bone	interstitial fluid	reproductive system
cardiac muscle	loose connective tissue	respiratory system
cartilage	lymphatic system	skeletal muscle
circulatory system	muscle tissue	skeletal system
connective tissue	muscular system	smooth muscle
digestive system	negative feedback	tissue
endocrine system	nervous system	urinary system
epithelial tissue	nervous tissue	
fibrous connective tissue	neuron	

Word Roots

cardi- = heart (*cardiac muscle*: striated muscle that forms the contractile tissue of the heart)

endo- = inner (*endocrine system*: the animal organ system that cooperates with the nervous system in regulating body functions and maintaining homeostasis)

epi- = above, over (*epithelial tissue*: a sheet of tightly packed cells lining organs, body cavities, and covering external surfaces)

homeo- = same; **-stasis** = standing, posture (*homeostasis*: the steady-state physiological condition of the body)

inter- = between (*interstitial fluid*: an aqueous solution that surrounds body cells and through which materials pass back and forth between the blood and the body tissues)

neuro- = nerve (*neuron*: a nerve cell; the fundamental structural and functional unit of the nervous system, specialized for carrying signals from one location in the body to another)

physio- = nature; **-logy** = the scientific study of a subject (*physiology*: the study of the functioning of an organism's structures)

CHAPTER 21

Nutrition and Digestion

Chapter Objectives

Opening Essay

Explain why obesity is increasing in the United States.

Obtaining and Processing Food

21.1 Define and distinguish between carnivores, herbivores, omnivores, suspension feeders, substrate feeders, fluid feeders, and bulk feeders.

21.2 Describe the four stages of food processing. Explain how animals are protected against self-digestion.

21.3 Compare the structures and functions of a gastrovascular cavity and an alimentary canal. Describe the specialized digestive systems of an earthworm, a grasshopper, and a bird.

Human Digestive System

21.4 Describe the main components of the human alimentary canal and the associated digestive glands.

21.5 Describe the functional components of saliva and the types and functions of the teeth in humans.

21.6 Explain how swallowing occurs and how food is directed away from the trachea.

21.7 Explain how the Heimlich maneuver is performed.

21.8 Relate the structure of the stomach to its functions. Describe the functions of the secretions of the stomach. Finally, explain why the stomach does not digest itself.

21.9 Describe the causes and treatments of heartburn, GERD, and gastric ulcers.

21.10 Describe the different types of chemical digestion that occur in the small intestine. Explain how the structure of the small intestine promotes nutrient absorption.

21.11 Explain how the liver helps to regulate the chemical composition of blood.

21.12 Describe the structures and functions of the colon and rectum. Note the causes of diarrhea and constipation.

21.13 Compare the digestive tracts of carnivores and herbivores. Describe how the digestive tracts of a koala and a coyote are specialized to digest cellulose.

21.13 Describe the process of ruminant digestion.

Nutrition

21.14 List the three nutritional needs common to all animals.

21.15 Define the basal metabolic rate. Explain how energy is obtained and stored in the body.

21.16 Describe the four classes of essential nutrients. Distinguish between undernutrition and malnutrition.

21.17 Define and distinguish between vitamins and minerals. Distinguish between water-soluble and fat-soluble vitamins. Define the essential minerals and explain why each is important in our diet.

21.17 Define the Recommended Dietary Allowances and explain how they contribute to good health.

21.18 Explain how scientists determine the levels of vitamins and minerals needed in the diet for good health.

21.18 Explain why, since 1998, the United States has required the addition of folic acid to certain foods.

21.19 Describe the types of information found on food labels.

21.20 Describe the obesity epidemic in the United States. Describe the role of leptin in weight management. Explain why cravings for fat may have once been adaptive.

21.21 Describe the best approach to weight control.

21.22 Explain how diet can influence the risks of cardiovascular disease and cancer.

Lecture Outline

I. Introduction

  A. All animals must eat to provide

    1. energy and

    2. the building blocks used to assemble new molecules.

  B. Animals also need essential

    1. vitamins and

    2. minerals.

  C. The modern human diet in developed countries allows access to relatively cheap and available calorie-dense foods.

  D. This diet, combined with sedentary jobs and inactive lifestyles, has led to an obesity crisis in the United States leading to

    1. 68% of people categorized as overweight and

    2. 100 million people categorized as obese.

  E. Thus, the modern diet appears to be contributing to shorter, less healthy lives.

II. Obtaining and Processing Food

  A. 21.1 Animals obtain and ingest their food in a variety of ways

    1. Most animals have one of three kinds of diets.

      a. Herbivores eat plants and include cattle, snails, and sea urchins.

      b. Carnivores eat meat and include lions, hawks, and spiders.

      c. Omnivores eat plants and other animals and include humans, roaches, raccoons, and crows.

    2. Animals obtain and ingest their food in different ways.

      a. Suspension feeders sift small organisms or food particles from water.

      b. Substrate feeders live in or on their food source and eat their way through it.

      c. Fluid feeders suck nutrient-rich fluids from a living host.

      d. Bulk feeders ingest large pieces of food.

B. 21.2 Overview: Food processing occurs in four stages

    1. Food is processed in four stages.

       a. Ingestion is the act of eating.

       b. Digestion is the breaking down of food into molecules **small** enough for the body to absorb.

       c. Absorption is the take up of the products of digestion, usually by the cells lining the digestive tract.

       d. Elimination is the removal of undigested materials out of the digestive tract.

C. 21.3 Digestion occurs in specialized compartments

    1. Sponges digest food in vacuoles.

    2. Most animals digest food in compartments.

    3. Cnidarians and flatworms have a **gastrovascular cavity** with a single opening, the **mouth**.

       a. Food enters the mouth.

       b. Enzymes break down the food.

       c. Food particles move into cells lining the compartment.

       d. Undigested materials are expelled back out the mouth.

    4. Most animals have an **alimentary canal** with

       a. a mouth,

       b. an anus, and

       c. specialized regions associated with one-way flow of food.

    5. The normal one-way flow moves food

       a. into the **pharynx** or throat,

       b. down the **esophagus** to a

          i. crop where food is softened and stored,

          ii. gizzard, where food is ground and stored, and/or

          iii. mach where food is ground and stored,

       c. to the **intestines**, where chemical digestion and nutrient absorption occur, and finally

       d. undigested materials are expelled through the **anus**.

III. The Human Digestive System

    A. 21.4 The human digestive system consists of an alimentary canal and accessory glands

       1. In humans, food is

          a. ingested and chewed in the mouth or **oral cavity**,

          b. pushed by the tongue into the pharynx,

          c. moved along by alternating waves of contraction and relaxation by smooth muscle in the walls of the canal in a process called **peristalsis**, and

          d. moved in and out of the stomach by **sphincters**.

          e. The final steps of digestion and nutrient absorption in humans occur in the small intestine.

          f. Undigested materials move through the large intestine, feces are stored in the rectum, and then expelled out the anus.

    B. 21.5 Digestion begins in the oral cavity

       1. Mechanical and chemical digestion begin in the mouth.

       2. Chewing cuts, smashes, and grinds food, making it easier to swallow.

3. The tongue
  a. tastes,
  b. shapes the food into a ball called a **bolus**, and
  c. moves it toward the pharynx.

C. Salivary glands **release**
  1. a slippery glycoprotein that moistens and lubricates food for easier swallowing,
  2. buffers that neutralize acids,
  3. salivary enzyme amylase that begins the hydrolysis of starch, and
  4. antibacterial agents that kill some bacteria ingested with food.

D. 21.6 After swallowing, peristalsis moves food through the esophagus to the stomach
  1. Air moves from the pharynx,
    a. into the larynx,
    b. past the vocal cords in the voice box,
    c. into the trachea, and
    d. into the lungs.
  2. Swallowed food and drink move from the pharynx,
    a. into the esophagus, and
    b. into the stomach.
  3. During swallowing,
    a. the tip of the larynx moves upward,
    b. preventing the food from entering the trachea.

E. 21.7 CONNECTION: The Heimlich maneuver can save lives
  1. The Heimlich maneuver
    a. involves a forceful elevation of the diaphragm,
    b. pushes air into the trachea, and
    c. can dislodge food from the pharynx or trachea during choking.
  2. Brain damage will occur within minutes if no airway is open.

F. 21.8 The stomach stores food and breaks it down with acid and enzymes
  1. The stomach can stretch and store up to 2 liters of food and drink.
  2. Some chemical digestion occurs in the stomach.
  3. The stomach secretes **gastric juice**, made up of
    a. mucus,
    b. a protein-digesting enzyme, and
    c. strong acid with a pH of about 2 that
      i. kills ingested bacteria,
      ii. breaks apart cells in food, and
      iii. denatures proteins.
  4. Pepsinogen and HCl produce active pepsin.
    a. Pepsinogen, H^+, and Cl^- are secreted into the lumen of the stomach.
    b. HCL converts some pepsinogen to pepsin.
    c. Pepsin helps activate more pepsinogen, starting a chain reaction.
    d. Pepsin begins the chemical digestion of proteins.
  5. What prevents the gastric juices from digesting the walls of the stomach?
    a. The secretion of pepsin in the inactive form of pepsinogen helps protect the cells of the gastric glands.
    b. Mucus helps protect the stomach lining against HCl and pepsin.
    c. New cells lining the stomach are produced about every three days to those that have been damaged.

G. 21.9 CONNECTION: Digestive ailments include acid reflux and gastric ulcers
   1. Acid reflux of chyme in the stomach back into the esophagus causes the feeling of heartburn.
   2. Gastroesophageal reflux disease (GERD) results from frequent and severe acid reflux that harms the lining of the esophagus.
   3. Open sores in the lining of the stomach, called ulcers, may form.
   4. Bacterial infections (*Helicobacter pylori*) in the stomach and duodenum can produce ulcers.
H. 21.10 The small intestine is the major organ of chemical digestion and nutrient absorption
   1. The small intestine is
      a. named for its smaller diameter,
      b. about 6 meters long,
      c. the site of much chemical digestion, and
      d. where most nutrients are absorbed.
   2. The first 25 cm of the small intestine is the **duodenum**, where chyme squirted from the stomach mixes with digestive juices from the pancreas, liver, gallbladder, and gland cells in the intestinal wall.
      a. The **pancreas** produces pancreatic juice containing a mixture of digestive enzymes and an alkaline solution rich in bicarbonate.
      b. The **liver** produces bile, which is stored in the **gallbladder** until it is needed. Bile breaks up fats into small droplets that are more susceptible to attack by digestive enzymes.
      c. The intestinal wall produces digestive enzymes.
   3. The surface area for absorption in the small intestine is greatly increased by
      a. folds of the intestinal lining,
      b. fingerlike projections called **villi**, and
      c. tiny projections of the surface of intestinal cells called **microvilli**.
   4. Nutrients pass into epithelial cells by
      a. diffusion and
      b. against concentration gradients.
   5. Fatty acids and glycerol are
      a. recombined into fats,
      b. coated with proteins, and
      c. transported into lymph vessels.
   6. Other absorbed nutrients such as amino acids and sugars pass
      a. out of the intestinal epithelium,
      b. across the thin walls of the capillaries into blood, and finally
      c. to the liver.
I. 21.11 One of the liver's many functions is processing nutrient-laden blood from the intestines
   1. Blood from the digestive tract drains
      a. into the **hepatic portal vein**
      b. to the liver.
   2. The liver performs many functions. The liver
      a. converts glucose in blood to glycogen,
      b. stores glycogen and releases sugars back into the blood as needed,

  c. synthesizes many proteins including blood clotting proteins and lipoproteins that transport fats and cholesterol to body cells,

  d. modifies substances absorbed in the digestive tract into less toxic forms, and

  e. produces bile.

J. 21.12 The large intestine reclaims water and compacts the feces

 1. The **large intestine,** or **colon,**

  a. is about 1.5 m long and 5 cm in diameter,

  b. has a pouch called the **cecum** near its junction with the small intestine, which bears a small fingerlike extension, the **appendix,**

  c. contains large populations of *E. coli*, which produce important vitamins,

  d. absorbs these vitamins and water into the bloodstream, and

  e. helps form firm feces, which are stored in the **rectum** until elimination.

 2. Diarrhea occurs when too little water is reclaimed from the contents of the large intestine.

 3. Constipation occurs when too much water is reclaimed.

K. 21.13 EVOLUTION CONNECTION: Evolutionary adaptations of vertebrate digestive systems relate to diet

 1. The length of the digestive tract often correlates with diet. In general, the alimentary canals relative to their body size are

  a. longer in herbivores and omnivores and

  b. shorter in carnivores.

 2. Many herbivores have specializations of the gut that promote the growth of cellulose-digesting bacteria and protists because these animals lack the enzymes needed to digest cellulose in plants.

 3. These mutualistic organisms may be housed in

  a. the cecum, in a coyote or koala,

  b. the large intestine and the cecum in rabbits and some rodents, or

  c. the stomach of **ruminants** such as cattle, sheep, and deer.

IV. Nutrition

A. 21.14 Overview: An animal's diet must satisfy three needs

 1. All animals have the same basic nutritional needs. Animals must obtain

  a. fuel to power all body activities,

  b. organic molecules to build the animal's own molecules, and

  c. essential nutrients, or substances the animal cannot make for itself.

B. 21.15 Chemical energy powers the body

 1. Cellular respiration produces the body's energy currency, ATP,

  a. by oxidizing organic molecules digested from food and

  b. usually using carbohydrates or fats as fuel.

 2. A gram of fat has more than twice as many calories as a gram of carbohydrate or protein.

 3. The energy content of food is measured in **kilocalories** (1 **kcal** = 1,000 calories).

 4. Dietary calories are actually kilocalories and are written as Calories.

 5. The rate of energy consumption by an animal is called its **metabolic rate**, the sum of all the energy-requiring biochemical reactions over a given interval of time.

 6. The **basal metabolic rate** (**BMR**) is the energy a resting animal requires each day.

 7. The metabolic rate is the BMR plus the energy needed for physical activity.

 8. Excess energy is stored as glycogen or fat.

C. 21.16 An animal's diet must supply essential nutrients

  1. Essential nutrients cannot be made from any raw material.

  2. There are four classes of essential nutrients.

  a. Essential fatty acids, such as linoleic acid, are

  i. used to make phospholipids of cell membranes and

  ii. found in seeds, grains, and vegetables.

  b. Essential amino acids are

  i. used to make proteins and

  ii. found in meats, eggs, and milk.

  c. Vitamins are organic nutrients discussed in module 21.17.

  d. Minerals are simple inorganic nutrients discussed in module 21.17.

  3. Malnutrition is a chronic deficiency in calories or one or more essential nutrients. The most common type of human malnutrition is protein deficiency.

  4. Undernutrition occurs when

  a. diets do not supply sufficient chemical energy or

  b. a person suffers from anorexia nervosa or bulimia.

D. 21.17 A healthy human diet includes 13 vitamins and many essential minerals

  1. Essential vitamins and minerals are

  a. required in minute amounts and

  b. absolutely essential to good health.

  2. Vitamins are organic nutrients that may be

  a. water-soluble, such as vitamins B and C, or

  b. fat-soluble, such as vitamins A, D, E, and K.

  3. Minerals are simple inorganic nutrients.

  a. Calcium and phosphorus are required in larger amounts.

  b. Iron is needed to make hemoglobin.

  c. Iodine is required to make thyroid hormones.

  d. Most people ingest more salt than they need.

  4. The **Recommended Dietary Allowances (RDAs)** are

  a. the minimum amounts of nutrients that are needed each day and

  b. determined by a national scientific panel.

  5. Overdoses of vitamins can be harmful.

  a. In general, excess water-soluble vitamins will be eliminated in urine.

  b. However, excess fat-soluble vitamins can accumulate to toxic levels in body fat.

E. 21.18 SCIENTIFIC DISCOVERY: Scientists use observations and experiments to determine nutritional needs

  1. Many insights into human nutrition have come from epidemiology, the study of human health and diseases within populations.

  a. The essential need for vitamin C was revealed by the high incidence of scurvy in sailors on long sea voyages.

  b. The need for folic acid to prevent neural tube defects in newborns was revealed by studies of pregnant women of low socioeconomic status. Since 1998, folic acid has been added to foods such as bread and cereals sold in the United States.

F. 21.19 CONNECTION: Food labels provide nutritional information

  1. Food labels indicate

  a. serving size,

  b. calories per serving,

    c. amounts of selected nutrients per serving and as a percentage of daily value, and

    d. recommendations for daily limits of selected nutrients.

G. 21.20 EVOLUTION CONNECTION: The human health problem of obesity may reflect our evolutionary past

  1. Overnourishment is the consumption of more food energy than is needed for normal metabolism.

  2. Obesity is the excessive accumulation of fat.

  3. The World Health Organization recognizes obesity as a major global health problem.

  4. In the United States, the percentage of obese people has doubled to more than 30% in the past two decades. More than 35% are overweight.

  5. Weight problems often begin at a young age.

    a. 15% of children and adolescents in the United States are obese.

    b. Another 17% are overweight.

  6. Obesity leads to

    a. type 2 diabetes,

    b. cancer of the colon and breasts, and

    c. cardiovascular disease.

  7. Obesity is estimated to be a factor in 300,000 deaths per year in the United States.

  8. A 15-year study published in 2010 indicates that obesity now surpasses smoking in its contribution to disease and the shortening of healthy life spans.

  9. The complexity of weight control in humans is evident from studies of the hormone leptin.

 10. Leptin

    a. is produced by adipose (fat) cells and

    b. suppresses appetite.

    c. Obese children who have an inherited mutant form of the leptin gene lose weight after leptin treatments.

    d. However, high levels in otherwise healthy people do not suppress appetite.

H. 21.21 CONNECTION: What are the health risks and benefits of weight loss plans?

  1. Why are so many people overweight? Is it

    a. lack of exercise,

    b. the amount of food,

    c. the quality of food, or

    d. a combination of the above?

  2. The U.S. market for weight loss products and services has gone from about $60 million a year in 1999 to more than $48 billion a year today.

  3. Weight loss diets may

    a. help individuals lose weight but

    b. have health risks leading to malnourishment.

  4. Some severely obese individuals may be candidates for weight-loss surgery.

  5. Scientific studies of weight-loss diets indicate that the best way to lose weight and keep it off is to

    a. increase exercise and

    b. eat a balanced diet with adequate amounts of all essential nutrients.

I. 21.22 CONNECTION: Diet can influence risk of cardiovascular disease and cancer

  1. A healthy diet may reduce the risk of

    a. cardiovascular disease and

    b. cancer.

2. Two main types of cholesterol occur in the blood.

    a. Low-density lipoproteins (LDL) contribute to

        i. blocked blood vessels and

        ii. higher blood pressure.

    b. High-density lipoproteins (HDL) help to reduce blocked blood vessels.

        i. Exercise increases HDL levels.

        ii. Smoking decreases HDL levels.

        iii. Trans fats in the diet tend to increase LDL levels.

        iv. Eating mainly unsaturated fats tends to lower LDL levels.

3. The relationship between food and health is complex.

4. The American Cancer Society recommends

    a. regular exercise and

    b. a diverse diet of healthy foods with an emphasis on plant sources.

Chapter Guide to Teaching Resources

Obtaining and Processing Food (21.1–21.3)

Student Misconceptions and Concerns

- Students are likely familiar with the basics of the digestive system and the different types of animal diets. However, they are less likely to understand the distinctions between chemical and mechanical digestion and the specific roles of enzymes. An extra effort may be needed to differentiate between these important components of the digestive process. (21.2–21.3)

Teaching Tips

- If you have just completed Chapter 20, you may wish to point out the similarities between the ciliary mucus mechanism used to trap debris inhaled into our respiratory tract (Module 20.4) and the suspension feeding systems of clams. (21.1)

- Humans are omnivores. Consider contrasting the teeth of a carnivore (perhaps a cat), an herbivore (perhaps a rodent or bovine), and a human to reveal the intermediate pattern of omnivore teeth. If appropriate skeletal materials are unavailable, good images can suffice. (21.1)

- If your class size permits, consider demonstrating the process of chemical digestion in the human mouth by distributing crackers to students. Have students chew the crackers and hold them in their mouths without swallowing. The sweet taste they may notice is produced by the sugars produced by the chemical breakdown of starch by amylase, a digestive enzyme found in human saliva. (21.2)

- Challenge your students to explain why digestive tubes are more efficient than gastrovascular cavities (such as those found in cnidarians). Point out the advantages of the part-by-part specialization of the digestive tract permitted by the one-way flow of materials through a digestive tube with openings on both ends (mouth and anus). One-way digestive tracts are types of "disassembly" lines. (21.3)

Human Digestive System (21.4–21.13)

Student Misconceptions and Concerns

- Students often confuse the structures and functions of the trachea and esophagus. You might point out that the trachea has a structure and function like the hose of a vacuum cleaner. The rigid ribbed walls of the trachea keep the tube open as air is sucked through it. The esophagus, however, relies upon rhythmic changes in the shape of the walls (peristalsis) to push food toward the stomach. If the esophagus had stiff walls, it would not be able to perform this function. (21.4)

- Students often confuse pain in the intestines with pain in the stomach. The looping nature of the colon causes fecal material to pass closely to the stomach on its way down the digestive tract. This may cause "stomach" pains before the need to defecate or the more painful contractions of the intestines associated with diarrhea. Young children therefore sometimes confuse the need to defecate with an upset stomach. (21.4)

Teaching Tips

- Ask your students to identify the structures and processes of the human digestive tract that promote one-way flow. Peristalsis in the esophagus, stomach, and intestines, plus the operation of sphincters along the esophagus and stomach, encourage one-way flow. Of course, an exception occurs during vomiting, when contractions of the abdominal cavity force the stomach contents back up the digestive tract and the upper (cardiac) sphincter opens. (21.4)

- The role of saliva in causing food particles to adhere into a bolus and lubricating it for easy passage can be demonstrated by eating crackers or pretzels. You might wish to challenge your students to see how many pretzels/crackers they can chew and swallow in a short period of time, without the use of any beverages. The main factor limiting the speed of this consumption is the ability to produce sufficient saliva. (21.5)

- If you have not already discussed the functional significance of the structure of human teeth, consider the following exercise. Challenge your students to explain why the teeth in their mouths have different shapes. Help them to understand the form and function relationships of sharp incisors (best suited for cutting and biting) and the flatter, blunter surfaces of molars (more effective at smashing and grinding). (21.5)

- Demonstrate the process of peristalsis: move a racquet ball or golf ball through a tube sock by squeezing behind the ball. (21.6)

- Students often invert the "y" and "n" of pharynx and larynx. Consider emphasizing the "inks" sound in these words. This mistake is nearly as common as pronouncing "nuclear" as "nucular"! (21.6)

- The esophagus is so efficient at peristalsis that it can propel liquid water along its length against the forces of gravity. If one of your students is willing to endure a little discomfort, have the student fill his/her mouth with water and then bend over at the waist, so that the mouth is lower than the stomach. Ask the student to swallow, then to remain bent over for a further 20–30 seconds. Then ask them a simple question. In answering, your student will demonstrate that his/her mouth is now empty. (Some students might recognize this as a potential cure for hiccups.) It is possible that some water in the pharynx will leak back out the nasal passageway. Thus, this demonstration is best performed using water rather than carbonated beverages! (21.6)

- Slurping a beverage by inhaling while sipping creates the risk of aspirating fluid into the trachea. Such simple behaviors can be most illustrative to students who have not carefully analyzed such phenomena. (21.7)

- You might ask students to try to model aspects of the Heimlich maneuver while seated in class. At the end of normal exhalation, ask students to try to forcefully expel even more air. They will likely notice that they contract their abdominal region, similar to the forces applied during the Heimlich maneuver, to create additional expulsive force. (21.7)

- As noted by the authors, one of the important roles of stomach acids is to kill pathogens (mostly bacteria) that we ingest with our meals. Although it is best to wash our hands before we eat, saliva and stomach acids serve as a backup system. (21.8)

- The anticipation of a meal may result in an increase in the peristaltic activity of an empty stomach. The movement of gas pockets in the stomach and intestines lead to the sounds of a hungry stomach "growling." (21.8)

- The finding that most human ulcers result from *Helicobacter pylori* infections represented a significant shift in medical understanding, and led to the 2005 Nobel Prize in Medicine being awarded to Drs. Robin Warren and Barry Marshall. This new explanation helps to illustrate the tentative nature of scientific knowledge, and the importance of the willingness to reject a hypothesis if another offers a better explanation. (21.9)

- The same process of emulsification that helps break down fats in the small intestine also helps keep oil permanently mixed with vinegar in some commercial salad dressings. (21.10)

- A person who continues to vomit after emptying the stomach might eventually bring up a small amount of bitter-tasting green fluid. This is likely to be bile piled up from the small intestine! (21.10)

- The liver is often said to "filter" the blood. However, unlike a coffee or air filter, the liver does not trap particles. Instead, chemicals are degraded by the liver into less toxic forms. (21.11)

- Students might wonder why they might need to take another dose of aspirin or other drug every four hours. What happened to the first dose? The liver is often involved in the breakdown of these medicines, which are eliminated from the bloodstream over time. (21.11)

- If a person's gallbladder is removed, they will continue to produce bile; however, they will no longer have the capacity to release large amounts of it corresponding to the ingestion of a particularly fatty meal. (21.11)

- Bacteria in the large intestine ferment some of the indigestible carbohydrates, releasing methane, carbon dioxide, and other gases. Most adult humans produce about 500 milliliters of this gas (flatulus) each day. A diet particularly high in certain carbohydrate-rich foods (such as beans) can greatly increase the quantity of flatulus that is produced. (21.12)

- In a 2009 report, the UN estimated that worldwide, approximately 1.5 million children (under the age of 5) die each year from diarrhea. They note that the total annual deaths from diarrhea exceed the combined deaths caused by AIDS, malaria, and measles. (21.12)

- Many sharks have a spiral valve inside the intestine that increases the surface area in contact with the intestinal contents. (21.13)

- Before discussing the digestive tracts of carnivores and herbivores, have your students guess about the differences between them. Which digestive tract do they expect will be longer, and why do they think so? Beginning lectures with such basic questions stimulates student interest and exposes both their background knowledge and their misconceptions. (21.13)

Nutrition (21.14–21.22)

Student Misconceptions and Concerns

- Given new choices and greater freedom away from home, young college students frequently experiment with their diets. The details on nutritional requirements are worth additional emphasis in lecture. (21.14–21.22)

- Advertising frequently creates false expectations about simple shortcuts to dieting. Consider emphasizing the importance of a well-balanced diet and exercise. (21.14–21.22)

- Students may struggle with the concept that a pound of fat contains more than twice the calories of a pound of sugar. It might seem that a pound of food would simply add a pound of weight. (You might wish to remind them that fiber and water have no caloric value, but still add to the weight of food.) They may also have never understood the concept of dietary calories, but just tried to avoid fatty foods. Consider encouraging class discussions that explore student misconceptions about calories, body weight, and healthy diets. (21.14–21.22)

Teaching Tips

- Before discussing nutrition, challenge your students to explain why we need to eat. Module 21.14 identifies three resources obtained from diet. (21.14)

- Basal metabolic rates change throughout a lifetime and typically decline with age. The high caloric needs of a growing child decrease in adulthood. College students might already be experiencing increased weight gain due in part to the reduced caloric needs of adulthood. Few students appreciate these fundamental changes in caloric demands. (21.15)

- Physical activity, which often remains high in active college students, also tends to decline throughout life. Few students appreciate the need to maintain physical activity throughout adulthood and/or reduce caloric intake. (21.15)

- A gram of fat stores more than twice the energy of a gram of polysaccharide such as starch. You might elaborate with a simple calculation to demonstrate how a person's body weight would vary if the energy stored in body fat were stored instead in carbohydrates. If a 100-kg man carried 25% body fat, he would have 25 kg of fat in his body. Fat stores about 2.25 times more energy per gram than carbohydrate. What would be the man's weight if he stored the energy in the fat in the form of carbohydrate? (2.25 × 25 = 56.25 kg of carbohydrate + 75 kg = 131.25 kg total body weight, an increase of 31.25%) (21.15)

- One of the challenges zookeepers face is to determine the essential nutrients required in the diets of exotic animals. Without an appreciation of the natural diet of a rare animal, certain dietary requirements may remain undetected, resulting in malnourishment. (21.16)

- The U.S. Department of Health and Human Services provides their Dietary Guidelines for All Americans at www.health.gov/dietaryguidelines. (21.16–21.19)

- Students are often surprised to learn that the mineral iron in our diets is the same iron we use as a building material. You might wish to point out that like the rust formed by the reaction of oxygen and iron, blood is also red, due to the bonding of oxygen to iron in our red blood cells. Furthermore, the familiar "metal" taste we experience when we have a cut in our mouth is due to the presence of iron in our blood. (21.17)

- Students who take vitamins might recall that fat-soluble vitamins are often taken as gel capsules (such as vitamin E) while water-soluble vitamins are taken in crushable pill form. (21.17)

- Table 21.17A illustrates the details of vitamin requirements for humans. Students might benefit from a comparison of this table and the label from a bottle of daily vitamins. (21.17–21.19)

- Three of the four main types of organic molecules are sources of calories. Students can examine a nutrition label on a package of food to identify these three groups (carbohydrates, fats, and proteins). Challenge students to think of the fourth category of organic molecule that is not a significant source of dietary calories (nucleotides, which include ATP and are components of DNA and RNA). (21.19)

- Consider an assignment in which all students keep track for one complete (and typical) day the number of grams of fat, carbohydrates, and proteins that they consume. They can obtain most of this information from food labels. Students should compare the relative amounts of each group. They might be surprised at the relatively high amount of protein in their diets. (21.19)

- According to the U.S. Department of Agriculture, U.S. consumption of added fats and oils is among the highest in the world. (21.20)

- Consider asking your students to research the average per capita consumption of certain foods in the United States—anything from a fruit or vegetable to a type of meat or a dairy product such as butter or ice cream—on the Internet. Have each student email you the annual per capita consumption figure, along with the address of the website. You might then want to compile the data from the most reliable sources and present the results to the class. You can also use this as an opportunity to provide students with guidance about gathering scientific information, particularly from online sources. (21.20–21.21)

- Research suggests that physical activity remains an important aspect of health, independent of body weight. Certain studies have concluded that sedentary people of normal body weight might be less healthy than very physically active people who are overweight. (21.21)

- Margarine commonly comes in liquid squeeze containers, in tubs, and in sticks. These forms reflect increasing amounts of hydrogenation, gradually increasing in firmness from a liquid, to a firmer spread, to a solid stick of margarine. As noted in the text, recent studies have suggested that unsaturated oils become increasingly unhealthy as they are hydrogenated. Public attention to hydrogenation and the health risks of the trans fats that result are causing many people to cut their consumption of trans fats. (21.22)

- The American Cancer Society's website, www.cancer.org, has extensive information on the relationship between diet and cancer. Search within their website for "Common Questions About Diet and Cancer." (21.22)

Key Terms

absorption
alimentary canal
anus
appendix
basal metabolic rate
  (BMR)
bile
bolus
bulk feeders
carnivores
cecum
chyme
colon
crop
digestion
duodenum
elimination
esophagus
essential amino acids
essential fatty acids
essential nutrients

feces
fluid feeders
gallbladder
gastric juice
gastrin
gastrovascular cavity
gizzard
hepatic portal vein
herbivores
high-density
  lipoproteins (HDLs)
ingestion
intestine
kilocalorie (kcal)
large intestine
liver
low-density
  lipoproteins (LDLs)
malnutrition
metabolic rate
microvilli

mineral
mouth
obesity
omnivores
oral cavity
pancreas
peristalsis
pharynx
Recommended Dietary
  Allowances (RDAs)
rectum
ruminants
salivary glands
small intestine
sphincter
stomach
substrate feeders
suspension feeders
villi
vitamin

Word Roots

carni- = flesh; **-vora** = eat (*carnivore*: an animal that mainly eats other animals)

chymo- = juice (*chyme*: the mixture of partially digested food and digestive juices formed in the stomach)

gastro- = stomach; **-vascula** = a little vessel (*gastric juice*: the collection of fluids [mucus, enzymes, and acid] secreted by the stomach; *gastrin*: a digestive hormone that stimulates the secretion of gastric juice; *gastrovascular cavity*: a central cavity in the body of certain animals that functions in both the digestion and distribution of nutrients)

herb- = grass (*herbivore*: an animal that mainly eats plants or algae)

kilo- = thousand (*kilocalorie*: the quantity of heat equal to 1,000 calories, used to measure the energy content of food, and usually referred to as a "calorie")

micro- = small; **-villi** = shaggy hair (*microvillus* [plural, *microvilli*]: one of the many small, finger-like microscopic projections on the epithelial cells that serve to increase the surface area of the lumen in the small intestine)

omni- = all (*omnivore*: an animal that consumes both meat and plant material)

peri- = around; **-stalsis** = a constriction (*peristalsis*: rhythmic waves of contraction of smooth muscle that push food along the digestive tract)

villius- = shaggy hair (*villus* [plural, *villi*]: one of many fingerlike projections of the inner surface of the small intestine, which serve to increase surface area)

CHAPTER 22

Gas Exchange

Chapter Objectives

Opening Essay

Explain how geese can fly at altitudes higher than the summit of Mt. Everest. Explain how humans adjust to life at high altitudes.

Mechanisms of Gas Exchange

22.1 Describe the three main phases of gas exchange in a human.

22.2 Describe the properties of respiratory surfaces. Describe four types of respiratory surfaces and the kinds of animals that use them.

22.3 Explain how the amount of oxygen available in air compares to that available in cold and warm fresh water and cold and warm salt water.

22.3 Explain how the structure and movements of fish gills maximize oxygen exchange.

22.4 Explain why breathing air is easier than using water for gas exchange.

22.4 Describe the tracheal system of insects.

22.5 Describe the respiratory structures of the fossil animal *Tiktaalik*, and explain why these features have led scientists to conclude that it likely lived in shallow water.

22.5 Explain how the metabolic rate of a vertebrate corresponds to the nature of its respiratory system.

The Human Respiratory System

22.6 Describe the structures and corresponding functions of a mammalian respiratory system. Describe the causes and symptoms of respiratory distress syndrome and COPD.

22.7 Describe the impact of smoking on human health.

22.8 Compare the mechanisms and efficiencies of lung ventilation in humans and birds.

22.9 Explain how breathing is controlled in humans.

Transport of Gases in the Human Body

22.10 Explain how blood transports gases between the lungs and tissues of the body.

22.11 Describe the functions of hemoglobin. Explain how carbon dioxide is transported in the blood.

22.12 Explain how a human fetus obtains oxygen prior to and immediately after birth.

Lecture Outline

I. Introduction

   A. People cannot survive for long in the air at the world's highest peaks in the Himalayan Mountains.

   B. Yet twice a year, flocks of geese migrate over the Himalayas.

   C. How can geese fly where people cannot breathe?

      1. Geese have more efficient lungs than humans, and

      2. their hemoglobin has a very high affinity for oxygen.

II. Mechanisms of Gas Exchange

   A. 22.1 Overview: Gas exchange in humans involves breathing, transport of gases, and exchange with body cells

      1. The process of **gas exchange** is sometimes called respiration, the interchange of

         a. O_2 and the waste product CO_2

         b. between an organism and its environment.

      2. Three phases of gas exchange occur in humans and other animals with lungs:

         a. breathing,

         b. transport of oxygen and carbon dioxide in blood, and

         c. exchange of gases with body cells.

            i. Body tissues take up oxygen and

            ii. release carbon dioxide.

      3. Cellular respiration requires a continuous supply of oxygen and the disposal of carbon dioxide.

   B. 22.2 Animals exchange O_2 and CO_2 across moist body surfaces

      1. Respiratory surfaces must be

         a. moist for diffusion of O_2 and CO_2 and

         b. thin, to best facilitate diffusion.

      2. The skin may be used for gas exchange in animals that are

         a. wet and

         b. small.

         c. Earthworms are an example.

      3. Most animals have specialized body parts that promote gas exchange:

         a. **gills** in fish and amphibians,

         b. **tracheal systems** in arthropods, and

         c. **lungs** in tetrapods that live on land, such as

            i. amphibians,

            ii. reptiles, including birds, and

            iii. mammals.

   C. 22.3 Gills are adapted for gas exchange in aquatic environments

      1. Gills

         a. are extensions of the body,

         b. increase the surface to volume ratio, and

         c. increase the surface area for gas exchange.

            i. Oxygen is absorbed.

            ii. Carbon dioxide is released.

2. In a fish, gas exchange is enhanced by

    a. ventilation of the gills (moving water past the gills) and

    b. countercurrent flow of water and blood.

3. Gas exchange with water has its limits.

    a. Water holds only about 3% of the oxygen in air.

    b. Cold water holds more oxygen than warm water.

    c. Fresh water holds more oxygen than salt water.

    d. Turbulent water holds more oxygen than still water.

D. 22.4 The tracheal system of insects provides direct exchange between the air and body cells

    1. Compared to water, using air to breathe has two big advantages.

        a. Air contains higher concentrations of O_2 than water.

        b. Air is lighter and easier to move than water.

    2. However, air-breathing animals lose water through their respiratory surfaces.

    3. Insect tracheal systems use tiny branching tubes that

        a. reduce water loss and

        b. pipe air directly to cells.

E. 22.5 EVOLUTION CONNECTION: The evolution of lungs facilitated the movement of tetrapods onto land

    1. Tetrapods seem to have evolved in shallow water.

        a. Fossil fish with legs had lungs and gills.

        b. Legs may have helped them lift up to gulp air.

        c. The fossil fish *Tiktaalik*

            i. lived about 375 million years ago and

            ii. illustrates these air-breathing adaptations.

    2. The first tetrapods on land diverged into three major lineages.

        a. Amphibians use small lungs and their body surfaces.

        b. Nonbird reptiles have

            i. lower metabolic rates and

            ii. simpler lungs.

        c. Birds and mammals have

            i. higher metabolic rates and

            ii. more complex lungs.

III. The Human Respiratory System

A. 22.6 In mammals, branching tubes convey air to lungs located in the chest cavity

    1. The **diaphragm**

        a. separates the abdominal cavity from the thoracic cavity and

        b. helps ventilate the lungs.

    2. In mammals, air is inhaled through the nostrils into the nasal cavity. Air is

        a. filtered by hairs and mucus surfaces,

        b. warmed and humidified, and

        c. sampled for odors.

    3. From the nasal cavity, air next passes

        a. to the **pharynx**,

        b. then **larynx**, past the **vocal cords**,

        c. into the **trachea**, held open by cartilage rings,

        d. into the paired **bronchi**,

  e. into **bronchioles**, and finally

  f. to the **alveoli**, grapelike clusters of air sacs, where gas exchange occurs.

 4. Alveoli are well adapted for gas exchange with high surface areas of capillaries

 5. In alveoli,

  a. O_2 diffuses into the blood and

  b. CO_2 diffuses out of the blood.

 6. **Surfactants** are specialized secretions required to keep the walls of the small alveoli from sticking shut.

  a. Babies born 6 weeks or more before their due date often struggle with respiratory distress syndrome due to an inadequate amount of lung surfactant.

  b. Artificial surfactants are now administered to preterm infants.

 7. Exposure to pollutants can cause continual irritation and inflammation of the lungs.

  a. Examples of common lung pollutants include

   i. air pollution and

   ii. tobacco smoke.

  b. Chronic obstructive pulmonary disease (COPD) can result limiting

   i. lung ventilation and

   ii. gas exchange.

B. 22.7 CONNECTION: Smoking is a serious assault on the respiratory system

 1. Mucus and cilia in the respiratory passages

  a. sweep contaminant-laden mucus up and out of the airways and

  b. can be damaged by smoking.

 2. One of the worst sources of lung-damaging air pollutants is tobacco smoke, containing more than 4,000 chemicals.

 3. Without healthy cilia, smokers must cough to clear dirty mucus from the trachea.

 4. Smoking can cause

  a. lung cancer,

  b. cardiovascular disease, and

  c. emphysema.

 5. Smoking accounts for 90% of all lung cancer cases.

 6. Smoking increases the risk of other types of cancer.

 7. Smoking also

  a. increases the risk of heart attacks and strokes,

  b. raises blood pressure, and

  c. increases harmful types of cholesterol.

 8. Every year in the United States, smoking

  a. kills about 440,000 people,

  b. more than all the deaths from accidents, alcohol, drug abuse, HIV, and murders combined.

 9. Adults who smoke die 13–14 years earlier than nonsmokers.

C. 22.8 Negative pressure breathing ventilates your lungs

 1. **Breathing** is the alternate inhalation and exhalation of air (ventilation).

 2. In mammals, inhalation occurs when

  a. the rib cage expands,

  b. the diaphragm moves downward,

  c. the pressure around the lungs decreases, and

  d. air is drawn into the respiratory tract.

3. This type of ventilation is called **negative pressure breathing.**

4. Exhalation occurs when

    a. the rib cage contracts,

    b. the diaphragm moves upward,

    c. the pressure around the lungs increases, and

    d. air is forced out of the respiratory tract.

5. Not all air is expelled during exhalation.

    a. Some air still remains in the trachea, bronchi, bronchioles, and alveoli.

    b. This remaining air is "dead air."

    c. Thus, inhalation mixes fresh air with dead air.

6. One-way flow of air in birds

    a. reduces dead air and

    b. increases their ability to obtain oxygen.

D. 22.9 Breathing is automatically controlled

    1. Breathing is usually under automatic control.

    2. Breathing control centers in the brain sense and respond to CO_2 levels in the blood.

    3. A drop in blood pH increases the rate and depth of breathing.

IV. Transport of Gases in the Human Body

A. 22.10 Blood transports respiratory gases

    1. The heart pumps blood to two regions.

        a. The right side pumps oxygen-poor blood to the lungs.

        b. The left side pumps oxygen-rich blood to the body.

    2. In the lungs, blood picks up O_2 and drops off CO_2.

    3. In the body tissues, blood drops off O_2 and picks up CO_2.

    4. A mixture of gases, such as air, exerts pressure.

        a. Each kind of gas in a mixture accounts for a portion of the total pressure of the mixture.

        b. Thus, each gas has a **partial pressure**.

        c. The exchange of gases between capillaries and the surrounding cells is based on partial pressures.

        d. Molecules of each kind of gas diffuse down a gradient of its own partial pressure, moving from regions of

            i. higher partial pressure to

            ii. lower partial pressure.

    5. Gases move from areas of higher concentration to areas of lower concentration.

        a. Gases in the alveoli of the lungs have more O_2 and less CO_2 than gases in the blood.

            i. O_2 moves from the alveoli of the lungs into the blood.

            ii. CO_2 moves from the blood into the alveoli of the lungs.

        b. The tissues have more CO_2 and less O_2 than gases in the blood.

            i. CO_2 moves from the tissues into the blood.

            ii. O_2 moves from the blood into the tissues.

B. 22.11 Hemoglobin carries O_2, helps transport CO_2, and buffers the blood

    1. Most animals transport O_2 bound to proteins called respiratory pigments.

        a. Blue, copper-containing pigment is used by

            i. molluscs and

            ii. arthropods.

> b. Red, iron-containing **hemoglobin**
>> i. is used by almost all vertebrates and many invertebrates and
>> ii. transports oxygen, buffers blood, and transports CO_2.
> 2. Most CO_2 in the blood enters red blood cells.
> 3. Some CO_2 combines with hemoglobin.
> 4. Other CO_2 reacts with water, forming carbonic acid, which then breaks apart into
>> a. hydrogen ions and
>> b. bicarbonate ions in a reversible reaction.
>> c. Hemoglobin binds most of the H^+ produced by this reaction, minimizing the change in blood pH.

C. 22.12 CONNECTION: The human fetus exchanges gases with the mother's blood
> 1. A human fetus does not breathe with its lungs. Instead, it exchanges gases with maternal blood in the placenta.
> 2. In the placenta, capillaries of maternal blood and fetal blood run next to each other. The fetus and mother do not share the same blood.
> 3. Fetal hemoglobin
>> a. attracts O_2 more strongly than adult hemoglobin and
>> b. takes oxygen from maternal blood.
> 4. At birth
>> a. CO_2 in fetal blood increases and
>> b. breathing control centers initiate breathing.
> 5. Smoking during pregnancy reduces the supply of oxygen to the fetus by up to 25%.

Chapter Guide to Teaching Resources

Mechanisms of Gas Exchange (22.1–22.5)

Student Misconceptions and Concerns

- As the authors note (in Module 22.1), it is important to distinguish between the use of the word respiration in the context of the whole organism (breathing) and in the context of cells (cellular respiration). (22.1)

- Respiratory structures such as gills, lungs, and insect tracheal systems are highly branched, reflecting an adaptation to increase the surface area and ultimately the surface-to-volume ratio of the animal. Students might not realize the common principles of adaptations to increase surface-to-volume ratios in the highly branched respiratory structures, as well as in the circulatory system (for example, the small size of red blood cells and tiny size of capillaries), discussed in detail in the next chapter. You might consider expanding on this principle as you address other systems that reflect such adaptations (for example, greater surface area of the digestive system for absorption of nutrients). (22.1–22.5)

Teaching Tips

- You may want to point out that in scientific artwork, it is common to identify blood vessels in the arterial system by coloring them red, and blood vessels in the venous system by coloring them blue. As experienced biologists, such expectations can be so routine that we forget that we might need to point this out to our students. (22.1)

- Salamanders in the family Plethodontidae are unusual terrestrial vertebrates that survive mainly on land as adults, yet have no lungs. The adults acquire all of their oxygen through their skin. Consider discussing with your class how this is possible. Their relatively small size, slow metabolic rates, preference for cool environments, and minimal physical activity all permit the absence of lungs. (22.2)

- Students struggling to recall the conditions that increase the oxygen content of water might benefit by picturing in their mind a scenario that includes all the best conditions. A pool at the base of a waterfall, generated from melting snow, has a very high oxygen content because the water is (a) fresh, (b) cool, and (c) turbulent. (22.3)

- As the authors note in Module 22.3, the basic principles of countercurrent exchange apply to the transfer of gases and temperature. Countercurrent exchange as it applies to temperature is addressed in Chapter 25. (22.3)

- Challenge your class to explain why fish gills do not work well in air. As noted in Modules 22.2 and 22.3, respiratory surfaces need to remain moist. In addition, the surface area of the gills is greatly reduced as the filaments adhere to each other. You can visually demonstrate this point by simply lifting your hand and spreading your fingers apart, noting that gills are spaced like this in water. In air (bring your fingers together), the filaments adhere into one larger mass with less surface area. (22.3)

- You might mention to your class that most animals use tracheal systems. After all, insects are by far the dominant type of animal on Earth (at least 70% of all known animal species). Therefore, whatever insects do is automatically the most common animal adaptation! (22.4)

- In a very general sense, the tracheal system of insects is like the ductwork bringing outside air into the individual offices of a high-rise building. (But unlike a tracheal system, the air is removed from the building by another system.) (22.4)

- Many aquatic amphibians, such as the axolotl salamander, use gills, lungs, and skin surfaces for gas exchange. As noted in Module 22.5, this appears to be true of the first tetrapods such as *Tiktaalik*. (22.5)

The Human Respiratory System (22.6–22.9)

Student Misconceptions and Concerns

- Students often confuse the structures and functions of the trachea and esophagus. To help them distinguish, point out that the trachea has a structure and function like the hose of a vacuum cleaner. The rigid ribbed walls of the trachea keep the tube open as air is sucked through it. The esophagus, however, relies upon rhythmic changes in the shape of the walls (peristalsis) to push food toward the stomach. If the esophagus had stiff walls, it would not be able to perform this function. (22.6)

- Students might misunderstand how the cilia lining our respiratory passages work. Cilia do not filter the air like a comb. Instead, cilia are covered by a layer of mucus. Dust particles adhere to sticky mucus, which is then swept up the respiratory tract by the cilia. If students clear their throats, they will identify the fate of this mucus. We swallow after clearing our throats!

Teaching Tips

- The basic principles of the vocal cords can be demonstrated by inflating a balloon and letting air out, while stretching the neck of the balloon. If the balloon neck is stretched tightly, it will produce high-pitched sounds; when it is relaxed, it will produce lower-pitched sounds. (22.6)

- Students often appreciate explanations that help them understand their own experiences. When we struggle with respiratory infections or allergies, especially when the air is dry, thick mucus accumulates in our branchial system. A long, warm shower hydrates these mucus films, facilitating their movement up and out of our respiratory systems. Although students might have heard this advice, they might not have fully understood the mechanisms. (Sipping hot tea also helps to hydrate these mucus surfaces.) (22.6)

- The impact of smoking on public health is described in detail in Module 22.7. Despite this increasingly available information, many students still choose to smoke. Consider including some exercise in your class that will provide students with an opportunity to better understand the public health consequences of smoking. (22.7)

- In its relaxed state, the human diaphragm is domed upward toward the heart. Contracting the diaphragm pushes down on the intestines and stomach, forcing the abdominal region outward. Thus, it can be more difficult to inhale after having consumed a large volume of food and/or drink. (22.8)

- Some of your students may have been taught to breathe deeply by actively extending their stomach outwards. Ask your class to explain why this permits them to take a deeper breath. (The answer: it allows the diaphragm to move down with less resistance from body organs in the abdominal cavity.) (22.8)

- As noted in Module 22.9, the breathing control centers in the brain are based upon the concentration of carbon dioxide in the blood (and the resulting changes in pH). Challenge your students to explain why this system is usually sufficient to provide adequate levels of oxygen in the blood. (The by-product of aerobic respiration is carbon dioxide.) (22.9)

Transport of Gases in the Human Body (22.10–22.12)

Student Misconceptions and Concerns

- Many students still struggle with the concept of diffusion as the main mechanism of gas transport. Before discussing gas transport, ask your class to explain why oxygen moves out of the blood in body tissues, but into the blood in the lungs. Why don't these processes proceed in the opposite direction? (22.10–22.12)

- Many students struggle with fundamental aspects of fetal circulation and respiration. Students might assume that the mother's blood flows through the umbilical cord into the fetus. Students might also expect that the fetus is somehow breathing air. Nobody likes to be embarrassed by ignorance, so gauging these and many other misconceptions can be a challenge. To better understand your students' background knowledge consider giving a short quiz on fundamental points before lecturing on the subject. (22.10–22.12)

Teaching Tips

- Figure 22.10 is an especially helpful depiction of the movements of gases in the human respiratory system. The figure includes all of the main sites where oxygen is consumed, the alveoli where gas exchange occurs in the lungs, and the separate movement of oxygenated and deoxygenated blood through the heart. (22.10)

- Students are often surprised to learn that the mineral iron in our diets is the same iron we use for building automobiles, pots, and pans. You might wish to point out that like the rust formed by the reaction of oxygen and iron, blood is also red, due to the bonding of oxygen to iron in our red blood cells. Furthermore, the familiar "metal" taste we experience when we have a cut in our mouth is due to the presence of iron in our blood. (22.11)

- Consider challenging your class to explain why a mother's hemoglobin will release oxygen to the fetus. As noted in Module 22.12, fetal hemoglobin has a stronger affinity for oxygen. This is like an adult pulling a toy away from a child. (22.12)

Key Terms

alveoli (singular, alveolus)	gas exchange	surfactant
breathing control center	gills	trachea
bronchi (singular, bronchus)	hemoglobin	tracheal system
bronchioles	larynx	ventilation
countercurrent exchange	lungs	vital capacity
diaphragm	negative pressure breathing	vocal cords
	partial pressure	
	pharynx	

Word Roots

alveol- = a cavity (*alveolus* [plural, *alveoli*]: one of the millions of tiny dead-end sacs within vertebrate lungs where gas exchange occurs)

bronch- = branch (*bronchiole*: a thin breathing tube that branches from a bronchus within a lung; *bronchus* [plural, *bronchi*]: one of a pair of breathing tubes that branch from the trachea into the lungs)

counter- = opposite (*countercurrent exchange*: the transfer of a substance or heat between two fluids flowing in opposite directions)

hemo- = blood (*hemoglobin*: an iron-containing protein in red blood cells that reversibly binds O_2 and transports it to body tissues)

CHAPTER 23

Circulation

Chapter Objectives

Opening Essay

Describe the adaptations of giraffes and humans to circulate blood against the pull of gravity.

Circulatory Systems

23.1 Describe the general functions of a circulatory system.

23.1 Compare the structures and functions of gastrovascular cavities, open circulatory systems, and closed circulatory systems.

23.2 Compare the cardiovascular systems of a fish, an amphibian, a reptile, a bird, and a mammal.

The Human Cardiovascular System and Heart

23.3 Describe the pathway of blood through the mammalian cardiovascular system. Note the names of all blood vessels and heart chambers identified in Figure 23.3A, B.

23.4 Distinguish between diastole and systole. Explain why blood moves in one direction through the heart.

23.5 Explain how heartbeats are controlled.

23.6 Define a heart attack and cardiovascular disease. Explain what causes them and what can be done to reduce the chances of developing cardiovascular disease.

Structure and Function of Blood Vessels

23.7 Relate the structure of blood vessels to their function.

23.8 Explain how and why blood pressure changes as blood moves away from the heart. Explain how blood is moved back to the heart.

23.9 Explain how blood pressure is measured. Give examples of normal and high blood pressure readings. Describe lifestyle changes that can help to reduce high blood pressure.

23.10 Explain how blood flow through capillaries is regulated.

23.11 Explain how the structure of a capillary relates to its functions.

Structure and Function of Blood

23.12 Describe the components of blood and their functions.

23.13 Describe the structure, function, and production of red blood cells. Explain why exercising at high altitudes, injecting synthetic EPO, and blood doping increase red blood cell concentrations.

23.14 Describe the process of blood clotting.

23.15 Define leukemia and describe the most common forms of treatment.

Lecture Outline

I. Introduction

A. In many animals, the pull of gravity influences the flow of blood through the body.

B. To regulate the pressure of blood in the head, the circulatory system of a giraffe uses

    1. special valves,

    2. saclike sinuses, and

    3. other mechanisms.

C. In humans, special one-way valves in veins prevent blood from flowing back down the legs.

II. Circulatory Systems

A. 23.1 Circulatory systems facilitate exchange with all body tissues

    1. All cells must

        a. receive nutrients,

        b. exchange gases, and

        c. remove wastes.

    2. Diffusion alone is inadequate for large and complex bodies.

    3. In most animals, **circulatory systems** facilitate these exchanges.

    4. An internal transport system assists diffusion by moving materials between

        a. surfaces of the body and

        b. internal tissues.

    5. A gastrovascular cavity in cnidarians and flatworms

        a. promotes digestion and

        b. distributes substances.

    6. Most animals use a true circulatory system that consists of a

        a. circulatory fluid (blood),

        b. muscular pump (heart), and

        c. set of tubes (blood vessels) to carry the fluid.

    7. **Open circulatory systems** are found in arthropods and many molluscs and consist of

        a. a heart,

        b. open-ended vessels, and

        c. blood that directly bathes the cells and functions as the interstitial fluid.

    8. **Closed circulatory systems** are found in vertebrates, earthworms, squids, and octopuses and consist of

        a. a heart and

        b. vessels that confine blood, keeping it distinct from interstitial fluid.

    9. The vertebrate circulatory system is often called a **cardiovascular system**, including three types of vessels.

        a. **Arteries** carry blood away from the heart.

        b. **Veins** return blood to the heart.

        c. **Capillaries** convey blood between arteries and veins.

    10. The cardiovascular system of a fish includes a heart with two main chambers:

        a. The **atrium** receives blood from veins.

        b. The **ventricle** pumps blood to gills via large arteries. These large arteries branch into

            i. **arterioles** that give rise to

      ii. capillaries, the smallest blood vessels that branch into networks called **capillary beds**.

      iii. Capillaries converge into **venules**, which in turn converge into larger veins.

B. 23.2 EVOLUTION CONNECTION: Vertebrate cardiovascular systems reflect evolution

  1. A two-chambered heart

    a. is characteristic of fish and

    b. pumps blood in a **single circulation** in which blood moves

      i. from gill capillaries,

      ii. to systemic capillaries, and

      iii. back to the heart.

  2. Land vertebrates have a **double circulation** consisting of a separate

    a. pulmonary circuit and

    b. systemic circuit.

  3. Three-chambered hearts

    a. are found in amphibians, turtles, snakes, and lizards and

    b. consist of

      i. two atria and

      ii. one undivided ventricle.

    c. This arrangement generally separates oxygen-poor and oxygen-rich blood.

  4. Four-chambered hearts

    a. are found in crocodilians, birds, and mammals and

    b. consist of

      i. two atria and

      ii. two ventricles.

    c. These two circuits do not mix

      i. oxygen-rich and

      ii. oxygen-poor blood.

III. The Human Cardiovascular System and Heart

A. 23.3 The human cardiovascular system illustrates the double circulation of mammals

  1. Blood flow through the double circulatory system of humans

    a. drains from the **superior vena cava** (from the head and arms) or **inferior vena cava** (from the lower trunk and legs) into the right atrium,

    b. moves out to the lungs via the **pulmonary artery**,

    c. returns to the left atrium through the **pulmonary vein**, and

    d. leaves the heart through the **aorta**.

B. 23.4 The heart contracts and relaxes rhythmically

  1. The repeated contraction and relaxation of pumping blood is called the **cardiac cycle**. The cycle consists of two main phases.

    a. During **diastole**, blood flows

      i. from veins

      ii. into heart chambers.

    b. During **systole**, blood flows

      i. from atria

      ii. into ventricles.

  2. Cardiac output is the amount of blood pumped per minute from the ventricles.

  3. Heart rate is the number of heart beats per minute.

  4. Heart valves prevent the backflow of blood.

5. A **heart murmur**

    a. is a defect in one or more heart valves that

    b. permits a backflow of blood and

    c. reduces the cardiac output.

C. 23.5 The SA node sets the tempo of the heartbeat

    1. The **SA (sinoatrial)** node

        a. generates electrical signals in atria and

        b. sets the rate of heart contractions.

    2. The **AV (atrioventricular)** node

        a. relays these signals to the ventricles and

        b. causes ventricular contraction.

    3. An electrocardiogram (ECG) records electrical changes in the heart.

    4. Heart rates normally adjust to body needs.

    5. Abnormal rhythms may occur in a heart attack.

    6. Automatic external defibrillators (AEDs)

        a. shock the heart,

        b. reset the SA node, and

        c. save thousands of lives.

D. 23.6 CONNECTION: What is a heart attack?

    1. A **heart attack**

        a. is damage or death of cardiac muscle and

        b. usually results from a blocked coronary artery.

    2. **Cardiovascular diseases** are disorders of the heart and blood vessels. These include

        a. a **stroke**, death of brain tissue from blocked or ruptured arteries in the head and

        b. **atherosclerosis**, in which fatty deposits in the walls of arteries narrow the blood vessels and restrict blood flow.

IV. Structure and Function of Blood Vessels

A. 23.7 The structure of blood vessels fits their functions

    1. Capillaries

        a. have thin walls consisting of a single layer of epithelial cells,

        b. are narrow, about as wide as one red blood cell, and

        c. increase surface area for gas and fluid exchange with the interstitial fluid.

    2. Arteries and veins

        a. are lined by a single layer of epithelial cells and

        b. have elastic fibers in an outer connective tissue layer that allows these vessels to recoil after stretching.

        c. Arteries contain a thick layer of smooth muscle in their walls that can constrict and reduce blood flow.

        d. Veins have one-way valves that restrict backward flow of blood.

B. 23.8 Blood pressure and velocity reflect the structure and arrangement of blood vessels

    1. **Blood pressure**

        a. is the force blood exerts on vessel walls,

        b. depends on cardiac output and resistance of vessels to expansion, and

        c. decreases as blood moves away from the heart.

    2. Blood pressure is

        a. highest in arteries and

        b. lowest in veins.

3. **Blood pressure** is measured as
    a. systolic pressure—caused by ventricular contraction and
    b. diastolic pressure—low pressure between contractions.
4. How does blood travel against gravity, up legs?
    a. Veins are squeezed by pressure from muscle contractions between
        i. two muscles or
        ii. muscles and bone or skin.
    b. One-way valves limit blood flow to one direction, toward the heart.
C. 23.9 CONNECTION: Measuring blood pressure can reveal cardiovascular problems
    1. A typical blood pressure for a healthy young adult is about 120/70.
    2. Blood pressure is commonly measured using a sphygmomanometer.
    3. **Hypertension** is a serious cardiovascular problem in which blood pressure is persistent at or above
        a. 140 systolic and/or
        b. 90 diastolic.
    4. Hypertension causes
        a. the heart to work harder, weakening the heart over time,
        b. increased plaque formation from tiny ruptures, and
        c. increased risk of blood clot formation.
    5. Hypertension can contribute to
        a. heart attacks,
        b. strokes, and/or
        c. kidney failure.
D. 23.10 Smooth muscle controls the distribution of blood
    1. Blood flow through capillaries is restricted by precapillary sphincters.
    2. By opening and closing these precapillary sphincters, blood flow to particular regions can be increased or decreased.
    3. Only about 5–10% of capillaries are open at one time.
E. 23.11 Capillaries allow the transfer of substances through their walls
    1. Capillaries have very thin walls.
    2. Substances leave blood and enter interstitial fluid by
        a. diffusion and
        b. pressure-driven flow through clefts between epithelial cells.
    3. Blood pressure forces fluid out of capillaries at the arterial end.
    4. Osmotic pressure draws in fluid at the venous end.

V. Structure and Function of Blood

A. 23.12 Blood consists of red and white blood cells suspended in plasma
    1. Blood consists of several types of cells suspended in a liquid called **plasma**, which
        a. is about 90% water and
        b. contains many different substances.
    2. Two classes of cells are suspended in blood plasma.
        a. **Red blood cells** or **erythrocytes** transport O_2 bound to hemoglobin.
        b. **White blood cells**, or **leukocytes**,
            i. function inside and outside the circulatory system and
            ii. fight infections and cancer.
            iii. Monocytes and neutrophils are white blood cells called **phagocytes**, which engulf and digest bacteria and debris from our own dead cells.

B. 23.13 CONNECTION: Too few or too many red blood cells can be unhealthy

    1. Anemia can be caused by low amounts of

        a. hemoglobin or

        b. red blood cells.

        c. Anemia causes fatigue due to lack of oxygen in tissues.

    2. The hormone **erythropoietin (EPO)** regulates red blood cell production.

    3. Some athletes artificially increase red blood cell production by

        a. training at high altitudes,

        b. injecting erythropoietin, and

        c. withdrawing, storing, and then reinjecting them just before a competition.

        d. Abuse of these methods can lead to clotting, stroke, heart failure, or even death.

C. 23.14 Blood clots plug leaks when blood vessels are injured

    1. When a blood vessel is damaged

        a. **platelets** rapidly adhere to the exposed connective tissue and

        b. a cluster of sticky platelets forms a plug.

        c. Clotting factors released from platelets and in the plasma help trigger the conversion of the plasma protein **fibrinogen** to **fibrin**, a threadlike protein that helps form a clot that plugs the leak.

    2. Within an hour after a fibrin clot forms, the platelets contract, pulling the torn edges closer together.

    3. Chemicals released by platelets also stimulate cell division in smooth muscle and connective tissue, initiating the healing process.

D. 23.15 CONNECTION: Stem cells offer a potential cure for blood cell diseases

    1. Multipotent stem cells

        a. are unspecialized and

        b. replace themselves throughout the life of an organism.

    2. Multipotent stem cells can differentiate into two main types of stem cells.

        a. Lymphoid stem cells can in turn produce two types of lymphocytes, which function in the immune system.

        b. Myeloid stem cells can differentiate into

            i. erythrocytes,

            ii. other white blood cells, and

            iii. platelets.

    3. Leukemia

        a. is cancer of white blood cells,

        b. results in extra leukocytes that do not function properly, and

        c. is usually fatal unless treated.

    4. Leukemia may be treated by

        a. radiation,

        b. chemotherapy, or

        c. the replacement of cancerous bone marrow with healthy bone marrow.

Chapter Guide to Teaching Resources

Circulatory Systems (23.1–23.2)

Student Misconceptions and Concerns

- Students might need to be reminded about the changes in surface-to-volume ratios as organisms increase in size. As any organism gets larger (maintaining the same proportions) the need for a circulatory system coupled with a respiratory system increases, since the increase in surface area does not keep up with the increase in volume. (23.1–23.2)

- Students might not realize that closed circulatory systems are capable of greater pressures when fluids remain confined to limited spaces. (23.1–23.2)

Teaching Tips

- If you have not included Chapter 20 in your course, you may want to show your class Figure 20.13A. This figure provides a general demonstration of the types of systems required by organisms too large to exchange all materials at the surface of the body. (23.1)

- A gastrovascular cavity, seen in cnidarians and flatworms, absorbs and distributes nutrients throughout the organism's body. The word root vascula (meaning "little vessel") represents the circulatory function of these systems. As noted in Module 23.1, gastrovascular cavities are not effective in larger animals. (23.1)

- The following analogy to a house might help students distinguish between open and closed circulatory systems. The flow of air through a home with a blower furnace is an open system, in which the furnace propels air through ducts that open into rooms, and the air is later collected by vents that channel air back to the furnace. In this open system, air pressure and currents are generally low. In contrast, the plumbing systems of most homes are much more like a closed system in which water, under high pressure, is contained in pipes. The analogy is not perfect, because water pipes do eventually open up into sinks and bathrooms, before draining into the sewage system. (23.1)

- Challenge students to explain why closed circulatory systems have evolved in squids and octopuses, but not in clams or snails. The greater amount of muscular activity in squids and octopuses may have favored these more efficient systems of delivery. (23.1–23.2)

- To help students understand the need for a circulatory system, consider this analogy. Small islands are like small animals: No inner part is very far from the edges. However, large countries, like large animals, have considerable interior areas located far from their borders. Therefore, large countries such as the United States, Canada, and China require an internal system of roads and railways to transport many goods from ocean ports to cities located deep in these countries. These roads and railways move materials from ports in the same way that blood and blood vessels move them from respiratory surfaces. (23.1–23.2)

- There are many simple demonstrations of diffusion that can be performed. If you use a video imager or overhead projector, add a single drop of food coloring into a beaker of water with bright illumination. The slow dissipation of the dye will serve as a colorful and dramatic example of materials moving from a higher to a lower level of concentration. (23.1–23.2)

- The three-chambered heart of amphibians and turtles should not be seen as a necessary "intermediate" stage in some predestined evolution of a four-chambered heart. Instead, the three-chambered heart conveys advantages not permitted by the complete subdivision of the ventricle. In amphibians and turtles, the circuit to the lungs can be bypassed when diving underwater. When breathing is not possible, blood can be rerouted past the lungs. Thus, a loss in efficiency conveys an advantage in flexibility. This fundamental principle, in which efficiency and flexibility are traded against each other, is illustrated in many systems in living organisms. (23.2)

The Human Cardiovascular System and Heart (23.3–23.6)

Student Misconceptions and Concerns

- Students often expect that the blood flowing through the heart supplies the heart muscle. The need for coronary arteries and veins is not clear to them. (The thickness of the walls of the heart does not permit efficient diffusion, and furthermore, the oxygen content of the blood in the right atrium and ventricle is very low.) (23.4–23.6)

- Students often develop an incorrect mental model of how atherosclerosis occurs. In a home, drainpipes grow narrower as materials accumulate on their inside surface. However, in atherosclerosis, the blood vessels narrow through an accumulation of materials within the walls themselves. In the pipe analogy, atherosclerosis is a pipe with thicker walls, which shrink the size of the lumen. (23.6)

Teaching Tips

- When discussing the way blood flows through four-chambered hearts, it is helpful to remind students that the heart is essentially two pumps. The right side collects from the body and propels to the lungs; the left side propels from the lungs out to the body. Having them memorize this sequence as right-to-left helps students recall the correct atrial and ventricular sequences. (23.3)

- Students often benefit from brief, concrete demonstrations of abstract ideas. When discussing the cardiac cycle, take the time to have students quickly take their own pulse as they are seated in class to help them relate the lecture topic to their own anatomy. This very short activity will provide a small break in the lecture routine and refocus the attention of those students whose minds may have begun to wander. (23.4)

- Having students take their own pulses also provides an opportunity to stimulate further curiosity. You may want to assign students to measure and record the variation in their pulse rates during the day's different activities, perhaps a) upon arrival to a class and after 20 minutes sitting in the class, b) before and after drinking coffee, or c) prior to and during exercise. (23.4)

- The specialized junctions that promote signal conduction between cardiac cells are specifically identified in Figure 20.6 in Chapter 20. (23.5)

- Before explaining the functions of the SA node, consider asking your students to explain why the atria contract before the ventricles contract. Posing a question and asking for an explanation rather than simply lecturing students often generates a more active interest in the subject matter. (23.5)

- Strokes can result from the blockage of or rupture of a blood vessel in the brain. Thus, clot-busting drugs may either help resolve a brain clot or lead to disastrous bleeding. (23.6)

- Cardiovascular disease affects more than the blood vessels of the heart and brain. Many of the same risk factors that promote cardiovascular disease are associated with poor circulation to a penis, potentially leading to erectile dysfunction. (23.6)

The Structure and Function of Blood Vessels (23.7–23.11)

Student Misconceptions and Concerns

- Students may need to be reminded of the definitions of an artery and vein, especially when discussing blood flow to and from the heart. Although veins generally carry oxygen-poor blood, the pulmonary artery transports low-oxygen blood to the lungs. The main difference between arteries and veins is the direction of flow (away from or toward the heart). Due to their structure, arteries are better able to resist the higher pressures generated by ventricular contractions. Veins generally experience lower pressure and are structurally less resistant. (23.7)

- Students often struggle to explain how blood is propelled up their legs to return to their hearts. Frequently, students will suggest that the heart itself must provide sufficient force to move blood completely around the body. However, such pressures would destroy delicate capillaries. Other student hypotheses might include attributing a negative, siphoning effect to the heart. (Although the heart can generate a small pull, it is not sufficient to return blood up their legs and trunk to the heart.) Let them wonder long enough to stimulate critical thinking and motivate them to learn the answer. After explaining the role of skeletal muscles and one-way valves in veins, you might also note that it has been suggested that students will be more alert in class and even perform better on tests if they wiggle their legs. Challenge students to explain why this might work and why locking their knees when standing might have the opposite effect. (And enjoy watching some of your students deliberately wiggling their legs on the next exam!) (23.8)

Teaching Tips

- The photo in Figure 23.7A demonstrates the narrow width of capillaries. Notice that the diameter of the capillaries barely permits the passage of red blood cells. (Also note that Figure 23.7B shows a capillary diameter much greater than in the photograph.) Challenge your students to explain why such a small size is adaptive. (Answer: it increases the surface area of capillaries and places red blood cells adjacent to the capillary walls for efficient gas exchange.) (23.7)

- One function of the circulatory system that is rarely discussed is the transport of heat. Blood vessels near the surface of the body expand when the body is overheated, releasing some of this excess heat to the environment. Conversely, during periods of exposure to cold, blood is shunted away from the skin to conserve heat. (23.7)

- Veins on the back of our hands can reveal many of these same principles of venous blood flow. If students keep their hands down below their heart for several minutes, such as during note taking or typing, they might notice their veins starting to bulge. Students can watch the veins empty by simply lifting their hands up to eye level. As we get older, such phenomena are even easier to see. Some instructors may be comfortable enough (and old enough!) to demonstrate this effect to their students. (23.8)

- Contracting the hand into a fist helps propel blood back up the arms to the heart. Skin pulled tight on the back of the hand compresses veins against the underlying ligaments and bones. With this example "in hand," students may better understand the propulsive forces moving venous blood back to the heart. (23.8)

- Students may not relate the structure of the walls of arteries to blood pressure. Consider noting the presence of smooth muscle in the walls of arteries (Figure 23.7C). If these muscles contract, they narrow the arteries and increase pressure. (23.7–23.9)

- Students might wonder why they are discouraged from swimming soon after eating a meal. Blood flow during exercise involves the diversion of blood away from the gut and to major muscle groups likely involved in swimming. This can lead to indigestion or muscle cramping. However, the greatest risk of swimming with a full stomach is more likely that even a small amount of vomit could clog an air passageway. (23.10)

- Figure 23.11B depicts the movements of fluid out of and back into capillaries because of changes in osmotic pressure. The text references Module 24.3 for further discussion of the role of the lymphatic system in fluid removal. If you do not plan on addressing Chapter 24, consider including the role of lymphatic vessels in your discussion of Chapter 23. (23.11)

- Students who have little practice interpreting electron micrographs might benefit from a closer analysis of Figure 23.11A, in which an electron micrograph is paired with explanatory figure. For example, simply recognizing nuclei in micrographs can be an important starting point in interpreting cellular details and gaining a sense of scale. (23.11)

Structure and Function of Blood (23.12–23.15)

Student Misconceptions and Concerns

- Students with limited backgrounds in anatomy and physiology might not appreciate the diverse functions of plasma, instead thinking of blood as a transporter of oxygen and carbon dioxide. Figure 23.12 lists the many functions performed by plasma. (23.12)

- Students might have heard about blood thinners, thinking that somehow these substances make blood more fluid (like watering down syrup). The term actually refers to substances that make blood clotting less likely. Anticoagulants are specifically addressed in Module 23.14. (23.12–23.15)

Teaching Tips

- If you have a small fiber-optic lamp available, shining the light through your fingertips in a darkened room creates a red glow. This provides a dramatic example of the abundance of hemoglobin in red blood cells in the capillaries of our bodies. (23.12)

- You might note that one of the effects of aspirin is to block platelet aggregation. For additional details about the use of aspirin to prevent and treat heart disease, search the American Heart Association website at www.heart.org using the key word "aspirin." (23.12–23.15)

- Discuss the relationship between the structure and functions of erythrocytes. In Module 23.12, the authors note that the absence of a nucleus permits these cells to carry a greater amount of hemoglobin. But why is an erythrocyte dented in the middle? Wouldn't it seem more likely to be shaped like a hockey puck? The indentation in the center of an erythrocyte might increase its flexibility, permitting easier passage through small capillaries. Encourage students to contribute other ideas on the adaptive advantages of this unique shape (including a higher surface to volume ratio). (23.12)

- Just for fun, you might have your students pause for exactly 5 seconds and then note that during that period of time they each replaced 10 million red blood cells. In just 155 seconds, each person (on average) produces as many red blood cells as there are people in the United States! (23.13)

- Levels of anemia are often higher in college women, who may be under academic or personal stress and hence less likely to eat a well-balanced diet. Consider mentioning this in class and noting the many sources of iron available to women (the American Heart Association website cited previously may be useful). (23.13)

- Students are often surprised to learn that the mineral iron in our diets is the same iron we use for building automobiles, pots, and pans. You might wish to point out that, like the rust formed by the reaction of oxygen and iron, blood is also red, due to the bonding of oxygen to iron in our red blood cells. Furthermore, the familiar "metal" taste we experience when we have a cut in our mouth is due to the presence of iron in our blood. (23.13)

- If your class is large in size, you may have at least one student who is a hemophiliac, or who has a close family member with hemophilia. If the student is willing, consider having him/her share some of the details of the routine necessary to manage hemophilia. Generating empathy for the challenges of various ailments can be an important part of an education. (23.14)

- Advances in stem cell research continue, along with political controversy over whether or not such research should be funded by the federal government. You may want to consider bringing recent articles about stem cell research to class, or encourage your students to find a recent article about some aspect of stem cells and email it to you. (23.15)

Key Terms

anemia	diastole	pulmonary artery
aorta	double circulation	pulmonary circuit
arteriole	erythrocyte	pulmonary vein
artery	erythropoietin (EPO)	pulse
atherosclerosis	fibrin	red blood cell
AV (atrioventricular)	fibrinogen	SA (sinoatrial) node
node	heart	single circulation
atrium (plural, atria)	heart attack	stem cell
blood	heart murmur	stroke
blood pressure	heart rate	superior vena cava
capillary	hypertension	systemic circuit
capillary bed	inferior vena cava	systole
cardiac cycle	leukemia	vein
cardiac output	leukocyte	ventricle
cardiovascular disease	open circulatory system	venule
cardiovascular system	phagocyte	white blood cell
circulatory system	plasma	
closed circulatory system	platelet	

Word Roots

atrio- = a vestibule (*atrium* [plural, *atria*]: a heart chamber that receives blood from the veins); **-ventriculo** = ventricle (*atrioventricular node*: a region of specialized heart muscle tissue between the left and right atria)

capill- = hairlike [here, in the sense of a tube with a very small diameter] (*capillary*: microscopic blood vessel that conveys blood between an arteriole and a venule)

cardi- = heart; **-vascula** = a little vessel (*cardiovascular disease*: any disease of the heart or blood vessels; *cardiovascular system*: a closed circulatory system with a heart and branching network of arteries, capillaries, and veins)

erythro- = red; **-cyto** = cell (*erythrocyte*: a red blood cell); **-poiet** = produce (*erythropoietin*: a hormone that stimulates the production of erythrocytes; secreted by the kidney when tissues of the body do not receive enough oxygen)

fibrino- = a fiber (*fibrin*: the activated form of the blood-clotting protein fibrinogen, which aggregates into threads that form the fabric of a blood clot); **-gen** = produce (*fibrinogen*: the plasma protein that is activated to form a clot when a blood vessel is injured)

hyper- = high (*hypertension*: abnormally high blood pressure, or a persistent blood pressure above 140/90)

leuko- = white (*leukemia*: a cancer of the blood or bone marrow characterized by the production of an abnormally high number of leukocytes); **-cyto** = cell (*leukocyte*: a white blood cell)

phago- = eat; **-cyto-** = cell (*phagocyte*: a white blood cell that engulfs bacteria, foreign proteins, and the remains of dead body cells)

pulmo- = a lung (*pulmonary artery*: an artery that transports blood from the heart to the lungs; *pulmonary circuit*: one of the two main blood circuits in terrestrial vertebrates; responsible for conveying blood between the heart and the lungs; *pulmonary vein*: a vein that transports blood from the lungs to the heart)

CHAPTER **24**

The Immune System

Chapter Objectives

Opening Essay

Describe the functions of neutrophils.

Innate Immunity

24.1 Describe the nature of innate defenses in invertebrates and vertebrates.

24.2 Describe the steps of the inflammatory response and explain how they help to prevent the spread of disease.

24.3 Describe the structure and functions of the lymphatic system.

Adaptive Immunity

24.4 Describe the specific nature of adaptive immune system responses. Define the terms antigen, antibody, passive immunity, and active immunity.

24.5 Describe the development and functions of B lymphocytes and T lymphocytes. Define and distinguish between the humoral immune response and the cell-mediated immune response.

24.6 Describe the nature of antigens. Explain how an antigen and an antibody interact.

24.7 Describe the process of clonal selection and compare a primary immune response to a secondary immune response.

24.8 Describe the specific structure of an antibody and relate its shape to its functions.

24.9 Describe four effector mechanisms of the humoral immune system. Explain how antibodies work with innate defenses to form a complete defense system.

24.10 Describe the production and uses of monoclonal antibodies.

24.11 Describe the specific functions of helper T cells and how they interact with other cells.

24.12 Explain how cytotoxic T cells destroy infected body cells.

24.13 Explain how HIV infects cells, multiplies, and causes disease.

24.14 Explain why it has been difficult to develop a successful treatment for AIDS.

24.15 Explain how the immune system identifies the body's own molecules and how this system complicates organ transplantations.

Disorders of the Immune System

24.16 Describe how the malfunction or failure of the immune system can cause disease.

24.17 Explain why allergies occur and what causes anaphylactic shock.

Lecture Outline

I. Introduction

    A. Neutrophils are

        1. a kind of white blood cell,

        2. capable of recognizing and destroying foreign invaders, and

        3. part of the body's immune system.

    B. The human body's immune system

        1. recognizes agents that cause disease and

        2. attacks them.

II. Innate Immunity

    A. 24.1 All animals have innate immunity

        1. Nearly everything in the environment teems with **pathogens**, agents that cause disease.

        2. The immune system is the body's system of defenses against agents that cause disease.

        3. Innate immunity is a series of defenses that

            a. act immediately upon infection and

            b. are the same whether or not the pathogen has been encountered before.

        4. Invertebrates rely solely on innate immunity, which may consist of

            a. an exoskeleton,

            b. low pH,

            c. the enzyme lysozyme, and

            d. immune cells capable of phagocytosis, cellular ingestion and digestion of foreign substances.

        5. Vertebrates have innate and adaptive immunity.

        6. Vertebrate innate immunity includes

            a. barriers such as skin and mucous membranes,

            b. interferons, proteins produced by virus-infected cells, that help to limit the cell-to-cell spread of viruses,

            c. neutrophils (phagocytic cells),

            d. macrophages, large phagocytic cells that wander through the interstitial fluid,

            e. natural killer cells that attack cancer cells and virus-infected cells, and

            f. a **complement system**, a group of about 30 kinds of proteins that can act with other defense mechanisms.

    B. 24.2 Inflammation mobilizes the innate immune response

        1. Tissue damage triggers the **inflammatory response**, a major component of our innate immunity, which can

            a. disinfect and clean infected tissues and

            b. limit the spread of infection to surrounding tissues.

        2. Bacterial infections can bring about an overwhelming systemic inflammatory response leading to septic shock, characterized by

            a. very high fever and

            b. low blood pressure.

    C. 24.3 The lymphatic system becomes a crucial battleground during infection

        1. The lymphatic system is

            a. involved in innate and adaptive immunity and

      b. consists of a network of
         i. lymphatic vessels,
         ii. lymph nodes, and
         iii. lymph.

  2. Lymphatic vessels
      a. collect fluid from body tissues and
      b. return it as **lymph** to the blood.

  3. Lymph organs
      a. include the spleen and lymph nodes and
      b. are packed with white blood cells that fight infections.

  4. As lymph circulates through lymphatic organs it
      a. collects
         i. microbes,
         ii. parts of microbes, and
         iii. microbial toxins, and
      b. transports them to lymphatic organs where
         i. macrophages in lymphatic organs engulf the invaders and
         ii. lymphocytes may mount an adaptive immune response.

III. Adaptive Immunity

A. 24.4 The adaptive immune response counters specific invaders
  1. Our immune system responds to foreign molecules called **antigens**, which elicit the adaptive immune response.
  2. The adaptive immune system
      a. is found only in the vertebrates,
      b. reacts to specific pathogens, and
      c. "remembers" an invader.
  3. Infection or vaccination triggers **active immunity**.
  4. Vaccination, or immunization, exposes the immune system to a **vaccine**,
      a. a harmless variant or
      b. part of a disease-causing microbe.
  5. We can temporarily acquire **passive immunity** by receiving premade antibodies.

B. 24.5 Lymphocytes mount a dual defense
  1. Lymphocytes
      a. are white blood cells that spend most of their time in the tissues and organs of the lymphatic system,
      b. are responsible for adaptive immunity, and
      c. originate from stem cells in the bone marrow.
         i. B lymphocytes or **B cells** continue developing in bone marrow.
         ii. T lymphocytes or **T cells** develop further in the thymus.
  2. B cells
      a. participate in the **humoral immune response** and
      b. secrete antibodies into the blood and lymph.
  3. T cells
      a. participate in the **cell-mediated immune response**,
      b. attack cells infected with bacteria or viruses, and
      c. promote phagocytosis by other white blood cells and by stimulating B cells to produce antibodies.

4. Millions of kinds of B cells and T cells

    a. each with different **antigen receptors**, capable of binding one specific type of antigen,

    b. wait in the lymphatic system,

    c. where they may respond to invaders.

C. 24.6 Antigens have specific regions where antibodies bind to them

  1. Antigens

    a. are molecules that elicit the adaptive immune response,

    b. usually do not belong to the host animal, and

    c. are proteins or large polysaccharides on the surfaces of viruses or foreign cells.

  2. **Antigenic determinants** are specific regions on an antigen where antibodies bind.

    a. An antigen usually has several different determinants.

    b. The antigen-binding site of an antibody and an antigenic determinant have complementary shapes.

D. 24.7 Clonal selection musters defensive forces against specific antigens

  1. When an antigen enters the body it activates only a small subset of lymphocytes that have complementary receptors.

  2. In **clonal selection**, the selected lymphocyte cells

    a. multiply into clones of short-lived **effector cells**, specialized for defending against the antigen that triggered the response, and

    b. multiply into **memory cells**, which confer long-term immunity.

    c. **Plasma cells** are the effector cells produced during clonal selection of B cells.

  3. The clonal selection of B cells occurs in two responses.

    a. In the **primary immune response**, clonal selection produces

      i. effector cells and

      ii. memory cells that may confer lifelong immunity.

    b. In the **secondary immune response**, memory cells are activated by a second exposure to the same antigen.

  4. Primary vs. secondary immune responses

    a. The primary immune response

      i. occurs upon first exposure to an antigen and

      ii. is slower than the secondary immune response.

    b. The secondary immune response

      i. occurs upon second exposure to an antigen and

      ii. is faster and stronger than the primary immune response.

E. 24.8 Antibodies are the weapons of the humoral immune response

  1. Antibodies are secreted

    a. by plasma (effector) B cells,

    b. into the blood and lymph.

  2. An antibody molecule

    a. is Y-shaped and

    b. has two **antigen-binding sites** specific to the antigenic determinants that elicited its secretion.

F. 24.9 Antibodies mark antigens for elimination

  1. Antibodies promote antigen elimination through several mechanisms:

    a. neutralization, binding to surface proteins on a virus or bacterium and blocking its ability to infect a host,

    b. agglutination, using both binding sites of an antibody to join invading cells together into a clump,

    c. precipitation, similar to agglutination, except that the antibody molecules link dissolved antigen molecules together, and

    d. activation of the complement system by antigen-antibody complexes.

G. 24.10 CONNECTION: Monoclonal antibodies are powerful tools in the lab and clinic

  1. Monoclonal antibodies (mAb) are

    a. identical antibodies

    b. produced by cells that are all descendants of a single, hybrid cell.

  2. To make the hybrid cell with desirable properties, two cells are fused.

    a. A cancerous tumor cell, able to multiply indefinitely, is fused to

    b. a normal antibody-producing B cell, which is producing the desired antibody.

  3. Monoclonal antibodies are useful in

    a. research,

    b. diagnosis (such as home pregnancy tests), and

    c. treatment of certain cancers.

H. 24.11 Helper T cells stimulate the humoral and cell-mediated immune responses

  1. In the cell-mediated immune response, an **antigen-presenting cell** displays

    a. a foreign antigen (a **nonself molecule**) and

    b. one of the body's own **self proteins**

    c. to a helper T cell.

  2. The helper T cell's receptors

    a. recognize the self–nonself complexes and

    b. the interaction activates the helper T cells.

  3. The helper T cell can then activate

    a. cytotoxic T cells, which attack body cells that are infected with pathogens, and

    b. B cells.

I. 24.12 Cytotoxic T cells destroy infected body cells

  1. Cytotoxic T cells

    a. are the only T cells that kill infected cells,

    b. bind to infected body cells, and

    c. destroy them.

  2. Cytotoxic T cells also play a role in protecting the body against the spread of some cancers.

J. 24.13 CONNECTION: HIV destroys helper T cells, compromising the body's defenses

  1. AIDS (acquired immunodeficiency syndrome), results from infection by **HIV**, the **human immunodeficiency virus**.

    a. Since 1981, AIDS has killed more than 27 million people and more than 33 million people live today with HIV.

    b. In 2008,

      i. 2.7 million people were newly infected with HIV and

      ii. over 2 million died, including 300,000 children under age 15.

    c. Most AIDS infections and deaths occur in nonindustrialized nations of southern Asia and sub-Saharan Africa.

  2. The AIDS virus usually attacks helper T cells impairing the

    a. cell-mediated immune response and

    b. humoral immune response,

    c. opening the way for **opportunistic infections**.

3. AIDS patients typically die from

    a. opportunistic infections and

    b. cancers

    c. that would normally be resisted by a person with a healthy immune system.

4. Until there is a vaccine or a cure, the best way to stop AIDS is to educate people about how the virus is transmitted.

K. 24.14 EVOLUTION CONNECTION: The rapid evolution of HIV complicates AIDS treatment

  1. HIV mutates very quickly.

  2. New strains are resistant to AIDS drugs.

  3. Drug-resistant strains now infect new patients.

L. 24.15 The immune system depends on our molecular fingerprints

  1. The immune system normally reacts

    a. only against nonself substances and

    b. not against self.

  2. Transplanted organs may be rejected because the transplanted cells lack the unique "fingerprint" of the patient's self proteins, called **major histocompatibility complex (MHC) molecules**.

  3. Donors are used that most closely match the patients' tissues.

  4. Transplants between identical twins do not typically have this problem.

IV. Disorders of the Immune System

A. 24.16 CONNECTION: Malfunction or failure of the immune system causes disease

  1. **Autoimmune diseases** occur when the immune system turns against the body's own molecules.

  2. Examples of autoimmune diseases include

    a. lupus,

    b. rheumatoid arthritis,

    c. insulin-dependent diabetes mellitus, and

    d. multiple sclerosis.

  3. **Immunodeficiency diseases** occur when an immune response is

    a. defective or

    b. absent.

  4. The immune system may be weakened by

    a. physical stress or

    b. emotional stress.

    c. Students are more likely to be sick during a week of exams.

B. 24.17 CONNECTION: Allergies are overreactions to certain environmental antigens

  1. **Allergies** are hypersensitive (exaggerated) responses to otherwise harmless antigens in our surroundings.

  2. Antigens that cause allergies are called **allergens**.

  3. Allergic reactions typically occur

    a. very rapidly and

    b. in response to tiny amounts of an allergen.

  4. Allergic reactions can occur in many parts of the body, including

    a. nasal passages,

    b. bronchi, and

    c. skin.

5. The symptoms of an allergy result from a two-stage reaction.
   a. The first stage, called sensitization, occurs when a person is first exposed to an allergen.
   b. The second stage begins when the person is exposed to the same allergen later.
      i. The allergen binds to mast cells.
      ii. Mast cells release histamine, causing irritation, itchy skin, and tears.
6. **Antihistamines**
   a. interfere with histamine's action,
   b. provide temporary relief, but
   c. often make people drowsy.
7. **Anaphylactic shock**
   a. is an extreme life-threatening allergic reaction and
   b. can be treated with injections of epinephrine.

Chapter Guide to Teaching Resources

Innate Immunity (24.1–24.3)

Student Misconceptions and Concerns

- Students may be frustrated by the amount of detail about the immune system provided in this chapter, and struggle to organize information about the many types of cells and responses. Asking them to create or complete tables, similar to the one in Figure 24.1, can help your students manage the information presented in the textbook and in your class discussions. (24.1–24.3)

Teaching Tips

- Students might be interested to learn that interferons are now mass-produced using recombinant DNA technology. Clinical studies are under way to explore their use in treating viral infections and cancer. (24.1)

- In an interesting article on the effectiveness of common hygiene methods, "Hygiene of the Skin: When Is Clean Too Clean?" Elaine Larson reviews the relationship between skin hygiene and infection. It can be found at the CDC website at www.cdc.gov/ncidod/eid/vol7no2/larson.htm. (24.1)

- The inflammatory response described in Module 24.2 and characterized in Figure 24.2 provides a good student hook for this chapter. The inflammatory response is a reaction that is immediately apparent, with characteristics that can cause alarm. Students are typically more interested in subjects that have obvious relevance to their lives, including potential threats to their health! (24.2)

- Excessive amounts of iron in the human body can promote bacterial infections and other disease. Searching for the key words "iron supplements bacteria" on the CDC website at www.cdc.gov will turn up many articles on this subject. (24.2–24.3)

- During a medical examination, a physician might feel for tenderness in the throat, axillary (armpit), and inguinal (groin) regions. Students are unlikely to appreciate the significance of this part of the exam. Making this connection for them can add relevance to your class discussions and generate additional interest in the subject. (24.3)

Adaptive Immunity (24.4–24.15)

Student Misconceptions and Concerns

- For students with limited science backgrounds, this section of the chapter can be particularly difficult; for some, it is the most challenging part of the textbook. Students must have a solid knowledge of the properties of different cells and their interactions, and understand that repeated exposure to antigens generates new interactions. The challenge is similar to explaining a new sport to someone unfamiliar to the game. (Imagine explaining the rules and strategies of football or poker to someone who had never heard of them.) Instructors might consider slowing their pace and using learning aids such as reference lists of cell types and their functions, or diagrams that remind students of these cellular interactions. (24.4–24.15)

- Having students read relevant material before it is addressed in lecture is one of the best ways to improve student comprehension. Before lecturing on a topic, identify specific textbook modules that should be read before you address them in class. Reading before lecture can lay a foundation that makes the lecture much more meaningful. However, it helps in other ways, too. As students listen in lecture, they know if definitions in lecture are included in the book, and students are already aware of which figures outline certain processes. (24.4–24.15)

- The concept of nonspecific and specific defenses is sometimes difficult for students new to the subject. Some analogies, such as the following, might help. Clothing can be considered a general defense against heat loss, minor surface abrasions, and minor chemical damage such as sunburn. Sunscreen is a specific defense, intended to limit exposure to ultraviolet radiation in particular. (24.4)

Teaching Tips

- The old saying "Give a man a fish and you have fed him for today; teach a man to fish and you have fed him for a lifetime" can be compared to the concept of passive and active immunity. Passive immunity, like the gift of a fish, is temporary. However, active immunity, like the ability to fish, can last a lifetime! (24.4)

- Many analogies can be developed relating to the cells and molecules involved in the immune response. In Module 24.4, the authors note that lymphocytes, which can respond to any antigen, resemble a standing army of soldiers in which each soldier is able to recognize a unique form of the enemy. (24.5)

- The authors suggest that the specific "fit" between an antigen and an antibody is like the relationship between a lock and a key. You might further this analogy by noting that the tremendous diversity of antibodies is like having a set of keys for virtually every possible type of lock. (24.6)

- Our own learning experiences provide an analogy to the greater swiftness and intensity of a secondary immune response. When first presented with a problem, we may struggle to determine how best to respond. However, with that first experience behind us, we expect to respond more quickly and effectively when we meet that challenge again. Although in each circumstance we benefit from a certain type of memory (experiential in one case, chemical in the other) their mechanisms are quite different. Consider noting these similarities and differences in your class discussion of primary and secondary immune responses. (24.7)

- Challenge your class to explain the adaptive advantages of antibodies' Y-shaped structure. Why aren't antibodies just made up of a single heavy and a single light chain? (Biologists have theorized that the Y shape permits the bonding together of two antigens or antigen-presenting surfaces, allowing a chain reaction or form of clumping.) (24.8–24.9)

- Figure 24.9 depicts four effector mechanisms and their consequences. This figure organizes the information and relates the processes to each other, making comparisons easier. Such figures are especially helpful for students. Highlighting such figures in your lecture helps students follow up after class discussions by identifying the most relevant sections of their textbook assignments. (24.9)

- Once produced, monoclonal antibodies have the ability to specifically identify one particular antigen and bind to it. Challenge your class to think of analogies to this reaction. As you and your class evaluate the analogies, help your class check the analogy against a proper understanding of monoclonal antibody properties (an important point in this chapter). (One possible analogy might be the use of a Phillips screwdriver to turn only Phillips-shaped screw heads.) (24.10)

- The authors note that the recognition by a helper T cell of a self protein and a foreign antigen in combination is like the two-key system used by banks to access safe-deposit boxes. (24.11)

- Your students might find the descriptions in Modules 24.11 and 24.12 to be particularly confusing, as the interaction of many cell types are described. Figures 24.11 and 24.12 help to simplify the details of these interactions. (24.11–24.12)

- The destruction of an infected cell by a cytotoxic T cell provides an obvious opportunity for a fight analogy. The two cells become interlocked "in battle," the infected cell develops "puncture wounds," and a fatal poison is absorbed into these "wounds." (24.12)

- The Centers for Disease Control and Prevention has extensive information about AIDS and other public health threats on its website at www.cdc.gov. (24.13–24.14)

- Students often do not understand how disproportionately distributed cases of HIV and AIDS now are in our world. Consider assigning students to identify the regions of the world most affected by HIV-AIDS by performing Internet research. The web site http://unaidstoday.org is a good starting point. (24.13–24.14)

- Despite efforts to educate the general public, many misconceptions about AIDS persist. A list of 18 common misconceptions can be found at the web site www.gng.org/currents/teachers/hiv101/misconceptions.html. (24.13–24.14)

- Students may enter your course knowing that the best types of tissue transplants are from a closely matched donor. However, what does it mean to have a tissue "match"? Few students can explain the specific reasons behind the need for tissue matching, or how such matching is done. Challenge your students to explain why we try to ensure a match between the tissues of a donor and a recipient. By posing such general questions, instructors can raise interest in the specific details of the answers. (24.15)

Disorders of the Immune System (24.16–24.17)

Student Misconceptions and Concerns

- Student interest in diseases and allergies can provide motivation for learning in this final chapter section. However, researching a medical subject without the necessary background to fully understand it often leads to confusion. Consider probing for misunderstandings about autoimmune diseases and allergies by asking students about their causes and treatments. (24.16–24.17)

- Students may believe that anything "natural" is somehow good. In addition to the many natural poisons found in animals and plants, our allergic responses to pollen, molds, and other environmental allergens remind us that "natural" is not always healthy. (24.16–24.17)

Teaching Tips

- Although the triggers of autoimmune diseases are not well understood, it does appear that autoimmune diseases are not communicable, and cannot be caught through exposure to others with the disease. Family histories of autoimmune diseases do suggest some degree of heritability, at least of predisposition. Thus, some family members may share degrees of a common autoimmune disease. (24.16)

- Allergic contact dermatitis occurs when an allergen triggers an immune response on the skin. One example is the rash that results from exposure to poison ivy. (24.17)

- As noted in Module 24.17, antihistamines are drugs that interfere with the action of histamine. They provide temporary relief from the symptoms of allergic reactions. Therefore, a person suffering from a severe reaction to poison ivy might find some relief by taking antihistamines. Unfortunately, antihistamines can also produce drowsiness. (24.17)

Key Terms

active immunity
adaptive immunity
AIDS (acquired immunodeficiency syndrome)
allergens
allergies
antibody
antigen
antigen receptor
antigen-binding site
antigenic determinant
antigen-presenting cell (APC)
antihistamine
autoimmune disease
B cell
cell-mediated immune response

clonal selection
complement system
cytotoxic T cell
effector cell
helper T cell
histamine
HIV (human immuno deficiency virus)
humoral immune response
immune system
immunodeficiency disease
inflammatory response
innate immunity
interferon
lymph
lymph nodes
lymphatic system
lymphocytes
macrophage

major histocompatibility molecules (MHC)
memory cell
monoclonal antibody
natural killer cell
neutrophil
nonself molecule
opportunistic infections
passive immunity
pathogens
phagocytosis
plasma cell
primary immune response
secondary immune response
self protein
T cell
vaccination
vaccine

Word Roots

anti- = against; **-gen** = produce (*antigen*: any molecule that elicits an adaptive immune response)

auto- = self (*autoimmune disease*: an immunological disorder in which the immune system attacks the body's own molecules)

cyto- = cell (*cytotoxic T cell*: a type of lymphocyte that attacks body cells infected with pathogens)

immuno- = safe (*immune system*: an animal body's system of defenses against agents that cause disease or illness)

in- = into; **-flam** = flame (*inflammatory response*: the warm, red, and swollen reaction to tissue damage)

macro- = large; **-phage** = eat (*macrophage*: a large, phagocytic white blood cell that destroys microbes)

neutro- = neutral; **-phil** = loving (*neutrophil*: an innate, defensive, phagocytic white blood cell that can engulf bacteria and viruses in infected tissue)

patho- = disease, suffering; **-gen** = produce (*pathogen*: a disease-causing agent)

phago- = eat; **-cyto** = cell (*phagocytosis*: cellular "eating": cellular ingestion and digestion of foreign molecules)

CHAPTER 25

Control of Body Temperature and Water Balance

Chapter Objectives

Opening Essay

Explain how bear physiology adjusts during a period of dormancy.

Thermoregulation

25.1 Distinguish between endotherms and ectotherms, providing examples of each.

25.2 Describe the four ways that heat is gained or lost by an animal.

25.3 Describe the five general categories of adaptations that help animals thermoregulate. Provide specific examples of each.

Osmoregulation and Excretion

25.4 Describe the osmoregulatory challenges and associated adaptations of freshwater and saltwater fish, terrestrial arthropods, and terrestrial vertebrates.

25.5 Describe the three ways that animals eliminate nitrogenous wastes, and the advantages and disadvantages of each method.

25.6 Describe the general and specific structure of the human kidney. Explain how this organ promotes homeostasis.

25.7 Describe the four major processes by which the human excretory system produces and disposes of urine.

25.8 Describe the key events in the process of converting filtrate into urine in the kidneys.

25.9 Explain how antidiuretic hormone contributes to homeostasis.

25.10 Explain how a dialysis machine functions.

Lecture Outline

I. Introduction

A. During cold winters, bears are often dormant.

B. Physiological processes aid homeostasis, keeping the body temperature about 5°C below normal.

    1. Body fat and dense fur provide insulation.

    2. Blood flow to extremities is reduced.

    3. Nitrogen-containing wastes are metabolized differently.

C. Homeostasis is the maintenance of steady internal conditions despite fluctuations in the external environment.

D. Examples of homeostasis include

    1. *thermoregulation*—the maintenance of internal temperature within narrow limits,

    2. *osmoregulation*—the control of the gain and loss of water and solutes, and

    3. *excretion*—the disposal of nitrogen-containing wastes.

II. Thermoregulation

A. 25.1 An animal's regulation of body temperature helps maintain homeostasis

    1. Thermoregulation is

        a. the process by which animals maintain an internal temperature within a tolerable range and

        b. a form of homeostasis.

    2. Ectothermic animals

        a. gain most of their heat from external sources and

        b. include many fish, most amphibians, lizards, and most invertebrates.

    3. Endothermic animals

        a. derive body heat mainly from their metabolism and

        b. include birds, mammals, a few reptiles and fish, and many insects.

B. 25.2 Heat is gained or lost in four ways

    1. Heat exchange with the environment may occur by

        a. *conduction*—the transfer of heat by direct contact,

        b. *convection*—the transfer of heat by movement of air or liquid past a surface,

        c. *radiation*—the emission of electromagnetic waves, or

        d. *evaporation*—the loss of heat from the surface of a liquid that is losing some of its molecules as a gas.

C. 25.3 Thermoregulation involves adaptations that balance heat gain and loss

    1. Five general categories of adaptations help animals thermoregulate.

    2. Increased metabolic heat production occurs when

        a. hormonal changes boost the metabolic rate in birds and mammals,

        b. birds and mammals shiver,

        c. organisms increase their physical activity, and

        d. honeybees cluster and shiver.

    3. Insulation is provided by

        a. hair,

        b. feathers, and

        c. fat layers.

    4. Circulatory adaptations include

        a. increased or decreased blood flow to skin and

        b. countercurrent heat exchange, with warm and cold blood flowing in opposite directions.

    5. Evaporative cooling may involve

        a. sweating,

        b. panting, or

        c. spreading saliva on body surfaces.

    6. Behavioral responses

        a. are used by endotherms and ectotherms and

        b. include

            i. moving to the sun or shade,

    ii. migrating, and

    iii. bathing.

III. Osmoregulation and Excretion

A. 25.4 Animals balance the level of water and solutes through osmoregulation

  1. Osmoregulation is the homeostatic control of the uptake and loss of water and solutes such as salt and other ions.

  2. Osmosis is one process whereby animals regulate their uptake and loss of fluids.

  3. Osmoconformers

    a. have body fluids with a solute concentration equal to that of seawater,

    b. face no substantial challenges in water balance, and

    c. include many marine invertebrates.

  4. Osmoregulators

    a. have body fluids whose solute concentrations differ from that of their environment,

    b. must actively regulate water movement, and

    c. include

      i. many land animals,

      ii. freshwater animals such as trout, and

      iii. marine vertebrates such as sharks.

  5. Freshwater fish

    a. gain water by osmosis (mainly through gills),

    b. lose salt by diffusion to the more dilute environment,

    c. take in salt through their gills and in food, and

    d. excrete excess water in dilute **urine**.

  6. Saltwater fish

    a. lose water by osmosis from the gills and body surface,

    b. drink seawater, and

    c. use their gills and kidneys to excrete excess salt.

  7. Land animals

    a. face the risk of dehydration,

    b. lose water by evaporation and waste disposal,

    c. gain water by drinking and eating, and

    d. conserve water by

      i. reproductive adaptations,

      ii. behavior adaptations,

      iii. waterproof skin, and

      iv. efficient kidneys.

B. 25.5 EVOLUTION CONNECTION: A variety of ways to dispose of nitrogenous wastes has evolved in animals

  1. Metabolism produces toxic by-products.

  2. Nitrogenous wastes are toxic breakdown products of proteins and nucleic acids.

  3. Animals dispose of nitrogenous wastes in different ways.

  4. Ammonia (NH_3) is

    a. poisonous,

    b. too toxic to be stored in the body,

    c. soluble in water, and

    d. easily disposed of by aquatic animals.

5. **Urea** is

    a. produced in the vertebrate liver by combining ammonia and carbon dioxide,

    b. less toxic,

    c. easier to store, and

    d. highly soluble in water.

6. **Uric acid** is

    a. excreted by some land animals (insects, land snails, and many reptiles),

    b. relatively nontoxic,

    c. largely insoluble in water,

    d. excreted as a semisolid paste, conserving water, but

    e. more energy expensive to produce.

C. 25.6 The urinary system plays several major roles in homeostasis

  1. The **urinary system**

    a. forms and excretes urine and

    b. regulates water and solutes in body fluids.

  2. In humans, the kidneys are the main processing centers of the urinary system.

  3. **Nephrons**

    a. are the functional units of the kidneys,

    b. extract a fluid **filtrate** from the blood, and

    c. refine the filtrate to produce **urine**.

  4. Urine is

    a. drained from the kidneys by **ureters**,

    b. stored in the **urinary bladder**, and

    c. expelled through the **urethra**.

D. 25.7 Overview: The key processes of the urinary system are filtration, reabsorption, secretion, and excretion

  1. **Filtration**

    a. Blood pressure forces water and many small molecules through a capillary wall into the start of the kidney tubule.

  2. **Reabsorption**

    a. refines the filtrate,

    b. reclaims valuable solutes (such as glucose, salt, and amino acids) from the filtrate, and

    c. returns these to the blood.

  3. Substances in the blood are transported into the filtrate by the process of **secretion**.

  4. By **excretion** the final product, urine, is excreted via the ureters, urinary bladder, and urethra.

E. 25.8 Blood filtrate is refined to urine through reabsorption and secretion

  1. Reabsorption in the proximal and distal tubules removes

    a. nutrients,

    b. salt, and

    c. water.

  2. pH is regulated by

    a. reabsorption of HCO_3^- and

    b. secretion of H^+.

  3. High NaCl concentration in the medulla promotes reabsorption of water.

F. 25.9 Hormones regulate the urinary system

    1. Antidiuretic hormone (ADH) regulates the amount of water excreted by the kidneys by

        a. signaling nephrons to reabsorb water from the filtrate, returning it to the blood, and

        b. decreasing the amount of water excreted.

    2. Diuretics

        a. inhibit the release of ADH and

        b. include alcohol and caffeine.

G. 25.10 CONNECTION: Kidney dialysis can be lifesaving

    1. Kidney failure can result from

        a. hypertension,

        b. diabetes, and

        c. prolonged use of common drugs, including alcohol.

    2. A dialysis machine

        a. removes wastes from the blood and

        b. maintains its solute concentration.

Chapter Guide to Teaching Resources

Thermoregulation (25.1–25.3)

Student Misconceptions and Concerns

- The concept of homeostasis may be new to some students, who have never considered how organisms must adjust to subtle changes in environmental conditions. Analogies to other systems that engage in self-regulation, such as the water regulation of a toilet or the temperature regulation of a furnace, may help. (25.1–25.3)

- One role of the circulatory system rarely discussed is the transport of heat. Blood vessels near the surface of the body expand when we overheat, releasing some of this excess to the environment. Conversely, during periods of exposure to cold, blood is shunted away from the skin to conserve heat. (25.1–25.3)

Teaching Tips

- The terms warm-blooded and cold-blooded are less precise than endotherm and ectotherm. Encourage students to discuss why the latter two terms are preferable. (25.1)

- Ask your students to explain the adaptive advantages of endothermy and ectothermy. You might prompt the discussion by noting that endotherms consume about 10 times as many calories as ectotherms of equivalent body mass. What advantages might be worth this additional "cost" for endotherms? (25.1)

- The heat generated by aerobic metabolism is analogous to the heat generated by the engine of an automobile. In both cases, the heat is a by-product of the process. In the winter, this excess heat helps keep the body and the interior of the car warm. In the summer, both the body and the automobile's engine must work to keep from overheating. (25.1)

- Have students list the many factors that affect heat gain and loss during periods of physical activity, then have them identify which of the four physical processes for exchanging heat are involved. The factors include (a) the person's physical condition, (b) the level of physical activity, (c) the age of the person (younger people tend to have higher metabolic rates), (d) the person's level of hydration (which in turn affects the amount of sweating and evaporative cooling), (e) the level of environmental humidity (higher levels decrease evaporative cooling), (f) the intensity of the wind (greater intensity promotes evaporative cooling), (g) the intensity of sunlight, and (h) the color of the person's clothing (which affects the amount of light energy the body absorbs). (25.2–25.3)

- You can extend the exercise by challenging your class to identify environmental conditions when it would be too hot to play an outdoor sport. That is, when as a parent or coach would you want to prevent practice or a game because it is dangerously hot? (25.2–25.3)

- As an alternative to this, challenge students to identify a human example of each of the four physical processes that involve heat exchange with the environment and that promote thermoregulation. Or, to check student comprehension, describe such examples and challenge the class to match the examples to the correct terminology. (25.2–25.3)

- Some students will be familiar with the foam insulation wrap applied around home water pipes. These forms of insulation are especially necessary when hot- and cold-water pipes run parallel and in close proximity to each other. Without the insulation, heat would be easily transferred from hot-water to cold-water pipes, in a situation similar to countercurrent heat exchange systems in animals. (25.3)

Osmoregulation and Excretion (25.4–25.10)

Student Misconceptions and Concerns

- The idea that a freshwater fish never drinks can be conceptually challenging, especially for students who have heard the old saying "drinks like a fish"! Consider introducing your discussion of osmoregulation with this remarkable and seemingly counterintuitive fact to generate interest. (25.4)

- The kidney's role in filtration and selective reabsorption may initially be confusing to many students. The process is a bit like cleaning up a closet by removing all the contents and then selectively returning to it what you wish to store. (25.5–25.9)

- Before addressing the human urinary system, challenge each student in your class to explain how a drink of water may end up as urine. Consider having students write out their answers on a 3 × 5 card in class. This quick survey will likely reveal misunderstandings that would otherwise be concealed by quiet students' reluctance to speak up. Students might suggest that some sort of tube transports fluid from the digestive tract to the kidneys or urinary bladder. Such surveys provide a useful means of gauging the initial assumptions of your students as they approach a new subject. (25.6)

Teaching Tips

- Students may better understand the challenges of osmoregulation in freshwater fish if they are reminded of what occurs when humans soak their hands in water. Students will likely recall that this causes the skin on their hands to wrinkle, and some may have noticed that their skin wrinkles even faster in soapy water. Skin absorbs water by osmosis (just as a freshwater fish gains water). Oils on our skin reduce the influx of water. Soapy water, which washes away these oils, speeds up the process. The wrinkling occurs because the skin can expand only in certain areas, creating puckers. (25.4)

- Student experience with osmoregulation not pertaining to their bodies may be quite limited. However, many students are familiar with the pasty white color of bird droppings. Consider beginning your discussion of nitrogenous wastes by asking your class to explain why bird droppings are white. (25.5)

- A moderately full human urinary bladder holds about 500 ml (or 1 pint) of fluid. The bladder's maximum capacity may be up to double that volume, although if overdistended, it may burst! (25.6)

- Students must understand that blood consists of two main components, cells and plasma. If your course has not covered Chapter 23, consider assigning Module 23.12 to ensure that they have this important background knowledge. (25.6–25.7)

- During the production of urine, blood cells remain within blood vessels, and components of the plasma are filtered out and selectively reabsorbed. Students may appreciate this important distinction early on in the discussion of renal functions. (25.6–25.7)

- Some drugs are excreted in urine. This is the basis of drug testing using samples of a person's urine. Making this simple connection can help generate interest and improve comprehension in your students. (25.7)

- Many students do not know about interstitial fluid or its functions. They may think that blood delivers nutrients directly to cells, perhaps through direct contact between capillaries and cells. Instead, interstitial fluids typically act as an intermediate and promote homeostasis in many ways. Interstitial fluid is discussed in detail in Module 23.7, which may not have been addressed previously in your class. (25.7–25.8)

- Students may be particularly interested in the diuretic effects of alcohol and caffeine. The text notes that the diuretic effects of alcohol may contribute to some of the symptoms of a hangover. However, the concentration of alcohol and caffeine are important factors. Higher urine output resulting from the high consumption of low-alcohol (1–5%) beer may largely be the consequence of increased water consumption. Drinks with higher alcohol levels, such as shots of hard liquor (gin, vodka, whiskey) or higher caffeine levels (espresso) and low fluid volume would be expected to better reveal the diuretic effects. (25.9)

- The loss of one kidney in a human typically results in enlargement of the remaining kidney, a process known as compensatory hypertrophy. As your time permits, this can provide material for a class discussion or for a special-topic assignment for students with a particular interest. (25.10)

- The unfortunate shortage of kidneys and other organs available for transplant is a major health issue. Consider discussing this problem with your class. Many state and federal organ donation organizations can by located by a quick Internet search. The National Kidney Foundation site, www.kidney.org/atoz/atozTopic_Organ-Tissue-Donation.cfm, includes information on kidney donation. (25.10)

Key Terms

ammonia	countercurrent heat exchange	excretion
antidiuretic hormone	dialysis	filtrate
(ADH)	distal tubule	filtration
Bowman's capsule	ectotherm	glomerulus (plural, glomeruli)
collecting duct	endotherm	loop of Henle

nephron	renal cortex	urethra
osmoconformer	renal medulla	uric acid
osmoregulation	secretion	urinary bladder
osmoregulator	thermoregulation	urinary system
proximal tubule	urea	urine
reabsorption	ureter	

Word Roots

anti- = against; **-diure** = urinate (*antidiuretic hormone*: a hormone made by the hypothalamus and secreted by the posterior pituitary that promotes water retention by the kidneys)

counter- = opposite (*countercurrent heat exchange*: parallel blood vessels that convey warm and cold blood in opposite directions, maximizing heat transfer to the cold blood)

dia- = through; **-lyso** = loosen (*dialysis*: the separation and disposal of metabolic wastes from the blood by mechanical means; an artificial method of performing the functions of the kidneys)

ecto- = outside; **-therm** = heat (*ectotherm*: an animal that warms itself mainly by absorbing heat from its surroundings)

endo- = within; **-therm** = heat (*endotherm*: an animal that derives most of its body heat from its own metabolism)

glomer- = a ball (*glomerulus*: the ball of capillaries in the nephron of the vertebrate kidney surrounded by Bowman's capsule; together, the glomerulus and Bowman's capsule produce filtrate from blood)

osmo- = pushing; **-conform** = the same (*osmoconformer*: an organism whose body fluids have a solute concentration equal to that of its surroundings); **-regula** = regular (*osmoregulation*: the control of the gain and loss of water and dissolved solutes in an organism; *osmoregulator*: an organism whose body fluids have a solute concentration different from that of its environment and that must use energy to control water loss or gain)

reni- = a kidney; **cortex-** = shell (*renal cortex*: the outer portion of the vertebrate kidney; *renal medulla*: the inner portion of the vertebrate kidney)

thermo- = heat; **-regula** = regular (*thermoregulation*: the maintenance of internal temperature within a range that allows cells to function efficiently)

CHAPTER 26

Hormones and the Endocrine System

Chapter Objectives

Opening Essay

Explain how testosterone affects male lions.

The Nature of Chemical Regulation

26.1   Compare the mechanisms and functions of the endocrine and nervous systems, noting areas of overlap.

26.1   Distinguish between hormones, local regulators, pheromones, and neurotransmitters.

26.2   Distinguish between the two major classes of vertebrate hormones and compare the two general mechanisms by which hormones trigger changes in target cells.

The Vertebrate Endocrine System

26.3   Describe the different types of vertebrate endocrine organs noting their specific functions.

26.4   Describe the functions of and interrelationships between the hypothalamus and the anterior and posterior pituitary glands.

Hormones and Homeostasis

26.5   Describe the functions of the thyroid gland. Describe the symptoms of hypothyroidism, hyperthyroidism, and goiter.

26.6   Explain how the thyroid and parathyroid glands maintain calcium homeostasis.

26.7   Explain how insulin and glucagon manage blood glucose levels.

26.8   Compare the causes and symptoms of type 1 diabetes, type 2 diabetes, and hypoglycemia.

26.9   Compare the functions of the hormones released by the adrenal medulla and the adrenal cortex. Describe the benefits and risks of using glucocorticoid drugs.

26.10 Describe the three major categories of sex hormones and their functions.

26.11 Describe the diverse functions of prolactin in vertebrate groups.

Lecture Outline

I. Introduction

A. In lions, the hormone testosterone promotes the development and maintenance of male traits including

1. growth and maintenance of the mane and

2. increased height and weight.

II. The Nature of Chemical Regulation

A. 26.1 Chemical signals coordinate body functions
1. The **endocrine system**
   a. consists of all hormone-secreting cells and
   b. works with the nervous system in regulating body activities.
2. The nervous system also
   a. communicates,
   b. regulates, and
   c. uses electrical signals via nerve cells.
3. Comparing the endocrine and nervous systems
   a. the nervous system reacts faster.
   b. the responses of the endocrine system last longer.
4. **Hormones are**
   a. chemical signals,
   b. produced by endocrine glands,
   c. usually carried in the blood, and
   d. responsible for specific changes in **target cells**.
5. Hormones may also be released from specialized nerve cells called **neurosecretory cells**.

B. 26.2 Hormones affect target cells using two main signaling mechanisms
1. Two major classes of molecules function as hormones in vertebrates.
   a. The first class includes hydrophilic (water-soluble), **amino-acid-derived hormones**. Among these are
      i.   proteins,
      ii. peptides, and
      iii. amines.
   b. The second class of hormones are **steroid hormones**, which include small, hydrophobic molecules made from cholesterol.
2. Hormone signaling involves three key events:
   a. reception,
   b. signal transduction, and
   c. response.
3. An **amino-acid-derived hormone**
   a. binds to plasma-membrane receptors on target cells and
   b. initiates a signal transduction pathway.
4. A **steroid hormone** can
   a. diffuse through plasma membranes,
   b. bind to a receptor protein in the cytoplasm or nucleus, and
   c. form a hormone-receptor complex that carries out the transduction of the hormonal signal.

III. The Vertebrate Endocrine System

A. 26.3 Overview: The vertebrate endocrine system consists of more than a dozen major glands
1. Some endocrine glands (such as the thyroid) primarily secrete hormones into the blood.
2. Other glands (such as the pancreas) have
   a. endocrine and

     b. nonendocrine functions.

   3. Other organs (such as the stomach) are primarily nonendocrine but have some cells that secrete hormones.

   4. The following figure shows the locations of the major endocrine glands.

   5. The following table summarizes the main hormones produced by the major endocrine glands and indicates how they
     a. function and
     b. are controlled.

   6. Two endocrine glands are not discussed further.
     a. The **pineal gland**
       i. is pea-sized, located near the center of the brain, and
      ii. secretes melatonin, a hormone that links environmental light conditions with biological rhythms.
     b. The **thymus gland**
       i. lies above the heart, under the breastbone, and
      ii. secretes a peptide that stimulates the development of T cells.

B. 26.4 The hypothalamus, which is closely tied to the pituitary, connects the nervous and endocrine systems
   1. The **hypothalamus**
     a. blurs the distinction between endocrine and nervous systems,
     b. receives input from nerves about the internal conditions of the body and the external environment,
     c. responds by sending out appropriate nervous or endocrine signals, and
     d. uses the pituitary gland to exert master control over the endocrine system.
   2. The **pituitary gland** consists of two parts.
     a. The **posterior pituitary**
       i. is composed of nervous tissue,
      ii. is an extension of the hypothalamus, and
      iii. stores and secretes oxytocin and ADH, which are made in the hypothalamus.
   3. The **anterior pituitary**
     a. synthesizes and secretes hormones that control the activity of other glands and
     b. is controlled by two types of hormones released from the hypothalamus:
       i. **releasing hormones** stimulate the anterior pituitary, and
      ii. **inhibiting hormones** inhibit the anterior pituitary.
   4. Pituitary secretions include
     a. growth hormone (GH) that promotes protein synthesis and the use of body fat for energy metabolism,
     b. endorphins that function as natural painkillers, and
     c. TRH (TSH-releasing hormone) that stimulates the thyroid (another endocrine gland) to release thyroxine.

IV. Hormones and Homeostatis

  A. 26.5 The thyroid regulates development and metabolism
   1. The **thyroid gland** is located in the neck, just under the larynx (voice box).
   2. The thyroid gland produces two similar hormones,
     a. thyroxine (T_4) and
     b. triiodothyronine (T_3).

3. These hormones regulate many aspects of
   a. metabolism,
   b. reproduction, and
   c. development.
4. Thyroid imbalance can cause disease.
   a. Hyperthyroidism
      i.   results from too much T_4 and T_3 in the blood,
      ii. leads to high blood pressure, loss of weight, overheating, and irritability, and
      iii. produces Graves' disease.
   b. Hypothyroidism
      i. results from too little T_4 and T_3 in the blood and
      ii. leads to low blood pressure, being overweight, and often feeling cold and lethargic.
5. Iodine deficiency can produce a **goiter**, an enlargement of the thyroid. In this condition,
   a. the thyroid gland cannot synthesize adequate amounts of T_4 and T_3, and
   b. the thyroid gland enlarges.
B. 26.6 Hormones from the thyroid and parathyroid glands maintain calcium homeostasis
   1. Blood calcium level is regulated by **antagonistic hormones** each working to oppose the actions of the other hormone:
      a. **calcitonin**, from the thyroid, lowers the calcium level in the blood, and
      b. **parathyroid hormone (PTH)**, from the **parathyroid glands**, raises the calcium level in the blood.
C. 26.7 Pancreatic hormones regulate blood glucose levels
   1. The **pancreas** secretes two hormones that control blood glucose:
      a. **insulin** signals cells to use and store glucose, and
      b. **glucagon** causes cells to release stored glucose into the blood.
D. 26.8 CONNECTION: Diabetes is a common endocrine disorder
   1. Diabetes mellitus
      a. affects about 8% of the U.S. population and
      b. results from a
         i. lack of insulin or
         ii. failure of cells to respond to insulin.
   2. There are three types of diabetes mellitus.
      a. Type 1 (insulin-dependent) is
         i. an autoimmune disease
         ii. caused by the destruction of insulin-producing cells.
      b. Type 2 (non-insulin-dependent) is
         i.   caused by a reduced response to insulin,
         ii. associated with being overweight and underactive, and
         iii. the cause of more than 90% of diabetes.
      c. Gestational diabetes
         i. can affect any pregnant woman and
         ii. lead to dangerously large babies, which can complicate delivery.

E. 26.9 The adrenal glands mobilize responses to stress
   1. The endocrine system includes two **adrenal glands**, sitting on top of each kidney.
   2. Each adrenal gland is made of two glands fused together, the
      a. adrenal medulla and
      b. adrenal cortex.
   3. Both glands secrete hormones that enable the body to respond to stress.
   4. Nerve signals from the hypothalamus stimulate the adrenal medulla to secrete
      a. epinephrine (adrenaline) and
      b. norepinephrine (noradrenaline).
   5. These hormones quickly trigger the "fight-or-flight" responses, which are short-term responses to stress.
   6. **Adrenocorticotropic hormone (ACTH)** from the pituitary causes the adrenal cortex to secrete
      a. glucocorticoids and
      b. mineralocorticoids.
   7. The effects of these hormones cause long-term responses to stress.
F. 26.10 The gonads secrete sex hormones
   1. Steroid sex hormones
      a. affect growth,
      b. affect development, and
      c. regulate reproductive cycles and sexual behavior.
   2. Sex hormones include
      a. estrogens, which maintain the female reproductive system and promote the development of female characteristics,
      b. progestins, such as progesterone, which prepare and maintain the uterus to support a developing embryo, and
      c. androgens, such as **testosterone**, which stimulate the development and maintenance of the male reproductive system.
   3. The synthesis of sex hormones by the gonads is regulated by the
      a. hypothalamus and
      b. pituitary.
G. 26.11 EVOLUTION CONNECTION: A single hormone can perform a variety of functions in different animals
   1. The peptide hormone prolactin (PRL) in humans stimulates mammary glands to grow and produce milk during late pregnancy.
   2. Suckling by a newborn stimulates further release of PRL.
   3. High PRL during nursing inhibits ovulation.
   4. PRL has many roles unrelated to childbirth, suggesting that PRL is an ancient hormone diversified through evolution.
      a. In some nonhuman mammals, PRL stimulates nest building.
      b. In birds, PRL regulates fat metabolism and reproduction.
      c. In amphibians, PRL stimulates movement to water.
      d. In fish that migrate between salt and fresh water, PRL helps regulate salt and water balance.

Chapter Guide to Teaching Resources

The Nature of Chemical Regulation (26.1–26.2)

Student Misconceptions and Concerns

- Student comprehension of the two mechanisms by which hormones trigger changes in target cells relies upon a good understanding of cell membranes and basic cellular chemistry. If these subjects have not been taught recently in your course, consider giving students a brief refresher before distinguishing between these mechanisms. (26.1–26.2)

- Students might not appreciate the diverse ways in which coordination and communication are achieved between the body's cells. Endocrine signals generally work like a radio transmitter, sending signals outward. Only target cells, like people with radios tuned to a particular frequency, will receive the signal. In contrast, the nervous system provides a direct, two-way connection between the sender and receiver, much more like a land-based telephone call. (26.1–26.2)

Teaching Tips

- The nervous and endocrine systems coordinate and regulate most other systems of the body. You might consider comparing the speed and duration of each system's response. The nervous system generally responds faster but for a shorter duration than the endocrine system. This helps to explain why it takes many minutes for a person to calm down after a very upsetting event. The hormones do not clear quickly from the systems. (26.1)

- The two mechanisms by which hormones trigger changes in target cells can be compared using this analogy. If a house is like a cell, ringing the doorbell and having someone answer it is like using a signal-transduction pathway. Pushing the doorbell, like a hormone binding to plasma-membrane receptors, causes an internal change. Using steroid hormones, on the other hand, is like walking up to the house, opening the door, and walking inside to deliver a message. Here the signal passes through the surface and into the interior of the home/cell to directly communicate the message. (26.2)

The Vertebrate Endocrine System (26.3–26.4)

Student Misconceptions and Concerns

- Appreciating the precise actions of hormones requires a thorough understanding of the specificity of target cells. The fact that only certain target cells will respond to a given hormone signal allows hormones to be "broadcast" generally throughout the circulatory system without affecting every single cell. (26.3)

- The abuse of growth hormones and steroids is of great concern in the world of professional and amateur sports. Although this is mentioned briefly in the text, consider emphasizing further the potential negative consequences of the abuse of these powerful hormones. The National Institute of Health provides additional details on its website at www.drugabuse.gov/ResearchReports/Steroids/AnabolicSteroids.html. (26.4)

Teaching Tips

- Growth hormone levels typically decline as we age. Recent studies suggest that injections of engineered human growth hormone may promote muscle growth and decrease body fat.

However, additional research is necessary to fully appreciate the benefits and potential risks of human growth hormone injections in the elderly. (26.3)

- Morphine and other opiates bind to the same cell receptors that naturally bind endorphins, producing powerful pain-killing effects. (26.4)

- Students may not have carefully considered the benefits of pain. Consider emphasizing the adaptive nature of pain to your class. The authors note the risks of stopping pain in an injured part of the body. Based on this, challenge students to propose explanations as to why endorphins nonetheless evolved. (26.4)

Hormones and Homeostasis (26.5–26.11)

Student Misconceptions and Concerns

- Many students struggle to remember the basic structures, functions, and locations of the major vertebrate organs. Understanding and remembering the specific control mechanisms are typically beyond their background knowledge entering a general biology college course. Students will appreciate any reminders or reference materials that help them to organize this information. (26.5–26.11)

- As the section title indicates, a central theme of endocrine function is the maintenance of homeostasis. Repeatedly framing the details of hormonal and glandular function in the context of homeostasis can increase levels of student comprehension. (26.5–26.11)

Teaching Tips

- Hypothyroidism produces symptoms that are like turning down a furnace during a cold winter. When thyroid levels are low, cells produce ATP and heat at a slower rate, and the person feels colder and is more lethargic than others in the same room. This reminds students that aerobic respiration produces heat and ATP. Hyperthyroidism is just the opposite, with an overproduction of heat as the consequence. (26.5)

- The use of calcitonin and parathyroid hormone to hold blood calcium levels steady is similar to the use of a furnace and air conditioner in a home to keep temperatures steady. The same analogy can be applied to the contrasting functions of insulin and glucagon. (26.6–26.7)

- Scientists are exploring the use of pancreatic cell transplants as a new source of insulin for patients with type 1 diabetes. Pancreatic cells may be derived from donors and/or modified from other cells using stem cell technology. One website devoted to this subject is http://diabetes.niddk.nih.gov/dm/pubs/pancreaticislet/. (26.7–26.8)

- The effects of the "fight or flight" response will likely last many minutes after the initial events that triggered the response. Telling such a person to calm down is unlikely to help. Instead, removing the person from the stimulus (if possible), engaging in mild exercise such as walking, and allowing many minutes of time will more likely reverse the condition. (26.9)

- In humans, differences in the concentrations of sex hormones decrease between the sexes in late adulthood. Differences in secondary sexual characteristics such as muscle tone and hair growth may diminish as a natural part of aging. Students with interests in geriatrics may enjoy assignments or extra credit to investigate this topic. (26.10)

- The shifting functions of prolactin reflect the kind of "remodeling" frequently found in evolution. Typically, new structures and functions result from modifications of ancestral structures and functions. In this case, as reproductive strategies evolved, the functional significance of prolactin was remodeled. (26.11)

Key Terms

adrenal cortex
adrenal gland
adrenal medulla
adrenocorticotropic
 hormone (ACTH)
amino-acid-derived
 hormones
androgen
antagonistic hormones
anterior pituitary
calcitonin
corticosteroid
diabetes mellitus
endocrine gland
endocrine system
endorphin
epinephrine

estrogen
glucagon
glucocorticoid
goiter
gonad
growth hormone (GH)
hormone
hypoglycemia
hypothalamus
inhibiting hormone
insulin
mineralocorticoid
neurosecretory cell
norepinephrine
pancreas
parathyroid glands
parathyroid hormone (PTH)

pineal gland
pituitary gland
posterior pituitary
progestin
prolactin (PRL)
releasing hormone
steroid hormone
target cell
testosterone
TRH-releasing hormone
triiodothyronine (T3)
thymus gland
thyroid gland
thyroid-stimulating hormone
 (TSH)
thyroxine (T4)

Word Roots

ad- = above; **-renal** = kidney (*adrenal gland*: an endocrine gland that sits on top of the kidney and secretes hormones that regulate the stress response; *adrenal medulla*: the central portion of an adrenal gland, controlled by nerve signals; secretes the fight-or-flight hormones epinephrine and norepinephrine)

andro- = male; **-gen** = produce (*androgens*: the principal male steroid hormones, such as testosterone, which stimulate the development and maintenance of the male reproductive system and secondary sex characteristics)

cortex- = shell (*adrenal cortex*: the outer portion of an adrenal gland, controlled by ACTH from the anterior pituitary; secretes hormones called glucocorticoids and mineralocorticoids)

-cortico = the shell (*corticosteroid*: a steroid sex hormone secreted by the gonads that promotes the development and maintenance of the male reproductive system and male body features)

endo- = within (*endorphin*: a pain-inhibiting hormone produced by the brain and anterior pituitary)

epi- = above, over (*epinephrine*: an amine hormone, also called adrenaline, secreted by the adrenal medulla that prepares body organs for action)

gluco- = sweet (*glucagon*: a peptide hormone, secreted by the islets of Langerhans in the pancreas, that raises the level of glucose in the blood; *glucocorticoid*: a corticosteroid hormone secreted by the adrenal cortex that increases the blood glucose level and helps maintain the body's response to long-term stress)

glyco- = sugar (*hypoglycemia*: an abnormally low level of glucose in the blood that results when the pancreas secretes too much insulin into the blood)

hypo- = below (*hypothalamus*: the ventral part of the vertebrate forebrain, located below the thalamus, that functions in maintaining homeostasis, especially in coordinating the endocrine and nervous systems);

-lact = milk (*prolactin*: a protein hormone secreted by the anterior pituitary that stimulates milk production in mammals)

neuro- = nerve (*neurosecretory cell*: a nerve cell that synthesizes hormones and secretes them into the blood, and also conducts nerve signals)

para- = beside, near (*parathyroid glands*: four endocrine glands, embedded in the surface of the thyroid gland, that secrete parathyroid hormone and raise blood calcium levels)

pro- = before; **gest-** = carry (*progestin*: one of a family of steroid hormones produced by the mammalian ovary that prepare the uterus for pregnancy)

tri- = three; **-iodo** = violet (*triiodothyronine*: an amine hormone secreted by the thyroid gland that stimulates metabolism in virtually all body tissues)

CHAPTER 27

Reproduction and Embryonic Development

Chapter Objectives

Opening Essay

Explain how the increased use of fertility drugs has impacted the number of multiple births in the United States. Describe the increased health risks that multiple births involve.

Asexual and Sexual Reproduction

27.1–27.2 Compare the types, advantages, and disadvantages of asexual and sexual reproduction.

Human Reproduction

27.3–27.4 Describe the structures and functions of the female and male human reproductive systems.

27.5 Describe and compare the processes and products of spermatogenesis and oogenesis.

27.6 Describe the events of and control of the menstrual cycle. Note the specific functions of releasing hormone, FSH, LH, estrogen, and progesterone.

27.7 Describe the nature of the most common sexually transmitted diseases. Note their agents of infection, symptoms, and methods of treatment.

27.8 Describe the most common forms of birth control and explain how each works. Compare the failure rates, advantages, and disadvantages of each method. Explain which methods help reduce the risk of STDs.

Principles of Embryonic Development

27.9 Relate the structure of sperm to its role in fertilization. Describe the mechanisms that prevent more than one sperm from fertilizing an egg and that prevent hybridization between different species.

27.10 Describe the process and results of cleavage. Explain how identical and nonidentical twins form.

27.11 Describe the process of gastrulation and the resulting arrangement of the embryo.

27.12 Explain how organs form after the development of a gastrula.

27.13 Explain how changes in cell shape, induction, cell migration, and apoptosis contribute to development.

27.14 Explain how the one-dimensional information in DNA is used to direct the three-dimensional form of an embryo.

Human Development

27.15 Describe the initial embryonic stages and the formation and functions of the extraembryonic membranes in humans.

27.16 Describe the main changes that occur during each of the trimesters of human development.

27.17 Explain how labor begins and describe the main events of the three stages of labor.

27.18 Describe the common causes of human infertility and the technologies currently available to help couples conceive.

Lecture Outline

I. Introduction

- **A.** Fertility drugs
  - **1.** increase the number of eggs that are ovulated and
  - **2.** have allowed thousands of infertile couples to have babies.
- **B.** Ten percent of women taking fertility drugs become pregnant with more than one embryo.
- **C.** Newborns from multiple births are
  - **1.** more likely to be premature,
  - **2.** more likely to have lower birth weights, and
  - **3.** less likely to survive.

II. Asexual and Sexual Reproduction

- **A.** 27.1 Asexual reproduction results in the generation of genetically identical offspring
  - **1. Asexual reproduction**
    - **a.** is the creation of genetically identical offspring by one parent,
    - **b.** is a very rapid form of reproduction, and
    - **c.** can proceed via
      - **i.** budding,
      - **ii.** fission, or
      - **iii.** fragmentation/regeneration.
- **B.** 27.2 Sexual reproduction results in the generation of genetically unique offspring
  - **1. Sexual reproduction**
    - **a.** is the creation of offspring by **fertilization** and
    - **b.** joins two haploid sex cells or **gametes** to form a diploid ($2n$) **zygote**.
  - **2.** The male gamete, the **sperm**,
    - **a.** is relatively small and
    - **b.** moves by means of a flagellum.
  - **3.** The female gamete, the **egg**,
    - **a.** is a much larger cell and
    - **b.** is not self-propelled.
  - **4.** Some organisms, such as sea anemones, can reproduce both
    - **a.** asexually and
    - **b.** sexually.
  - **5.** Some animals exhibit **hermaphroditism** in which an individual has both female and male reproductive systems.

6. Hermaphroditism makes it easier to find a mate for animals that are solitary or less mobile.
7. Hermaphrodites may
   a. exchange gametes with other individuals or
   b. fertilize their own eggs.
8. **External fertilization**
   a. occurs when eggs and sperm are discharged near each other and
   b. is used by many fish and amphibian species.
9. **Internal fertilization**
   a. occurs when sperm is deposited in or near the female reproductive tract and
   b. is used by some fish and amphibian species and nearly all terrestrial animals.

III. Human Reproduction

A. 27.3 Reproductive anatomy of the human female
   1. Both sexes in humans have
      a. a set of **gonads** where gametes are produced,
      b. ducts for gamete transport, and
      c. structures for copulation.
   2. **Ovaries** contain **follicles** that
      a. nurture eggs and
      b. produce sex hormones.
   3. An immature egg is ejected from the follicle in a process called **ovulation**.
   4. **Oviducts** convey eggs to the uterus where a fertilized egg develops.
   5. The **uterus** opens into the **vagina** through the **cervix**.
   6. The vagina
      a. receives the penis during sexual intercourse and
      b. forms the birth canal.
B. 27.4 Reproductive anatomy of the human male
   1. **Testes** (singular, *testis*) produce
      a. sperm and
      b. male hormones.
   2. The **epididymis** stores sperm as they develop further.
   3. Several glands contribute to semen. These are the
      a. **seminal vesicles,**
      b. **prostate gland**, and
      c. **bulbourethral glands**.
   4. During **ejaculation**
      a. **sperm** is expelled from the epididymis,
      b. the seminal vesicles, prostate, and bulbourethral glands secrete into the urethra, and
      c. **semen** is formed and expelled from the **penis**.
   5. Sperm production
      a. is regulated by a negative feedback system of hormones and
      b. involves the
         i. hypothalamus,
         ii. anterior pituitary, and
         iii. testes.

C. 27.5 The formation of sperm and egg cells requires meiosis

   1. Spermatogenesis occurs in **seminiferous tubules**.

      a. Primary spermatocytes

         i. are formed by mitosis and

         ii. divide by meiosis I to produce secondary spermatocytes.

      b. Secondary spermatocytes

         i. divide by meiosis II to produce round spermatids,

         ii. spermatids differentiate into elongate sperm, and

         iii. mature sperm are released into seminiferous tubules.

   2. Oogenesis begins before birth when a diploid cell in each developing follicle begins meiosis.

      a. Each month about one **primary oocyte** resumes meiosis.

      b. A **secondary oocyte** arrested at metaphase of meiosis II is ovulated.

      c. Meiosis of the ovum is completed after fertilization.

   3. Oogenesis and spermatogenesis are

      a. alike in that both produce haploid gametes but

      b. different in that

         i. oogenesis produces only one mature egg and polar bodies that degenerate and

         ii. spermatogenesis produces four mature gametes.

D. 27.6 Hormones synchronize cyclic changes in the ovary and uterus

   1. About every 28 days

      a. the hypothalamus signals the anterior pituitary to secrete follicle-stimulating hormone (FSH) and luteinizing hormone (LH),

      b. which trigger the growth of a follicle and ovulation, the release of an egg.

   2. After ovulation, the ovarian follicle becomes the corpus luteum.

   3. The corpus luteum secretes estrogen and progesterone, which

      a. stimulate the endometrium to thicken,

      b. prepare the uterus for implantation of the embryo, and

      c. inhibit the hypothalamus, reducing FSH and LH secretion.

   4. If the egg is fertilized

      a. the embryo releases hormones that maintain the uterine lining and

      b. menstruation does not occur.

   5. If the egg is not fertilized

      a. the drop in LH shuts down the corpus luteum and its hormones,

      b. menstruation is triggered, and

      c. the hypothalamus and pituitary stimulate development of a new follicle.

E. 27.7 CONNECTION: Sexual activity can transmit disease

   1. Sexually transmitted diseases (STDs) caused by bacteria can often be cured.

   2. Chlamydia

      a. is the most common bacterial STD,

      b. often produces no symptoms, and

      c. can lead to pelvic inflammatory disease and infertility.

   3. Viral diseases

      a. such as **genital herpes** and HIV,

      b. can only be controlled.

   4. The best way to avoid the spread of STDs is abstinence.

   5. Latex condoms provide the best protection against disease transmission for "safer sex."

F. 27.8 CONNECTION: Contraception can prevent unwanted pregnancy

    1. Contraception is the deliberate prevention of pregnancy.

        a. Several forms of contraception can prevent pregnancy, with varying degrees of success.

IV. Principles of Embryonic Development

    A. 27.9 Fertilization results in a zygote and triggers embryonic development

        1. Embryonic development begins with fertilization,

            a. the union of sperm and egg,

            b. to form a diploid zygote.

        2. Sperm are adapted to reach and fertilize an egg. Sperm have

            a. a streamlined shape, which moves easily through fluids,

            b. many mitochondria, which provide ATP for tail movements, and

            c. a head that contains a haploid nucleus and is tipped with an acrosome containing enzymes that help it penetrate the egg.

        3. During fertilization,

            a. sperm squeeze past follicle cells,

            b. acrosomal enzymes digest the egg's jelly coat,

            c. a sperm binds to egg receptors,

            d. sperm and egg plasma membranes fuse,

            e. the sperm nucleus enters the egg cytoplasm,

            f. the vitelline layer separates and becomes impenetrable, and

            g. the egg and sperm nuclei fuse.

    B. 27.10 **Cleavage** produces a ball of cells from the zygote

        1. Cleavage is a rapid series of cell divisions that produces

            a. more cells,

            b. smaller cells, and

            c. a fluid-filled embryo called a blastula.

    C. 27.11 Gastrulation produces a three-layered embryo

        1. During **gastrulation**

            a. cells migrate to new locations,

            b. a rudimentary digestive cavity forms, and

            c. the basic body plan of three layers is established with

                i. **ectoderm** outside—becomes skin and nervous systems,

                ii. **endoderm** inside—becomes digestive tract,

                iii. **mesoderm** in the middle—becomes muscle and bone.

    D. 27.12 Organs start to form after gastrulation

        1. Organs develop from the three embryonic layers.

            a. The stiff **notochord** forms the main axis of the body and is later replaced by the vertebral column in most chordates.

            b. The **neural tube** develops above the notochord and will become the

                i. brain and

                ii. spinal cord.

        2. As the embryo elongates, paired somites

            a. form along the sides of the notochord,

            b. hollow out to form a coelom, and

            c. eventually contribute to muscles, bone, and other connective tissues.

        3. Other systems develop at the same time.

E. 27.13 Multiple processes give form to the developing animal
 1. Tissues and organs develop by
    a. changes in cell shape,
    b. cell migration, and
    c. programmed cell death (also called **apoptosis**).
 2. Through **induction**, adjacent cells and cell layers
    a. influence each other's differentiation
    b. via chemical signals.
F. 227.14 EVOLUTION CONNECTION: Pattern formation during embryonic development is controlled by ancient genes
 1. **Pattern formation**,
    a. the emergence of the parts of a structure in their correct relative positions,
    b. involves the response of genes to spatial variations of chemicals in the embryo, and
    c. results in tissues and organs developing in their proper positions at the correct times.
 2. **Homeotic genes**
    a. contain common nucleotide sequences (**homeoboxes**),
    b. guide pattern formation in embryos, and
    c. occur in diverse groups such as
       i. prokaryotes,
       ii. yeast,
       iii. plants, and
       iv. animals.
 3. Homeotic genes reveal the shared evolutionary history of life.

V. Human Development

A. 27.15 The embryo and placenta take shape during the first month of pregnancy
 1. Pregnancy, or **gestation**, is the carrying of developing young within the female reproductive tract.
 2. Human pregnancy
    a. averages 266 days (38 weeks) from fertilization or
    b. 40 weeks (9 months) from the start of the last menstrual period.
 3. Human development begins with fertilization in the oviduct.
 4. Cleavage produces a **blastocyst** whose
    a. inner cell mass becomes the embryo and the
    b. trophoblast, the outer cell layer, which
       i. attaches to the uterine wall and
       ii. forms part of the **placenta**.
 5. Gastrulation occurs and organs develop from the three embryonic layers.
 6. Four extraembryonic membranes develop.
    a. The **amnion**
       i. surrounds the embryo and
       ii. forms a fluid-filled amniotic cavity that protects the embryo.
    b. The **yolk sac**,
       i. in reptiles, stores yolk,
       ii. in humans, does not store yolk but is a source of the first germ cells and blood cells.

c. The **allantois**
   i. contributes to the umbilical cord,
   ii. forms part of the urinary bladder, and
   iii. in reptiles, stores embryonic waste.
d. The **chorion**
   i. contributes to the placenta and
   ii. secretes **human chorionic gonadotropin** (**HCG**), which prevents menstruation in mammals.

7. The placenta is a
   a. close association of
      i. embryonic chorion and
      ii. mother's blood vessels, and
   b. site of
      i. gas exchange—from mother to embryo,
      ii. nutrient exchange—from mother to embryo, and
      iii. waste exchange—from embryo to mother.

B. 27.16 Human development from conception to birth is divided into three trimesters
   1. The first **trimester** is the period of greatest change.
      a. The embryo forms, looking like other vertebrate embryos.
      b. Extraembryonic membranes form.
      c. All major organ systems are established.
      d. After 9 weeks after fertilization, the embryo is called a fetus and
         i. can move its arms and legs and
         ii. starts to look distinctly human.
   2. During the second trimester,
      a. there is a great increase in the size of the fetus, and
      b. human features are refined.
      c. At 20 weeks, the fetus
         i. is about 19 cm long (7.6 in.)
         ii. weighs about 0.5 kg (1 lb.).
   3. The third trimester is also a time of rapid growth.
      a. The circulatory and respiratory systems mature.
      b. Muscles thicken and the skeleton hardens.
      c. The third trimester ends with birth.
      d. Babies born as early as 24 weeks may survive only with extensive medical care.

C. 27.17 Childbirth is induced by hormones and other chemical signals
   1. Hormonal changes induce birth.
      a. Estrogen makes the uterus more sensitive to oxytocin.
      b. Oxytocin acts with prostaglandins to initiate labor.
      c. The cervix dilates to about 10 cm.
      d. The baby is expelled by strong uterine contractions.
      e. The placenta dislodges and is expelled after the baby.
   2. Labor occurs in three stages:
      a. dilation of the cervix,
      b. expulsion, delivery of the infant,
      c. delivery of the placenta.

D. 27.18 CONNECTION: Reproductive technologies increase our reproductive options

    1. New techniques can help many infertile couples.

        a. About 15% of couples wanting children are infertile.

        b. Drug therapies can help address problems of impotence (erectile dysfunction) and induce ovulation.

        c. Assisted reproductive technologies (**ART**) require eggs to be harvested from the ovaries, fertilized, and returned to a woman's body.

        d. In vitro fertilization (**IVF**) is the most common assisted reproductive technology. Fertilization occurs in a culture dish and an early embryo is implanted in the uterus.

Chapter Guide to Teaching Resources

Asexual and Sexual Reproduction (27.1–27.2)

Student Misconceptions and Concerns

- Students do not often understand the costs and benefits of asexual and sexual reproduction. Consider discussing the advantages and disadvantages of each of these forms of reproduction. Encourage students to focus on the compromises involved in any adaptation. There is simply no one "best" way for all animals to reproduce. (27.1–27.2)

- Many students expect that hermaphroditic animals simply fertilize themselves. Although this may be common in some animals, the exchange of gametes between hermaphrodites also occurs, as noted in the text. (27.2)

Teaching Tips

- Aphid life cycles usually alternate between asexual and sexual reproductive strategies during a single year. Consider challenging your class to explain why aphids (and other animals) do this. In general, sexual reproduction is most common in times of stress, and may be related to overpopulation or environmental change in which diversity may be favored. (27.1)

- Many salamander species use spermatophores to transfer sperm from the male to the female. Spermatophores are reproductive structures produced by males during courtship. Sperm is deposited atop a gelatinous base attached to the substrate. The female moves over the spermatophore, removes some or all of the sperm from the cap, and stores the sperm in her reproductive tract (a spermatheca) until the time of egg deposition. Thus, sperm transfer is external but fertilization is internal. (27.2)

Human Reproduction (27.3–27.8)

Student Misconceptions and Concerns

- Students' background knowledge of human reproductive biology is likely to be quite uneven. Furthermore, the embarrassment frequently associated with this topic makes it difficult for teachers to fairly assess what students know. The best advice may be to not assume too much. (27.3–27.8)

- Embarrassment with the subject of human reproductive biology may make open discussions uncomfortable for some students. Good clear textbook and media assignments that can be studied privately and opportunities to ask anonymous questions provide additional avenues to address sensitive content and questions. (27.3–27.8)

- Students often believe that drugs are available to cure most STDs. However, viral infections, including HIV, HPV, and herpes, should be assumed to be lifelong. (27.7–27.8)

Teaching Tips

- Ectopic pregnancies occur when an embryo implants anywhere other than the uterus. Most frequently, ectopic pregnancies occur in the oviducts. However, the structure of the oviduct cannot accommodate the growth of a fetus. Surgical removal of the fetus, resulting in an abortion, is thus often required for the sake of the mother's health. Many of those who believe that abortion is wrong in general, may consider abortions acceptable in the case of ectopic pregnancy, in that it may literally save the life of the mother. (27.3)

- Endometriosis is an inflammatory condition in which the endometrium spreads beyond the uterus. It can lead to painful menstrual cycles and infertility. The Endometriosis Association website, www.endometriosisassn.org, is a good resource for additional information. (27.3)

- Men in your class will be well aware of physiological changes in the scrotum associated with thermoregulation. When a man enters into cool water, the scrotum is pulled tight and the testes are held close to the body. During a warm shower or bath, the scrotum relaxes and the testes are held far away from the body. (27.4)

- Testicular cancer is the most common form of cancer in men between 15 and 35 years of age. Students can find information about testicular cancer and how to perform a self-exam at the website for the American Cancer Society at www.cancer.org. (27.4)

- Students often confuse semen and sperm. Most of a human ejaculate consists of glandular products. In fact, there is no visible difference to the naked eye in the ejaculate of a fertile or sterile man. (27.4)

- Ask students to explain why polar bodies are produced during oogenesis and why they have so little cytoplasm. Challenge your students to explain why polar bodies are not produced in spermatogenesis. (Answer: Polar bodies are produced during oogenesis to eliminate nuclear material. Their smaller size is an adaptation to conserve cytoplasm during reduction division. During spermatogenesis, four functional spermatozoa are produced and no nuclear material is discarded.) (27.5)

- Students might wonder why a woman's body goes through menstrual cycles. Why not just sustain the endometrium continuously? One hypothesis suggests that because the uterus is a good environment in which bacteria can grow, menstrual cycles are a way to "flush" the system and discourage microbial growth. (27.6)

- Many home pregnancy tests rely upon antibodies to HCG. (27.6)

- The Sexuality Information and Education Council of the U.S. (SIECUS) is a national, non-profit organization that affirms that sexuality is a natural and healthy part of living. Its website at www.siecus.org is an excellent source of information related to this chapter. (27.7)

- Although people infected with sexually transmitted diseases might have no apparent symptoms, they may still be capable of infecting partners. This important point is worth repeating to young college audiences who may be overly optimistic about the health of their partners. (27.7)

- Chlamydia is the most common sexually transmitted bacterial infection in the United States. (27.7)

- Students often mistakenly equate contraception with prevention of sexually transmitted diseases. As you review the forms of birth control, consider pointing out the strategies that provide little or no protection against STDs. The pill, for example, does nothing to prevent disease transmission. Consider pointing out that methods that greatly reduce the transmission of disease (condoms used with spermicides) are also effective forms of birth control. (27.8)

Principles of Embryonic Development (27.9–27.14)

Student Misconceptions and Concerns

- The descriptions of basic development addresses questions that students may have never thought to ask. How do we get so many cells (trillions!) in our adult bodies? How do basic tissues, organs, and organ systems form? What mechanisms permit the coordinated development of the body? Before beginning this chapter, consider challenging your students with some of these fundamental questions: How did you get a heart, a brain, and ears? What determined when you were ready to be born? How did you get nutrients and oxygen before you could eat or breathe? (27.9–27.14)

- Many students do not realize that their nervous system is hollow, and do not consequently relate the formation of the neural tube to the structure of a fully developed adult nervous system. While discussing formation of the neural tube, you may want to anticipate the subject matter of Chapter 28 by emphasizing that the fluid-filled ventricles of the brain and the central canal of the spinal cord are spaces. (27.12)

Teaching Tips

- The authors note in Module 27.9 that the process of sea urchin development is discussed because sea urchins exhibit fundamental details that are found in the development of most vertebrates. These similarities are a consequence of our shared ancestry and provide strong evidence of evolution. (27.9)

- Reproductive isolating mechanisms are generally classified into prezygotic and postzygotic categories. Module 27.9 discusses some of the ways that hybridization is prevented by species-specific biochemical interactions between the sperm and the egg. (27.9)

- Cleavage is largely a process of subdivision with no growth. This process is a bit like cutting up a pie into pieces. With every division, more pieces are produced, but the pieces are smaller and the pie itself does not increase in size. Similarly, cleavage increases the number of cells while decreasing their size. (27.10)

- Cleavage in humans is a very slow process, taking up to 12 hours for each division. (27.10)

- Cleavage results in an uneven distribution of cytoplasmic elements into the daughter blastomeres (embryonic cells produced by cleavage). Some students might benefit from this simple analogy: Imagine baking a pie that is filled with one can of apple pie filling and one can of cherry pie filling. The contents of each can are poured into opposite ends of the pie and are not mixed. When the pie is served, some pieces will contain only apples, some only cherries, and some combinations of both. This disproportionate division of pie contents is like the disproportionate division of cytoplasmic elements during cleavage. (27.10)

- You might wish to reflect on the somewhat famous quote of Lewis Wolpert, who in 1986 said, "It is not birth, marriage, or death, but gastrulation, which is truly the most important time in your life." The development and arrangement of the basic embryonic layers (ectoderm: skin and nervous system; mesoderm: muscle and bone; and endoderm: digestive tract) establishes the basic body plan. (27.11)

- Gastrulation establishes the basic body plan by positioning the future systems of the body in relationship to each other. This essential element of gastrulation is a crucial event that is a prerequisite for later developmental events (and thus is the basis of the quote directly above). (27.11)

- The colors used in the text to depict the three layers of embryonic tissue are standards used in embryology. Blue represents ectoderm and its derivatives, red represents mesoderm and its derivatives, and yellow represents endoderm and its derivatives. (27.11)

- Neural crest cells are often referred to as the fourth layer of embryonic tissue because these cells give rise to a variety of tissues in diverse locations in the body. Neural crest cells and their derivatives are not addressed in Chapter 27. (27.11)

- The notochord functions as a sort of scaffolding upon which the embryo develops, especially important before a vertebral column develops. In the lancelet (amphioxus), the notochord is the adult skeletal structure along the long axis of the body. (27.12)

- The alignment of the notochord and neural tube is not accidental. Cellular communication between the notochord and neural plate results in the parallel alignment of the neural tube to the notochord (which forms first). (27.12)

- Apoptosis is a sort of editing mechanism that permits the selective destruction of embryonic structures. Examples of apoptosis in normal development (such as the formation of fingers discussed in Module 27.13) are abundant. For example, extensive apoptosis during vertebrate brain development functions as a sort of "neural pruning" of the developing nervous system (neural "tree"), resulting in the final neural configurations. (27.13)

- In every construction project, there must be some coordination of effort: someone has to be in charge. Homeotic genes perform this coordinating function, signaling when and where structures are to form. (27.14)

- The discovery of homeotic genes and their functions permitted insight into the evolution of homologous structures. Small changes in homeotic genes permit the rearrangement of ancestral parts into new configurations, which may serve new functions. Biologists had long wondered how major changes might evolve relatively quickly. Minor changes in the directions provided by these genes can result in major changes in structure. (27.14)

Human Development (27.15–27.18)

Student Misconceptions and Concerns

- Students often think that maternal and fetal blood merge together. Consider spending additional time to note the close association but distinct separation maintained between these two circulatory systems. (27.15)

- The extraembryonic membranes surrounding a human embryo are rarely understood by college students outside of the health sciences. These extraembryonic membranes can be viewed as analogous to the life-support systems used by astronauts. (27.15)

- Students frequently confuse the terms infertility and impotence. Care should be used to carefully distinguish these terms. (27.18)

- Few students understand that many STDs can lead to infertility. For example, chlamydia is the most frequently reported bacterial sexually transmitted disease, according to the CDC. Infertility is a common consequence of chlamydia infections. (27.18)

Teaching Tips

- All vertebrates develop in a fluid environment. Fish and amphibians typically lay their eggs in water. Amniotes (reptiles and mammals) are defined by the presence of an amniotic sac, a self-contained aquatic system that surrounds the embryo with water inside the egg. The evolution of the amniotic egg eliminated the need to reproduce near water, freeing amniotes to reproduce underground, in deserts, and in trees! (27.15)

- Morning sickness typically occurs during the first trimester of pregnancy and subsides during the second. However, a great deal of variation in the timing and degree of symptoms has been observed. Unfortunately, the precise cause of morning sickness remains unknown. (27.16)

- Most human babies weigh 3–4 kilograms (kg) at birth. Birth weights much larger or smaller than this are associated with increased mortality. This is an example of stabilizing selection, which is discussed in Module 13.13. (27.16)

- When discussing the dilation of the cervix as part of labor, it might be useful to note that cigarettes are 90–100 mm long. Thus, a fully dilated cervix is about as wide as a cigarette is long. (27.17)

- The many benefits of breastfeeding are noted in a summary report of the American Medical Association, which can be found at www.ama-assn.org/ama/no-index/about-ama/15169.shtml. (27.17)

- Impotence is often caused by cardiovascular disease. Students may be unaware of the extent to which smoking, poor diet, and lack of exercise can therefore contribute to sexual problems. (27.18)

- The fate of surplus frozen embryos (sometimes called snowflake babies) produced by in vitro fertilization is often debated. Some people have suggested that they be used as sources of stem cells. Others regard this as akin to abortion and therefore unacceptable. Students may find it engaging to research and discuss the scientific and ethical issues raised by these embryos. (27.18)

Key Terms

allantois	embryo	seminal vesicle
amnion	fertilization	sexual reproduction
asexual reproduction	homeotic genes	sexually transmitted disease
blastocoel	internal fertilization	(STDs)
blastocyst	neural tube	testes (singular, testis)
bulbourethral gland	notochord	trimesters
cleavage	penis	tubal ligation
clitoris	prostate gland	yolk sac
conception	rhythm method	zygote
contraception	secondary oocyte	

Word Roots

a- = not, without (*asexual reproduction*: a type of reproduction involving only one parent that produces genetically identical offspring)

blast- = bud, sprout; **-coel** = opening (*blastocoel*: the fluid-filled cavity inside a blastocyst)

-cyst = sac, bladder (*blastocyst*: a mammalian embryo made up of a hollow ball of cells)

contra- = against (*contraception*: the deliberate prevention of pregnancy)

fertil- = fruitful (*fertilization*: the union of the nucleus of a sperm cell with the nucleus of an egg cell, producing a zygote)

noto- = the back; **-chord** = a string (*notochord*: a flexible, cartilage-like, longitudinal rod located between the digestive tract and nerve cord in chordate animals)

sem- = seed (*seminal vesicle*: a gland in males that secretes a fluid component of semen that lubricates and nourishes sperm)

tri- = three (*trimester*: a three-month period)

CHAPTER 28

Nervous Systems

Chapter Objectives

Opening Essay

Explain how spinal cords may be injured and why the damage is often traumatic.

Nervous System Structure and Function

28.1 Describe the structural and functional subdivisions of the nervous system. Describe the three parts of a reflex, distinguishing the three types of neurons that may be involved in the reaction.

28.2 Describe the structures and functions of neurons and myelin sheaths.

Nerve Signals and Their Transmission

28.3 Define a resting potential and explain how it is created.

28.4 Explain how an action potential is produced and the resting membrane potential restored.

28.5 Explain (a) how an action potential propagates itself along a neuron, (b) why action potentials move in only one direction, and (c) how action potentials relay different intensities of information.

28.6 Compare the structures, functions, and locations of electrical and chemical synapses.

28.7 Compare excitatory and inhibitory neurotransmitters. Explain how the number and location of bound neurotransmitters influence a receiving cell.

28.8 Describe the types and functions of neurotransmitters known in humans.

28.9 Explain how drugs can alter chemical synapses.

An Overview of Animal Nervous Systems

28.10 Describe the diversity of animal nervous systems and provide examples. Explain how the structure of the nervous system relates to the ways animals interact with their environment.

28.11 Describe the general structure of the brain, spinal cord, and associated nerves of vertebrates. Describe the formation, location, and functions of cerebrospinal fluid.

28.12 Compare the functions of the motor nervous system and autonomic nervous system.

28.12 Compare the structures, functions, and interrelationships of the parasympathetic, sympathetic, and enteric divisions of the peripheral nervous system.

28.13 Explain how the vertebrate brain develops from an embryonic tube.

The Human Brain

28.14–28.15 Describe the main parts and functions of the human brain. Detail the structures and functions of the cerebral cortex.

28.16 Explain how injuries, illness, and surgery provide insight into the functions of the brain.

28.17 Explain how fMRI scans help us understand brain functions.

28.18 Explain how the brain regulates sleep and arousal.

28.19 Describe the structure and functions of the limbic system. Describe the properties of short-term, long-term, and skill memories.

28.20 Describe the causes, symptoms, and treatments of schizophrenia, depression, Alzheimer's disease, and Parkinson's disease.

Lecture Outline

I. Introduction

A. Spinal cord injuries disrupt communication between
  1. the central nervous system (brain and spinal cord) and
  2. the rest of the body.
B. Over 250,000 Americans are living with spinal cord injuries.
C. Spinal cord injuries
  1. happen more often to men,
  2. happen mostly to people in their teens and 20s,
  3. are caused by vehicle accidents, gunshots, and falls, and
  4. are usually permanent because the spinal cord cannot be repaired.

II. Nervous System Structure and Function

A. 28.1 Nervous systems receive sensory input, interpret it, and send out appropriate commands
  1. The **nervous system**
    a. obtains sensory information, **sensory input**,
    b. processes sensory information, **integration**, and
    c. sends commands to effector cells (muscles) that carry out appropriate responses, **motor output**.
  2. The **central nervous system** (**CNS**) consists of the
    a. brain and
    b. spinal cord (vertebrates).
  3. The **peripheral nervous system** (**PNS**)
    a. is located outside the CNS and
    b. consists of
      i. **nerves** (bundles of neurons wrapped in connective tissue) and
      ii. **ganglia** (clusters of neuron cell bodies).
  4. Sensory neurons
    a. convey signals from sensory receptors
    b. to the CNS.
  5. Interneurons
    a. are located entirely in the CNS,

   b. integrate information, and

   c. send it to motor neurons.

  6. Motor neurons convey signals to effector cells.

 B. 28.2 Neurons are the functional units of nervous systems

  1. Neurons are

   a. cells specialized for carrying signals and

   b. the functional units of the nervous system.

  2. A neuron consists of

   a. a **cell body** and

   b. two types of extensions (fibers) that conduct signals,

    i. **dendrites** and

    ii. **axons.**

  3. Myelin sheaths

   a. enclose axons,

   b. form a cellular insulation, and

   c. speed up signal transmission.

III. Nerve Signals and Their Transmission

 A. 28.3 Nerve function depends on charge differences across neuron membranes

  1. At rest, a neuron's plasma membrane has potential energy—the **membrane potential**, in which

   a. just inside the cell is slightly negative and

   b. just outside the cell is slightly positive.

  2. The **resting potential** is the voltage across the plasma membrane of a resting neuron.

  3. The resting potential exists because of differences in ion concentration of the fluids inside and outside the neuron.

   a. Inside the neuron

    i. K^+ is high and

    ii. Na^+ is low.

   b. Outside the neuron

    i. K^+ is low and

    ii. Na^+ is high.

 B. 28.4 A nerve signal begins as a change in the membrane potential

  1. A **stimulus** is any factor that causes a nerve signal to be generated. A stimulus

   a. alters the permeability of a portion of the membrane,

   b. allows ions to pass through, and

   c. changes the membrane's voltage.

  2. A nerve signal, called an **action potential**, is

   a. a change in the membrane voltage,

   b. from the resting potential,

   c. to a maximum level, and

   d. back to the resting potential.

 C. 28.5 The action potential propagates itself along the axon

  1. Action potentials are

   a. self-propagated in a one-way chain reaction along a neuron and

   b. all-or-none events.

  2. The frequency of action potentials (but not their strength) changes with the strength of the stimulus.

D. 28.6 Neurons communicate at synapses

    1. Synapses are junctions where signals are transmitted between

        a. two neurons or

        b. between neurons and effector cells.

    2. Electrical signals pass between cells at electrical synapses.

    3. At chemical synapses

        a. the ending (presynaptic) cell secretes a chemical signal, a **neurotransmitter**,

        b. the neurotransmitter crosses the **synaptic cleft**, and

        c. the neurotransmitter binds to a specific receptor on the surface of the receiving (postsynaptic) cell.

E. 28.7 Chemical synapses enable complex information to be processed

    1. Some neurotransmitters

        a. excite a receiving cell, and

        b. others inhibit a receiving cell's activity by decreasing its ability to develop action potentials.

    2. A receiving neuron's membrane may receive signals

        a. that are both excitatory and inhibitory and

        b. from many different sending neurons.

    3. The summation of excitation and inhibition determines if a neuron will transmit a nerve signal.

F. 28.8 A variety of small molecules function as neurotransmitters

    1. Many small, nitrogen-containing molecules are neurotransmitters.

        a. Acetylcholine is a neurotransmitter

            i. in the brain and

            ii. at synapses between motor neurons and muscle cells.

        b. Biogenic amines

            i. are important neurotransmitters in the CNS and

            ii. include serotonin and dopamine, which affect sleep, mood, and attention.

        c. Many neuropeptides

            i. consist of relatively short chains of amino acids important in the CNS and

            ii. include endorphins, decreasing our perception of pain.

        d. Nitric oxide

            i. is a dissolved gas and

            ii. triggers erections during sexual arousal in men.

G. 28.9 CONNECTION: Many drugs act at chemical synapses

    1. Many psychoactive drugs

        a. act at synapses and

        b. affect neurotransmitter action.

    2. Caffeine counters the effect of inhibitory neurotransmitters.

    3. Nicotine acts as a stimulant by binding to acetylcholine receptors.

    4. Alcohol is a depressant.

IV. An Overview of Animal Nervous Systems

    A. 28.10 EVOLUTION CONNECTION: The evolution of animal nervous systems reflects changes in body symmetry

        1. Radially symmetrical animals have a nervous system arranged in a weblike system of neurons called a nerve net.

2. Most bilaterally symmetrical animals evolved
   a. **cephalization**, the concentration of the nervous system at the head end, and
   b. **centralization**, the presence of a central nervous system distinct from a peripheral nervous system.
B. 28.11 Vertebrate nervous systems are highly centralized
   1. In the vertebrates, the central nervous system (CNS)
      a. consists of the **brain** and **spinal cord** and
      b. includes spaces filled with cerebrospinal fluid
         i. forming **ventricles** of the brain,
         ii. forming the **central canal** of the spinal cord, and
         iii. surrounding the brain.
   2. The vertebrate peripheral nervous system (PNS) consists of
      a. cranial nerves,
      b. spinal nerves, and
      c. ganglia.
   3. The PNS can be divided into two functional components:
      a. the **motor system**, mostly voluntary, and
      b. the **autonomic nervous system**, mostly involuntary.
   4. The motor nervous system
      a. carries signals to and from skeletal muscles and
      b. mainly responds to external stimuli.
   5. The autonomic nervous system
      a. regulates the internal environment and
      b. controls smooth and cardiac muscle and organs and glands of the digestive, cardio-vascular, excretory, and endocrine systems.
C. 28.12 The peripheral nervous system of vertebrates is a functional hierarchy
   1. The autonomic nervous system is composed of three divisions.
      a. The **parasympathetic division** primes the body for activities that gain and conserve energy for the body.
      b. The **sympathetic division** prepares the body for intense, energy-consuming activities.
      c. The **enteric division** consists of networks of neurons in the digestive tract, pancreas, and gallbladder that control secretion and peristalsis.
D. 28.13 The vertebrate brain develops from three anterior bulges of the neural tube
   1. The vertebrate brain evolved by the enlargement and subdivision of the
      a. **forebrain**,
      b. **midbrain**, and
      c. **hindbrain**.
   2. In the course of vertebrate evolution, the forebrain and hindbrain gradually became subdivided
      a. structurally and
      b. functionally.
   3. In birds and mammals the **cerebrum**
      a. is much larger and
      b. correlates with their sophisticated behavior.

V. The Human Brain

A. 28.14 The structure of a living supercomputer: The human brain

   1. The human brain is

      a. more powerful than the most sophisticated computer and

      b. composed of three main parts:

         i. forebrain,

         ii. midbrain, and

         iii. hindbrain.

   2. The midbrain, subdivisions of the hindbrain, the thalamus, and the hypothalamus

      a. conduct information to and from higher brain centers,

      b. regulate homeostatic functions,

      c. keep track of body position, and

      d. sort sensory information.

   3. The cerebrum is

      a. part of the forebrain and

      b. the largest and most complex part of the brain.

      c. Most of the cerebrum's integrative power resides in the cerebral cortex of the two **cerebral hemispheres**.

B. 28.15 The cerebral cortex is a mosaic of specialized, interactive regions

   1. The cerebral cortex

      a. is less than 5 mm thick and

      b. accounts for 80% of the total human brain mass.

   2. Specialized integrative regions of the cerebral cortex include

      a. the somatosensory cortex and

      b. centers for vision, hearing, taste, and smell.

   3. The motor cortex directs responses.

   4. Association areas

      a. make up most of the cerebrum and

      b. are concerned with higher mental activities such as reasoning and language.

   5. In a phenomenon known as **lateralization**, right and left cerebral hemispheres tend to specialize in different mental tasks.

C. 28.16 CONNECTION: Injuries and brain operations provide insight into brain function

   1. Brain injuries and surgeries reveal brain functions.

      a. Phineas Gage had a 13-pound steel rod pierce his skull, which resulted in negative changes to his personality.

      b. Stimulation of the cerebral cortex during surgeries caused patients to recall sensations and memories.

      c. Cutting the corpus callosum revealed information about brain lateralization.

D. 28.17 CONNECTION: fMRI scans can provide insight into brain structure and function

   1. Functional magnetic resonance imaging (fMRI) is

      a. a scanning and imaging technology used to study brain functions,

      b. used on conscious patients,

      c. monitors changes in blood oxygen usage in the brain, and

      d. correlates to regions of intense brain function.

E. 28.18 Several parts of the brain regulate sleep and arousal

   1. Sleep and arousal involve activity by the

      a. hypothalamus,

      b. medulla oblongata,

    c. pons, and

    d. neurons of the reticular formation.

  2. Sleep

    a. is essential for survival,

    b. is an active state, and

    c. may be involved in consolidating learning and memory.

F. 28.19 The limbic system is involved in emotions, memory, and learning

  1. The **limbic system** is

    a. a functional group of integrating centers in the

      i. cerebral cortex,

      ii. thalamus,

      iii. hypothalamus, and

    b. involved in

      i. emotions such as nurturing infants and bonding emotionally to other people,

      ii. memory, and

      iii. learning.

G. 28.20 CONNECTION: Changes in brain physiology can produce neurological disorders

  1. Many neurological disorders can be linked to changes in brain physiology, including

    a. schizophrenia,

    b. major depression,

    c. Alzheimer's disease, and

    d. Parkinson's disease.

  2. **Schizophrenia** is

    a. a severe mental disturbance and

    b. characterized by psychotic episodes in which patients lose the ability to distinguish reality.

  3. Depression

    a. Two broad forms of depressive illness have been identified:

      i. **major depression** and

      ii. **bipolar disorder**, manic-depressive disorder.

    b. Treatments may include selective serotonin reuptake inhibitors (SSRIs), which increase the amount of time serotonin is available to stimulate certain neurons in the brain.

  4. **Alzheimer's disease** is

    a. characterized by confusion, memory loss, and personality changes and

    b. difficult to diagnosis.

  5. **Parkinson's disease** is

    a. a motor disorder and

    b. characterized by

      i. difficulty in initiating movements,

      ii. slowness of movement, and

      iii. rigidity.

Chapter Guide to Teaching Resources

Nervous System Structure and Function (28.1–28.2)

Student Misconceptions and Concerns

- As students absorb additional details, often they lose sight of the fundamental functions of the nervous system, creating the risk that they will miss the forest for the trees. Remember to regularly connect the three fundamental functions of the nervous system, 1) sensory input, 2) integration, and 3) motor output, to an image of the PNS and CNS, noting where these functions occur (as in Figure 28.1A, for example). Returning to this or another familiar figure throughout lectures on the nervous system can help to remind students of key functions while allowing them to visually organize additional information. Such figures serve as "intellectual anchors" for a discussion. (28.1)

- Students often confuse the terms spinal column, spinal cord, spine, and backbone. They may fail to distinguish between the series of bones (vertebrae) and the extension of the central nervous system (the spinal cord) that runs through them. Figure 28.12B can help to clarify any confusion. (28.1–28.2)

Teaching Tips

- Challenge students to explain the adaptive advantages of reflexes. What is the benefit of an "automatic" response to a stimulus? (28.1)

- Challenge your students to provide examples of computer systems that have the same three functions as the nervous system. For example, many automobiles use built-in computers that detect signals indicating engine performance, interpret the signals, and then send signals to make adjustments. (28.1)

- The proportion of neurons to glial cells in the brain is often quite surprising to students who might have little appreciation for the roles or even the existence of glial cells. Like the president of the United States or the head of any major organization, neurons have a large "support staff" of cells that help them perform their function. (28.2)

- Myelination is like the insulation on an electrical cord that ensures the wires are only exposed in specific locations. Breaks in this insulation, like disruption of myelin sheaths, will reduce the effectiveness of signal conduction. (28.2)

- Myelin sheaths and the nodes of Ranvier may also be described using the following analogy: Imagine that you are preparing a long hot dog (axon), maybe one 20 inches long. However, your hot dog buns (myelin) are only 6 inches long. You use three buns spaced 1 inch apart. That leaves two gaps (nodes of Ranvier), 1 inch each, separating the buns. If you really want to make the point, you could find a fake hot dog item and bring along three hot dog buns. (28.2)

Nerve Signals and Their Transmission (28.3–28.9)

Student Misconceptions and Concerns

- The abstract and complex nature of action potentials requires a careful and gradual discussion. Students with minimal backgrounds in cell biology are likely to struggle with this concept. Consider an initial presentation that provides an overview of the movement of charges before addressing the specific details. (28.3–28.9)

- Students who lack a background in chemistry and electricity are likely to struggle with the basic process of action potentials. Assumptions about the limited permeability of membranes, charges on ions, and natural electrical attractions may be unfamiliar to them. Students who read carefully through the text before action potentials are discussed in class are much more likely to understand the related lecture(s). (28.3–28.9)

- Consider presenting the diverse actions of neurotransmitters and related drugs in a table for quick and easy reference during lecture. Many students will have an interest in a particular drug, but soon forget the related effect if it was discussed earlier. A table permits easy reference to check drug effects. (28.3–28.9)

Teaching Tips

- Students may require a review of the basic concept of potential energy. A simple demonstration in class, such as holding an object and then letting it plummet to the floor, can provide a quick, clear demonstration. As noted in the text, potential electrical energy can be stored in a battery. (28.3)

- Students might benefit most by first learning how sodium and potassium ions move during an action potential before addressing the resulting changes in membrane potential. (28.4)

- Students may better comprehend the idea of the threshold for an action potential by considering an analogy to the various annoying stimuli in our lives. A blaring TV might be annoying, but one tolerates it for a while. However, a person can reach a "threshold" where he or she is stimulated enough to get up and turn it off. (28.4)

- An action potential spreading along the length of an axon retains its strength. The overall process is therefore like the "wave" sometimes created by audiences at sporting events. (28.5)

- Challenge students to explain how the intensity of a signal can be expressed when the strength of an action potential signal is steady. As noted in the text, signal intensity is communicated by the frequency of the signals. This is like knocking on a door again and again to communicate urgency. (28.5)

- The transmission of a signal across a chemical synapse is like driving along a road to a river, then taking a ferry across the river, then driving away on a road on the other side. The movement of the traveler (or the signal) continues, but changes mechanisms along the way. (28.6)

- The authors compare a neuron's diverse contacts with other neurons (potentially, hundreds of them) to a living circuit board. (28.7)

- Another analogy to the diverse signal input to a neuron might be helpful, even amusing. A neuron receiving diverse and potentially opposing signals is like a sports team hearing the crowd cheering for and against them. Game shows often demonstrate similar situations, as players' decisions are influenced by the shouted suggestions of the audience. (28.7)

- Students may have heard about chemical imbalances in the brain without specifically knowing what this means. Abnormal concentrations of neurotransmitters in the central nervous system resulting from disease or chemical exposure can change our ability to perceive and respond to our world. Many drugs, both legal and illegal, can create imbalances with potentially disastrous consequences. (28.8–28.9)

- The treatment of psychological disorders is complicated by the diversity of neurotransmitters and their interactions. Therefore, predicting how a specific prescription drug will function in a particular patient is often difficult. Students may begin with the assumption that scientists currently understand much more about these complex reactions than we actually do. Emphasizing the need for additional research in these fields may encourage students to ponder career directions they have not previously considered. (28.8–28.9)

- Here is a bit of logic you might share with your students. Ask your students if they would avoid purchasing prescription drugs from a pharmacist convicted of some crime. If the answer is yes, ask why? The likely response will be that one might not trust a criminal pharmacist to carefully provide medicine. Why, then, you might wonder aloud, would anyone trust the quality of illegal drugs obtained from criminals (who are not likely trained pharmacists) who sell them on the street? (28.8–28.9)

An Overview of Animal Nervous Systems (28.10–28.13)

Student Misconceptions and Concerns

- Students may think of the human brain as completely unique. Yet, the anatomical components of the human brain mirror the basic components found in many other vertebrates. These similarities are so extensive that sheep brains are often studied in biology laboratories to better understand human anatomy. (28.10–28.11)

- Students often think of the motor nervous system as "voluntary" and directed by conscious thoughts. You might point out to your students that they are not likely concentrating on contracting the various muscles needed to maintain their posture as they sit in class. As noted in Module 28.12, many skeletal muscles are actually controlled by reflexes. (28.12)

Teaching Tips

- Before addressing Modules 28.10–28.13, consider challenging your students to explain what we mean by a "head" in an animal. Why are heads concentrated on one end of the body? Why is the mouth usually, but not always, associated with the head? (The opening to the digestive tract of a planarian is in the middle of the body.) An analogy might be made to an airplane, whose pilot sits inside the cockpit in front gathering and processing information about where the plane is headed. Why are all six of our major senses (taste, smell, sight, touch, sound, and balance) all centered in our heads? (28.10)

- Students often are surprised to learn that their brain is hollow, although some students may know that the central nervous system is surrounded by cerebrospinal fluid. The basic development of the brain and spinal cord from an embryonic tube is addressed in Module 28.13. (28.11)

- Students often remember the functions of the autonomic nervous system better by thinking of them as "automatic." (28.12)

- Students may remember the functions of the sympathetic division as "sympathetic" to our problems. For example, the sympathetic nervous system may react to stressful situations by preparing us to fight or to run (although we often choose to do neither). (28.12)

- The automatic functions of the enteric division may not be appreciated by your students. You might note that given our busy days, with so many activities and obligations, we are fortunate that our digestive system can secrete, mix, propel, and absorb our meals without our focused mental attention! Can you imagine adding all that to our to-do list? (28.12)

- Many of the sympathetic division responses are the products of hormones released into the bloodstream. These responses cannot be quickly reversed. You might want to encourage students to think of how long it usually takes for them or others to calm down after having become extremely nervous or upset. Time and separation from the source of stress are usually required. For example, those who take a long walk in order to calm down often find, in the mild exercise and the retreat from the situation, an emotional comfort that also makes biological sense. (28.12)

- The basic organization of the embryonic brain of humans is very similar to the early developmental stages in fish, amphibians, reptiles, and other mammals. The formation of a neural tube and subdivision into three and then five brain regions reflects the common ancestry of vertebrates. For biology teachers, such connections are commonplace. However, pointing out such evidence of evolution can help students understand why evolution has been widely accepted by the scientific community as a fundamental process of life. (28.13)

The Human Brain (28.14–28.20)

Student Misconceptions and Concerns

- Students often think of vertebrate skulls as just a place to house the brain. In most vertebrates, the brain is a relatively small item housed deep in the skull. The skull also houses all the major sense organs, is the site of firm muscle attachments, and is the entry point for the respiratory and digestive systems. (28.14–28.20)

- Popular media often suggests that lateralization is a fixed human trait; i.e., certain people are "left-brained" while others are "right-brained." Students might therefore believe that they are one or the other. As biology frequently reveals, little about life is that clear and distinct. The traits associated with each side of the brain are matters of degree, and studies of surgical procedures, disease, and injury have revealed that the brain's hemispheres have considerable plasticity. (28.15)

Teaching Tips

- Tables such as 28.14, which provide summaries of structures and functions, can relieve lectures from the repetition of tedious detail. Instead, more class time can be spent on more interesting and meaningful aspects of the topic. Such tables also facilitate the creation of matching questions on exams! (28.14)

- As students learn about the structure and function of the cerebral cortex, they are actually using these sets of cells to think about these cells. As student understanding grows, these sets of cells become increasingly aware of their own properties, in a process that is like looking in a mirror! (28.15)

- Module 28.16 notes that the cerebrum lacks cells that can detect pain. Consider challenging your students to explain the source of the pain during a headache. (Some headaches can result from pain outside the brain. For example, sinus pressure, muscle tension, or a toothache can be considered a type of headache. Vascular headaches can result from pain receptors in overstretched or over constricted blood vessels of the brain.) (28.16)

- Much of what we know about brain function comes from damage caused by accidents or disease. Challenge your students to consider the limits of these "natural" experiments. (For instance, disease or damage may have multiple physiological effects, making it difficult to trace them to the malfunction of a particular brain region.) Corroborating data from other technologies, such as fMRI scans, helps verify earlier results. Reviewing the different approaches to understanding the brain reveals how multiple, independent lines of evidence increase confidence in results. (28.16–28.17)

- As noted in Module 28.18, sleep seems to be involved in learning and memory. Study strategies that involve cramming large amounts of information into the memory in a short period of time may not permit enough sleep and review for deeper understanding. Students who engage in such practices may easily be confused on an exam. The strategy of processing smaller amounts of information over a longer period of time, allowing for both rest and frequent review, is likely to result in the retention of a better-integrated body of information. (28.18)

- Moving information from short-term memory to long-term memory requires frequent rehearsal. Using note cards to create questions and answers based upon the information for an exam is one form of rehearsal that can be very effective when studying basic information. This chapter helps students understand the underlying physiological basis of many successful study techniques. (28.19)

- The strong emotional reactions to scents and music that many humans have experienced are properties of our limbic system. (28.19)

- The text notes that nearly 20 million American adults are affected by depression. However, many students may be unaware what proportion of the population this number represents. Does 20 million represent a large or small fraction of the people in our country? Consider surveying your class to see how many have an idea of the size of the U.S. population and what fraction of people therefore suffer from depression. The current U.S. population, about 311–312 million, is estimated at the website www.census.gov/main/www/popclock.html. (28.20)

- The frequent occurrence of the neurological disorders discussed in Module 28.20 makes it likely that many of your students will know someone who is affected by such a disorder or may even be coping with one themselves. Topics such as these, which often have immediate relevance to students' lives and tend to arouse both sympathy and curiosity, create excellent opportunities for class discussions and further exploration outside of class. (28.20)

- Students may wonder why diseases of old age (such as Alzheimer's, cancer, and cardio-vascular disease) have not been selected against by natural selection. Consider challenging your class to explain why diseases of old age may not be subject to strong selective pressures. Many students will not realize that diseases that strike primarily after the most common age of reproduction experience reduced selective pressure. (28.20)

Key Terms

Alzheimer's disease (AD)	biogenic amine	dendrites
amygdala	central canal	enteric division
autonomic nervous system	centralization	forebrain
axon	cerebellum	ganglia (singular, ganglion)
basal nuclei	cerebral hemispheres	gray matter
	circadian rhythm	hindbrain
	corpus callosum	hippocampus

integration
interneurons
major depression
medulla oblongata
midbrain
motor neurons
motor output
motor system
nerve

nerve cords
nerve net
nervous systems
neurotransmitter
parasympathetic division
Parkinson's disease
sensory input
sensory neurons
stimulus

sympathetic division
synaptic terminal
synaptic vesicle
thalamus
threshold
ventricle
white matter

Word Roots

auto- = self (*autonomic nervous system*: the component of the vertebrate peripheral nervous system that regulates the internal environment)

bio- = life; **-genic** = producing (*biogenic amine*: a neurotransmitter derived from an amino acid)

circa- = a circle (*circadian rhythm*: a biological cycle of about 24 hours that is controlled by a biological clock, usually under the influence of environmental cues; a pattern of activity that is repeated daily)

corpus = body; **callos-** = hard (*corpus callosum*: the thick band of nerve fibers that connect the right and left cerebral hemispheres in placental mammals)

dendro- = tree (*dendrite*: a branched neuron fiber that conveys signals from its tip inward, towards the cell body of the neuron)

hippo- = horse (*hippocampus*: the integrative center of the cerebrum, and the part of the limbic system that plays a central role in memory and learning; in cross-section, its outline resembles a seahorse)

inter- = between (*interneuron*: a nerve cell, located entirely within the central nervous system, that integrates sensory signals and may relay command signals to motor neurons)

neuro- = nerve; **trans-** = across (*neurotransmitter*: a chemical messenger that carries information from a transmitting neuron to a receiving cell, either another neuron or an effector cell)

para- = near (*parasympathetic division*: the set of neurons in the autonomic nervous system that generally promotes body activities that gain and conserve energy, such as digestion and reduced heart rate)

syn- = together (*synaptic terminal*: the tip of a transmitting neuron's axon, where signals are sent to another neuron or to an effector cell)

CHAPTER 29

The Senses

Chapter Objectives

Opening Essay

Explain how bats and some marine mammals use echolocation to better understand their environments.

Sensory Reception

29.1 Describe the essential roles of sensory receptors. Explain how electromagnetic receptors help the hammerhead shark perceive its world.

29.2 Define sensory transduction, receptor potential, and sensory adaptation, and provide examples of each.

29.3 Describe the five general categories of sensory receptors found in animals, and provide examples of each.

Hearing and Balance

29.4 List the structures of the ear in the sequence in which they participate in hearing. Describe the possible causes of hearing loss. Explain how the cochlea distinguishes sounds of different pitch.

29.5 Explain how body position and movement are sensed in the inner ear.

29.6 Explain what causes motion sickness and what can be done to prevent it.

Vision

29.7 Compare the structures and functions of the eye cups of planarians, the compound eyes of insects and crustaceans, and the single-lens eyes of humans.

29.8 Describe the parts of the human eye and their functions.

29.8 Compare the mechanisms used to focus the eyes of a squid and a human.

29.9 Explain the causes and symptoms of myopia, hyperopia, presbyopia, and astigmatism.

29.10 Compare the structures, functions, distributions, and densities of rods and cones. Explain how light is perceived in the retina.

Taste and Smell

29.11 Explain how odor and taste receptors function.

29.12 Describe the characteristics of human "supertasters," and their potential implications for health.

29.13 Describe the role of the central nervous system in sensory perception.

Lecture Outline

I. Introduction

  A. Bats use echolocation to detect their environment.
  B. High-pitched sounds are
    1. produced in their larynx and
    2. emitted from their mouths and noses.
  C. Their brains process the time delay and spatial arrangement of the echoes to determine the size, shape, location, speed, and direction of objects in their environment.
  D. Marine mammals
    1. include dolphins, killer whales, and sperm whales,
    2. produce ultrasonic clicking sounds in their nasal passages,
    3. focus the sound by bouncing it off of skull bones and an oil-filled structure in their forehead, and
    4. receive the echo in a narrow window of bone behind the jaw.
  E. Echolocation has also been observed in some species of cave-dwelling birds and forest-dwelling shrews.

II. Sensory Reception

  A. 29.1 Sensory organs share a common cellular basis
    1. All animal senses originate in **sensory receptors**, specialized cells or neurons that are tuned to the
      a. conditions of the external world and
      b. the internal organs.
    2. All sensory receptors
      a. trigger an action potential and
      b. send information to the central nervous system.
      c. Sensation depends on the part of the brain that receives the action potential.
  B. 29.2 Sensory receptors convert stimulus energy to action potentials
    1. Sensory receptors detect stimuli.
    2. All stimuli represent forms of energy.
    3. In a process called **sensory transduction**, receptors
      a. detect one type of signal (the stimulus) and
      b. convert the signal to another type, an electrical signal.
    4. When a sensory receptor cell in a taste bud detects sugar molecules,
      a. sugar molecules enter the taste bud,
      b. sugar molecules bind to sweet receptors, specific protein molecules embedded in a taste receptor cell membrane, and
      c. the binding triggers a signal transduction pathway that causes some ion channels in the membrane to close and others to open.
      d. These changes in the flow of ions create a graded change in membrane potential called a **receptor potential**.
    5. The stronger the stimulus,
      a. the more neurotransmitter released by the receptor cell and
      b. the more frequently the sensory neuron transmits action potentials to the brain.
    6. Repeated stimuli may lead to **sensory adaptation**, the tendency of some sensory receptors to become less sensitive when they are stimulated repeatedly.

C. 29.3 Specialized sensory receptors detect five categories of stimuli

   1. There are five categories of sensory receptors.

      a. Pain receptors detect dangerous stimuli including high heat and pressure.

      b. Thermoreceptors detect heat or cold.

      c. Mechanoreceptors respond to

         i. mechanical energy,

         ii. touch,

         iii. pressure, and

         iv. sound.

      d. Chemoreceptors

         i. include sensory receptors in our nose and taste buds and

         ii. respond to chemicals.

      e. Electromagnetic receptors respond to

         i. electricity,

         ii. magnetism, and

         iii. light (sensed by photoreceptors).

III. Hearing and Balance

  A. 29.4 The ear converts air pressure waves to action potentials that are perceived as sound

   1. The human ear channels sound waves

      a. from the **outer ear** with a flap-like **pinna**,

      b. down the **auditory canal**,

      c. to the **eardrum**, which separates the outer ear from the middle ear,

      d. to a chain of bones in the **middle ear** (malleus, incus, and stapes), and

      e. to the fluid in the coiled **cochlea** in the **inner ear**.

      f. The **Eustachian tube** connects the pharynx to the middle ear, permitting pressure equalization.

   2. Pressure waves transmitted to the fluid of the cochlea

      a. bend hair cells in the **organ of Corti** against the **basilar membrane** and

      b. trigger nerve signals to the brain.

   3. Louder sounds generate more action potentials.

   4. Various pitches stimulate different regions of the organ of Corti.

   5. Deafness is the loss of hearing.

   6. Deafness can be caused by the inability to detect sounds resulting from

      a. middle-ear infections,

      b. a ruptured eardrum, or

      c. stiffening of the middle-ear bones.

   7. Deafness

      a. can also result from damage to sensory receptors or neurons and

      b. is often progressive and permanent.

  B. 29.5 The inner ear houses our organs of balance

   1. Three organs in the inner ear detect body position and movement. These include

      a. three semicircular canals and

      b. two chambers, the utricle and the saccule.

      c. All three of these structures operate on the same principle: the bending of hairs on hair cells.

   2. The three **semicircular canals** detect changes in the head's rotation or angular movement.

3. The utricle and saccule detect the position of the head with respect to gravity.

C. 29.6 CONNECTION: What causes motion sickness?

1. Motion sickness may be caused by conflicting signals between the

    a. inner ear and

    b. eyes.

2. Motion sickness can be a severe problem for astronauts.

3. Motion sickness may be reduced by

    a. closings the eyes,

    b. limiting head movements,

    c. focusing on a stable horizon,

    d. sedatives such as dramamine or bonine, or

    e. long-lasting, drug-containing skin patches.

IV. Vision

A. 29.7 EVOLUTION CONNECTION: Several types of eyes have evolved independently among animals

1. The ability to detect light plays a central role in the lives of nearly all animals.

2. All animal light detectors are based on cells called **photoreceptors** that contain pigment molecules that absorb light.

3. Most invertebrate eyes include some kind of light-detecting organ.

4. One of the simplest organs is the **eye cup**,

    a. used by planarians,

    b. which senses light intensity and direction.

5. Two major types of image-forming eyes have evolved in the invertebrates.

    a. Compound eyes of insects

        i. consist of up to several thousand light-detectors called ommatidia,

        ii. function as acute motion detectors, and

        iii. usually provide excellent color vision.

    b. In **single-lens eyes**

        i. light enters the front center of the eye through a small opening, the **pupil**, controlled by an **iris**,

        ii. passes through a single disklike **lens**, and

        iii. is focused onto the **retina**, which consists of many photoreceptor cells.

        iv. The center of focus is the **fovea**, where photoreceptor cells are highly concentrated.

        v. Single-lens eyes

            (I) evolved independently in the vertebrates but

            (II) are similar in structure.

B. 29.8 Humans have single-lens eyes that focus by changing position or shape

1. The outer surface of the human eyeball is a tough, whitish layer of connective tissue called the **sclera**.

    a. At the front of the eye, the sclera becomes the transparent **cornea**, which

        i. lets light into the eye and

        ii. also helps focus light.

    b. The sclera surrounds a pigmented layer called the **choroid**. The anterior choroid forms the iris, which gives the eye its color.

2. The lens and ciliary body divide the eye into two fluid-filled chambers.

    a. The large chamber behind the lens is filled with a jellylike **vitreous humor**.

b. The smaller chamber in front of the lens contains the thinner **aqueous humor**.

c. These humors

    i. help maintain the shape of the eyeball and

    ii. circulate nutrients and oxygen to the lens, iris, and cornea.

3. The **conjunctiva**

  a. lines the inner surface of the eyelids and folds back over the white of the eye (but not the cornea).

  b. Conjunctivitis is an inflammation of the conjuctiva by bacteria or a virus.

4. A gland above the eye secretes tears that

  a. clean and

  b. moisten the eye.

5. The lens focuses light onto the retina by bending light rays. Focusing can occur in two ways.

  a. In squids and fishes, the lens focuses by moving back and forth.

  b. In mammals, the lens focuses by changing shape using

    i. muscles attached to the choroid and

    ii. ligaments that suspend the lens.

C. 29.9 CONNECTION: Artificial lenses or surgery can correct focusing problems

  1. Visual acuity is the ability of the eyes to distinguish fine detail.

    a. Visual acuity is measured by reading standardized eye charts from a distance of 20 feet.

    b. The ability to see normally at 20 feet is 20/20 vision.

  2. Three vision problems are common.

    a. Nearsightedness is the inability to focus on distant objects, usually caused by an eyeball that is too long.

    b. Farsightedness is the inability to focus on close objects, usually caused by an eyeball that is too short.

    c. Astigmatism is blurred vision caused by a misshapen lens or cornea.

    d. Corrective lenses can bend light rays to compensate for each of these problems.

D. 29.10 The human retina contains two types of photoreceptors: rods and cones

  1. The human retina contains two types of photoreceptors.

    a. Rods

      i. contain the visual pigment rhodopsin, which can absorb dim light, and

      ii. can detect shades of gray in dim light.

    b. Cones

      i. contain the visual pigment photopsin, which absorbs bright colored light, and

      ii. allow us to see color in bright light.

  2. When rhodopsin and photopsin absorb light,

    a. they change chemically, and

    b. the change alters the permeability of the cell's membrane.

    c. The resulting receptor potential triggers a change in the release of neurotransmitter from the synaptic terminals.

    d. This release initiates a complex integration process in the retina.

V. Taste and Smell

A. 29.11 Taste and odor receptors detect chemicals present in solution or air

  1. Taste and smell depend on chemoreceptors that detect specific chemicals in the environment.

    2. Chemoreceptors

        a. in taste buds detect molecules in solution and

        b. lining the nasal cavity detect airborne molecules.

B. Taste and smell interact. Much of what we taste is really smell.

C. Taste receptors

    1. are located in taste buds on the tongue and

    2. produce five taste sensations:

        a. sweet,

        b. salty,

        c. sour,

        d. bitter, and

        e. umami (the savory flavor of meats and cheeses).

D. 29.12 CONNECTION: "Supertasters" have a heightened sense of taste

    1. About 25% of humans are "supertasters" with up to three times the sensitivity to bitter.

    2. Supertasters are more likely to

        a. avoid spinach, broccoli, cabbage, coffee, and alcoholic beverages and

        b. be obese.

E. 29.13 Review: The central nervous system couples stimulus with response

    1. The nervous system

        a. receives sensory information,

        b. integrates it, and

        c. commands appropriate responses, either an action or no action.

Chapter Guide to Teaching Resources

Sensory Reception (29.1–29.3)

Student Misconceptions and Concerns

- The concept of sensory transduction, as applied to any particular sense organ, is typically new to most students. Students' familiarity with numerous forms of digital technology may help them make a connection. CD players, DVD recordings, and MP3 players rely upon electricity and signal conversions to store and generate sounds and images. (29.2)

Teaching Tips

- You might want to ask your students to consider the uneven distribution of sensory receptors in the human body. Sensory receptors may be concentrated in regions where environmental inputs are focused, such as the eyes and ears, or spread more generally, such as skin or the walls of the digestive tract. (29.1)

- Students can better understand sensory adaptation by thinking about events in their lives. Perhaps they notice a distinct smell in the hallways and laboratories of the science facilities at your school. However, after a few minutes, we tend not to notice the smells as much. These experiences illustrate sensory adaptation. (29.2)

- In elementary school, students often learn that there are five senses (taste, smell, touch, sight, and hearing). Consider matching these five senses to the types of specialized sensory receptor described in Module 29.3. (29.3)

Hearing and Balance (29.4–29.6)

Student Misconceptions and Concerns

- Lectures on the sensory systems of humans present numerous opportunities to relate new information to familiar student experiences. For example, the functions of the pinna of the ear can be demonstrated by cupping one hand around the pinna, boosting its ability to detect sound. Consider other simple demonstrations and explanations relating common experiences to the structure and function of the senses. (29.4–29.6)

- The natural tendency to wonder about our world seems to fade with increasing education. Discussions of the human sensory systems can rekindle that curiosity in your students, if time is available to field their questions. Perhaps you might have your class ask questions about their sensory experiences on 3×5 cards, which you can later answer selectively as time permits. (29.4–29.6)

Teaching Tips

- The range of human hearing and the effect of age can be demonstrated by a popular high-pitched ringtone. Searching "high-pitched ringtone" through Google will reveal multiple sites where the pitch can be heard and downloaded. (It is sometimes also called a "mosquito" ringtone.) This can also offer the opportunity to discuss the potentially damaging effect of loud noises on the delicate structures of the ear. (29.4)

- MP3 players and similar devices have increased our opportunities to damage our hearing. In addition, listening to loud music while actively exercising outdoors can interfere with the detection of danger or vital communication. Consider discussing these important safety concerns with your class. (29.4)

- Consider asking your students why they each have two ears. In general, they help us locate the source of a sound. If a sound is louder in one ear, then that ear is probably closer to the source. In general, when sound is of equal volume in both ears, we are either facing directly towards or away from the source. Of course, there are exceptions. (29.4)

- Students might wonder why their voice played back on a recording sounds different from what they hear when they speak. When we hear our own voice, many of the vibrations are transferred from our throat to our ear via bones and cartilage. These materials transfer the sound differently and thus do not sound the same as our voice transmitted through air. (29.4)

- The lumping together of hearing and balance in the five senses learned in elementary school may result in a decreased appreciation for the sense of balance. Yet, hearing and balance are clearly separate senses. (Hearing-impaired people can still walk!) Consider asking your students to close their eyes and tilt their heads in different directions. How can they tell the position of their heads? In addition to the semicircular canals, stretch receptors in the neck provide positional information. (29.5)

- Ask your class to consider the hypothesis that motion sickness results from mixed sensory inputs from the eyes and balance organs. For example, do students agree that they might be able to read while traveling down a straight highway, but become sick if they read on a winding road? How might standing on the outside of a boat be different from standing deep inside a boat, unable to see the horizon? Considering the causes of motion sickness affords an opportunity to practice informed critical thinking. (29.6)

Vision (29.7–29.10)

Student Misconceptions and Concerns

- Many common visual phenomena may have been noticed but not understood by students. Students have experienced or know about floating specks in the visual field, difficulty focusing on text late at night, and colorblindness. However, few students have the ability to accurately explain these and many other phenomena related to vision. These familiar subjects of curiosity can be used in your class to encourage reflective critical thought using the information provided in Modules 29.7–29.10. Insight into their explanations and other questions can be found in the Teaching Tips that follow. (29.7–29.10)

Teaching Tips

- Optical illusions can reveal the mental gymnastics our mind performs to make sense of our visual world. Consider searching "optical illusions" on the Internet to identify some examples to share with your class. (29.7)

- Cataracts, a clouding of the lens of the eye, are a common vision problem. Extensive exposure to ultraviolet (UV) light is one known cause of cataracts. Using eyeglasses and/or sunglasses with 100% UV coating can reduce exposure to UV light. (29.7)

- Bits of cellular debris often drift within the vitreous humor, temporarily showing up in our field of view. These bits are commonly called "floaters." (29.8)

- Some students might be familiar with the test for glaucoma in which a puff of air is shot at the eye. This blast of air distorts the eyeball and provides a measurement of the internal pressure. Dribbling a basketball and squeezing a tennis ball are examples of other tests of internal pressure. (29.8)

- The ciliary muscles of the eye can become fatigued if one focuses closely for long periods. Students who spend hours reading might find it difficult to focus closely, especially at the end of a long day. Staring off into the distance is relaxing in part because the ciliary muscles can relax. (29.8)

- The lacrimal canal connects the inner corner of the eye to the sinus cavity. Our noses might run when we cry because some surplus tears drain into our nose. (29.8)

- Challenge students to explain why an image appears clearer as we move closer to it. In general, it has to do with the number of rods and cones in the retina that are used to form the image. When we see an object at a distance, perhaps using only 10% of our field of vision, we use a proportional amount of rods and cones to form the image (about 10%). When we move closer, the image forms a larger percentage of our field of view and a proportionally higher number of rods and cones paint the picture. Like the images displayed on computer monitors or printed in newspapers, this image is formed by a series of dots: the more dots used to form the picture, the clearer the image. (29.9)

- The inheritance patterns of colorblindness are discussed in Module 9.22. (29.10)

- A dark pigment layer behind the rods and cones absorbs light that has passed through these photoreceptor cells. This prevents reflected light from interfering with the detection of new light. Albino vertebrate pupils appear red because the light transmitted through the retina is not absorbed by a pigment layer and instead reflects off red blood cells in the choroid layer of the eye. (29.10)

Taste and Smell (29.11–29.13)

Student Misconceptions and Concerns

- We tend to think the world is that which we perceive. These modules on the sensory systems provide hints of the world that other organisms detect. From sounds and wavelengths above and below our spectrum to concentrations of scents beyond our detection, other organisms may perceive the world very differently from us. Consider encouraging your students to imagine the world as other organisms perceive it and thereby gain insight into their existence. (29.11–29.13)

Teaching Tips

- Students that have sampled colognes or perfumes may have noticed that after an initial sniff, the scent tends to linger. Assuming that the scented liquid was not touched to the nose region, the lingering smell may result from its persistence in the mucus covering the sensory cells. Without the cilia of the olfactory region to sweep away the mucus containing the scent, the smell might last much longer. (29.11)

- Module 29.12 describes the heightened sensitivity of supertasters, people who have an increased ability to detect bitter flavors. If students are not assigned this module, you may consider challenging your class to predict some of the consequences. As noted in Module 29.12, supertasters may be less likely to eat a well-balanced diet that includes vegetables, leading to an increased risk of obesity and colon cancer. (29.12)

- You may wish to challenge your students who engage in sports to reflect on strategies that improved their performance. In addition to cardiovascular conditioning, basic motor skills, and strategy, students might list concentration and focus. Focus and concentration increase our awareness of the world around us and permit quick adjustments to changes in that environment. Humans acquire an advantage in sports, just as animals do in life-sustaining or life-threatening situations, by paying close attention to their perceptions. (29.13)

Key Terms

aqueous humor	farsightedness	pupil
astigmatism	fovea	receptor potential
auditory canal	hair cells	retina
basilar membrane	inner ear	rhodopsin
chemoreceptor	iris	rods
choroid	lens	sclera
cochlea	mechanoreceptor	semicircular canals
compound eye	nearsightedness	sensory adaptation
cones	middle ear	sensory receptor
conjuctiva	organ of Corti	sensory transduction
cornea	outer ear	stretch receptor
eardrum	pain receptor	single-lens eye
electromagnetic receptor	photopsin	thermoreceptor
Eustachian tube	photoreceptor	visual acuity
eye cup	pinna	vitreous humor

Word Roots

aqua- = water (*aqueous humor*: the clear, watery solution that fills the space between the lens and the cornea in the vertebrate eye)

audit- = hearing (*auditory canal*: part of the vertebrate outer ear that channels sound waves from the pinna or outer body surface to the eardrum)

chemo- = chemical (*chemoreceptor*: a sensory receptor that detects chemical changes within the body or a specific kind of molecule in the external environment)

coch- = a snail (*cochlea*: a coiled tube in the inner ear of birds and mammals that contains the hearing organ, the organ of Corti)

electro- = electricity (*electromagnetic receptor*: a sensory receptor that detects energy of different wavelengths, such as electricity, magnetism, and light)

fovea- = a pit (*fovea*: the eye's center of focus, a location of high photoreceptor concentration on the retina)

mechano- = an instrument (*mechanoreceptor*: a sensory receptor that detects physical deformations in the body's environment associated with pressure, touch, stretch, motion, or sound)

photo- = light (*photopsin*: one of a family of visual pigments in the cones of the vertebrate eye that absorb bright, colored light; *photoreceptor*: a type of electromagnetic receptor that detects light)

rhodo- = red (*rhodopsin*: a visual pigment located in the rods of the vertebrate eye that absorbs dim light)

sclero- = hard (*sclera*: a tough layer of connective tissue forming the outer surface of the vertebrate eye)

semi- = half (*semicircular canals*: fluid-filled channels in the inner ear that detect changes in the head's rate of rotation or angular movement)

thermo- = heat (*thermoreceptor*: a sensory receptor that detects heat or cold)

vitre- = glass (*vitreous humor*: the jellylike substance that fills the space behind the lens in the vertebrate eye)

CHAPTER 30

How Animals Move

Chapter Objectives

Opening Essay

Describe the adaptations of horses that increase speed.

Movement and Locomotion

30.1   Describe the diverse methods of locomotion found among animals, and the forces each method must overcome.

30.2   Describe the three main types of skeletons, their advantages and disadvantages, and provide examples of each.

The Vertebrate Skeleton

30.3   Describe the common features of terrestrial vertebrate skeletons, distinguishing between the axial and appendicular skeletons. Explain how homeotic genes relate to the absence of limbs in snakes.

30.4   Describe the complex structure of bone, noting the major tissues and their relationship to blood-forming tissues.

30.5   Explain why bones break and how we can help them heal. Describe the causes of osteoporosis.

30.6   Describe three types of joints and provide examples of each.

Muscle Contraction and Movement

30.7   Explain how muscles and the skeleton interact to produce movement. Explain how muscles relengthen once contracted.

30.8   Describe the structure and arrangement of the filaments found in a muscle cell.

30.9   Explain at the cellular level how a muscle cell contracts.

30.10   Explain how a motor neuron signals a muscle fiber to contract.

30.10   Describe the role of calcium in a muscle contraction.

30.10   Explain how motor units control muscle contraction.

30.11   Explain what causes muscle fatigue. Distinguish between aerobic and anaerobic exercise, noting the advantages of each.

30.12   Compare the structure and functions of slow, intermediate, and fast muscle fibers. Explain why some people seem to be natural sprinters or long distance runners.

Lecture Outline

I. Introduction

   A. Horses are well adapted for long-distance running with legs that are

      1. long and

      2. light.

II. Movement and Locomotion

   A. 30.1: Locomotion requires energy to overcome friction and gravity

      1. Animal movement

         a. is very diverse but

         b. relies on the same cellular mechanisms, moving protein strands against one another using energy.

      2. Locomotion

         a. is active travel from place to place and

         b. requires energy to overcome friction and gravity.

      3. An animal swimming is

         a. supported by water but

         b. slowed by friction.

      4. An animal walking, hopping, or running

         a. involves less overall friction between air and the animal,

         b. must resist gravity, and

         c. requires good balance.

      5. An animal burrowing or crawling

         a. must overcome great friction between the animal and the ground,

         b. is more stable with respect to gravity,

         c. may move by side-to-side undulations (such as snakes), or

         d. may move by a form of peristalsis (such as worms).

      6. An animal flying uses its wings as airfoils to generate lift.

      7. Flying has evolved in very few groups of animals. Flying animals include

         a. most insects,

         b. reptiles, including birds, and

         c. bats (mammals).

      8. Animal movement results from a collaboration between muscles and a skeletal system to overcome

         a. friction and

         b. gravity.

   B. 30.2 Skeletons function in support, movement, and protection

      1. Skeletons provide

         a. body support,

         b. movement by working with muscles, and

         c. protection of internal organs.

      2. There are three main types of animal skeletons:

         a. hydrostatic skeletons,

         b. exoskeletons, and

         c. endoskeletons.

      3. Hydrostatic skeletons are

         a. fluid held under pressure in a closed body compartment and

> **b.** found in worms and cnidarians.
>
> **c.** Hydrostatic skeletons
>
> > **i.** help protect other body parts by cushioning them from shocks,
> >
> > **ii.** give the body shape, and
> >
> > **iii.** provide support for muscle action.
>
> **4. Exoskeletons** are rigid external skeletons that consist of
>
> > **a.** chitin and protein in arthropods and
> >
> > **b.** calcium carbonate shells in molluscs.
> >
> > **c.** Exoskeletons must be shed to permit growth.
>
> **5. Endoskeletons** consist of hard or leathery supporting elements situated among the soft tissues of an animal. They may be made of
>
> > **a.** cartilage or cartilage and bone (vertebrates),
> >
> > **b.** spicules (sponges), or
> >
> > **c.** hard plates (echinoderms).

III. The Vertebrate Skeleton

> **A.** 30.3 EVOLUTION CONNECTION: Vertebrate skeletons are variations on an ancient theme
>
> > **1.** The vertebrate skeletal system provided
> >
> > > **a.** the structural support and
> > >
> > > **b.** means of location
> > >
> > > **c.** that enabled tetrapods to colonize land.
> >
> > **2.** The human skeleton consists of an
> >
> > > **a. axial skeleton**
> > >
> > > > **i.** that supports the axis or trunk of the body and
> > > >
> > > > **ii.** consists of the skull, vertebrae, and ribs and
> > >
> > > **b. appendicular skeleton**
> > >
> > > > **i.** that includes the appendages and the bones that anchor the appendage and
> > > >
> > > > **ii.** consists of the arms, legs, shoulders, and pelvic girdles.
> >
> > **3.** Vertebrate bodies reveal variations of this basic skeletal arrangement.
> >
> > **4.** Master control (homeotic) genes
> >
> > > **a.** are active during early development and
> > >
> > > **b.** direct the arrangement of the skeleton.
> > >
> > > **c.** Vertebrate evolution has included changes in these master control genes.
>
> **B.** 30.4 Bones are complex living organs
>
> > **1.** Cartilage at the ends of bones
> >
> > > **a.** cushions joints and
> > >
> > > **b.** reduces friction of movements.
> >
> > **2.** Fibrous connective tissue covering most of the outer surface of bone forms new bone in the event of a fracture.
> >
> > **3.** Bone cells
> >
> > > **a.** live in a matrix of flexible protein fibers and hard calcium salts and
> > >
> > > **b.** are kept alive by blood vessels, hormones, and nerves.
> >
> > **4.** Long bones have
> >
> > > **a.** a central cavity storing fatty **yellow bone marrow** and
> > >
> > > **b.** spongy bone located at the ends of bones containing **red bone marrow**, a specialized tissue that produces blood cells.

C. 30.5 CONNECTION: Healthy bones resist stress and heal from injuries

    1. Bone cells

        a. repair bones and

        b. reshape bones throughout life.

    2. Broken bones

        a. are realigned and immobilized and

        b. bone cells build new bone, healing the break.

    3. Osteoporosis is

        a. a bone disease,

        b. characterized by low bone mass and structural deterioration, and

        c. less likely if a person

            i. has high levels of calcium in the diet,

            ii. exercises regularly, and

            iii. does not smoke.

D. 30.6 Joints permit different types of movement

    1. Joints allow limited movement of bones.

    2. Different joints permit various movements.

        a. Ball-and-socket joints enable rotation in the arms and legs.

        b. Hinge joints in the elbows and knees permit movement in a single plane.

        c. Pivot joints enable the rotation of the forearm at the elbow.

IV. Muscle Contraction and Movement

A. 30.7 The skeleton and muscles interact in movement

    1. Muscles and bones interact to produce movement.

    2. Muscles

        a. are connected to bones by **tendons** and

        b. can only contract, requiring an antagonistic muscle to

            i. reverse the action and

            ii. relengthen muscles.

B. 30.8 Each muscle cell has its own contractile apparatus

    1. Muscle fibers are cells that consist of bundles of myofibrils. Skeletal muscle cells

        a. are cylindrical,

        b. have many nuclei, and

        c. are oriented parallel to each other.

    2. Myofibrils contain overlapping

        a. thick filaments composed primarily of the protein **myosin** and

        b. thin filaments composed primarily of the protein **actin**.

    3. Sarcomeres are

        a. repeating groups of overlapping thick and thin filaments and

        b. the contractile unit—the fundamental unit of muscle action.

C. 30.9 A muscle contracts when thin filaments slide along thick filaments

    1. According to the sliding-filament model of muscle contraction, a sarcomere contracts (shortens) when its thin filaments slide across its thick filaments.

        a. Contraction shortens the sarcomere without changing the lengths of the thick and thin filaments.

        b. When the muscle is fully contracted, the thin filaments overlap in the middle of the sarcomere.

2. Myosin heads of the thick filaments

    a. *bind* ATP and

    b. *extend* to high-energy states.

3. Myosin heads then

    a. *attach* to binding sites on the actin molecules and

    b. *pull* the thin filaments toward the center of the sarcomere.

D. 30.10 Motor neurons stimulate muscle contraction

  1. A motor neuron

    a. carries an action potential to a muscle cell,

    b. releases the neurotransmitter acetylcholine from its synaptic terminal, and

    c. initiates a muscle contraction.

  2. An action potential in a muscle cell

    a. passes along T tubules and

    b. into the center of the muscle fiber.

  3. Calcium ions

    a. are released from the endoplasmic reticulum and

    b. initiate muscle contraction by moving the regulatory protein tropomyosin away from the myosin-binding sites on actin.

  4. A **motor unit** consists of

    a. a neuron and

    b. the set of muscle fibers it controls.

  5. More forceful muscle contractions result when additional motor units are activated.

E. 30.11 CONNECTION: Aerobic respiration supplies most of the energy for exercise

  1. Aerobic respiration

    a. requires a constant supply of glucose and oxygen and

    b. provides most of the ATP used to power muscle movement during exercise.

  2. The anaerobic process of lactic acid fermentation

    a. can provide ATP faster than aerobic respiration but

    b. is less efficient.

F. 30.12 CONNECTION: Characteristics of muscle fiber affect athletic performance

  1. Depending on the pathway they use to generate ATP, muscle fibers can be classified as

    a. slow,

    b. intermediate, or

    c. fast.

  2. Most muscles have a combination of fiber types, which can be affected by exercise.

  3. Muscles can adapt to exercise by increasing the

    a. levels of myoglobin,

    b. number of mitochondria, and/or

    c. number of capillaries going to muscles.

Chapter Guide to Teaching Resources

Movement and Locomotion (30.1–30.2)

Student Misconceptions and Concerns

- Students may struggle to understand the physics of the mechanisms of movement and the resistant forces that are overcome. Students may not have had a physics course or be able to recall basic principles of force and motion. Consider addressing the fundamental concepts of friction and resistance before addressing examples of terrestrial, aquatic, and aerial locomotion. (30.1)

- As noted in the following, many analogies can be developed to help illustrate the fundamental differences between hydrostatic skeletons, exoskeletons, and endoskeletons. Although students may be able to distinguish between these types of skeletons, appreciating the advantages and disadvantages of each is typically more challenging. Students may need to be reminded why each system is adaptive for the particular organisms in which it is found. (30.2)

Teaching Tips

- Aquatic turtles generally have a more streamlined profile than their terrestrial relatives such as box turtles. (30.1)

- Students may not have considered the impact of drag forces on the efficiency of movement through air or water. The tapered trailing end of a boat or automobile may reduce drag and improve efficiency. Rowing a boat with a blunted end reveals the turbulence that trails the craft in the water. This contrasts with the more even flow of water past the tapered rear end of a canoe. The structural advantage of a tapered tail can be observed in the conical end of a jet and that of a fast-moving fish. (30.1)

- As a laboratory exercise, challenge students to observe the movements of an earthworm and describe the mechanism outlined in Module 30.1. Students will require a thorough understanding of the muscle layers, setae, hydrostatic skeleton, and internal compartmentalization of an earthworm's body before they can offer detailed explanations. (30.1)

- Challenge your students to distinguish between flying and gliding. Despite the names of flying squirrels and flying fish, these animals glide. One distinction between gliding and flying is the ability to gain and maintain altitude. (30.1)

- The internal pressure exerted by the water enclosed in a water balloon determines the balloon's physical shape and properties, much as it does in a hydrostatic skeleton. Internal fluid pressure also helps to increase the stiffness of leaves. (30.2)

- Like a suit of armor, an exoskeleton must be rebuilt to permit growth. Similarly, as children grow, we must provide larger clothing to cover the surface of their bodies. (30.2)

- An exoskeleton is generally similar to the structure of a piece of M&M candy. The hard outer coating provides firm support and protection for the soft interior. (30.2)

The Vertebrate Skeleton (30.3–30.6)

Student Misconceptions and Concerns

- Students often think of bones as static structures that provide support. The continuous growth of bone is a nonstop sculpting process that allows our bones to accommodate the dynamic effects of mass and motion. (30.3–30.6)

- General definitions of tissue often fail to include extracellular substances. In endoskeletons and exoskeletons, such substances play vital roles in mineral storage and resisting the dynamic forces of movement. (30.3–30.6)

Teaching Tips

- Students often struggle to distinguish the series of vertebrae forming the vertebral column from the actual nervous tissue of the spinal cord. They may benefit from instructors making a clear distinction between these related structures when the axial skeleton is first introduced. (30.3)

- Most vertebrate skulls do much more than house the brain. In most vertebrates, the brain is a relatively small structure housed deep in the skull. A vertebrate skull typically houses all the major sense organs, serves as the site of firm muscle attachments, and is the entry point for the respiratory and digestive systems. (30.3)

- The pectoral girdle is attached much more loosely to the axial skeleton than the pelvic girdle, in which the sacral vertebrae are firmly attached to the ilium on each side of the body. Challenge your students to explain why the pectoral and pelvic girdles have such different relationships to the axial skeleton. (The propulsive forces of the rear legs can best drive the body through the direct transfer of forces with a firmly attached pelvic girdle. The more loosely arranged pectoral girdle permits a broader range of motion and flexibility, but at the expense of the efficient transfer of forces.) (30.3)

- Students may have encountered hyaline cartilage at the ends of chicken bones during a meal. If the ends of bones have been exposed during cooking, the cartilage dehydrates and does not appear white and glossy. However, if a joint has been separated after cooking, such as a thigh that has been dislocated from the drumstick of a chicken, the glossiness of the white cartilage, which reduces friction, can be appreciated. (30.4)

- People do not often consume the nutritious elements inside of bone (although these tissues provide flavoring in soups that include a soup bone). However, in times and places with limited nutritional resources, boiling bones and/or breaking them open allows access to these additional nutrients. (30.4)

- Astronauts typically suffer from bone loss. After months of time in the microgravity of space, the problem can become significant. Biomedical researchers working with NASA are trying to better understand the causes of bone loss so that they can develop methods to limit it. (30.5)

- Consider challenging your students to identify examples of human-engineered structures that reflect the properties of the three types of joints described in Module 30.6. The authors already note the similarity between a hinge joint in our elbow and the hinge of a door. (30.6)

Muscle Contraction and Movement (30.7–30.12)

Student Misconceptions and Concerns

- As the generation of ATP is discussed, students should be cautioned against the idea that "energy is created" when it is converted from one form to another. This might be a good time to review the principle of conservation of energy (the first law of thermodynamics, addressed in Module 5.10). (30.7–30.12)

- Muscle cells are only able to contract. None can actively relengthen. Challenge your students to explain how muscle cells return to their extended length. (Answer: Opposing muscles or other forces, such as gravity, act in opposition to relengthen muscle cells when they relax.) (30.7)

- The actual mechanism of skeletal muscle contraction, the bending of myosin heads, is not well understood by most students. Consider focusing on this fundamental question as an introduction, exploring the answer as the detail of muscle structure is explored. (30.8–30.9)

- Students often fail to realize that aerobic metabolism is a process generally similar to the burning of wood or the burning of gasoline in an automobile engine. Noting these general similarities can help students better comprehend both the overall reaction and the heat generation associated with these processes. (30.10–30.11)

Teaching Tips

- The structure of a tendon is very similar to that of a steel cable. In a tendon, collagen fibers are neatly arranged and slightly twisted together. Steel wire in a cable has a similar design. The twist in both structures permits a limited amount of stretch to prevent the tendon or cable from snapping when a strong force is suddenly applied. (30.7)

- Students might wonder why skeletal muscle cells have many nuclei. One of the limits of cell size is the ability of a nucleus to control the cytoplasm. As the cytoplasmic volume increases, additional nuclei have been adaptive. A general analogy is that of a day-care center. At some point, as additional children are accepted into the center, more supervisors are required. There is a limit to the number of children that can be responsibly supervised by a single person, just as there is a limit to the amount of cytoplasm that can be controlled by one nucleus. (30.8)

- Students might need help understanding how the contraction of sarcomeres over microscopic distances results in the perceptible motions of our body. Consider explaining it like this: Imagine we have a train with 100 cars that are all 20 feet long. If we shorten each car by 1 foot, how much shorter will the train be? (100 feet.) The collective contraction of sarcomeres adds up to much larger movements. (30.9)

- One way to help explain motor units is to provide an analogy with the controls for the sets of lights in your classroom (if you are so equipped). Each set of lights is controlled by its own switch. The lights in one set all turn on or off (or perhaps dim) together. The total amount of light in the room depends upon how many sets of lights are turned on. Just as in muscles, if a room requires more refined lighting, more switches (more motor units) will control fewer lights each (fewer muscle cells per motor unit). (30.10)

- During cellular respiration, our cells convert about 40% of our food energy to useful work. The other 60% of the energy is released as heat. We use this heat to maintain a relatively steady body temperature near 37°C (98–99°F). This is about the same amount of heat generated by a 75 watt incandescent light bulb. When we exercise our muscles, we need more ATP. The extra production of ATP results in an excess production of heat. Thus, we generally produce too much heat when we exercise, and have evolved various mechanisms to dissipate this heat into our environment (such as sweating and increasing blood flow to the surface of our body). (30.11)

- As noted in Module 30.12, exercise stimulates the production of additional myofibrils. Thus, muscle growth is primarily a consequence of an increase in cell size due to the addition of myofibrils. (Additional mitochondria and blood vessels also contribute to the increase in muscle mass). (30.12)

- The differences between dark meat and white meat in birds such as chickens reflect differences in types of skeletal muscle fibers. Unlike humans, these birds have muscles made up primarily of just one type of muscle fiber. Dark meat contains higher amounts of myoglobin, fat, and capillaries, which are associated with sustained exertion. White meat, with less fat, less myoglobin, and fewer capillaries, is associated with quick bursts of energy, such as the contractions of the pectoral muscles to generate lift during takeoff. Artificial selection has resulted in variations on these basic differences. (30.12)

Key Terms

actin	hydrostatic skeleton	osteoporosis
appendicular skeleton	ligaments	pivot joints
axial skeleton	locomotion	red bone marrow
ball-and-socket joints	motor unit	sarcomere
endoskeleton	muscle fibers	thick filaments
exoskeleton	myofibrils	thin filaments
hinge joints	myosin	yellow bone marrow

Word Roots

endo- = within (*endoskeleton*: a hard skeleton located within the soft tissues of an animal)

exo- = outside (*exoskeleton*: a hard external skeleton that protects an animal and provides points of attachment for muscles)

hydro- = water (*hydrostatic skeleton*: a skeletal system composed of fluid held under pressure in a closed body compartment; the main skeleton of most cnidarians, flatworms, nematodes, and annelids)

liga- = bound or tied (*ligament*: a type of fibrous connective tissue that joins bones together at joints)

myo- = muscle; **-fibro** = fiber (*myofibril*: one of the contractile threads, made up of sarcomeres, that are arranged together in longitudinal bundles to form a muscle fiber)

osteo- = bone; **por-** = passage, pore (*osteoporosis*: a skeletal disorder characterized by thinning, porous, and easily broken bones)

sarco- = flesh; **-mere** = a part (*sarcomere*: the fundamental unit of muscle contraction, composed of thin filaments of actin and thick filaments of myosin)

CHAPTER 31

Plant Structure, Growth, and Reproduction

Chapter Objectives

Opening Essay

Describe the size and location of the tallest trees in the world. Explain how these trees interact with other forms of life.

Plant Structure and Function

31.1 Explain how the cultivation of wheat has changed over the past 10,000 years. Describe the consequences of improved wheat production for human society.

31.2 Compare the structure of monocots and eudicots.

31.3 Compare the structures and functions of roots, stems, and leaves. Explain how "pinching back" a plant helps make it bushier.

31.4 Distinguish between a taproot, stolon, rhizome, tuber, bulb, petiole, and tendril, and indicate common examples of each from a vegetable garden. Identify the basic plant organ that is modified in each example.

31.5 Define a tissue system. Describe the three main types of tissue systems found in young eudicot roots, stems, and leaves. Compare the arrangements of these tissue systems in the roots, stems, and leaves of monocots and eudicots.

31.6 Describe the three unique structures found in most plant cells. Describe the structures and functions of the five major types of plant cells.

Plant Growth

31.7 Distinguish between (a) indeterminate and determinate growth and (b) annuals, biennials, and perennials.

31.7–31.8 Describe and compare primary and secondary growth. Explain how a tree grows. Describe the location of the new and old tissues and how tree rings are produced.

Reproduction of Flowering Plants

31.9 Describe the parts of a flower and their functions. Relate this structure to the overall life cycle of an angiosperm.

31.10 Describe the processes and events that lead to double fertilization. Describe the advantages of double fertilization.

31.11 Explain how a seed forms. Compare the structures of eudicot and monocot seeds and explain the significance of seed dormancy.

31.12 Describe the structure and functions of fruit. Describe some of the adaptations of fruits that promote seed dispersal.

31.13 Describe and compare germination in bean and corn plants.

31.14 Describe four examples of cloning in plants. Compare the advantages and disadvantages of asexual versus sexual reproduction.

31.15 Describe plant adaptations that permit very long lives.

Lecture Outline

I. Introduction

A. Some plants, such as coast redwoods, are among the largest and oldest organisms on Earth.

B. Coast redwoods are gymnosperms, a kind of plant that bears seeds on cones.

C. Angiosperms, or flowering plants, bear seeds in fruits.

D. Most plants are angiosperms, which will be the focus of this unit on plant structure.

II. Plant Structure and Function

A. 31.1 CONNECTION: People have manipulated plants since prehistoric times

    1. Humans have engaged in agriculture for about 10,000 years.

    2. Genetic manipulation of crop plants such as wheat began with cross-pollination of plants with desirable traits.

    3. Today many crop plants are genetically modified using DNA technology.

B. 31.2 The two major groups of angiosperms are the monocots and the eudicots

    1. Monocots and eudicots differ in

        a. number of **cotyledons** (seed leaves),

        b. pattern of leaf venation,

        c. arrangement of stem vascular tissue,

        d. number of flower parts, and

        e. root structure.

    2. **Monocots**, such as wheat and corn, have

        a. one cotyledon,

        b. parallel leaf venation,

        c. scattered vascular bundles,

        d. flower parts in threes or multiples of three, and

        e. fibrous roots.

    3. **Eudicots**, which are most plants, have

        a. two cotyledons,

        b. branched leaf venation,

        c. a ring of vascular bundles,

        d. flower parts in fours or fives (or multiples), and

        e. a taproot system.

C. 31.3 A typical plant body contains three basic organs: roots, stems, and leaves

    1. Plant **organs** consist of several types of tissues that together carry out particular functions.

    2. Plants use a **root system** to

        a. anchor the plant in the soil,

        b. absorb and transport water and minerals, and

        c. store food.

        d. Root hairs

            i. are tiny tubular projections off of roots that

            ii. greatly increase the surface area for absorption.

3. Plants use a **shoot system** to absorb the sun's energy and carbon dioxide from the air.
4. A shoot system consists of
   a. **stems**,
   b. **leaves**, and
   c. adaptations for reproduction.
5. A stem has
   a. **nodes**, the points at which leaves are attached, and
   b. **internodes**, the portions of the stem between nodes.
6. Plants typically have two kinds of buds.
   a. **Terminal buds** are at the apex of stems, with developing leaves and a compact series of nodes and internodes.
   b. **Axillary buds** are found in the angles formed by the leaf and the stem.
7. In many plants, the terminal bud produces hormones that inhibit growth of the axillary buds in a phenomenon called **apical dominance**.
8. Plant root and shoot systems are interdependent.
   a. Plant roots depend on shoots for carbohydrates produced via photosynthesis.
   b. Plant shoots depend on roots for water and minerals.
D. 31.4 Many plants have modified roots, stems, and leaves
   1. Modifications of plant parts are adaptations for various functions, including
      a. food or water storage,
      b. asexual reproduction,
      c. protection,
      d. climbing, and
      e. photosynthesis.
   2. Stems may be modified as
      a. stolons, for asexual reproduction,
      b. **tubers**, for storage and asexual reproduction,
      c. **rhizomes**, for storage and asexual reproduction, or
      d. cactus stems, for water storage and photosynthesis.
   3. Leaves may be modified for
      a. climbing, such as a pea plant **tendril**, or
      b. protection, such as a cactus spine.
E. 31.5 Three tissue systems make up the plant body
   1. The organs of plants contain **tissues**, which are a group of cells that together perform a specialized function. For example
      a. **xylem** tissue contains water-conducting cells that convey water and dissolved minerals upward from roots and
      b. **phloem** tissue contains cells that transport sugars and other organic nutrients from leaves or storage tissues to other parts of the plant.
   2. Each plant organ (root, stem, or leaf) has three types of tissues.
      a. **Dermal tissue** provides a protective outer covering.
      b. **Vascular tissue** provides support and long-distance transport.
      c. **Ground tissue** composes the bulk of the plant body and is involved in
         i. food production,
         ii. storage, and
         iii. support.
   3. **Dermal tissues** form
      a. a layer of tightly packed cells called the **epidermis**,

b. the first line of defense against damage and infection, and

c. a waxy layer called the **cuticle**, which reduces water loss.

4. Vascular tissue

    a. is composed of xylem and phloem and

    b. arranged in

        i. **a vascular cylinder** in a root or

        ii. **vascular bundles** in stems.

5. Ground tissues lie between dermal and vascular tissue.

    a. Eudicot stem ground tissue is divided into **pith** and **cortex**.

    b. Leaf ground tissue is called **mesophyll**.

6. In a leaf, the epidermis is interrupted by tiny pores called **stomata**, which allow exchange of CO_2 and O_2 between

    a. the surrounding air and

    b. the photosynthetic cells inside the leaf.

    c. Each stoma is flanked by two **guard cells** that regulate the opening and closing of the stoma.

F. 31.6 Plant cells are diverse in structure and function

1. Plant cells have three structures that distinguish them from animal cells:

    a. chloroplasts, the site of photosynthesis,

    b. a central vacuole containing fluid that helps maintain cell turgor (firmness), and

    c. a protective cell wall composed of cellulose.

2. Plant cell walls

    a. Some plant cell walls have two layers.

        i. A primary cell wall forms the outermost layer.

        ii. A secondary cell wall forms a tough layer inside the primary wall.

    b. A sticky layer called the middle lamella lies between adjacent plant cells.

    c. Openings in cell walls called plasmodesmata allow cells to communicate and exchange materials easily.

3. Plant cell structure is related to function.

4. There are five major types of plant cells with different functions:

    a. parenchyma cells,

    b. collenchyma cells,

    c. sclerenchyma cells,

    d. water-conducting cells, and

    e. food-conducting cells.

5. Parenchyma cells

    a. are the most abundant type of cell in most plants,

    b. usually have only a thin and flexible primary cell wall,

    c. perform most of the metabolic functions of a plant, and

    d. can divide and differentiate into other types of plant cells under certain conditions.

6. Collenchyma cells

    a. lack a secondary cell wall,

    b. have an unevenly thickened primary cell wall, and

    c. provide flexible support in actively growing parts of the plant.

7. Sclerenchyma cells

    a. have a thick secondary cell wall usually strengthened with lignin, the main chemical component of wood,

    b. cannot elongate at maturity and are therefore found only in regions of the plant that have stopped growing in length, and

    c. when mature are dead, with their cell walls forming most of the rigid skeleton that supports the plant.

  8. Two types of sclerenchyma cells are

    a. fibers, long and slender cells usually arranged in bundles, and

    b. sclereids, shorter than fibers, have thick, irregular and very hard secondary cell walls that impart the hardness present in nut shells and pear tissue.

  9. Xylem tissue of angiosperms includes two types of water-conducting cells, **tracheids** and **vessel elements**. Both cell types

    a. have rigid, lignin-containing secondary cell walls,

    b. are dead at maturity, and

    c. form chains with overlapping ends that create tubes within vascular tissue.

  10. Food-conducting cells known as **sieve-tube elements** (or members)

    a. remain alive at maturity but lack most organelles and

    b. have end walls, called **sieve plates**, with pores that allow fluid to flow from cell to cell along the sieve tube.

  11. Alongside each sieve-tube element is at least one **companion cell**, which is connected to surrounding sieve-tube elements by numerous plasmodesmata. Companion cells produce and transport proteins to sieve-tube elements.

III. Plant Growth

  A. 31.7 Primary growth lengthens roots and shoots

    1. Animal growth is **determinate**, stopping after a certain size is reached.

    2. Plant growth is **indeterminate**, continuing throughout a plant's life.

    3. Plants are categorized based on how long they live.

      a. Annuals complete their life cycle in one year.

      b. Biennials complete their life cycle in two years.

      c. Perennials live for many years.

    4. Plant growth occurs in specialized tissues called **meristems**, consisting of undifferentiated cells that divide when conditions permit.

    5. Apical meristems are found at the tips of roots and shoots.

    6. Primary growth

      a. occurs at apical meristems,

      b. allows roots to push downward through the soil, and

      c. allows shoots to grow upward toward the sun.

    7. The apical meristems of root tips are covered by a **root cap**.

    8. Root growth occurs behind the root cap in three zones.

      a. Zone of cell division includes the apical meristem and cells derived from it.

      b. Zone of cell elongation, where cells lengthen by as much as 10 times.

      c. Zone of differentiation, where cells differentiate into dermal, vascular, and ground tissues, including the formation of **primary xylem** and **primary phloem**.

  B. 31.8 Secondary growth increases the diameter of woody plants

    1. Secondary growth

      a. is an increase in thickness of stems and roots and

      b. occurs at lateral meristems.

    2. Lateral meristems are areas of active cell division that exist in two cylinders that extend along the length of roots and shoots.

     a. Vascular cambium is a lateral meristem that lies between primary xylem and primary phloem.

     b. Cork cambium is a lateral meristem that lies at the outer edge of the stem cortex.

  3. Vascular cambium produces cells in two directions.

     a. Secondary xylem produces **wood** toward the interior of the stem.

     b. Secondary phloem produces the inner bark toward the exterior of the stem.

  4. Cork cambium produces

     a. cells in one direction,

     b. the outer **bark**, which is composed of cork cells.

  5. Wood annual rings show layers of secondary xylem.

     a. In temperate regions, periods of dormancy stop growth of secondary xylem.

     b. Rings occur in areas when new growth starts each year.

  6. The bark (secondary phloem and cork) is sloughed off over time.

  7. Wood rays

     a. consist of parenchyma cells that radiate from the stem's center and

     b. function in

        i. lateral transport of water and nutrients,

        ii. storage of starch, and

        iii. wound repair.

  8. Most transport occurs near the vascular cambium.

     a. Sapwood near the vascular cambium conducts xylem sap.

     b. Heartwood consists of older layers of secondary xylem that no longer transports water and instead stores resins and wastes.

     c. Secondary phloem near the vascular cambium transports sugars.

IV. Reproduction of Flowering Plants

  A. 31.9 The flower is the organ of sexual reproduction in angiosperms

  1. Flowers typically contain four types of highly modified leaves called floral organs.

     a. Sepals enclose and protect a flower bud.

     b. Petals are showy and attract pollinators.

     c. Stamens are male reproductive structures.

     d. Carpels are female reproductive structures.

  2. A **stamen** has two parts.

     a. An **anther** produces pollen, which house cells that develop into sperm.

     b. A stalk (filament) elevates the anther.

  3. A **carpel** has three parts.

     a. The **stigma** is the landing platform for pollen.

     b. The **ovary** houses one or more **ovules**, in which each ovule contains a developing egg and supporting cells.

     c. A slender neck (style) leads to an ovary.

  4. The term **pistil** is sometimes used to refer to a single carpel or a group of fused carpels.

  5. In the life cycle of a generalized angiosperm,

     a. fertilization occurs in an ovule,

     b. the ovary develops into a fruit,

     c. the ovule develops into the seed containing the embryo,

     d. the seed **germinates** in a suitable habitat, and

     e. the embryo develops into a seedling and then mature plant.

B. 31.10 The development of pollen and ovules culminates in fertilization

  1. Plant life cycles involve alternating diploid (2n) and haploid (n) generations.

    a. The diploid generation is called the **sporophyte**.

      i. Specialized diploid cells in anthers and ovules undergo meiosis to produce haploid spores.

      ii. The haploid spores undergo mitosis and produce the haploid generation.

    b. The haploid generation is called the **gametophyte**, which produces gametes via mitosis.

    c. At fertilization, gametes from male and female gametophytes unite to produce a diploid zygote.

  2. Pollen grains are the male gametophytes.

    a. A cell in the anther undergoes meiosis to produce four haploid spores.

    b. Each spore then divides via mitosis to produce two cells:

      i. the tube cell and

      ii. generative cell.

    c. A tough wall forms around the cells to produce a pollen grain.

    d. Pollen grains are released from the anther.

  3. The female gametophyte is an **embryo sac**.

    a. A cell in the ovule undergoes meiosis to produce four haploid spores.

    b. Three of the spores degenerate.

    c. The surviving spore undergoes a series of mitotic divisions to produce the embryo sac.

    d. One cell within the embryo sac is a haploid egg ready to be fertilized.

    e. One central cell within the embryo sac has two nuclei and will produce **endosperm**.

  4. Pollination is the transfer of pollen from anther to stigma.

  5. Pollen may be carried by wind, water, and animals.

  6. As a pollen grain germinates,

    a. the tube cell gives rise to the pollen tube, which grows downward into the ovary, and

    b. the generative cell divides by mitosis, producing two sperm.

  7. At fertilization,

    a. one sperm fertilizes the haploid egg to produce a diploid zygote, and

    b. another sperm fuses with the diploid central cell nucleus to produce a triploid (3n) cell that will give rise to the **endosperm**, which nourishes the developing embryo.

  8. This formation of a diploid zygote and a triploid nucleus is called **double fertilization**.

C. 31.11 The ovule develops into a seed

  1. After fertilization, the ovule, containing the triploid central cell and the diploid zygote, begins developing into a seed.

  2. The seed stockpiles proteins, oils, and starches.

  3. The zygote first divides by mitosis to produce two cells.

    a. One cell becomes the embryo.

    b. The other cell divides to form a thread of cells that pushes the embryo into the endosperm.

  4. The result of embryonic development in the ovule is a mature seed, including

    a. an endosperm,

    b. one or two cotyledons,

    c. a root,

d. a shoot, and

e. a tough **seed coat**.

5. Seed dormancy

    a. is a period when embryonic growth and development are suspended and

    b. allows for germination when conditions are favorable.

6. Eudicot seeds have

    a. two cotyledons,

    b. apical meristems that lack protective sheaths, and

    c. no endosperm because the fleshy cotyledons absorbed the endosperm nutrients as the seed formed.

7. Monocot seeds have

    a. a single cotyledon,

    b. an embryonic root and shoot with protective sheaths, and

    c. endosperm.

D. 31.12 The ovary develops into a fruit

    1. Hormonal changes induced by fertilization trigger the ovary to develop into a **fruit**.

    2. Fruit

        a. houses and protects seeds and

        b. aids in their dispersal.

    3. After pollination, a pea plant flower

        a. drops its petals,

        b. the ovary starts to grow, expanding tremendously, and its wall thickens, and

        c. a pod forms, holding the peas, or seeds.

    4. Mature fruits may be fleshy or dry.

        a. Fleshy fruits include oranges, tomatoes, and grapes.

        b. Dry fruits include beans, nuts, and grains.

E. 31.13 Seed germination continues the life cycle

    1. At germination, a seed

        a. takes up water and

        b. resumes growth and development.

    2. In eudicot seedlings

        a. the embryonic root of a bean emerges first and grows downward, and

        b. shoots emerge from the soil with the apical meristem "hooked" downward to protect it.

    3. In monocot seedlings, the shoots are covered by a protective sheath and emerge straight from the soil.

F. 31.14 Asexual reproduction produces plant clones

    1. Most plants are capable of asexual reproduction, producing genetically identical offspring (**clones**).

    2. Asexual reproduction can be advantageous in very stable environments.

    3. Clones naturally result from

        a. fragmentation, the separation of a parent plant into parts that develop into whole plants, such as occurs in a garlic bulb,

        b. root sprouts, and

        c. runners.

    4. Plants are often propagated by taking cuttings, which can produce roots.

    5. Plants can be cultured on specialized media in tubes.

G. 31.15 EVOLUTION CONNECTION: Evolutionary adaptations allow some trees to live very long lives

1. Some plants can survive a very long time.
   a. Some coast redwoods can be 2,000–3,000 years old.
   b. The oldest organism on Earth is thought to be a 4,600 year old bristlecone pine (*Pinus longaeva*) named Methuselah.
2. A long life increases evolutionary fitness by increasing the number of reproductive opportunities.
3. Several adaptations allow some plants to live much longer than animals.
   a. Meristem tissues allow for continued growth and repair throughout life.
   b. A decentralized vascular (circulatory) system allows part of a tree to survive damage and regrow.
   c. Plants produce defensive compounds that help protect them.
   d. Plants have a well-adapted hormonal control system that coordinates all of these behaviors.

Chapter Guide to Teaching Resources

Plant Structure and Function (31.1–31.6)

Student Misconceptions and Concerns

- Students often fail to see the specific applications of fundamental principles of biology. For example, many structural adaptations increase the surface-to-volume ratio in plants and animals. The divisions within the human lung, as well as microvilli, leaves, and root hairs, are examples. Increased surface areas are typically found where something is exchanged: gases exchanged at respiratory surfaces, nutrients absorbed by microvilli, light absorbed by leaves, and water and minerals absorbed by root hairs. If this chapter is one of the final topics addressed in your course, illustrating these broad principles with examples from a variety of subjects can serve as a unifying review. (31.2)

- Students may not understand turgor, although they encounter it in their lives. The shape of a water balloon is different from the shape of an uninflated balloon due to internal fluid pressure (turgor). A plant in need of water may have drooping leaves, a consequence of decreased turgor. (31.6)

Teaching Tips

- The impact of the green revolution and the continued improvement of agricultural techniques may be little appreciated by your students. Yet as the text notes in Module 13.1, from 1940 to 1980, world wheat production doubled while the cost of production was cut in half. Consider sharing and discussing the importance of these developments as they relate to modern economies and the world's population. (31.1)

- Figure 31.2 provides a visually simple but important comparison of monocots and eudicots. By referring to this figure in class, students will be able to absorb more details during lecture that they can then review at their leisure. (31.2)

- Consider bringing living examples of monocots and eudicots to class or taking a short trip outside during a related lab to quickly compare examples. If you have a lawn nearby, examples of monocots should be abundant! (31.2)

- Challenge your students to suggest circumstances when apical growth is more adaptive for a plant, and other situations in which branching would be more favorable. (31.3)

- The modifications of the three plant organs described in Module 31.4 reveal the remodeling nature of evolution. As Francois Jacob noted, evolution works more like a tinkerer than an engineer. The common ancestry of eudicots is revealed by the diverse modifications of three basic plant organs derived from the shared ancestors. Your students' appreciation of the enormous evidence in support of evolution will grow if you note such examples frequently throughout your course. (31.4)

- Module 31.5 can be particularly problematic for students with limited backgrounds in plant biology. The basic structures and functions of tissues and subtypes of plants are introduced, and monocots and eudicots are compared. The terminology is extensive. Students may benefit most by creating their own mini-glossary for quick reference and study before, during, and after related lectures. (31.5)

- The functions of human epidermis have some analogues in plants. As in plants, our epidermis serves as a defense against physical damage and infectious organisms. In addition, oils on our skin help us retain water (and keep the epidermis flexible). (31.5)

- Cellulose is the most abundant organic compound on Earth. Students often find this fact worth remembering. (31.6)

- Students will remember the function of phloem more easily if you remind them that both phloem and food start with an "F" sound. (31.6)

Plant Growth (31.7–31.8)

Student Misconceptions and Concerns

- Students often expect determinate growth in plants, because it is characteristic of humans. However, most plant species show indeterminate growth and are capable of growing as long as they can live. (31.7)

- Students typically expect that as a tree grows taller, the trunk will "stretch" upward along its entire length. This expectation arises naturally from the experience of our own growth as humans. However, as a tree grows, the entire trunk does not increase in size. Instead, growth occurs at the upper ends and through expansion of the trunk. Therefore, initials carved into the trunk of a tree will remain at that height as long as the tree is upright and healthy. (31.8)

Teaching Tips

- Lobsters are one of the few animals that show indeterminate growth. (31.7)

- Students may not realize that the cork used to seal a wine bottle is the same cork that is discussed in Module 31.8. (31.8)

- Students may not appreciate the many important functions of tree bark. Carving into bark, or peeling it away from a trunk, exposes the inner tissues to pathogens. In many ways, the functions of human skin and bark are similar. (31.8)

Reproduction of Flowering Plants (31.9–31.15)

Student Misconceptions and Concerns

- The development of the male and female gametophytes in flowers is often not as well understood by students who are more familiar with animals. A thorough review of the alternation of generations life cycle of plants is helpful before discussing the details of plant sexual reproduction. (31.10–31.12)

- Students' knowledge of sexual reproduction in animals often results in an expectation of similar processes in plants. The double fertilization typical of angiosperms requires extra time and attention to distinguish it from processes seen in animals. (31.10)

- The distinction between fruits and vegetables is a frequent, if trivial, point of contention. Module 31.12 specifically notes the structures and functions of fruits. To promote further understanding, consider discussing what the term "vegetable" means as well. (31.12)

Teaching Tips

- The authors note in Module 31.9 that Modules 17.8 and 17.9 provide important background information on the sexual life cycle of a flowering plant. If these modules have not been addressed previously, consider adding them to the Chapter 31 assignment. (31.9)

- More students will recall that stamens are the male organs if they emphasize the word's last syllable. (31.9)

- The four main parts of a flower, which are modified leaves, represent additional examples of evolutionary remodeling. (31.9)

- Plants that produce lightweight, windborne pollen are the major sources of allergies, because the pollen remains in the air longer than heavier pollen grains. (31.10)

- Coconut milk is an example of liquid endosperm. Coconut meat is solid endosperm. (31.11)

- Seed dispersal mechanisms are diverse and reflect specific adaptive strategies. The inventor of Velcro was inspired by the seed dispersal mechanisms of the common burdock plant. (31.12)

- Seed production in plants clearly illustrates the ability of organisms to produce more offspring than can survive, a premise of natural selection. While discussing seed production, consider reminding students of this important principle, which is well illustrated in plants. (31.13)

- Depending upon your prior discussions of animal reproduction and diversity, you might challenge your students to identify natural examples of animal cloning. Cnidarians and flatworms are groups that are often mentioned as examples. (31.14)

- Consider challenging your class to compare the biology of animals and plants and the respective adaptations that lengthen their life spans. As discussed in Module 31.15, the regenerative capacity of plants promotes longevity. Do animals generally have the capacity to repair and replace organs? Stem cell research has recently revealed additional details about the ability to repair damaged or diseased tissues. Metabolic rates in animals have been generally correlated with longevity. How might the cellular metabolic rate of a mouse, which lives only a few years, compare with that found in a long-lived plant such as a redwood, which can live for centuries? (31.15)

Key Terms

annual
anther
apical dominance
apical meristem
axillary bud
bark
biennial
carpel
clone
collenchyma cell
companion cell
cork
cork cambium
cortex
cotyledon
cuticle
dermal tissue system
determinate growth
dicot
double fertilization
embryo sac
endodermis
endosperm
epidermis
eudicot
fiber
fragmentation
fruit
gametophyte
germinate

ground tissue system
guard cell
heartwood
indeterminate growth
internode
lateral meristem
leaves
meristem
mesophyll
monocot
node
organ
ovary
ovules
parenchyma cell
perennial
petal
phloem
pistil
pith
pollination
primary growth
primary phloem
primary xylem
rhizome
root cap
root hair
root system
sapwood
sclereid

sclerenchyma cell
secondary growth
secondary phloem
secondary xylem
seed coat
sepal
shoot system
sieve plate
sieve-tube elements
sporophyte
stamen
stem
stigma
stoma (plural, stomata)
tendril
terminal bud
tissue
tissue system
tracheid
tuber
vascular bundle
vascular cambium
vascular cylinder
vascular tissue system
vein
vessel element
wood
wood ray
xylem

Word Roots

ann- = year (*annual*: a plant that completes its life cycle in a single year or growing season)

anth- = a flower (*anther*: the sac in which pollen grains develop, located at the tip of a flower's stamen)

apic- = the tip (*apical dominance*: in a plant, the hormonal inhibition of axillary buds by a terminal bud)

bienn- = two years (*biennial*: a plant that requires two years to complete its life cycle)

carp- = a fruit (*carpel*: the female reproductive organ of a flower, consisting of the stigma, style, and ovary)

coll- = glue; **-enchyma** = an infusion (*collenchyma cell*: a flexible plant cell type that occurs in strands or cylinders that support young parts of the plant without restraining growth)

cuti- = the skin (*cuticle*: in plants, a waxy coating on the surface of stems and leaves that helps retain water)

derm- = skin (*dermal tissue system*: the outer protective covering of plants)

endo- = inner (*endosperm*: a nutrient-rich tissue formed by the union of a sperm cell with two polar nuclei during double fertilization, which provides nourishment to the developing embryo in angiosperm seeds); **derm-** = skin (*endodermis*: the innermost layer of the cortex in plant roots)

epi- = over (*epidermis*: the dermal tissue system in plants; the outer covering of animals)

gamet- = a wife or husband (*gametophyte*: the multicellular haploid form in organisms undergoing alternation of generations, which mitotically produces haploid gametes that unite and grow into the sporophyte generation)

inter- = between (*internode*: the segment of a plant stem between the points where leaves are attached)

later- = side (*lateral meristem*: a meristem such as vascular cambium or cork cambium that thickens the roots and shoots of woody plants)

meristo- = divided (*meristem*: plant tissue consisting of undifferentiated cells that divide and generate new cells and tissues)

meso- = middle; **-phyll** = a leaf (*mesophyll*: the green tissue in the interior of a leaf, which serves as its ground tissue system and provides the main site of photosynthesis)

perenni- = through the year (*perennial*: a plant that lives for many years)

phloe- = the bark of a tree (*phloem*: the portion of a plant's vascular tissue system, made up of sieve-tube members, that conveys phloem sap throughout a plant)

rhizo- = a root (*rhizome*: a horizontal stem that grows underground)

sclero- = hard (*sclereid*: a very hard, dead sclerenchyma cell found in nutshells and seed coats; *sclerenchyma cell*: a supportive cell with rigid secondary walls hardened with lignin)

sporo- = a seed; **-phyto** = a plant (*sporophyte*: the multicellular diploid form in the life cycle of organisms undergoing alternation of generations that results from a union of gametes and that meiotically produces haploid spores that grow into the gametophyte generation)

stam- = standing upright (*stamen*: the pollen-producing male reproductive organ of a flower, consisting of an anther and filament)

stom- = opening (*stoma* [plural, *stomata*]: a pore surrounded by guard cells in the epidermis of a leaf, responsible for gas exchange in the plant)

trachei- = the windpipe (*tracheid*: a tapered, porous plant cell that functions to conduct water and provide support; chains of tracheids or vessel elements make up the water-conducting supportive tubes in xylem)

vascbula- = a little vessel (*vascular bundle*: a strand of vascular tissues [both xylem and phloem] in a plant stem)

xyl- = wood (*xylem*: the tube-shaped, nonliving portion of the vascular system in plants that carries water and minerals from the roots to the rest of the plant)

CHAPTER 32

Plant Nutrition and Transport

Chapter Objectives

Opening Essay

Explain how plants can be used to clean up environmental toxins, describing examples and noting the pros and cons of this approach.

The Uptake and Transport of Plant Nutrients

32.1 Explain what happens to the materials that plants take up from the air and soil.

32.2 Compare the intracellular and extracellular movements of material into root xylem. Describe the function of the Casparian strip.

32.3 Explain how root pressure is generated.

32.3 Explain how the transpiration-cohesion-tension mechanism causes the ascent of xylem sap in a plant.

32.4 Explain how guard cells control transpiration. Describe three cues that contribute to stomatal opening at dawn.

32.5 Explain how, when, and where phloem conducts sap.

Plant Nutrients and the Soil

32.6 Explain how hydroponics help to determine which plant nutrients are essential.

32.6 Distinguish between micronutrients and macronutrients and note examples of each. List the six macronutrients that make up about 98% of a plant's dry weight.

32.7 Explain how fertilizers can prevent nutrient deficiencies in plants.

32.8 Describe the properties of different soil layers. Explain why topsoil is most important for plant growth. Explain how plants use cation exchange to absorb inorganic cations.

32.9 Explain how irrigation and the use of fertilizers impact agriculture. Describe techniques that minimize soil erosion and the buildup of salts in soils.

32.10 Compare the processes and products of organic and conventional agriculture.

32.11 Describe new strategies to improve the protein content of crops. Describe some of the benefits and concerns created by the genetic engineering of plants.

Plant Nutrition and Symbiosis

32.12 Explain how and why most plants depend upon bacteria to supply nitrogen.

32.13 Explain how fungi help most plants absorb nutrients from the soil. Describe the significance of plant-fungus symbiosis to the evolution of life on land. Describe the special relationship between legumes and nitrogen-fixing bacteria.

32.14 Describe examples of parasitic and carnivorous plants. Explain why carnivorous plants are most commonly found in acid bogs.

Lecture Outline

I. Introduction

A. Many plants can remove toxins such as heavy metals from soils by
   1. taking them up with their roots and
   2. storing them in their bodies.
B. After Hurricane Katrina, sunflowers were used to remove toxins from soils in some parts of New Orleans.

II. The Uptake and Transport of Plant Nutrients

A. 32.1 Plants acquire nutrients from air, water, and soil
   1. Plant growth uses
      a. air,
      b. water, and
      c. soil.
   2. Plants obtain water, minerals, and some oxygen from the soil.
   3. The sugars made by plants in photosynthesis use
      a. carbon and oxygen from the atmosphere and
      b. hydrogen from water.
   4. Plants use cellular respiration to break down some of these sugars
      a. obtaining energy and
      b. consuming oxygen.
   5. Plants must
      a. move water from its roots to its leaves and
      b. deliver sugars to specific areas of its body.
B. 32.2 The plasma membranes of root cells control solute uptake
   1. Root hairs greatly increase a root's absorptive surface.
   2. Water and solutes can move through the root's epidermis and cortex by going
      a. through cells,
      b. between cells, or
      c. through some combination of these routes.
   3. Once the water and solutes reach the endodermis, a continuous waxy barrier called the **Casparian strip**
      a. stops them from entering the xylem via cell walls and
      b. forces them to cross the selectively permeable plasma membrane of an endodermal cell to enter the xylem (water-conducting tissue) for transport upward.
C. 32.3 Transpiration pulls water up xylem vessels
   1. **Xylem sap** consists of
      a. water and
      b. dissolved inorganic nutrients.
   2. Xylem tissues of angiosperms consist of very thin tubes composed of two types of cells that conduct xylem sap up a plant:
      a. tracheids and
      b. vessel elements.
   3. What force moves xylem sap up against the downward pull of gravity?
      a. **Root pressure**, the accumulation of water in roots by osmosis, can push xylem sap up a few meters.

    b. Transpiration, the loss of water by evaporation from leaves (and other aerial parts of a plant)

        i. is regulated by guard cells surrounding stomata and

        ii. can move xylem sap to the top of the tallest tree.

  4. Transpiration can pull xylem sap up a tree because of two special properties of water:

    a. Cohesion is the sticking together of molecules of the same kind.

    b. Adhesion is the sticking together of molecules of different kinds.

  5. The overall process of this movement of xylem sap is called the **transpiration-cohesion-tension mechanism**. In this process,

    a. the air's pull on water creates a tension and

    b. that tension pulls on an unbroken chain of water molecules in the xylem

        i. held together by cohesion and

        ii. helped upward by adhesion.

  6. Therefore xylem sap moves up without any energy expenditure by the plant.

D. 32.4 Guard cells control transpiration

  1. A plant must make a trade-off between its need

    a. for water and

    b. to make food by photosynthesis.

  2. Stomata

    a. can open and close and

    b. help plants adjust their transpiration rates to changing environmental conditions.

    c. Guard cells control the opening of a stoma by changing shape.

  3. Stomata open when guard cells take up water in the following process:

    a. Potassium is actively taken up by guard cells from nearby cells.

    b. This creates an osmotic gradient and water follows.

    c. Uneven cell walls of guard cells cause them to bow when water is taken up.

    d. The bowing of the guard cells causes the pore of the stoma to open.

    e. When guard cells lose K^+ ions, the guard cells become flaccid and the stoma closes.

  4. Several factors influence guard cell activity.

    a. In general, stomata are open during the day and closed at night.

    b. Sunlight signals guard cells to accumulate K^+ and open stomata.

    c. Low CO_2 concentration in leaves also signals guard cells to open stomata.

    d. Plants have natural rhythms that help them close stomata at night to conserve water.

    e. Plants may also close stomata during the day to conserve water when necessary.

E. 32.5 Phloem transports sugars

  1. Phloem sap transports sugars

    a. made by photosynthesis and

    b. using a pressure flow mechanism.

  2. At a **sugar source**

    a. sugar is loaded into the phloem tube,

    b. sugar raises the solute concentration in the tube, and

    c. water follows, raising the pressure in the tube.

  3. At a **sugar sink**

    a. sugar is removed,

    b. water follows, and

    c. phloem sap flows from source to sink in a process called the **pressure flow mechanism**.

4. Plant biologists use aphids to study phloem sap.

    a. Pressure in the phloem sap force-feeds an aphid.

    b. If an aphid is severed at the stylet (sucking mouthpart) and only the stylet remains, phloem sap continues to flow into the stylet.

III. Plant Nutrients and the Soil

  A. 32.6 Plant health depends on a complete diet of essential inorganic nutrients

    1. A plant must obtain inorganic substances to survive and grow.

    2. Essential elements are those that a plant must obtain to

      a. complete its life cycle of growth and

      b. have reproductive success.

    3. There are 17 elements essential to plant growth and reproduction.

      a. There are nine **macronutrients** that plants require in relatively large amounts.

      b. There are eight **micronutrients** that plants require in relatively small amounts.

    4. Both types of nutrients have vital functions.

    5. Macronutrients are components of organic molecules and include (the first six make up 98% of a plant's dry weight)

      a. carbon,

      b. hydrogen,

      c. oxygen,

      d. nitrogen,

      e. sulfur,

      f. phosphorus,

      g. potassium,

      h. calcium, and

      i. magnesium.

    6. Micronutrients often act as cofactors and include

      a. chlorine,

      b. iron,

      c. manganese,

      d. boron,

      e. zinc,

      f. copper,

      g. nickel, and

      h. molybdenum.

  B. 32.7 CONNECTION: Fertilizers can help prevent nutrient deficiencies

    1. The availability of nutrients in soil affects plant growth and health.

    2. Growers can often determine which nutrients are missing from soil by looking at plant symptoms.

    3. Nitrogen shortage is the most common nutritional problem for plants.

    4. Fertilizers are compounds given to plants to promote growth.

    5. Nutrient deficiencies can be alleviated by adding to soil

      a. inorganic chemical fertilizers or

      b. compost, a soil-like mixture of decomposed organic matter.

  C. 32.8 Fertile soil supports plant growth

    1. Soil horizons are layers of soil with different characteristics.

      a. The A horizon, or **topsoil,**

        i. is subject to weathering and

   ii. contains **humus** (decayed organic matter) and many soil organisms.

  b. The B horizon primarily consists of

   i. clay and

   ii. dissolved elements.

  c. The C horizon consists of rocks of the "parent material" from which soil is formed.

 2. A soil's physical and chemical characteristics affect plant growth.

  a. Small rock and clay particles

   i. hold water and ions and

   ii. allow oxygen to diffuse into plant roots.

  b. Humus

   i. provides nutrients and

   ii. supports the growth of organisms that enhance soil fertility.

 3. Anions such as nitrate are readily available to plants because they are not bound to soil particles.

 4. Cations such as K^+ adhere to soil particles.

 5. In **cation exchange**, root hairs

  a. release H^+ ions, which displace cations from soil particles, and then

  b. absorb the free cations.

D. 32.9 CONNECTION: Soil conservation is essential to human life

 1. Human practices in agriculture have degraded soils.

  a. Irrigation can gradually make soil salty.

  b. Plowed lands are subject to erosion by wind and rain, which removes topsoil.

  c. Chemical fertilizers are costly and may contaminate groundwater.

 2. Good soil management includes

  a. water-conserving irrigation,

  b. erosion control, and

  c. the prudent use of herbicides and fertilizers.

E. 32.10 CONNECTION: Organic farmers follow principles of sustainable agriculture

 1. Organic farming promotes **sustainable agriculture**, a system embracing farming methods that are

  a. conservation-minded,

  b. environmentally safe, and

  c. profitable.

 2. The USDA has established guidelines for foods labeled "organic."

 3. Organic farming guidelines are intended to

  a. sustain biological diversity,

  b. maintain soil quality,

  c. reduce or eliminate the use of chemical pesticides,

  d. avoid use of genetically modified plants, and

  e. reduce or eliminate the use of chemical fertilizers.

F. 32.11 CONNECTION: Agricultural research is improving the yields and nutritional values of crops

 1. Advances in genetic engineering have led to many improvements in crops that

  a. are more resistant to disease and insects, reducing the need to use pesticides,

  b. are resistant to weed-killing herbicides, reducing the need to till the soil, which promotes erosion, and

  c. have improved nutritional quality, allowing less land to feed more people.

IV. Plant Nutrition and Symbiosis

A. 32.12 Most plants depend on bacteria to supply nitrogen

    1. The Earth's atmosphere consists of about 80% nitrogen.

    2. However, nitrogen deficiency is the most common nutritional problem in plants. Why is that?

        a. Plants cannot absorb nitrogen directly from the air.

        b. Instead, to be used by plants, nitrogen must be converted to ammonium (NH_4^+) or nitrate (NO_3^-).

    3. Soil bacteria can convert N_2 gas from the air into forms usable by plants via several processes.

        a. Nitrogen-fixing bacteria convert atmospheric N_2 to ammonia (NH_3) in a process called **nitrogen fixation**.

        b. Ammonifying bacteria add to the supply of ammonium by decomposing organic matter.

        c. Nitrifying bacteria convert ammonium to nitrates, the form most often taken up by plants.

B. 32.13 EVOLUTION CONNECTION: Plants have evolved symbiotic relationships that are mutually beneficial

    1. Most plants form mutually beneficial symbioses with fungi called **mycorrhizae**, which

        a. act like extensions of plant roots, increasing the area for absorption of water and minerals from soil,

        b. selectively absorb phosphate and other minerals from the soil,

        c. release growth factors and antibiotics into the soil, and

        d. have evolved with plants and were important to plants successfully invading land.

    2. Some plants form symbioses with nitrogen-fixing bacteria.

        a. Legumes (peas, beans, alfalfa, and others) form root nodules to house nitrogen-fixing symbionts in the genus *Rhizobium*.

        b. Other plants, such as alders, form symbioses with other kinds of nitrogen-fixing bacteria.

        c. Plants that form these associations are rich in nitrogen.

    3. Mycorrhizae and nitrogen-fixing bacteria benefit by receiving sugars from the plants they colonize.

C. 32.14 The plant kingdom includes epiphytes, parasites, and carnivores

    1. Some plants have nutritional adaptations that take advantage of other organisms.

    2. Epiphytes, including many orchids,

        a. grow anchored on other plants and

        b. absorb water and minerals from rain.

    3. Parasitic plants, such as dodder and mistletoe,

        a. may not use photosynthesis,

        b. use their roots to tap into the host plant's vascular system, and

        c. absorb sugars and minerals from the host plant.

    4. Carnivores, such as a sundew plant or Venus flytrap,

        a. capture and digest small animals such as insects,

        b. absorb inorganic elements from prey, and

        c. are found in nutrient-poor environments.

Chapter Guide to Teaching Resources

The Uptake and Transport of Plant Nutrients (32.1–32.5)

Student Misconceptions and Concerns

- These first five modules of Chapter 32 help to answer questions that students may never have asked. Often, answers are more significant if we first spend time pondering the questions. Consider starting these discussions by raising some of the basic questions noted by the authors, including: a) What is the source of the raw materials that make up a plant's body? b) Do plant roots act like a sponge, absorbing just about anything? c) What makes plant saps move up a plant, especially the really tall ones? (32.1–32.5)

- Although analogies are often useful, some of their particulars can be misleading. In many ways, the vascular tissues and movement of fluid through plants are unlike the circulatory system of vertebrates. Whereas vertebrates have a one-way flow of fluid propelled by a contracting heart through a contained tubular system, phloem sap, propelled instead by a pressure flow mechanism, can move in either direction. (32.5)

Teaching Tips

- Module 32.1 references the discussion of photosynthesis in Chapter 7. If you have not already addressed the content of Chapter 7, consider discussing the sources of carbon, hydrogen, and oxygen that are used in the construction of carbohydrates resulting from photosynthesis. (32.1)

- With the exception of small amounts of glycogen obtained from meat and lactose obtained from dairy products, humans get most of our dietary carbohydrates from plants. (32.1)

- Root hairs are yet another example of an adaptation to increase the surface area of an organism. The divisions within the human lung, as well as microvilli and plant leaves, are other examples. Increased surface areas are typically found where something is exchanged: gases exchanged at respiratory surfaces, nutrients absorbed by microvilli, light absorbed by leaves, and water and minerals absorbed by root hairs. If this chapter is one of the final topics addressed in your course, illustrating these broad principles with examples from a variety of subjects can provide a unifying review. (32.2)

- The cohesive property of water allows some insects to walk or stand on a liquid water surface. The cohesion and adhesion of water is also the reason why we need to dry ourselves off after taking a shower, since water still clings to our skin and hair. (32.3)

- Demonstrate or ask students to recall what happens when a soda straw is lifted out of a beverage: some of the beverage still sticks to the straw. This is an example of adhesion. (32.3)

- The change in shape of guard cells is due to internal fluid pressure, or turgor—important in many other organisms. Turgor helps maintain the shape of plant cells, gives structure to the hydrostatic skeletons of sea anemones and earthworms, and causes a penis to become firm upon erection. Before addressing guard cells, you may challenge your class to explain what leaves, earthworms, and an erect penis have in common. The answer is turgor. (32.4)

- Many phloem saps other than maple syrup are used commercially. For example, phloem sap from rubber trees native to the Brazilian Amazon was once the major source of rubber.

(Most rubber is now synthetically produced.) Pine oil, derived from pine tree resin, is the active ingredient in Pine-Sol cleaner. (32.5)

Plant Nutrients and the Soil (32.6–32.11)

Student Misconceptions and Concerns

- It is important to distinguish between the acquisition of nutrients and the acquisition of food. Plants, unlike animals, do not obtain their food from the environment. Instead, plants are autotrophs that generate their own food. The essential elements required by plants are not sources of calories. (32.6–32.11)

Teaching Tips

- Students might assume that macronutrients are large in size and micronutrients are small. Instead, the word roots macro and micro refer to the quantities of nutrients required in each category. (32.6)

- Students who know that most (78%) of Earth's atmosphere consists of nitrogen may be confused to learn that nitrogen shortage is the most common nutritional problem for plants. As Modules 32.7 and 32.12 indicate, plants cannot use nitrogen in its most common form, which is found in the atmosphere. However, they can use dissolved nitrate ions and ammonium ions. (32.7)

- Students with limited backgrounds in botany might be surprised to learn that roots need oxygen. Aeration of the soil by burrowing worms and other animals helps create small spaces for air. Highly compacted soils limit the movement of air and can interfere with plant survival. (32.8)

- The U.S. Department of Agriculture's Natural Resources Conservation Service provides numerous links and abundant information on soil conservation at www.nrcs.usda.gov/feature/. (32.9)

- At http://attra.ncat.org/organic.html, the National Sustainable Agriculture Information Service provides extensive online publications describing the USDA rules and requirements for certified organic farming. (32.10)

- Roundup Ready corn, a product manufactured by Monsanto, is resistant to the commercial herbicide Roundup. Thus, farmers can spray fields of Roundup Ready corn directly with Roundup, killing weeds but not the corn. An Internet search will quickly reveal the controversy over this and other genetically modified organisms (GMOs), which can encourage interesting discussions and promote critical thinking skills. Module 12.9 discusses some of the issues related to the use of GM organisms. (32.11)

Plant Nutrition and Symbiosis (32.12–32.14)

Student Misconceptions and Concerns

- Students often confuse the terms symbiosis and mutualism, falsely thinking that they mean the same thing. You might wish to clarify these terms to emphasize the more general meaning of symbiosis and the win/win nature of mutualism, a type of symbiosis. (32.12–32.14)

Teaching Tips

- With abundant antibacterial products now on the market, students may believe that all bacteria are harmful. Before addressing the mutualistic roles of soil bacteria and plants, challenge your students to explain why planting seeds in sterilized soil could be problematic. (32.12)

- Mycorrhizae provide an excellent example of a mutualistic relationship. Unless the various types of symbiotic relationships have already been discussed, consider illustrating mutualism and parasitism with the relationships in Modules 32.13–32.14. (32.13–32.14)

- For additional specific details on mycorrhizal relationships, see the literature exchange website for mycorrhiza at http://mycorrhiza.ag.utk.edu/. (32.13)

- The International Carnivorous Plant Society maintains a website at www.carnivorousplants.org. The site contains many beautiful photographs of carnivorous plants, answers to FAQs, and numerous related resources. (32.14)

Key Terms

adhesion	macronutrient	sugar source
Casparian strip	micronutrient	sustainable agriculture
cation exchange	mycorrhiza	topsoil
cohesion	nitrogen fixation	transpiration
compost	phloem sap	transpiration-cohesion-tension
essential element	pressure flow mechanism	mechanism
fertilizer	root pressure	xylem sap
humus	sugar sink	

Word Roots

fertil- = fruitful (*fertilizer*: compounds given to plants to promote their growth)

macro- = large (*macronutrient*: a chemical substance that an organism must obtain in relatively large amounts)

micro- = small (*micronutrient*: a chemical substance that an organism must obtain in very small amounts)

myco- = a fungus; **-rhizo** = a root (*mycorrhizae*: a mutualistic association of plant roots and fungi)

phloe- = the bark of a tree (*phloem sap*: the solution of sugars, other nutrients, and hormones conveyed throughout a plant via phloem tissue)

trans- = across (*transpiration*: the evaporation of water from parts of a plant, particularly the leaves; *transpiration-cohesion-tension mechanism*: the transport mechanism that drives the upward movement of water in plants)

xyl- = wood (*xylem sap*: the solution of inorganic nutrients conveyed in xylem tissue from a plant's roots to its shoots)

CHAPTER 33

Control Systems in Plants

Chapter Objectives

Opening Essay

Describe the pros and cons of using soybean phytoestrogens to address symptoms of menopause.

Plant Hormones

33.1 Describe the experiments and conclusions of the phototropism research performed by the Darwins, Boysen-Jensen, and Went. Explain why auxin does not seem to play the same role in sunflowers and other eudicots as it does in grasses.

33.2–33.7 Describe the functions of the five major types of plant hormones.

33.8 Describe the uses of plant hormones in modern agriculture and the ethical issues associated with their use.

Responses to Stimuli

33.9 Define phototropism, gravitropism, and thigmotropism. Explain how these reactions occur and describe their significance to plants.

33.10 Explain how biological clocks work and how they influence the lives of plants.

33.11 Distinguish between short-day plants and long-day plants. Explain why these terms can be misleading.

33.12 Describe the roles of phytochromes in plants.

33.13 Explain how plants defend themselves against herbivores. Describe the systemic acquired resistance defense response in plants.

Lecture Outline

I. Introduction

A. Soy protein is one of the few plant proteins that provide all of the essential amino acids.

B. Benefits of consuming soy include

   1. lowered risk of heart disease,

   2. high levels of antioxidants and fiber,

   3. low levels of fat, and

   4. lowering bad LDL cholesterol while maintaining good HDL levels.

C. Soy contains phytoestrogens, hormones that can reduce the symptoms of menopause in women and can help

   1. reduce the risks of heart disease and

   2. sustain bone mass.

D. However, high levels of estrogens appear to increase the risk of

    1. breast cancer and

    2. ovarian cancer.

II. Plant Hormones

  A. 33.1 Experiments on how plants turn toward light led to the discovery of a plant hormone

    1. Any growth response that results in plant organs curving toward or away from stimuli is called a **tropism**.

    2. The growth of a shoot in response to light is called **phototropism**.

      a. Moving toward sunlight helps a growing plant use sunlight to drive photosynthesis.

      b. Phototropism can result when the cells on the dark side of a plant stem elongate faster than those on the light side.

    3. Studies of plant responses to light led to the first evidence of plant **hormones**, a chemical signal

      a. produced in one part of the body and

      b. transported to other parts,

      c. where it acts on target cells to change their functioning.

    4. Charles Darwin and his son Francis conducted experiments that showed that the shoot tips of plants controlled their ability to grow toward light.

    5. The Darwins' experiments

      a. When plant tips were removed, plants did not grow toward light.

      b. When plant tips were covered with an opaque cap, they did not grow toward light.

      c. When plant tips were covered with a clear tip, they did grow toward light.

    6. Peter Boysen-Jensen later conducted experiments that showed that chemical signals produced in shoot tips were responsible for phototropism.

    7. Jensen's experiment

      a. When a gelatin block that allowed chemical diffusion was placed below the shoot tip, plants grew toward light.

      b. When a mica block that prevented chemical diffusion was placed below the shoot tip, plants did not grow toward light.

    8. A graduate student named Frits Went isolated the chemical hormone responsible for phototropism.

      a. Plant tips were placed on an agar block to allow the chemical signal molecules to diffuse from the plant tip to the agar.

      b. When agar blocks containing chemical signals were centered on the ends of "decapitated" plants, they grew straight.

      c. When agar blocks were offset to one side of the "decapitated" plants, they bent away from the side with the agar block.

      d. Went concluded that a chemical produced in the shoot tip was transferred down through the plant, and high concentration of that chemical increased cell elongation on the dark side of the plant.

    9. The chemical signal responsible for phototropism is a hormone that Went called auxin.

  B. 33.2 Five major types of hormones regulate plant growth and development

    1. Plant hormones

      a. are produced in very low concentrations but

      b. can have a profound effect on growth and development.

2. The binding of hormones to cell surface receptors triggers a signal transduction pathway that
    a. amplifies the hormonal signal and
    b. leads to a response or responses within the cell.
3. Plant biologists have identified five major types of plant hormones.
    a. Other important hormones exist, but will not be discussed here.
    b. Some of the hormones listed in Table 33.2 represent a group of related hormones.
4. As indicated in Table 33.2, each hormone has multiple effects, depending on
    a. its site of action,
    b. its concentration, and
    c. the developmental stage of the plant.
C. 33.3 Auxin stimulates the elongation of cells in young shoots
    1. **Auxin** is used for any chemical substance that promotes seedling elongation.
    2. Indoleacetic acid (IAA) is the
        a. major natural auxin found in plants and
        b. type of auxin referred to in Chapter 32.
    3. Auxin is produced in apical meristems at the tips of shoots.
    4. At different concentrations, auxin
        a. stimulates or inhibits the elongation of shoots and roots,
        b. may act by weakening cell walls, allowing them to stretch when cells take up water,
        c. stimulates the development of vascular tissues and cell division in the vascular cambium, promoting growth in stem diameter, and
        d. is produced by developing seeds and promotes the growth of fruit.
D. 33.4 Cytokinins stimulate cell division
    1. **Cytokinins**
        a. promote cytokinesis, or cell division,
        b. are produced in actively growing organs such as roots, embryos, and fruits, and
        c. move upward from roots through a plant,
            i.   balancing the effects of auxin from apical meristems and
            ii. causing lower buds to develop into branches.
E. 33.5 Gibberellins affect stem elongation and have numerous other effects
    1. **Gibberellins**
        a. promote cell elongation and cell division in stems and leaves and
        b. were named for a genus of fungi that produce the same chemical and cause "foolish seedling" disease, in which rice seedlings grew so tall and spindly that they toppled over before producing grain.
        c. There are more than 100 distinct gibberellins produced primarily in roots and young leaves.
    2. Gibberellins also promote
        a. fruit development and
        b. seed germination.
    3. In some plants, gibberellins interact antagonistically with abscisic acid.
F. 33.6 Abscisic acid inhibits many plant processes
    1. **Abscisic acid (ABA)** is a plant hormone that inhibits growth.
    2. High concentrations of ABA promote seed dormancy.
        a. ABA must be removed for germination to occur.
        b. The ratio of ABA to gibberellins controls germination.

3. ABA also acts as a "stress hormone," causing stomata to close when a plant is dehydrated.

G. 33.7 Ethylene triggers fruit ripening and other aging processes

   1. **Ethylene** is a

     a. gaseous by-product of coal combustion and

     b. naturally occurring plant hormone.

   2. Plants produce ethylene, which triggers

     a. fruit ripening and

     b. programmed cell death.

   3. Ethylene is also produced in response to stresses such as drought, flooding, injury, or infection.

   4. A changing ratio of auxin to ethylene, triggered mainly by shorter days, probably causes

     a. autumn color changes and

     b. the loss of leaves from deciduous trees.

H. 33.8 CONNECTION: Plant hormones have many agricultural uses

   1. Agricultural uses of plant hormones include

     a. control of fruit production, ripening, and dropping,

     b. production of seedless fruits, and

     c. use as weed killers.

   2. Agricultural uses of plant hormones

     a. help keep food prices down and can benefit the environment in aspects such as soil erosion, but

     b. may have dangerous side effects for humans and the environment.

III. Response to Stimuli

A. 33.9 Tropisms orient plant growth toward or away from environmental stimuli

   1. **Tropisms** are responses that cause plants to grow in response to environmental stimuli.

     a. Positive tropisms cause plants to grow toward a stimulus.

     b. Negative tropisms cause plants to grow away from a stimulus.

   2. Plants respond to various environmental stimuli.

     a. **Phototropism** is a response to light.

     b. **Gravitropism** is a response to gravity.

     c. **Thigmotropism** is a response to touch.

B. 33.10 Plants have internal clocks

   1. Plants display rhythmic behavior including the

     a. opening and closing of stomata and

     b. folding and unfolding of leaves and flowers.

   2. A **circadian rhythm**

     a. is an innate biological cycle of about 24 hours and

     b. may persist even when an organism is sheltered from environmental cues.

   3. Research on a variety of organisms indicates that circadian rhythms are controlled by internal timekeepers known as **biological clocks**.

   4. Environmental cues such as light/dark cycles keep biological clocks precisely synchronized.

   5. For most organisms, including plants, we know little about

     a. where the clocks are located or

      b. what kinds of cells are involved.

C. 33.11 Plants mark the seasons by measuring photoperiod

   1. Biological clocks can influence seasonal events including

      a. flowering,

      b. seed germination, and

      c. the onset of dormancy.

   2. The environmental stimulus plants most often use to detect the time of year is called **photoperiod**, the relative lengths of day and night.

   3. Plant flowering signals are determined by night length.

   4. **Short-day plants**, such as chrysanthemums and poinsettias

      a. generally flower in the late summer, fall, or winter

      b. when light periods shorten.

   5. **Long-day plants**, such as spinach, lettuce, and many cereal grains

      a. generally flower in late spring or early summer

      b. when light periods lengthen.

D. 33.12 Phytochromes are light detectors that may help set the biological clock

   1. **Phytochromes**

      a. are proteins with a light-absorbing component and

      b. may help plants set their biological clock and monitor photoperiod.

   2. Phytochromes detect light in the red and far-red wavelengths.

      a. One form of phytochrome absorbs red light (P_r).

      b. One form detects far-red light (P_{fr}).

      c. When P_r absorbs light, it is converted into P_{fr}.

      d. When P_{fr} absorbs light, it is converted into P_r.

      e. P_r is naturally produced during dark hours, while P_{fr} is broken down.

      f. The relative amounts of P_r and P_{fr} present in a plant change as day length changes.

E. 33.13 EVOLUTION CONNECTION: Defenses against herbivores and infectious microbes have evolved in plants

   1. **Herbivores** are animals that mainly eat plants.

   2. Plants use chemicals to defend themselves against herbivores and pathogens.

   3. Plants counter herbivores with

      a. physical defenses, such as thorns, and

      b. chemical defenses, such as distasteful or toxic compounds.

   4. Plants defend themselves against pathogens at several levels.

      a. The first line of defense against infection is the physical barrier of the plant's epidermis.

      b. If that fails, plant cells damaged by infection

         i. seal off the infected areas and

         ii. release microbe-killing chemicals that signal nearby cells to mount a similar chemical defense.

         iii. In addition, hormones trigger generalized defense responses in other organs in the process of **systemic acquired resistance**.

Chapter Guide to Teaching Resources

Plant Hormones (33.1–33.8)

Student Misconceptions and Concerns

- Students are likely to think of plants as static, inert objects that interact passively with their environments. Without careful study and consideration, it can be challenging for students to explain how plants interact with their surroundings. This section on plant hormones reveals some of the mechanisms used by plants to respond to changing environmental conditions. (33.1–33.8)

- Students are unlikely to know about the many manipulations of plants performed in modern agriculture. Learning about them will familiarize students with some of the more practical (and profitable) applications of scientific knowledge and perhaps reveal new career options. (33.1–33.8)

Teaching Tips

- Consider bringing in a plant that shows a distinct orientation in one direction. Before discussing phototropism, ask students to explain why the plant may have this orientation. You may also want to challenge them to predict how the plant will respond after several days in the classroom. (33.1)

- Students might not realize that angled growth can result from accelerated and/or retarded growth on one side. In Module 33.1, the authors note that accelerated growth appears to occur in grass shoots, but retarded growth occurs in sunflowers and other eudicots. (33.1)

- In Modules 33.2 and 33.3, the authors note that the effects of a particular hormone are determined by many factors, including the concentration, developmental stage of the plant, and presence and concentration of other hormones. Biology is highly complex (although some students might wish otherwise!). As you relate the diversity and complexity of life throughout your course, hormones and their interactions in plants and animals are wonderful examples. (33.2–33.3)

- Ask your students to explain how some seedless fruits are produced. It may be amusing for them to consider this question when they do not know how it is done! (33.3, 33.5, 33.8)

- In Module 33.4, the authors compare a basil plant with and without a terminal bud. In addition to details on the control of axillary bud growth, the experiment demonstrates an important principle of biology: Organisms must compromise. With limited resources, the basil plant's growth reflects a compromise between growth in height and growth of branches. (33.4)

- Although the similarities are limited, you may want to challenge students to identify human hormones that have effects like the plant hormones discussed in this chapter. For example, gibberellins and human growth hormone both promote growth. (33.5)

- Much of the content of biology courses may answer questions students have never thought to ask. Module 33.6 raises a few of these questions. What keeps seeds dispersed in autumn from sprouting in the winter? What keeps the seeds in fruit from germinating immediately? As we explore biology, it is useful to encourage curiosity first to make students receptive to the explanation. (33.6)

- Special bags made of a material that absorbs ethylene gas are now commercially available under brand names such as Green Bags. Their manufacturers claim that they extend the life of fruits and vegetables stored inside them. (33.7)

- As noted previously, the realities of biology mean that modern agriculture requires compromise. Human societies cannot last without a steady food supply, but they must also factor in the cost, quality, and environmental risks associated with its production. Make sure your students appreciate the key role of science and education in informing the important decisions we make as a society about our food and the environment. (33.8)

Responses to Stimuli (33.9–33.13)

Student Misconceptions and Concerns

- Students may struggle with the concept that plants respond actively to their environments. In addition to the internal changes in physiology produced by hormones, plants can also move in response to environmental stimuli. (33.9–33.13)

- Students may not understand why defenses against herbivores are not found in all plants. The production of distasteful or toxic compounds reveals an important evolutionary compromise. Is it adaptive to use more energy to produce chemical defenses, or better to divert the energy to regrowth? Plants, animals, and all life exist in a world of limited resources. As circumstances and organisms vary, the particular strategy that is most adaptive varies too. Specialization comes at a cost, and all adaptations represent compromise. (33.13)

Teaching Tips

- Photographs or living examples of a germinating seed and a climbing vine are very useful teaching aids for demonstrating gravitropism and thigmotropism, respectively. (33.9)

- Short video clips on plant tropisms can be found by searching "tropisms video" in Google. Such short clips can quickly illustrate these activities. (33.9)

- Encourage your students to focus on circadian rhythms by challenging them to identify those in their own lives. Sleep, physical activity, hunger, eating, drinking, and urination are not spread evenly throughout a 24-hour period. Recognizing these cycles in themselves helps students relate to such cycles in plants. (33.10)

- After addressing circadian rhythms which occur within a 24-hour day, Module 33.11 addresses seasonal biological cycles. Challenge students to identify seasonal biological cycles in animals in their region. If winters are cold in your area, annual changes may include the growth of thicker fur in mammals, hibernation, or migration to distant locations. (33.11)

- Module 33.12 describes a mechanism used by plants to measure the length of the night and respond to morning light. Figure 33.12A is especially helpful in explaining this reaction. Challenge your students to explain why the many types of receptors and signaling pathways that respond to light have been particularly advantageous to plants. Although light is important to animal activities, plants must be even more sensitive to it because of the import role played by light in photosynthesis. (33.12)

- Examples of natural selection often include simple predator-prey relationships. The complex relationships depicted in Figure 33.13A provide some additional examples of the evolution of complex systems. Challenge students to explain how the recruitment of parasitic wasps might have evolved in this system. Perhaps some plants under attack by caterpillars emitted variants of a chemical from their leaves that at that time was involved in some other unrelated reaction. However, the few plants that emitted a variant of this chemical attracted parasitic wasps. Such plants would be more likely to survive and reproduce. With each generation, the proportion of plants with this new ability to attract parasitic wasps would increase, and the trait would become common in subsequent generations. (33.13)

Key Terms

abscisic acid (ABA)	gibberellin	phototropism
auxin	gravitropism	phytochrome
biological clock	herbivore	short-day plant
circadian rhythm	hormone	systemic acquired resistance
cytokinin	long-day plant	thigmotropism
ethylene	photoperiod	tropism

Word Roots

ab- = off; **-scin** = to cut (*abscisic acid*: a plant hormone that inhibits cell division, promotes dormancy, and interacts with gibberellins in regulating seed germination)

aux- = grow, enlarge (*auxin*: a plant hormone, such as indoleacetic acid or a related compound, whose chief effect is to promote seedling elongation)

circ- = a circle (*circadian rhythm*: in an organism, a biological cycle of about 24 hours that is controlled by a biological clock, usually under the influence of environmental cues)

cyto- = cell; **-kine** = moving (*cytokinin*: one of a family of plant hormones that promotes cell division, retards aging in flowers and fruits, and may interact antagonistically with auxins in regulating plant growth and development)

gibb- = humped (*gibberellin*: one of a family of plant hormones that triggers the germination of seeds and interacts with auxins in regulating growth and fruit development)

gravi- = gravity; **-trop** = turn, change (*gravitropism*: a plant's growth response to gravity)

herbi- = plants; **-vora** = eat (*herbivore*: an animal that eats only plants or algae)

photo- = light (*phototropism*: the growth of a plant shoot toward or away from light)

phyto- = a plant; **-chromo** = color (*phytochrome*: a colored protein in plants that contains a special set of atoms that absorbs light)

thigmo- = a touch (*thigmotropism*: the growth movement of a plant in response to touch)

CHAPTER 34

The Biosphere: An Introduction to Earth's Diverse Environments

Chapter Objectives

Opening Essay

Compare the unusual ecology of the Himalayas and deep-sea hydrothermal vent communities.

The Biosphere

34.1 Define and distinguish between the different levels within ecosystems. Distinguish between the biotic and abiotic components of an ecosystem.

34.2 Summarize the subject and impact of Rachel Carson's influential book *Silent Spring*.

34.3 Describe the abiotic factors that influence life in the biosphere.

34.4 Describe the adaptations that enable pronghorns to survive in the open plains and shrub deserts of North America.

34.5 Explain how global climate patterns are influenced by solar energy input as well as the movement of Earth through space. Explain how landforms affect local climate.

34.5 Explain why the seasons of the year, prevailing winds, and ocean currents exist.

Aquatic Biomes

34.6 Describe the abiotic and biotic characteristics of the different ocean zones and adjacent aquatic biomes.

34.7 Describe the different types of freshwater biomes.

34.7 Explain how the properties of a river change between its source and its outlet, and how this impacts the biotic components of this biome.

Terrestrial Biomes

34.8 Explain why species in widely separated biomes may have similar features.

34.8 Explain why storms and fire are crucial factors in some biomes.

34.8–34.17 Describe the characteristics used to define terrestrial biomes. Then use these characteristics to define the major terrestrial biomes: tropical forests, savannas, deserts, chaparral, temperate grasslands, temperate forests, coniferous forests, tundra, and polar ice.

34.18 Explain how all parts of the biosphere are linked by the global water cycle.

Lecture Outline

I. Introduction

A. For most of life on Earth, the sun is the main source of energy.

B. But around hydrothermal vents, life depends on chemoautotrophic sulfur bacteria.

C. From the roof of the world to the deepest oceans, Earth's diverse environments are bursting with life.

II. The Biosphere

A. 34.1 Ecologists study how organisms interact with their environment at several levels

   1. Ecology is the scientific study of the interactions of organisms with their environments.

   2. Organisms can potentially be affected by many different variables, grouped into two major types.

     a. Biotic factors include all of the organisms in an area, the living component of the environment.

     b. Abiotic factors are the environment's nonliving component, the physical and chemical factors.

   3. An organism's habitat includes the biotic and abiotic factors present in its surroundings.

   4. Ecologists study environmental interactions at the levels of the

     a. organism,

     b. population, a group of individuals of the same species living in a particular geographic area,

     c. community, an assemblage of all the populations of organisms living close enough together for potential interaction, and

     d. ecosystem, both the abiotic and biotic components of the environment.

   5. Some ecologists take a wider perspective by studying **landscapes**, arrays of ecosystems usually visible from the air as distinctive patches.

   6. The **biosphere**

     a. extends from the atmosphere several kilometers above Earth to the depths of the oceans and

     b. is all of the Earth that is inhabited by life.

B. 34.2 CONNECTION: The science of ecology provides insight into environmental problems

   1. Human activities affect all parts of the biosphere.

     a. Cities, farms, and highways change the landscape.

     b. The widespread use of chemicals such as fertilizers and pesticides poses problems to people and other organisms.

   2. Two events raised questions about the long-term effects of widespread DDT use.

     a. The evolution of pesticide resistance in insects and

     b. Rachel Carson's 1962 book *Silent Spring*, which played a key role in the awakening of environmental awareness.

C. 34.3 Physical and chemical factors influence life in the biosphere

   1. The most important abiotic factors that determine the biosphere's structure and dynamics include

     a. the energy source, usually solar energy,

     b. temperature,

    c. abundance and type of water,

    d. nutrients,

    e. other aquatic factors such as availability of oxygen, and

    f. other terrestrial factors including wind and fire.

D. 34.4 EVOLUTION CONNECTION: Organisms are adapted to abiotic and biotic factors by natural selection

  1. One of the fundamental goals of ecology is to explain the distribution of organisms.

  2. The presence of a species in a particular place has two possible explanations.

    a. The species may have evolved from ancestors living in that location, or

    b. it may have dispersed to that location and been able to survive once it arrived.

  3. The pronghorn is a highly successful herbivorous running mammal of open country.

    a. It is a descendent of ancestors that roamed the open plains and shrub deserts of North America more than a million years ago.

    b. It is found nowhere else and is only distantly related to the many antelope species in Africa.

  4. A pronghorn's habitat is arid, windswept, and subject to extreme temperature fluctuations.

  5. Their ability to survive and reproduce under these conditions left offspring that carried their alleles into subsequent generations.

  6. Until around 12,000 years ago, one of their major predators was probably the now extinct American cheetah, similar to African cheetahs alive today.

  7. Ecologists hypothesize that the selection pressure of the cheetah's pursuit led to the pronghorn's blazing speed, which far exceeds that of its main present-day predator, the wolf.

  8. Like many large herbivores that live in open grasslands, the pronghorn also derives protection from living in herds.

  9. Populations of organisms are adapted to local environmental conditions, which may limit the distribution of organisms.

E. 34.5 Regional climate influences the distribution of terrestrial communities

  1. Climate often determines the distribution of communities.

  2. Earth's global climate patterns are largely determined by

    a. the input of solar energy and

    b. the planet's movement in space.

  3. Solar radiation varies with latitude.

    a. Equatorial regions receive sunlight more directly.

    b. Higher latitudes receive sunlight at more of a slant.

  4. Most climatic variations are due to the uneven heating of Earth's surface.

  5. Earth's permanent tilt causes the seasons.

    a. In June, the Northern Hemisphere of the Earth is tipped toward the sun.

    b. In December, the Northern Hemisphere of the Earth is tipped away from the sun.

    c. The reverse is true about the Southern Hemisphere, generating opposite seasons during the same time of year.

  6. The **tropics** are the region surrounding the equator between latitudes 23.5° north and 23.5° south.

  7. Uneven heating of the Earth causes rain and winds.

    a. The direct intense solar radiation in the tropics near the equator has an impact on the global patterns of rainfall and winds.

     b. The tropics experience the greatest annual input and least seasonal variation in solar radiation.

8. As the air rises in the tropics, it
     a. cools and releases much of its water content,
     b. produces abundant precipitation typical of most tropical regions, and
     c. creates an area of calm or very light winds known as the **doldrums**.

9. High altitude air masses
     a. lose their moisture over equatorial zones and then
     b. spread away from the equator.

10. The air then
     a. cools and descends again at latitudes of about 30° north and south and
     b. spreads back toward the equator creating the cooling **trade winds** that dominate the tropics.

11. As the air moves back toward the equator, it
     a. warms and
     b. picks up moisture.

12. The **temperate zones** are between the tropics and
     a. the Arctic Circle in the north and
     b. the Antarctic Circle in the south.
     c. The temperate zones have seasonal variations and more moderate temperatures than the tropics or the polar zones.

13. **Prevailing wind patterns** result from the combined effects of
     a. rising and falling air masses and
     b. Earth's rotation.
     c. In the tropics, Earth's rapidly moving surface deflects vertically circulating air, making the trade winds blow from east to west.
     d. In temperate zones, the slower-moving surface produces the **westerlies**, winds that blow from west to east.

14. **Ocean currents**, river-like flow patterns in the oceans, result from a combination of
     a. prevailing winds,
     b. the planet's rotation,
     c. unequal heating of surface waters, and
     d. the location and shapes of the continents.
     e. Ocean currents have a profound effect on regional climates.

15. Landforms can also affect local climate. For example, air temperature declines about 6°C with every 1,000-m increase in elevation.

16. Near mountains, rainfall is affected by
     a. location of mountains,
     b. prevailing winds, and
     c. ocean current patterns.

17. Climate and other abiotic factors of the environment control the global distribution of organisms.

18. The influence of these abiotic factors results in **biomes**, the major types of ecological associations that occupy broad geographic regions of land or water.

III. Aquatic Biomes

A. 34.6 Sunlight and substrate are key factors in the distribution of marine organisms

1. Aquatic biomes are shaped by the availability of

    a. light and

    b. nutrients.

2. Within the oceans the

    a. **pelagic realm** includes all open water,

    b. **benthic realm** the seafloor,

    c. **aphotic zone**, where there is insufficient light for photosynthesis, and

    d. **photic zone** where light penetration is sufficient for photosynthesis and **phytoplankton** can occur.

       i. **Zooplankton** are abundant in the pelagic photic zone.

       ii. Coral reefs also occur in the photic zone.

3. The marine environment includes distinctive biomes where the ocean meets the land or fresh water.

    a. **Intertidal zones** are where the ocean meets the land and the shore is

       i. pounded by waves during high tide and

       ii. exposed to the sun and drying winds during low tide.

    b. **Estuaries** are productive areas where rivers meet the ocean.

    c. **Wetlands** are transitional between aquatic and terrestrial ecosystems.

B. 34.7 Current, sunlight, and nutrients are important abiotic factors in freshwater biomes

1. Freshwater biomes

    a. cover less than 1% of the Earth,

    b. contain less than 0.01% of its water,

    c. harbor 6% of all described species, and

    d. include lakes, ponds, rivers, streams, and wetlands.

2. Freshwater biomes fall into two broad groups:

    a. standing water biomes (lakes and ponds) and

    b. flowing water biomes (rivers and streams).

IV. Terrestrial Biomes

A. 34.8 Terrestrial biomes reflect regional variations in climate

1. Terrestrial ecosystems are grouped into nine major types of biomes, distinguished primarily by their predominant vegetation.

2. The geographic distribution of plants and thus terrestrial biomes largely depends on climate. The key climate factors are

    a. temperature and

    b. precipitation.

3. The same type of biome may occur in geographically distant places if the climate is similar.

4. The current concern about global warming is generating intense interest in the effect of climate on vegetation patterns.

5. Scientists are documenting

    a. latitudinal shifts in biome borders and snow and ice coverage and

    b. changes in length of the growing season.

B. 34.9 Tropical forests cluster near the equator

1. Tropical forests

    a. occur in equatorial areas,

     b. experience warm temperatures and days that are 11–12 hours long year-round, and

     c. have variable rainfall.

  2. The tropical rain forest is among the most complex of all biomes.

     a. Tropical rain forests harbor enormous numbers of species.

     b. Large-scale human destruction of tropical rain forests continues to endanger many species.

C. 34.10 Savannas are grasslands with scattered trees

  1. Savannas

     a. are warm year-round,

     b. have 30–50 cm annual rainfall,

     c. experience dramatic seasonal variation,

     d. are dominated by grasses and scattered trees, and

     e. are mostly inhabited by large grazing mammals and insects.

D. 34.11 Deserts are defined by their dryness

  1. Deserts are the driest of all terrestrial biomes.

     a. They are characterized by low and unpredictable rainfall.

     b. Desertification, the conversion of semiarid regions to desert, is a significant environmental problem.

E. 34.12 Spiny shrubs dominate the chaparral

  1. The **chaparral** is a shrubland with

     a. cool, rainy winters and

     b. hot, dry summers.

     c. Vegetation is adapted to periodic fires.

F. 34.13 Temperate grasslands include the North American prairie

  1. Temperate grasslands

     a. are mostly treeless, except along rivers or streams,

     b. experience precipitation of about 25–75 cm per year, with periodic droughts and cold winters, and

     c. in North America have historically been grazed by large bison and pronghorn.

     d. Farms have replaced most of North America's temperate grasslands.

G. 34.14 Broadleaf trees dominate temperate forests

  1. Temperate broadleaf forests

     a. grow where there is sufficient moisture to support the growth of large trees and

     b. experience wide-ranging temperatures (-30°C to 30°C) and high annual precipitation (75–150 cm).

     c. Nearly all of the original broadleaf forests in North America have been drastically altered by agriculture and urban development.

H. 34.15 Coniferous forests are often dominated by a few species of trees

  1. Cone-bearing evergreen trees, such as spruce, pine, fir, and hemlock, dominate **coniferous forests**.

  2. The northern coniferous forest, or **taiga**, is the largest terrestrial biome on Earth. The taiga is characterized by

     a. long, cold winters and

     b. short, wet summers.

  3. Temperate rain forests of coastal North America are also coniferous forests.

I. 34.16 Long, bitter-cold winters characterize the tundra
  1. The **tundra** covers expansive areas of the Arctic between the taiga and the permanently frozen polar ice.
  2. The treeless arctic tundra
     a. is characterized by **permafrost**, continuously frozen subsoil, and
     b. experiences little precipitation.

J. 34.17 Polar ice covers the land at high latitudes
  1. **Polar ice** covers
     a. land north of the tundra,
     b. much of the Arctic Ocean, and
     c. the continent of Antarctica.
  2. Temperatures are extremely cold year-round and precipitation is very low.
  3. The terrestrial polar biome is closely intertwined with the neighboring marine biome.

K. 34.18 The global water cycle connects aquatic and terrestrial biomes
  1. Ecological subdivisions such as biomes are linked by
     a. nutrient cycles and
     b. the water cycle.
     c. Water in the form of precipitation and evaporation moves between the land, oceans, and atmosphere.
        i. Over the oceans, evaporation exceeds precipitation.
        ii. Over the land, precipitation exceeds evaporation.
  2. Human activities affect the global water cycle.
     a. The destruction of tropical rain forests reduces the amount of water vapor in the air.
     b. Pumping large amounts of groundwater to the surface for irrigation increases the rate of evaporation over land.

Chapter Guide to Teaching Resources

The Biosphere (34.1–34.5)

Student Misconceptions and Concerns

- Students may confuse the terms ecology and environmentalism. The science of ecology and the environmental issues that it often raises are related but distinct processes. (34.1–34.5)

Teaching Tips

- In the first chapter of the text, Module 1.2 introduces the levels of biological organization extending from an atom to the biosphere. Reviewing these with students will help them to place these ecology chapters in context. (34.1)

- A website devoted to Rachel Carson can be viewed at www.rachelcarson.org. (34.2)

- As a class focusing exercise, consider challenging students to make lists of all the abiotic components in a given ecosystem. You might suggest a particular place to consider, such as a nearby park or other nearby area of natural interest. They may work in class in small groups, or turn the lists in as a short homework assignment (perhaps via e-mail). (34.3)

- In general, the sun is the primary source of energy input to ecosystems. Hydrothermal vent communities are a clear exception. Some students might enjoy researching additional details about these ecosystems and the roles they might have played in the early evolution of life on Earth. One source of good information about hydrothermal vent communities is www.csa.com/discoveryguides/vent/websites.php. (34.3)

- Consider challenging your students to explain why organisms are typically limited to living in only certain parts of the biosphere. Module 34.4 notes that a species range may be limited by adaptations to particular environmental conditions. The same adaptations that permit survival under certain conditions may reduce survival rates under other conditions. Such trade-offs between specialization and generalization are a normal part of biology. If you want to emphasize the point with an analogy, you might note that choosing a particular major in college increases the student's skills in that field, but comes at the cost of detailed study in other fields. (34.4)

- Module 34.5 discusses the reasons why Earth's tilt causes seasons. Consider challenging your students, perhaps as a short in-class activity, to explain why it is typically cooler (a) further away from the equator and (b) during the winter months. Although you may not want to use class time on this activity every year, collecting student responses before your students read or learn about this in class can reveal misconceptions and areas of misunderstanding that will help direct your teaching for years to come. (34.5)

Aquatic Biomes (34.6–34.7)

Student Misconceptions and Concerns

- Students may benefit from a review of the general properties of water introduced in Modules 2.10–2.16, which provide insight into the abiotic properties of aquatic biomes. (34.6–34.7)

Teaching Tips

- Before addressing aquatic biomes, consider asking your students to explain (a) why fog frequently forms over large bodies of water in the spring and fall and (b) how life would be different in aquatic environments if ice sank when it froze. (34.6)

- Consider exploring with your students the many ways that the Gulf of Mexico was impacted by the BP 2010 spill and the natural mechanisms in this biome that are helping it to recover. (34.6)

- The turnover of lakes and ponds in the fall often results in noticeable changes such as fish kills and alterations in water color and smell. If you are addressing this subject in the fall or early winter, you might instruct students to watch for this phenomenon. (34.7)

- Before lecturing about rivers and streams, ask students to speculate about how the qualities of a stream change between its source and the point where it joins a larger body of water many kilometers downstream. In particular, how do water temperature, water clarity, water speed, and the types of fish inhabiting the water change as the water flows away from its source? (34.7)

- The speed of water plays a key role in the removal and deposition of sediment in rivers and streams. Near the outer edge of a curve, a river or stream will erode the bank. However, in places where the river slows, such as along the inside of curves, sediment tends to be deposited, resulting in the winding shape of mature rivers. Satellite images of such rivers, such as the Mississippi, reveal the extensive curvature of these systems. (34.7)

Terrestrial Biomes (34.8–34.18)

Student Misconceptions and Concerns

- Before addressing specific terrestrial biomes, consider providing some specific details about weather patterns with reference to the major factors that influence your local weather. Students may not understand the influences of mountains, large bodies of water, and latitude on the weather where they live, and will be engaged by an immediately observable, close-to-home example. (34.8–34.18)

Teaching Tips

- Many websites, some designed for pre-college students, introduce the diversity of biomes using varying degrees of detail and imagery. A list of them can be found at www.aresearchguide.com/biomes.html. (34.8–34.17)

- Consider preparing a chart that will help your students compare the characteristics of the major terrestrial biomes. Students who are just beginning college may still need help learning the best ways to organize information. (34.8–34.17)

- Challenge your students to identify unpredictable natural disturbances in the terrestrial biomes examined. How is each biome adapted to recover? What components of each biome are dependent upon these natural disturbances? Exploring the role of disturbances in ecosystems may provide encouragement to students saddened by negative human impacts on biomes. (34.8–34.17)

- In the 1960s and early 1970s, movies set in the American West were produced in portions of Europe with similar biomes. A Google search for "spaghetti westerns" will produce links to websites devoted to this genre of film. (34.11–34.12)

- Discussing the movements of water through your local community can help students relate to the concept of global water cycling at a local level. You may want to have them consider all of the possible inputs of water into your community and the possible routes of exit. Students may not realize the possibility that the outflow of water from one community is connected to the inflow of water into another community downstream. (34.17)

Key Terms

abiotic factor	ecosystem	taiga
aphotic zone	estuary	temperate broadleaf forest
benthic realm	habitat	temperate grassland
biomes	intertidal zone	temperate rain forests
biosphere	landscape	temperate zones
biotic factor	ocean currents	trade winds
chaparral	organism	tropical forests
community	pelagic realm	tropics
coniferous forests	permafrost	tundra
continental shelves	photic zone	westerlies
deserts	phytoplankton	wetlands
desertification	population	zooplankton
doldrums	prevailing winds	
ecology	savanna	

Word Roots

a- = without; **bio-** = life (*abiotic factor*: the nonliving chemical and physical components of an ecosystem)

-aphoto = light (*aphotic zone*: the region of an aquatic ecosystem beneath the photic zone, where light does not penetrate sufficiently for photosynthesis to occur)

bio- = life (*biome*: a defined area of ecologically similar communities of organisms; *biosphere*: the part of the Earth inhabited by life; *biotic factor*: a living component of an ecosystem)

bentho- = the depths of the sea (*benthic realm*: a seafloor, or the bottom of a freshwater lake, pond, river, or stream)

eco- = home (*ecology*: the scientific study of the interactions of organisms with their environments)

estuar- = the sea (*estuary*: the area where a freshwater stream or river merges with the ocean)

inter- = between (*intertidal zone*: the shallow zone of the ocean where land meets water)

pelag- = the sea (*pelagic realm*: all of the open-water areas of an ocean, excluding the intertidal zone)

perman- = remaining (*permafrost*: a permanently frozen stratum below the arctic tundra)

-photo = light (*photic zone*: the region of an aquatic ecosystem where light penetrates and photosynthesis occurs)

phyto- = a plant (*phytoplankton*: algae and photosynthetic bacteria that drift passively in aquatic environments)

zoo- = animal (*zooplankton*: animals [heterotrophs] that drift freely in aquatic environments)

CHAPTER 35

Behavioral Adaptations to the Environment

Chapter Objectives

Opening Essay

Describe the adaptations of prairie voles that lead to lifelong monogamy.

The Scientific Study of Behavior

35.1 Define and distinguish between the proximate and ultimate causes of behavior.

35.2 Describe the adaptive advantage of innate behaviors. Provide examples of fixed action patterns and note the adaptive advantage of each.

35.3 Describe the respective roles of genetics and the environment in shaping behavior.

Learning

35.4–35.11 Define the seven types of learning and note the adaptive advantages and examples of each.

35.5 Explain how bird song development involves innate behavior and experience.

35.6 Describe the problems that imprinting creates for captive breeding programs. Explain how these challenges were addressed for whooping cranes.

35.7 Define and compare kinesis, taxis, and the use of landmarks in animal movements.

35.8 Explain how cognitive maps help direct animal migrations.

35.9 Explain why associative learning depends upon memory.

35.10 Explain how alarm calls are used and learned in vervet monkeys.

35.11 Define cognition and describe an example.

Survival and Reproductive Success

35.12 Define search images and optimal foraging, providing examples of each.

35.13 Compare the types of signals used by nocturnal mammals and diurnal birds. Describe the complex social signals used in animal societies, including honeybees.

35.14 Explain how courtship rituals are adaptive.

35.15 Compare monogamous and polygamous relationships. Describe the circumstances that would favor each system and provide examples of each.

35.16 Explain how endocrine disruptors may be introduced into the environment and describe the consequences of this pollution.

Social Behavior and Sociobiology

35.17 Define social behavior and sociobiology, providing examples of each.

35.18 Define a territory and describe the ways in which territories are used, identified, and defended.

35.19 Define agonistic behavior and provide an example. Explain how agonistic behavior is adaptive.

35.20 Explain how dominance hierarchies are maintained and identify their adaptive value.

35.21 Define altruism and kin selection and describe examples of each.

35.22 Describe dominance hierarchies and reconciliation behavior in chimps.

35.23 Explain how genes and environmental factors contribute to human social behavior.

Lecture Outline

I. Introduction

A. Mating is one of the most fundamental activities in the animal world.

B. Male peacocks expend considerable time and energy trying to attract a mate.

C. Prairie voles

    1. share a nest,

    2. share in the care of their young, and

    3. mate for life.

II. The Scientific Study of Behavior

A. 35.1 Behavioral ecologists ask both proximate and ultimate questions

    1. Behavior encompasses a wide range of activities.

        a. A behavior is an action carried out by muscles or glands under the control of the nervous system in response to an environmental cue.

        b. Collectively, behavior is the sum of an animal's responses to internal and external environmental cues.

    2. Behavioral ecology is the study of behavior in an evolutionary context.

    3. The questions investigated by behavioral ecologists fall into two broad categories.

        a. Proximate questions concern the immediate reason for the behavior.

            i. How is it triggered by **stimuli** (environmental cues that cause a response)?

            ii. What physiological or anatomical mechanisms play a role?

            iii. What underlying genetic factors are at work?

            iv. Proximate causes are the answers to such questions about the immediate mechanism for behavior.

        b. Ultimate questions address why a particular behavior occurs. **Ultimate causes** are the evolutionary explanations for behavior.

B. 35.2 Fixed action patterns are innate behaviors

    1. Lorenz and Tinbergen were among the first to demonstrate the importance of **innate behavior**, behaviors that are

        a. under strong genetic control and

        b. are performed in virtually the same way by all individuals of a species.

2. Many of Lorenz's and Tinbergen's studies were concerned with behavioral sequences called **fixed action patterns (FAPs)**,
   a. an unchangeable series of actions
   b. triggered by a specific stimulus.
   c. Once initiated, the sequence is performed in its entirety, regardless of any changes in circumstances.
   d. Examples include
      i. reproductive behaviors and
      ii. behaviors that must be done correctly the first time to survive, such as a young chick hatched out on a cliff ledge, starting to fly.

C. 35.3 Behavior is the result of both genetic and environmental factors
   1. Animal behavior often involves a combination of genetic programming and environmental factors.
      a. Genetic engineering in fruit flies has been used to investigate genes that influence behavior. Genes have been identified that govern
         i. learning and memory,
         ii. internal clocks,
         iii. courtship, and
         iv. mating behaviors.
   2. Cross-fostering experiments are useful for studying environmental factors that affect behavior. Studies of rats reveal that behavioral changes can be passed to future generations,
      a. not through genes, but
      b. through the social environment.
      c. Interactions with the mother change the pattern of gene expression in the pups, thus affecting the development of parts of the neuroendocrine system that regulate the fight or flight response.

III. Learning

A. 35.4 Habituation is a simple type of learning
   1. **Learning** is modification of behavior as a result of specific experiences.
   2. Learning enables animals to change their behaviors in response to changing environmental conditions.
   3. There are various forms of learning, ranging from
      a. a simple behavioral change in response to a single stimulus to
      b. complex problem solving using entirely new behaviors.
   4. **Habituation** is one of the simplest forms of learning.
      a. An animal learns not to respond to a repeated stimulus that conveys little or no information.
      b. In terms of ultimate causation, habituation may increase fitness by allowing an animal's nervous system to focus on stimuli that signal
         i. food,
         ii. mates, or
         iii. real danger.

B. 35.5 Imprinting requires both innate behavior and experience
   1. **Imprinting** is
      a. generally irreversible learning and
      b. limited to a specific phase in an animal's life called a **sensitive period**.

c. Examples include
      i. a young bird learning to identify its parents and
      ii. song development in birds.
C. 35.6 CONNECTION: Imprinting poses problems and opportunities for conservation programs
   1. In attempting to save species that are at the edge of extinction, biologists sometimes try to increase their numbers in captivity.
   a. Artificial incubation in captivity is often successful.
   b. But without parents available as models for imprinting, the offspring may not learn appropriate behaviors.
   c. Biologists have invented new ways to save species that recognize the importance of parenting behavior.
D. 35.7 Animal movement may be a simple response to stimuli or require spatial learning
   1. Kinesis is a random movement in response to a stimulus. A kinesis may be
   a. merely starting or stopping,
   b. changing speed, or
   c. turning more or less frequently.
   2. Taxis is a response directed
   a. toward (positive taxis) or
   b. away from (negative taxis) a stimulus.
   c. Many stream fish, such as trout, exhibit positive taxis in the current, automatically swimming or orienting in an upstream direction.
   3. In **spatial learning**, animals establish memories of landmarks in their environment that indicate the locations of
   a. food,
   b. nest sites,
   c. prospective mates, and/or
   d. potential hazards.
   e. The digger wasp uses landmarks to keep track of her nests.
E. 35.8 Movements of animals may depend on cognitive maps
   1. An animal can move around its environment using landmarks alone.
   2. A **cognitive map**
   a. is a more powerful mechanism and
   b. uses an internal representation, or code, of the spatial relationships among objects in an animal's surroundings.
   c. The most extensive studies of cognitive maps involved animals that exhibit **migration**.
   3. Migrating animals often stay on course using a variety of cues.
   a. Gray whales seem to use the coastline to pilot their way north and south.
   b. Birds migrating at night navigate by the stars.
   c. Monarch butterflies appear to migrate using only innate responses to environmental cues.
   d. Some songbirds show the interaction of genes and experience in migration.
F. 35.9 Animals may learn to associate a stimulus or behavior with a response
   1. Associative learning is the ability to associate one environmental feature with another.
   a. In one type of learning, an animal learns to link a particular stimulus to a particular outcome. For example, a dog may expect to go for a walk if the owner picks up the leash.

    b. Trial-and-error learning is an animal's ability to learn to associate one of its own behaviors with a positive or negative effect.

    c. Memory is the key to all associative learning.

G. 35.10 Social learning employs observation and imitation of others

  1. Social learning is learning by observing the behavior of others.

    a. Many predators learn some of their basic hunting tactics by observing and imitating their mothers.

    b. Alarm calls of vervet monkeys in Kenya provide an interesting example of how performance of a behavior can improve through social learning.

H. 35.11 Problem-solving behavior relies on cognition

  1. Cognition is the ability of an animal's nervous system to perceive, store, integrate, and use information gathered by the senses.

    a. Some animals have complex cognitive abilities that include **problem solving**, the ability to apply past experience to novel situations.

    b. Problem-solving behavior

      i. is highly developed in some mammals, especially dolphins and primates, and

      ii. has been observed in some bird species.

IV. Survival and Reproductive Success

A. 35.12 Behavioral ecologists use cost-benefit analysis to study foraging

  1. Animals forage in a great many ways.

    a. Some animals, such as crows, are feeding "generalists."

    b. Other animals, such as koalas, are feeding "specialists."

  2. The mechanism that enables an animal to find particular foods efficiently is called a **search image**.

  3. Animals with food choices face trade-offs involved in selection. The amount of energy may vary considerably in

    a. locating,

    b. capturing, and

    c. preparing prey for consumption.

  4. Optimal foraging theory predicts that an animal's feeding behavior should provide

    a. maximal energy gain with minimal energy expense and

    b. minimal risk of being eaten while foraging.

    c. In England, a researcher tested part of this theory by studying insectivorous birds called wagtails, which often eat dung flies.

B. 35.13 Communication is an essential element of interactions between animals

  1. Interactions between animals depend on some form of signaling between the participating individuals.

  2. Animal communication includes

    a. sending,

    b. receiving, and

    c. responding to signals.

  3. Forms of communication vary considerably and many animals use more than one type of signal simultaneously.

    a. Nocturnal mammals use odor and sound.

    b. Diurnal birds use visual and auditory signals.

    c. Fish may use visual, electrical, and/or auditory signals.

    d. Honeybees "dance" to signal to other bees the location of a food source.

C. 35.14 Mating systems often involves elaborate courtship rituals
   1. Careful communication is an essential prerequisite for mating.
      a. In many species, prospective mates must perform an elaborate courtship ritual.
      b. The ritual confirms that individuals are of the same species, of the opposite sex, physically primed for mating, and not threats to each other.
D. 35.15 Mating behaviors and parental care enhance reproductive success
   1. Animal mating systems fall into three categories.
      a. Promiscuous systems have no
         i. strong pair-bonds or
         ii. lasting relationships between males and females.
      b. Monogamous systems have
         i. one male and one female and
         ii. both parents participating in parental care.
      c. Polygamous systems
         i. have one individual of one sex mating with several of the other and
         ii. usually consist of one male and many females.
   2. The needs of offspring and certainty of paternity help explain differences in
      a. mating systems and
      b. parental care by males.
E. 35.16 CONNECTION: Chemical pollutants can cause abnormal behavior
   1. Endocrine-disrupting chemicals in natural environments may cause
      a. abnormal behavior and
      b. reproductive abnormalities.
   2. Examples of the effects of endocrine-disrupting chemicals in natural environments include
      a. a drop in the intensity of nest-guarding behavior in certain male fish exposed to pollutants that mimic the female hormone estrogen and
      b. masculinization of female mosquitofish anatomy.

V. Social Behavior and Sociobiology

A. 35.17 Sociobiology places social behavior in an evolutionary context
   1. Biologists define **social behavior** as any kind of interaction between two or more animals, usually of the same species.
   2. **Sociobiology** applies evolutionary theory to the study and interpretation of social behavior to explain how social behaviors
      a. are adaptive and
      b. could have evolved by natural selection.
B. 35.18 Territorial behavior parcels out space and resources
   1. Many animals exhibit territorial behavior.
      a. A **territory** is an area, usually fixed in location,
         i. which individuals defend and
         ii. from which other members of the same species are usually excluded.
      b. Territories are usually used for
         i. feeding,
         ii. mating,
         iii. rearing young, or
         iv. a combination of these activities.

C. 35.19 Agonistic behavior often resolves confrontations between competitors

   1. In many species, conflicts that arise over limited resources, such as food, mates, or territories, are settled by agonistic behavior. **Agonistic behavior**

      a. is social behavior that consists of threats, rituals, and sometimes combat that determines which competitor gains access to a resource and

      b. can directly affect an individual's evolutionary fitness.

D. 35.20 Dominance hierarchies are maintained by agonistic behavior

   1. Many animals live in social groups maintained by agonistic behaviors.

   2. **Dominance hierarchy** is the ranking of individuals based on social interactions. Examples include

      a. pecking order in chickens and

      b. hierarchies among the females within a wolf pack.

E. 35.21 EVOLUTION CONNECTION: Altruistic acts can often be explained by the concept of inclusive fitness

   1. Many social behaviors are selfish because natural selection favors behaviors that maximize an individual's

      a. survival and

      b. reproductive success.

   2. **Altruism** is defined as behavior that reduces an individual's fitness while increasing the fitness of others in the population.

   3. The concept of **inclusive fitness** describes an individual's success at perpetuating its genes by

      a. producing its own offspring and

      b. helping close relatives, who likely share many of those genes, to produce offspring.

   4. Natural selection favoring altruistic behavior that benefits relatives is called **kin selection**. Thus, genes for altruism may be propagated if individuals that benefit from altruistic acts are themselves carrying those genes.

   5. A classic study of Belding's ground squirrel, which lives in regions of the western United States, provided empirical support for kin selection.

F. 35.22 SCIENTIFIC DISCOVERY: Jane Goodall revolutionized our understanding of chimpanzee behavior

   1. Dr. Jane Goodall has studied the behavior of chimpanzees in their natural habitat, in East Africa, since the early 1960s.

   2. Her research indicates that

      a. chimps make and use tools and

      b. male dominance hierarchies and reconciliation behaviors are integral parts of the lives of many primates.

G. 35.23 Human behavior is the result of both genetic and environmental factors

   1. Twins provide a natural laboratory for investigating the origins of complex behavioral traits.

   2. Results from twin studies consistently show that for complex behavioral traits such as general intelligence and personality characteristics, genetic differences account for roughly half the variation among individuals.

   3. Genes do not dictate behavior but, instead, cause tendencies to react to the environment in a certain way.

   4. The mechanisms and underlying genetics of behavior are proximate causes.

   5. Sociobiologists explore the ultimate causes of human behavior.

Chapter Guide to Teaching Resources

The Scientific Study of Behavior (35.1–35.3)

Student Misconceptions and Concerns

- Students may misunderstand inherited factors and the environment as strictly opposing influences on behavior. The dual impacts of nature and nurture in biology should become increasingly clear as students progress through your course. This chapter permits greater exploration of the roles of and interactions between genetic and environmental factors. (35.1–35.3)

- Distinguishing between proximate and ultimate causes may pose a challenge for some students. Students may imagine that organisms engage in behaviors intentionally, acting on a foresight far beyond their intellectual capacity. In fact, proximate causes reflect the immediate mechanism for a behavior that has been favored by natural selection (ultimate causes) with consequences that may occur much later in an organism's life. For example, animal migrations may be triggered by immediate environmental cues (proximate causes). Do animals migrate because of a vision of a better place far away, or because migration has been adaptive in prior generations of their species (ultimate causes)? (35.1–35.3)

Teaching Tips

- Consider the following analogy to help illustrate proximate and ultimate causes of behavior. If you write a term on the board during lecture, students are likely to write the term down in their notes. The proximate cause is a cue from you, the advantages of doing well on exams and good grades in general is more like an ultimate cause. (35.1)

- In Module 35.2, the authors make the following analogy. A fixed action pattern is like the series of steps performed automatically by a coffee vending machine. After money is inserted and a selection is made, a cup drops into place and coffee is dispensed, perhaps along with sugar and cream, depending on which button was pushed (that is, which particular fixed action pattern was triggered). You might challenge your students to suggest other examples drawn from their daily lives. (35.2)

- Module 35.3 describes the dual influence of genetics and the environment in shaping behavior and other phenotypic characteristics. You might note that despite the fact that identical twins share the same set of genes, phenotypic differences occur. Furthermore, as the module also notes, in some reptile species the sex of offspring is determined by the incubation temperature of the eggs rather than by genetics. (35.3)

Learning (35.4–35.11)

Student Misconceptions and Concerns

- Many students confuse the changes that occur during an individual's lifetime with evolutionary change in a species. These individual "adaptations to the environment" can reinforce Lamarckian misconceptions. (35.4–35.11)

- Students may not have considered the general ability of animals to engage in behavioral responses to their environment and the more limited ability of plants to do likewise. Students might not have considered the different mechanisms that plants and animals employ to move within ecosystems (see Modules 33.9–33.13). (35.4–35.11)

Teaching Tips

- Although it is important to stress the diverse examples of learning in animals, students tend to understand concepts best by first applying them to their own experiences. Many of the teaching tips in the following provide examples of learning that occur in our daily lives. (35.4–35.11)

- While discussing habituation, draw students' attention to the various sounds within your classroom that they might otherwise have "tuned out." Also point out that students might not be aware of the texture of the pen or pencil they are holding, the firmness of the seat, or the position of their feet on the floor. (35.4)

- Students might wonder why birds have an imprinting period in which they learn to identify their mother. Why, students might wonder, don't geese simply have an innate ability to recognize an adult female goose? The plasticity of imprinting permits offspring to identify their mother in particular (who has a greater genetic stake in their survival), rather than any adult female. (35.5)

- You may mention that the genetic bottleneck effect (Module 13.11) poses another significant risk to the long-term survival of whooping cranes. A new virus or other disease could cause the extinction of a species with such limited genetic diversity. (35.6)

- Challenge your students to think of times when they engaged in kinesis and when they, by contrast, engaged in taxis. It may be difficult to identify an occurrence of true kinesis, when a person was not moving toward or away from some environmental factor. Whether turning away from the sun, moving toward a buffet, or waiting in line, most human movements are directed toward or away from at least one environmental factor. Struggling to identify an example of true kinesis helps students focus on the distinctions between kinesis and taxis. (35.7)

- Examples of spatial learning are abundant in a college environment. Most students (and faculty) travel to and from their classrooms not by following road signs, but by referencing environmental landmarks. (35.7)

- Students who have lived for more than a few days in their dorm room have developed a cognitive map of the most common objects in their room. In the morning, a person might reach for the alarm clock or light switch without looking, since their cognitive map informs them where these items are located. A person might also have an immediate but inexplicable sense that something is "wrong" if they return to a familiar room in which items have been rearranged, without consciously realizing that the room is no longer consistent with their cognitive map. (35.8)

- Associative learning can lead to misleading conclusions. Correlated factors may not have a cause-and-effect relationship. Challenge your students to think of examples of misleading correlations. (35.9)

- There are abundant examples of social learning in humans. Children quickly mimic the behaviors, including language, and adopt the habits of those they interact with most regularly. Social learning also helps adults who are adapting to a foreign culture to adopt new habits in the proper context. (35.10)

- Students may have wondered about the intelligence of animals living in the world around them. Consider challenging your students to evaluate the importance of each type of learning in evaluating the intelligence of an organism. Can they agree on a common standard for determining which animals are the "smartest"? Which types of learning would be most important in defining intelligence? (35.11)

Survival and Reproductive Success (35.12–35.16)

Student Misconceptions and Concerns

- Some students may believe that humans are somehow exceptional and that their behavior is not governed by the principles of animal behavior. Other students may acknowledge these associations, but remain skeptical when it comes to individual examples. Behaviors, just like our biochemical and cellular structure, reveal our close kinship with animals and our descent from common ancestors. (35.12–35.16)

- It is difficult to think of the world as being more than we perceive. What we touch, see, hear, and smell appears to be the only reality to us as humans. Yet most mammals, our closest relatives, generally rely upon sound and odors beyond our human perceptions. (35.13)

Teaching Tips

- The concept of a search image is familiar to most people, although it may not go by this name. Ask your students if they can recall searching for a parent or friend, perhaps somewhere in a large store. As they scanned the crowd of people, do they remember watching for some particular characteristic of the person they were looking for, perhaps their height, the color of their clothing, or another distinctive feature? When we ask for help finding something we have lost, the first question we often answer is "What does it look like?" The description of the lost item or person helps the person who hears it form a search image. (35.12)

- All of us engage in some sort of cost-benefit analysis when selecting a restaurant. Distance, price, and the type of meal are all considered. Although a meal several hundred miles away might be better, few of us would travel such a distance. (35.12)

- Students who have taken a communications class will recognize the definition of animal communication. Sending, receiving, and responding to signals are all part of communication. Illustrate this point simply in class by noting how students respond to something you say, perhaps by writing an idea down in their notes. (35.13)

- Students may believe that mating behavior is just about attracting a mate. As the authors note in Module 35.14, mating behavior also functions to confirm that an individual is a member of the species, establish that they belong to the opposite sex, and signal their intentions. For some species, such as spiders, miscommunication can result in death! (35.14)

- The authors identify a specific and common misunderstanding in Module 35.15. Animal reproductive strategies, such as those that increase certainty of paternity among males, are not typically the result of a conscious awareness of intents and consequences. Instead, behaviors that increase the likelihood of paternity have been favored through natural selection. Adaptive strategies do not arise because animals are necessarily smart or wise, although from a limited and immediate perspective, this may appear to be the case. (35.15)

- The website for the EPA's Endocrine Disruptor Screening Program (EDSP) can be found at www.epa.gov/scipoly/oscpendo/. (35.16)

Social Behavior and Sociobiology (35.17–35.23)

Student Misconceptions and Concerns

- Students who have watched enough footage of animal behavior on television might believe that most animal disputes are resolved through dangerous combat. Modules 35.17–35.23 include many examples of agonistic behavior that reduce the likelihood of direct combat, perhaps through displays, vocalizations, or chemical communication. Peaceful strategies save energy and lives, although they seldom boost television ratings. (35.17–35.23)

Teaching Tips

- Students may not have considered the social and political significance of the study of sociobiology. Students may find an Internet search of the field especially interesting. If you are fairly new to this field, consider requiring students to email to you a link to a site discussing some aspect of human sociobiology. (35.17)

- Challenge your students to describe examples of territorial behavior in humans. How is human territorial behavior similar to and different from the territorial behavior described in Module 35.18? (35.18)

- Because of the adjectives' similar spelling, some students may confuse agonistic behavior with an agnostic philosophy. Although the distinctions are likely clear to you, consider pointing out that these are unrelated terms that are spelled similarly. (35.19)

- Pet dogs often respect the dominance hierarchy in their human families. The dog may display submissiveness towards some members and dominance towards others. It is likely that some students in your class will have observed these displays and will want to share their stories. (35.20)

- Before addressing the content of Module 35.21, challenge your students to explain how you can pass along your genes if you do not reproduce. Consider asking this question at the end of a lecture period, to be discussed at the start of the next class period. (35.21)

- Students will likely be interested in comparing the behavior of humans and chimpanzees, as described in Module 35.22. The many obvious similarities between human and chimp anatomy, physiology, and behavior will most likely further reinforce the concept of shared ancestry for your students. (35.22)

- Consider asking your students to explain why identical twins who have lived under the same conditions and in the same family do not behave exactly alike. Students might note the unique social interactions of each twin and the role of chance in the twins' lives. For example, the twins are likely to have attended school together, but not to have always sat in the same place, or always talked to the same people at the same time. (35.23)

Key Terms

agonistic behavior	cognitive map	imprinting
altruism	communication	inclusive fitness
associative learning	dominance hierarchy	innate behavior
behavior	fixed action patterns (FAPs)	kin selection
behavioral ecology	foraging	kinesis
cognition	habituation	learning

migration
monogamous
optimal foraging theory
polygamous
problem solving
promiscuous
proximate causes

proximate questions
search image
sensitive period
signal
social behavior
social learning
sociobiology

spatial learning
stimuli
taxis (plural, taxes)
territory
trial-and-error learning
ultimate questions
ultimate causes

Word Roots

agon- = a contest (*agonistic behavior*: confrontational behavior involving a contest waged by threats, displays, or actual combat, which settles disputes over limited resources, such as food or mates)

alter- = other (*altruism*: behavior that reduces an individual's fitness while increasing the fitness of another individual)

kine- = move (*kinesis*: a change in activity in response to a stimulus)

mono- = one; **-gamy** = reproduction (*monogamous*: a type of relationship in which one male mates with just one female)

poly- = many (*polygamous*: a type of relationship in which an individual of one sex mates with several of the other sex)

socio- = a companion (*sociobiology*: the study of the evolutionary basis of social behavior)

CHAPTER 36

Population Ecology

Chapter Objectives

Opening Essay

Compare the individual and group characteristics of emperor penguins.

Population Structure and Dynamics

36.1   Define a population and population ecology. Describe the general type of work performed by population ecologists.

36.2   Define population density and describe different types of dispersion patterns.

36.3   Explain how life tables are used to track mortality and survivorship in populations. Compare Type I, Type II, and Type III survivorship curves.

36.4   Describe and compare the exponential and logistic population growth models, illustrating both with examples. Explain the concept of carrying capacity.

36.5   Describe the factors that regulate growth in natural populations.

36.6   Define boom-and-bust cycles, explain why they occur, and provide examples.

36.7   Explain how life-history traits vary with environmental conditions and with population density. Compare r-selection and K-selection and indicate examples of each.

36.8   Describe the major challenges inherent in managing populations.

The Human Population

36.9   Explain how the structure of the world's human population has changed and continues to change. Describe the key factors that affect human population growth.

36.10 Explain how the age structure of a population can be used to predict changes in population size and social conditions.

36.11 Explain the concept of an ecological footprint. Describe the uneven use of natural resources in the world.

Lecture Outline

I. Introduction

   A. Individual emperor penguins face the rigors of the Antarctic climate and have special adaptations, including a

      1. downy underlayer of feathers for insulation and

      2. thick layer of fat for energy storage and insulation.

   B. The entire population of emperor penguins reflects group characteristics, including the

      1. survivorship of chicks and

      2. growth rate of the population.

C. Population ecologists study natural population
   1. structure and
   2. dynamics.

II. Population Structure and Dynamics

A. 36.1 Population ecology is the study of how and why populations change
   1. A **population** is a group of individuals of a single species that occupy the same general area.
   2. Individuals in a population
      a. rely on the same resources,
      b. are influenced by the same environmental factors, and
      c. are likely to interact and breed with one another.
   3. A population can be described by the number and distribution of individuals.
   4. Population dynamics, the interactions between biotic and abiotic factors, cause variations in population sizes.
   5. **Population ecology** is concerned with
      a. the changes in population size and
      b. factors that regulate populations over time.
   6. Populations
      a. increase through birth and immigration to an area and
      b. decrease through death and emigration out of an area.

B. 36.2 Density and dispersion patterns are important population variables
   1. **Population density** is the number of individuals of a species per unit area or volume.
   2. Examples of population density include the
      a. number of oak trees per square kilometer in a forest or
      b. number of earthworms per cubic meter in forest soil.
   3. Ecologists use a variety of sampling techniques to estimate population densities.
   4. Within a population's geographic range, local densities may vary greatly.
   5. The **dispersion pattern** of a population refers to the way individuals are spaced within their area.
   6. Dispersion patterns can be clumped, uniform, or random.
      a. In a **clumped pattern**
         i.   resources are often unequally distributed and
         ii. individuals are grouped in patches.
   7. In a **uniform pattern**, individuals are
      a. most likely interacting and
      b. equally spaced in the environment.
   8. In a **random pattern** of dispersion, the individuals in a population are spaced in an unpredictable way.

C. 36.3 Life tables track survivorship in populations
   1. **Life tables** track survivorship, the chance of an individual in a given population surviving to various ages.
   2. **Survivorship curves** plot survivorship as the proportion of individuals from an initial population that are alive at each age.
   3. There are three main types of survivorship curves.
      a. Type I
      b. Type II
      c. Type III

D. 36.4 Idealized models predict patterns of population growth

1. The rate of population increase under ideal conditions is called exponential growth. It can be calculated using the **exponential growth model** equation, $G = rN$, in which

   a. G is the growth rate of the population,

   b. N is the population size, and

   c. r is the **per capita rate of increase** (the average contribution of each individual to population growth).

2. Eventually, one or more **limiting factors** will restrict population growth.

3. The **logistic growth model** is a description of idealized population growth that is slowed by limiting factors as the population size increases.

4. To model logistic growth, the formula for exponential growth, rN, is multiplied by an expression that describes the effect of limiting factors on an increasing population size.

5. The symbol K stands for **carrying capacity**, the maximum population size that a particular environment can sustain. $$G = rN \frac{(K - N)}{K}$$

E. 36.5 Multiple factors may limit population growth

1. The logistic growth model predicts that population growth will slow and eventually stop as population density increases.

2. At increasing population densities, **density-dependent** rates result in

   a. declining births and

   b. increases in deaths.

3. **Intraspecific competition** is

   a. competition between individuals of the same species for limited resources and

   b. is a density-dependent factor that limits growth in natural populations.

4. Limiting factors may include

   a. food,

   b. nutrients,

   c. retreats for safety, or

   d. nesting sites.

5. In many natural populations, abiotic factors such as weather may affect population size well before density-dependent factors become important.

6. **Density-independent factors** are unrelated to population density. These may include

   a. fires,

   b. storms,

   c. habitat destruction by human activity, or

   d. seasonal changes in weather (for example, in aphids).

F. 36.6 Some populations have "boom-and-bust" cycles

1. Some populations fluctuate in density with regularity.

2. Boom-and-bust cycles may be due to

   a. food shortages or

   b. predator-prey interactions.

G. 36.7 EVOLUTION CONNECTION: Evolution shapes life histories

1. The traits that affect an organism's schedule of reproduction and death make up its **life history**.

2. Key life history traits include

   a. age of first reproduction,

   b. frequency of reproduction,

          c. number of offspring, and

          d. amount of parental care.

    3. Populations with so-called *r*-**selected** life history traits

          a. produce more offspring and

          b. grow rapidly in unpredictable environments.

    4. Populations with *K*-**selected** traits

          a. raise fewer offspring and

          b. maintain relatively stable populations.

    5. Most species fall between these two extremes.

    6. A long-term project in Trinidad

          a. studied guppy populations,

          b. provided direct evidence that life history traits can be shaped by natural selection, and

          c. demonstrated that questions about evolution can be tested by field experiments.

H. 36.8 CONNECTION: Principles of population ecology have practical applications

    1. **Sustainable resource management** involves

          a. harvesting crops and

          b. eliminating damage to the resource.

    2. The cod fishery off Newfoundland

          a. was overfished,

          b. collapsed in 1992, and

          c. still has not recovered.

    3. Resource managers use population ecology to determine sustainable yields.

III. The Human Population

A. 36.9 The human population continues to increase, but the growth rate is slowing

    1. The human population

          a. grew rapidly during the 20th century and

          b. currently stands at about 7 billion.

    2. The **demographic transition**

          a. is the shift from high birth and death rates,

          b. to low birth and death rates, and

          c. has lowered the rate of growth in developed countries.

    3. In the developing nations

          a. death rates have dropped,

          b. birth rates are still high, and

          c. these populations are growing rapidly.

    4. The **age structure** of a population

          a. is the proportion of individuals in different age groups and

          b. affects the future growth of the population.

    5. **Population momentum** is the continued growth that occurs

          a. despite reduced fertility and

          b. as a result of girls in the 0–14 age group of a previously expanding population reaching their childbearing years.

B. 36.10 CONNECTION: Age structures reveal social and economic trends

    1. Age-structure diagrams reveal

          a. a population's growth trends and

          b. social conditions.

C. 36.11 CONNECTION: An ecological footprint is a measure of resource consumption

    1. The U.S. Census Bureau projects a global population of

        a. 8 billion people within the next 20 years and

        b. 9.5 billion by mid-21st century.

    2. Do we have sufficient resources to sustain 8 or 9 billion people?

    3. To accommodate all the people expected to live on our planet by 2025, the world will have to *double* food production.

    4. An **ecological footprint** is an estimate of the amount of land required to provide the raw materials an individual or a nation consumes, including

        a. food,

        b. fuel,

        c. water,

        d. housing, and

        e. waste disposal.

    5. The United States

        a. has a very large ecological footprint, much greater than its own land, and

        b. is running on a large ecological deficit.

    6. Some researchers estimate that

        a. if everyone on Earth had the same standard of living as people living in the United States,

        b. we would need the resources of 4.5 planet Earths.

Chapter Guide to Teaching Resources

Population Structure and Dynamics (36.1–36.8)

Student Misconceptions and Concerns

- Many students who are not biology majors have trouble thinking about the evolution of systems. One analogy that can be developed, especially for economically-minded students, is the parallels to the "evolution" of businesses. Consider the introduction and expansion of McDonald's restaurants in the United States over the last 50 years. When McDonald's restaurants were just starting out, they experienced little competition, with access to many customers. The "population" of McDonald's restaurants in the United States grew exponentially (or nearly so), with few density-dependent factors. However, today McDonald's restaurants in the U.S. must compete with each other, as well as with many other fast-food restaurants, such as Burger King and Taco Bell. The population of McDonald's restaurants in the United States has stabilized because of this competition for customers, a density-dependent factor. A graph of the growth of McDonald's restaurants in the United States would likely resemble the lazy "S" shape. (36.1–36.8)

- Students often expect that spraying insecticides or using various killing devices (such as bug zappers) will make a significant impact in a pest population. As noted in Module 36.8, many pesticides kill both pests and their predators. Furthermore, most pest populations are *r*-selective and capable of recovering quickly, perhaps more quickly than their predators. Such considerations provide a classic illustration of the complexities inherent in biological systems and the often unexpected consequences of change. (36.8)

Teaching Tips

- A mark-recapture method not specifically addressed in this chapter can be used to estimate the size of a population. The following can serve as a demonstration or an activity for students working in small groups:

  a. Provide each group with an opaque bag (brown paper lunch bags work well) of about 200 dried lima beans (or any inexpensive small item that can be marked).

  b. Have each group draw out 40 beans.

  c. Mark each bean with a distinct pencil or ink mark.

  d. Return these marked beans back to the bag.

  e. Mix the beans in the bag by shaking or turning the bag. Note: Thorough mixing and random selection is essential to the mark-recapture method. You may wish to note here that this research method does not work well for wildlife populations that are territorial and thus do not mix.

  f. Draw out another 40 beans and count the number of marked beans in the sample.

  g. The formula for calculating the population size is as follows: The number of marked beans in the first sample × the total number in the second sample ÷ the number of recaptures in the second sample = the population size. Thus, if you started out with exactly 200 beans, sampled 40, marked them, and resampled 40 beans, we would expect that you would recapture 8 marked beans, based on the equation $40 \times 40 \div 8 = 200$. (36.1)

- A simple application of the dispersion pattern of a population would be to apply the concept to the population of humans on your college or university campus. Would students consider the distribution of people to be clumped, uniform, or random? Most campuses would likely represent a clumped pattern. It might be fun to discuss when, if ever, the human population on your campus represents a uniform or random pattern. (36.2)

- The Centers for Disease Control provide information and life tables for people living in the United States at their website, www.cdc.gov/nchs/products/life_tables.htm. (36.3)

- Exponential growth in a population is like compounded interest on a bank account. The growth of the account is initially small, but as the interest earns interest, the growth expands. $1,000 invested at 7% interest is worth more than $30,000 in 50 years. Consider assigning students to calculate the value of a simple interest bearing investment over a set period of years, as in the example just noted. Many online financial calculators can perform this task. (36.4)

- It is typically easier for students to understand a concept when the examples are familiar. Consider the biology of your region and identify a population that is likely to be well-known by your students, for instance, the population of squirrels on your campus. Challenge your students to identify limiting factors for that particular population. (36.5)

- Consider challenging your class to explain why the lynx and hare cycle does not result in the elimination of one or both of the species. Why don't we see hares hunted to extinction? Students may not have considered that predators encounter greater difficulty in finding prey when prey populations are low. This permits the recovery of the hare population, which in turn supports the recovery of the lynx population. (36.6)

- Compromise is a key principle of biology. No adaptation can be perfect, and no reproductive strategy can maximize all types of efforts. As the text notes, an organism cannot have a great number of offspring and invest great amounts of parental care in each one. Resources, including time, are limited. Have students imagine how different their lives would have been if they had been born as one of a set of quadruplets—or if they themselves were faced with the task of rearing four children at once! (36.7)

- Consider a class assignment exploring the collapse of the northern cod fishery and identifying other fish species in danger of overharvesting, as well as strategies to prevent this. As emphasized in Module 36.4, harvesting a population down to intermediate levels maximizes the sustained yield. (36.8)

- The sustainable management of the Alaskan fisheries is a good lesson in responsible resource management. Consider learning more about the management of halibut populations around Alaska as a positive example. (36.8)

The Human Population (36.9–36.11)

Student Misconceptions and Concerns

- Some students may not understand the impact of delayed reproduction on population growth. Working through the following example in class might help. Refer back to the text example of exponential growth in a population of bacteria (Module 36.4). What if one population reproduced every 20 minutes and another population reproduced every 40 minutes? Clearly, the 20-minute cycle would increase the population faster. (36.9–36.11)

- Students are often frustrated by the long list of environmental problems caused by humans, and students may begin to feel helpless as coverage of the issues goes on. You might consider directing them to specific websites for basic suggestions on what they can do to make a difference. A Google search of "what you can do environment" should yield many potentially good sites. (36.11)

Teaching Tips

- The U.S. government's Census Bureau sponsors a U.S. and World Population Clock at www.census.gov/main/www/popclock.html. It might be of special interest to note how near we are to a world population of 7 billion people (expected to be reached in 2011). (36.9)

- Module 36.10 provides a wonderful opportunity to discuss the social impact of human population changes in the United States. As noted in Module 36.10, Medicare and Social Security will be increasingly impacted as the U.S. population ages. You might want to discuss the occupational outlook for professions that will address the needs of the growing elderly population, and the opportunity to invest in companies that will capitalize on these changes. (36.10)

- Module 36.11 notes that the United States has an ecological footprint greater than the land area of the United States. Consider asking your class to explain how this is possible and what this means to other countries. The authors further note that the world's richest countries, with 15% of the global population, account for 36% of humanity's total footprint. (36.11)

Key Terms

age structure
carrying capacity
clumped dispersion
  pattern
demographic transition
density-dependent
density-independent
  factor
dispersion pattern
ecological footprint

exponential growth model
intraspecific competition
K-selection
life history
life table
limiting factors
logistic growth model
per capita rate of increase
population
population density

population ecology
population momentum
r-selection
random dispersion pattern
survivorship curve
sustainable resource
  management
uniform dispersion pattern

Word Roots

capit- = head (*per capita*: per person)

demo- = people; **-graphy** = writing (*demography*: the study of human populations)

intra- = within (*intraspecific competition*: competition between individuals of the same species for limited resources)

CHAPTER 37

Communities and Ecosystems

Chapter Objectives

Opening Essay

Describe the value and benefits of natural ecosystems.

Community Structure and Dynamics

37.1   Define a biological community. Explain why the study of community ecology is important.

37.2   Define interspecific competition, mutualism, predation, herbivory, and parasitism, and provide examples of each.

37.3   Define an ecological niche. Explain how interspecific competition can occur when the niches of two populations overlap.

37.4   Describe the mutualistic relationship between corals and dinoflagellates.

37.5   Define predation. Describe the protective strategies potential prey employ to avoid predators.

37.6   Explain why many plants have chemical toxins, spines, or thorns. Define coevolution and describe an example.

37.7   Explain how parasites and pathogens can affect community composition.

37.8   Identify and compare the trophic levels of terrestrial and aquatic food chains.

37.9   Explain how food chains interconnect to form food webs.

37.10   Describe the two components of species diversity. Explain why large fields of a single crop are vulnerable to devastating disease.

37.11   Define a keystone species. Explain why the long-spined sea urchin is considered a keystone species.

37.12   Explain how disturbances can benefit communities. Distinguish between primary and secondary succession.

37.13   Explain how invasive species can affect communities.

Ecosystem Structure and Dynamics

37.14   Compare the movement of energy and chemicals within and through ecosystems.

37.15   Compare the primary production of tropical rain forests, coral reefs, and open ocean. Explain why the differences between them exist.

37.16–37.17   Describe the movement of energy through a food chain. Explain why there are more producers than consumers and why eating meat counts as a great luxury.

37.18–37.21   Explain how carbon, nitrogen, and phosphorus cycle within ecosystems.

37.22   Explain how rapid eutrophication of aquatic ecosystems affects species diversity and oxygen levels.

37.23   Explain how human activities are threatening natural ecosystems.

Lecture Outline

I. Introduction

A. Natural ecosystems are valuable because they
  1. provide natural resources,
  2. support outdoor recreation, and
  3. provide natural services including
     a. buffering against hurricane damage,
     b. recycling nutrients,
     c. preventing erosion, and
     d. pollinating crops.

II. Community Structure and Dynamics

A. 37.1 A community includes all the organisms inhabiting a particular area
  1. Community ecology is concerned with factors that
     a. influence species composition and distribution of communities and
     b. affect community stability.
  2. A biological **community** is
     a. an assemblage of all the populations of organisms living close enough together for potential interaction and
     b. described by its species composition.
  3. The boundaries of a community vary with the research question to be investigated. For example, the boundaries of a community could be defined as
     a. a pond or
     b. the intestinal microbes of a pond organism.

B. 37.2 Interspecific interactions are fundamental to community structure
  1. **Interspecific interactions**
     a. are relationships with individuals of other species in the community,
     b. greatly affect population structure and dynamics, and
     c. can be categorized according to their effect on the interacting populations.
  2. **Interspecific competition** occurs when populations of two different species compete for the same limited resource.
     a. In **mutualism**, both populations benefit.
     b. In **predation**, one species (the predator) kills and eats another (the prey).
     c. In **herbivory**, an animal consumes plant parts or algae.
     d. In parasitism, the host plants or animals are victimized by parasites or pathogens.

C. 37.3 Competition may occur when a shared resource is limited
  1. An **ecological niche** is the sum of an organism's use of the biotic and abiotic resources in its environment.
  2. Interspecific competition occurs when the niches of two populations overlap.
  3. Competition lowers the carrying capacity of competing populations because the resources used by one population are not available to the other population.

D. 37.4 Mutualism benefits both partners
  1. Reef-building corals and photosynthetic dinoflagellates illustrate the win/win nature of mutualism. Photosynthetic dinoflagellates
     a. gain shelter in the cells of each coral polyp,
     b. produce sugars used by the polyps, and
     c. provide at least half of the energy used by the coral animals.

E. 37.5 EVOLUTION CONNECTION: Predation leads to diverse adaptations in prey species

 1. Predation benefits the predator but kills the prey.

 2. Prey adapt using protective strategies that include

  a. camouflage,

  b. mechanical defenses, and

  c. chemical defenses.

F. 37.6 EVOLUTION CONNECTION: Herbivory leads to diverse adaptations in plants

 1. Herbivores and plants undergo **coevolution**,

  a. a series of reciprocal evolutionary adaptations in two species,

  b. in which change in one species acts as a new selective force on another.

 2. A plant whose body parts have been eaten by an animal must expend energy to replace the loss.

  a. Thus, numerous defenses against herbivores have evolved in plants.

  b. Plant defenses against herbivores include

   i. spines and thorns and

   ii. chemical toxins.

G. 37.7 Parasites and pathogens can affect community composition

 1. A parasite lives on or in a host from which it obtains nourishment.

  a. Internal parasites include nematodes and tapeworms.

  b. External parasites include mosquitoes, ticks, and aphids.

 2. Pathogens are disease-causing microscopic parasites that include

  a. bacteria,

  b. viruses,

  c. fungi, or

  d. protists.

 3. Non-native pathogens can have rapid and dramatic impacts.

  a. The American chestnut was devastated by the chestnut blight protist.

  b. A fungus-like pathogen is currently causing sudden oak death on the West Coast.

 4. Non-native pathogens can cause a decline of the ecosystem.

H. 37.8 Trophic structure is a key factor in community dynamics

 1. The **trophic structure** of a community is a pattern of feeding relationships consisting of several different levels.

  a. The sequence of food transfer up the trophic levels is known as a **food chain**.

  b. The transfer of food moves chemical nutrients and energy from producers up through the trophic levels in a community.

 2. Producers

  a. are autotrophs and

  b. support all other trophic levels.

 3. Consumers are heterotrophs.

  a. Herbivores are **primary consumers**.

  b. Secondary consumers typically eat herbivores.

  c. Tertiary consumers typically eat secondary consumers.

  d. Quaternary consumers typically eat tertiary consumers.

 4. Detritivores derive their energy from **detritus**, the dead material produced at all the trophic levels.

 5. Decomposers

  a. are mainly prokaryotes and fungi and

b. secrete enzymes that digest molecules in organic materials and convert them into inorganic forms, in the process called **decomposition**.

I. 37.9 Food chains interconnect, forming food webs
   1. A **food web** is a network of interconnecting food chains.
   2. Notice that
     a. consumers may eat more than one type of producer and
     b. several species of consumers may feed on the same species of producer.

J. 37.10 Species diversity includes relative abundance and species richness
   1. **Species diversity** is defined by two components:
     a. species richness, the number of species in a community, and
     b. relative abundance, the proportional representation of a species in a community.
   2. Plant species diversity in a community affects the species diversity of animals.
   3. Species diversity has consequences for pathogens.
   4. Low species diversity is characteristic of most modern agricultural ecosystems.

K. 37.11 Keystone species have a disproportionate impact on diversity
   1. A **keystone species**
     a. is a species whose impact on its community is larger than its biomass or abundance indicates and
     b. occupies a niche that holds the rest of its community in place.
   2. Examples of keystone species in marine ecosystems include
     a. *Pisaster* sea stars and
     b. long-spined sea urchins.

L. 37.12 Disturbance is a prominent feature of most communities
   1. **Disturbances**
     a. are events that damage biological communities and
     b. include storms, fires, floods, droughts, overgrazing, or human activity.
     c. The types, frequency, and severity of disturbances vary from community to community.
   2. Communities change drastically following a severe disturbance that
     a. strips away vegetation and
     b. removes significant amounts of soil.
   3. **Ecological succession** results from colonization by a variety of species, which are replaced by a succession of other species.
   4. **Primary succession** begins in a virtually lifeless area with no soil.
   5. **Secondary succession** occurs when a disturbance destroys an existing community but leaves the soil intact.

M. 37.13 CONNECTION: Invasive species can devastate communities
   1. **Invasive species**
     a. are organisms that have been introduced into non-native habitats by human actions and
     b. have established themselves at the expense of native communities.
     c. The absence of natural enemies often allows rapid population growth of invasive species.
   2. Examples of invasive species include the deliberate introduction of
     a. rabbits into Australia and
     b. cane toads into Australia.

III. Ecosystem Structure and Dynamics

A. 37.14 Ecosystem ecology emphasizes energy flow and chemical cycling

1. An **ecosystem** consists of
   a. all the organisms in a community and
   b. the abiotic environment with which the organisms interact.
2. In an ecosystem,
   a. **energy flow** moves *through* the components of an ecosystem and
   b. **chemical cycling** is the transfer of materials *within* the ecosystem.
3. A terrarium
   a. represents the components of an ecosystem and
   b. illustrates the fundamentals of energy flow.

B. 37.15 Primary production sets the energy budget for ecosystems

1. **Primary production**
   a. is carried out by producers,
   b. is the amount of solar energy converted to chemical energy by an ecosystem's producers for a given area and during a given time period, and
   c. produces **biomass**, the amount of living organic material in an ecosystem.
2. Different ecosystems vary in their
   a. primary production and
   b. contribution to the total production of the biosphere.

C. 37.16 Energy supply limits the length of food chains

1. A caterpillar represents a primary consumer.
2. Of the organic compounds a caterpillar ingests, about
   a. 50% is eliminated in feces,
   b. 35% is used in cellular respiration, and
   c. 15% is used for growth.
3. A pyramid of production shows the flow of energy
   a. from producers to primary consumers and
   b. to higher trophic levels.
4. Only about 10% of the energy stored at each trophic level is available to the next level.

D. 37.17 CONNECTION: A pyramid of production explains the ecological cost of meat

1. When humans eat
   a. grain or fruit, we are primary consumers,
   b. beef or other meat from herbivores, we are secondary consumers, and
   c. fish like trout or salmon, we are tertiary or quaternary consumers.
2. Only about 10% of the chemical energy available in a trophic level is passed to the next higher trophic level.
3. Therefore, the human population has about ten times more energy available to it when people eat plants instead of the meat of herbivores.
4. Eating meat of any kind is expensive
   a. economically and
   b. environmentally.

E. 37.18 Chemicals are cycled between organic matter and abiotic reservoirs

1. Ecosystems are supplied with a continual influx of energy from the
   a. sun and
   b. Earth's interior.
2. Except for meteorites, there are no extraterrestrial sources of chemical elements.
3. Thus, life also depends on the recycling of chemicals.

4. **Biogeochemical cycles** include
   a. biotic components,
   b. abiotic components, and
   c. **abiotic reservoirs**, where a chemical accumulates or is stockpiled outside of living organisms.
5. Biogeochemical cycles can be
   a. local or
   b. global.

F. 37.19 The carbon cycle depends on photosynthesis and respiration
   1. Carbon is
      a. the major ingredient of all organic molecules and
      b. found in
         i.   the atmosphere,
         ii. fossil fuels, and
         iii. dissolved in carbon compounds in the ocean.
   2. The return of CO_2 to the atmosphere by respiration closely balances its removal by photosynthesis.
   3. The carbon cycle is affected by burning wood and fossil fuels.

G. 37.20 The phosphorus cycle depends on the weathering of rock
   1. Organisms require phosphorus for
      a. nucleic acids,
      b. phospholipids, and
      c. ATP.
   2. The phosphorus cycle does not have an atmospheric component.
   3. Rocks are the only source of phosphorus for terrestrial ecosystems.
   4. Plants absorb phosphate ions in the soil and build them into organic compounds.
   5. Phosphates are returned to the soil by decomposers.
   6. Phosphate levels in aquatic ecosystems are typically low enough to be a limiting factor.

H. 37.21 The nitrogen cycle depends on bacteria
   1. Nitrogen is
      a. an ingredient of proteins and nucleic acids,
      b. essential to the structure and functioning of all organisms, and
      c. a crucial and often limiting plant nutrient.
   2. Nitrogen has two abiotic reservoirs:
      a. the atmosphere, in which about 80% is nitrogen gas, and
      b. soil.
   3. **Nitrogen fixation**
      a. converts N_2 to compounds of nitrogen that can be used by plants and
      b. is carried out by some bacteria.

I. 37.22 CONNECTION: A rapid inflow of nutrients degrades aquatic ecosystems
   1. In aquatic ecosystems, primary production is limited by low nutrient levels of
      a. phosphorus and
      b. nitrogen.
   2. Over time, standing water ecosystems
      a. gradually accumulate nutrients from the decomposition of organic matter and fresh influx from the land, and
      b. primary production increases in a process known as eutrophication.

3. Eutrophication of lakes, rivers, and coastal waters
   a. depletes oxygen levels and
   b. decreases species diversity.
4. In many areas, phosphate pollution leading to eutrophication comes from
   a. agricultural fertilizers,
   b. pesticides,
   c. sewage treatment facilities, and
   d. runoff of animal waste from feedlots.
5. Eutrophication of aquatic systems may also result from increased levels of nitrogen from
   a. feedlots and
   b. applications of large amounts of fertilizer.
J. 37.23 CONNECTION: Ecosystem services are essential to human well-being
   1. Although agricultural and other managed ecosystems are necessary to supply our needs, we also depend on services provided by natural ecosystems.
   2. Healthy ecosystems
      a. supply fresh water and some foods,
      b. recycle nutrients,
      c. decompose wastes, and
      d. regulate climate and air quality.
   3. Enormous increases in food production have come at the expense of
      a. natural ecosystems and
      b. the services they provide.
   4. Human activities also threaten many forest ecosystems and the services they provide.

Chapter Guide to Teaching Resources

Community Structure and Dynamics (37.1–37.13)

Student Misconceptions and Concerns

- For many students, understanding ecosystems is like appreciating art. Although both are visible to the naked eye, some background is required to understand the method of composition, the significance of components, and the nature of interactions. The fundamentals introduced in this chapter are new ways to see generally familiar systems. (37.1–37.13)

- The concept of an ecological niche can be confusing. Ecologist Eugene Odum has suggested that an ecological niche is like an organism's habitat (address) and its occupation combined. (37.3)

- The idea that ecosystems are relatively stable is common. Natural disturbances of any sort (fires, earthquakes, floods, or strong storms) are typically viewed as tragic and damaging to ecosystems. Before beginning the topic of ecological disturbances, consider asking your students to briefly respond to news that a state or federal park has (a) been burned, (b) been struck by high winds and/or lightning, or (c) been temporarily flooded. In addition, consider asking what, if anything, should be done to prevent or repair this damage? (37.12)

Teaching Tips

- Many students have been exposed to diverse ecosystems only through television and movies, which have likely focused on a few species. Before discussing this chapter, consider showing the class a good video (it need not be long) about an ecosystem. The video can then serve as a shared recent experience to which you can relate the content of this chapter. Alternately, you can relate some of the basics of this chapter to a local or regional example with which most students are familiar. There may even be a distinct community on your campus, such as a pond, wooded area, etc., that students could visit and return from with new insights. (37.1–37.13)

- In human society, a community might be roughly equivalent to a local population, perhaps all the people living in a town or city. The definition of a biological community is more inclusive, comprising all of the populations of organisms living close enough together for potential interaction. (37.1)

- Examples of interspecific competition are as close as the nearest lawn. Although students may be more likely to think of animal examples, the various grasses and weeds in a lawn reveal different strategies in their competition for sunlight, moisture, and soil. (37.2)

- If your class includes students with business interests, they may enjoy the following analogy. To better understand competition, students might think about fast-food restaurants in your region. Challenge your students to identify the strategies employed by these restaurants to compete with each other. As each restaurant makes changes, does the other restaurant respond? Restaurants changing strategies in response to each other is analogous to coevolution. (37.2–37.3, 37.6)

- Students who are business-oriented may also enjoy this analogy. Many corporate leaders describe the best business deals as mutualistic, fostering a win-win relationship. For example, perhaps a new company creates a marketable product from another company's wastes. (37.4)

- Rattlesnakes are a good example of a highly specialized predator. Since they are unable to move fast enough to catch their prey, rattlesnakes typically ambush them, a process facilitated by their camouflaged bodies. Rattlesnakes often feed during the cooler parts of the day, using heat-detecting facial pits to identify prey before injecting them with fast-acting venom. The prey is immediately released (perhaps to avoid damage to the snake from struggling prey), but is disabled by the venom within seconds. The rattlesnake then uses a variety of senses to track the prey the short distance to where it has collapsed. (37.5)

- Coevolution is illustrated by organisms that exhibit reciprocal evolutionary adaptations. Challenge students to explain how rewarding a pollinator with nectar has benefited some plants. Why would plants that have adaptations for only certain pollinators have an advantage? In many cases, pollinators that are restricted to certain species are more likely to transport pollen between members of that species instead of wasting pollen by taking it to other species. (37.6)

- Pathogens are probably what most people refer to as germs. Students might believe that this general term refers to some specific type of organism. (37.7)

- Students have often had prior exposure to the concepts of food webs and food chains. Present a food web (perhaps Figure 37.9) to your class and challenge them to predict the consequences of a decrease or increase in the population of one of the organisms. This activity can help students understand how difficult it is to make precise predictions about these complex systems. (37.8–37.9)

- Diversity within a species has some of the same advantages as diversity within a community. In both situations, diversity limits the damage from a pathogen or predator specialized to attack one variation within a species or one species in a community. (37.10)

- Many keystone species have been identified in ecosystems, including sea otters, elephants, freshwater bass, and *Pisaster*, a sea star noted in Figure 37.11. Challenge your class to explain how the concept of keystone species impacts the efforts of conservation biologists. Why might some species be more important to conserve? (37.11)

- Before and after images of the impact and recovery of an ecosystem from a natural disaster can be more powerful than any verbal explanation of the process. Consider locating before and after images of ecosystems damaged by hurricanes, fire, or the 1980 eruption of Mt. St. Helens, to show recovery. (37.12)

- Depending upon your location and its circumstances, consider a short field trip on or near your campus to show disturbed regions and signs of recovery. (37.12)

- The United States Department of Agriculture sponsors the National Invasive Species Information Center, which maintains a website at www.invasivespeciesinfo.gov. (37.13)

- Students who are interested in wildlife may collect an animal to keep as a pet, or to admire for a few days. This might be a good time to remind them that if they hope to return a wild animal to its natural environment, they should do so quickly and return it to within a few feet of the spot of its collection. Reintroducing an organism to a nearby environment may spread disease and potentially extend the organism's natural range. Further, the introduction of commercial specimens from fish tanks, such as the marine algae Caulerpa dumped into the ocean, has had devastating consequences. The following website addresses this example www.invasivespeciesinfo.gov/aquatics/caulerpa.shtml. (37.13)

- The accidental introduction of the Brown Tree Snake into Guam during World War II has had devastating impact on the ecology and economy of Guam. Extensive details can be found at www.fort.usgs.gov/Resources/Education/BTS/. (37.13)

Ecosystem Structure and Dynamics (37.14–37.23)

Student Misconceptions and Concerns

- Without an understanding of basic physics and the inefficiency of aerobic metabolism, students might not understand how chemical energy in food is lost as heat. Consider expanding upon the explanations given in the book. (37.14)

- The environmental impact of eating farm animals is little appreciated by most students who otherwise may be concerned about global climate change and the conservation of natural ecosystems. This chapter section helps explain the basis of the increased costs associated with a diet that includes meat. (37.17)

- Students are unlikely to have any prior knowledge of biogeochemical cycles. Although some transfers between the biotic and abiotic components of ecosystems, such as the use of fertilizer on plants, may be known to them, the broader fact that the biosphere is a self-cycling system is not appreciated by most students. Before you lecture, consider asking your students to explain how carbon, phosphorus, and nitrogen cycle through the atmosphere. Pre-testing your students on their knowledge can confirm both what they understand and what they may need explained to them in more detail. (37.18–37.21)

Teaching Tips

- The heat generated as a by-product of metabolism, which is quite evident during strenuous exercise, is much like the heat produced by a running automobile engine. In both circumstances, heat is a by-product of the fuel-burning process. (37.14)

- Energy flow through an ecosystem is analogous to the flow of fuel through a car or electricity through a vacuum cleaner. These systems will not work without a steady input. NASA, however, must rely upon some closed systems for its spacecrafts. Students might enjoy investigating the recycling of gases and fluids in these systems. (37.14)

- Challenge students to explain why the areas of greatest primary production are near the equator. (Answer: Primary production is a consequence of photosynthesis. Regions near the equator receive the highest levels of solar input.) (37.15)

- Why do food chains and webs typically have only three to five levels? This question, which is seldom considered by students, is addressed directly in this section of the chapter. It can spark a good opening discussion before a lecture on food chains and food webs. (37.16)

- Some students might be interested in eating more proteins and fewer carbohydrates because of popular diet plans. But do high-protein diets always require the consumption of more meat? The many sources of plant proteins might be surprising to students. Some high-protein vegetarian options are described by the Vegetarian Society at its website, http://www.vegsoc.org/page.aspx?pid=781#dietary sources. (37.17)

- As you discuss the importance of the biogeochemical cycles, consider explaining the basic label information provided on a container of plant fertilizer. Consider an example that might be used on houseplants, and therefore more likely to be familiar to students. Typically, plant fertilizers contain various forms of nitrogen and phosphorus, which are essential chemicals for growth. (37.18–37.20)

- As rising atmospheric carbon dioxide levels affect global climate, carbon cycling has become an increasingly important issue. If your course will not cover Module 38.5, on global warming, consider including a brief discussion of the topic here. (37.19)

- Discussing the movements of water through your local community can help students better understand the concept of biogeochemical cycling. You may want to ask students to consider all of the possible inputs of water into your community as well as the possible routes of exit. (37.20)

- As noted in Module 37.20, phosphate contamination of aquatic systems typically leads to increased algal growth and potentially disastrous fish kills. (37.20)

- The nitrogen-fixing bacteria living in the roots of soybeans add nitrogen to the soil. Corn does not enjoy this same relationship with bacteria. However, by rotating corn and soybean crops, farmers can allow corn crops to use some of the nitrogen fixed by the soybean crop in the previous year. Such rotation has other benefits. Since corn is a monocot and soybeans are dicots, few pests attack both corn and soybeans. Thus, crop rotation also helps to control the pest populations that target each type of plant, reducing the need for other pest-fighting strategies. (37.21)

- The studies of the Hubbard Brook Experimental Forest (described well at www.hubbardbrook.org/ and in the previous edition of this *Concepts* textbook) provide an opportunity to explain how basic principles of scientific investigation are applied to ecological studies. Consider discussing the difficulties of conducting these broad experiments in other locations, where water cycling may not be so restricted and other biogeochemical cycles not as well defined. (37.22)

- Most human communities include at least one golf course where heavy chemical applications of fertilizers occur. Discuss with your students the environmental impact of replacing a natural prairie or forested ecosystem with a golf course, noting the change in species diversity and broader ecological impacts of applications of fertilizers and pesticides and the related increase in fossil fuel consumption. Immediate examples from your local community help students immediately relate to the topics of this chapter. (37.23)

Key Terms

abiotic reservoirs	ecological niche	nitrogen fixation
biogeochemical cycles	ecological succession	predation
biological control	ecosystem	primary consumer
biomass	energy flow	primary production
chemical cycling	food chain	primary succession
coevolution	food web	producers
community	herbivory	quaternary consumer
decomposers	interspecific competition	secondary consumer
decomposition	interspecific interactions	secondary succession
detritivore	invasive species	species diversity
detritus	keystone species	sustainability
disturbances	mutualism	tertiary consumer

Word Roots

a- = without; **bio-** = life (*abiotic reservoir*: a part of an ecosystem where a chemical, such as carbon or nitrogen, accumulates or is stockpiled outside of living organisms)

geo- = Earth (*biogeochemical cycle*: any of the various chemical circuits that involve both biotic and abiotic components of an ecosystem)

de- = from, down, out (*decomposer*: prokaryotes and fungi that secrete enzymes that digest organic material and break it down into inorganic forms)

detrit- = wear off (*detritus*: dead organic matter); **-vora** = eat (*detritivore*: an organism that consumes organic wastes and dead organisms)

herb- = grass; **-vora** = eat (*herbivory*: the consumption of plant material by an animal)

inter- = between (*interspecific interactions*: interactions between organisms of different species)

mutu- = reciprocal (*mutualism*: an interspecific relationship in which both partners benefit)

quatr- = four (*quaternary consumer*: an organism that eats tertiary consumers; the fourth step on the food chain)

terti- = three (*tertiary consumer*: an organism that eats secondary consumers; the third step on the food chain)

CHAPTER 38

Conservation Biology

Chapter Objectives

Opening Essay

Describe the causes of the decline of tigers in the world.

The Loss of Biodiversity

38.1 Describe the three components of biodiversity. Explain how human activities threaten biodiversity.

38.2 Describe the greatest current threats to biodiversity, providing examples of each.

38.2 Describe the process of biological magnification.

38.3–38.6 Describe the causes and consequences of global warming.

Conservation Biology and Restoration Ecology

38.7 Explain why the efforts to save the black-footed ferret and silversword plant from extinction are a good model for future conservation efforts.

38.8 Describe the goals of landscape ecology. Describe the significance of edges and movement corridors in maintaining biodiversity.

38.9 Describe the significance of biodiversity hotspots. Describe the challenges of protecting species that migrate or otherwise require great ranges.

38.10 Explain how zoned reserves are being used to protect ecosystems. Describe the success and ongoing challenges of such reserves in Costa Rica.

38.11 Describe the goals of the Yukon to Yellowstone Initiative. Explain why wolves are considered a keystone species and how their return to Yellowstone National Park has impacted the ecosystem there.

38.12 Describe the goals and methods of restoration ecology. Describe the goals and expected outcomes of the Kissimmee River Project.

38.13 Explain why sustainable development should be the ultimate goal for the long-term maintenance of human societies and the ecosystems that support them.

Lecture Outline

I. Introduction

A. Over the past century, wild tiger populations have been reduced from about 100,000 to 3,200.

B. Tigers are threatened by
   1. declining habitat,
   2. poaching, and
   3. human populations encroaching into their habitat.

II. The Loss of Biodiversity

A. 38.1 Loss of biodiversity includes the loss of ecosystem, species, and genes

1. Biodiversity has three levels:
   a. ecosystem diversity,
   b. species diversity, and
   c. genetic diversity.

2. As natural ecosystems are lost, so are essential services, including
   a. productivity of natural environments for human food supplies and
   b. the purification of water used by cities.

3. At present, scientists have described and formally named about 1.8 million species.
   a. It is difficult to estimate species loss.
   b. Species loss may be 1,000 times higher than at any time in the past 100,000 years.
   c. **Extirpation** is the loss of a single population of a species.
   d. **Extinction** is the irreversible loss of all populations of a species.

4. Because of the network of community interactions among populations of different species within an ecosystem,
   a. the loss of one species
   b. can negatively affect the species richness of an ecosystem.

5. Genetic diversity of a species is reduced if
   a. local populations are lost and
   b. the total number of individuals declines.

B. 38.2 CONNECTION: Habitat loss, invasive species, overharvesting, pollution, and climate change are major threats to biodiversity

1. Human alteration of habitats poses the greatest threat to biodiversity.

2. Habitation alteration is caused by
   a. agriculture,
   b. urban development,
   c. forestry,
   d. mining, and
   e. environmental pollution.

3. Invasive species rank second behind habitat destruction as a threat to biodiversity.

4. Invasive species
   a. compete with native species,
   b. prey on native species, and
   c. parasitize native species.

5. Overexploitation is the third major threat to biodiversity. Overharvesting has threatened rare trees,
   a. reduced populations of tigers, Galápagos tortoises, whales, and rhinoceroses, and
   b. depleted wild populations of game fish.

6. Human activities produce diverse pollutants that may affect ecosystems far from their source.
   a. The water cycle transfers pollutants from terrestrial to aquatic ecosystems.
   b. The release of chemicals into the atmosphere promoted the thinning of the **ozone layer**.

7. **Biological magnification** concentrates synthetic toxins that cannot be degraded by microorganisms.

C. 38.3 CONNECTION: Rapid warming is changing the global climate

1. The scientific debate about global warming is over.

2. Increased global temperatures caused by rising concentrations of greenhouse gases are changing climate patterns with grave consequences.
   a. Global temperature has risen 0.8°C in the last 100 years.
      i. 0.6°C of that increase occurred in the last three decades.
      ii. 2 to 4.5°C increases are likely by the end of the 21st century.
   b. Temperature increases are not distributed evenly.
   c. Precipitation patterns are changing too.
D. 38.4 CONNECTION: Human activities are responsible for rising concentrations of greenhouse gases
   1. Much of the rapid warming is the result of burning fossil fuels.
      a. Atmospheric CO_2 did not exceed 300 ppm for 650,000 years.
      b. The preindustrial concentration was below 300 ppm.
      c. Atmospheric CO_2 is approximately 385 ppm today.
      d. High levels of methane and nitrous oxide also trap heat.
E. 38.5 Global climate change affects biomes, ecosystems, communities, and populations
   1. Climate change in western North America has spawned catastrophic wildfires.
   2. The greatest impact of global climate change is affecting organisms that live at
      a. high latitudes and
      b. high elevations.
   3. Warming oceans threaten coral reef communities.
   4. Earlier arrival of warm temperatures in the spring is disturbing ecological communities.
      a. Birds and frogs have begun their breeding periods earlier.
      b. Migratory birds may experience mismatches, arriving after peak food availability has already passed.
   5. Climate change has also
      a. increased the range of disease-carrying mosquitoes and
      b. enabled bark beetles to reproduce faster, promoting the destruction of millions of acres of conifers in western North America.
F. 38.6 EVOLUTION CONNECTION: Climate change is an agent of natural selection
   1. **Phenotypic plasticity**
      a. has minimized the impact of global climate change on some species, and
      b. cases of microevolutionary changes have been observed.
      c. The rapidity of the environmental changes makes it unlikely that evolutionary processes will save many species from extinction.
   2. In Europe, the great tit bird
      a. has shifted it breeding season earlier, in an example of directional selection,
      b. favoring individuals that lay their eggs sooner, and
      c. better matching the earlier emergence of caterpillars.
   3. In the Yukon Territory of Canada,
      a. where the spring temperatures have increased by about 2°C,
      b. red squirrels have begun breeding earlier in the spring.

III. Conservation Biology and Restoration Ecology

A. 38.7 Protecting endangered populations is one goal of conservation biology
   1. **Conservation biology** is a goal-driven science that seeks to
      a. understand and
      b. counter the rapid loss of biodiversity.

2. Some conservation biologists direct their efforts at

   a. protecting populations and

   b. increasing endangered populations.

   c. Threats posed by human activities are also assessed.

3. The black-footed ferret in the United States

   a. is one of three ferret species worldwide and the only ferret found in North America,

   b. was reduced to just 18 individuals,

   c. has been bred in captivity, and

   d. was reintroduced into the wild.

4. In Hawaii, the silversword plants once abundant on the cinder cone of the volcano Mauna Kea

   a. were bred in greenhouses and

   b. reintroduced to reestablish wild populations.

B. 38.8 Sustaining ecosystems and landscapes is a conservation priority

   1. Conservation efforts are increasingly aimed at sustaining

      a. ecosystems and

      b. landscapes, a regional assemblage of interacting ecosystems.

   2. Landscape ecology is the application of ecological principles to the study of the structure and dynamics of a collection of ecosystems.

   3. Edges between ecosystems have distinct sets of features and species.

   4. The increased frequency and abruptness of edges caused by human activities can increase species loss.

   5. Movement corridors connecting isolated habitats may be helpful to fragmented populations.

C. 38.9 Establishing protected areas slows the loss of biodiversity

   1. To establish parks, wilderness areas, and other legally protected reserves, conservation biologists are applying their understanding of

      a. population,

      b. ecosystem, and

      c. landscape dynamics.

   2. Choosing locations for protection often focuses on **biodiversity hot spots**, relatively small areas with

      a. a large number of endangered and threatened species, and

      b. an exceptional concentration of **endemic species**, those that are found nowhere else.

   3. Migratory species pose a special problem for conservationists.

      a. Monarch butterflies occupy many areas.

      b. Sea turtles travel great distances.

D. 38.10 Zoned reserves are an attempt to reverse ecosystem disruption

   1. Zoned reserves are undisturbed wildlands surrounded by buffer zones of compatible economic development.

   2. Costa Rica has established many zoned reserves.

   3. Ecotourism

      a. is travel to natural areas for tourism and recreation and

      b. has become an important source of revenue for conservation efforts.

E. 38.11 CONNECTION: The Yellowstone to Yukon Conservation Initiative seeks to preserve biodiversity by connecting protected areas
   1. The Yellowstone to Yukon Conservation Initiative
      a. created a string of parks and reserves in a 3,200-km wildlife corridor,
      b. extends from Alaska south across Canada to northern Wyoming,
      c. included the reintroduction of wolf populations, considered a keystone species in this region, and
      d. sparked angry protests from some ranchers.
F. 38.12 CONNECTION: The study of how to restore degraded habitats is a developing science
   1. **Restoration ecology** uses ecological principles to restore degraded areas to their natural state, a process that may include
      a. detoxifying polluted ecosystems,
      b. replanting native vegetation, and
      c. returning waterways to their natural course.
   2. Large-scale restoration projects attempt to restore damaged landscapes.
   3. The Kissimmee River Restoration Project in Florida is
      a. restoring river flow and wetlands and
      b. improving wildlife habitat.
G. 38.13 Sustainable development is an ultimate goal
   1. Sustainable development
      a. seeks to improve the human condition while conserving biodiversity,
      b. depends on increasing and applying ecological knowledge, and
      c. values our linkages to the biosphere.
   2. We are most likely to
      a. save what we appreciate and
      b. appreciate what we understand.
   3. Now is the time to
      a. aggressively pursue more knowledge about life and
      b. work toward long-term sustainability.

Chapter Guide to Teaching Resources

The Biodiversity Crisis: An Overview (38.1–38.6)

Student Misconceptions and Concerns

- The importance of biodiversity may not be obvious to many students. Yet, as this chapter notes, biodiversity is inherently valuable on many levels. Consider challenging your class to explain why biodiversity matters, as an introduction to the subject. (38.1–38.6)

- Frustration can overwhelm students who are alarmed by the many problems addressed in this chapter. One way to address this is to provide meaningful ways for students to respond to this information (for example, changes in personal choices and informed voting). Several related websites are noted in the Teaching Tips that follow. (38.1–38.6)

- Students often confuse the causes and consequences of global warming and the destruction of the ozone layer. Instructors should take care to distinguish between these two global problems. (38.2)

Teaching Tips

- Consider referencing some of the following websites for basic ideas on what individuals can do to help address the loss of biodiversity:

  Conservation International: www.conservation.org/act/

  EPA: www.epa.gov/climatechange/wycd/index.html

  World Wildlife Fund: wwf.panda.org/about_our_earth/biodiversity/. (38.1)

- Genetic bottlenecks, which are a consequence of the loss of diversity within a species, are discussed in Module 13.11. Preventing genetic bottlenecks is essential to the long-term conservation of species. (38.1)

- Module 36.8 describes the impact of overfishing on cod populations off the east coast of North America. (38.2)

- You might wish to note the mission of the Nature Conservancy, an organization devoted to the purchase and protection of land across the world. Students can visit them on the web at www.nature.org. (38.2)

- One of the best websites devoted to the brown tree snake problem in Guam can be found at www.fort.usgs.gov/Resources/Education/BTS/. The story of this remarkable disaster is also chronicled in Mark Jaffe's 1994 book *And No Birds Sing: The Story of an Ecological Disaster,* which provides a wonderful example of the process of science and discovery. (38.2)

- Consider an analogy between the ozone layer and sunscreen applied to the skin. The thinning of the ozone layer is like putting on less and less sunscreen. In both situations, more harmful UV light penetrates the layers. (38.2)

- Modules 37.8, 37.9, and 37.16 discuss food chains, food webs, and the decreasing availability of energy at each higher trophic level. Student understanding of biological magnification depends upon comprehension of these facts. (38.2)

- Many students do not realize that greenhouses get very warm when exposed to strong sunlight. (Most of them have probably never even been inside a greenhouse.) However, most students understand that a closed car gets warmer when sitting in the sun (thus the need for the various windshield sun reflectors). The glass in the car functions like the glass in a greenhouse. (38.3-38.4)

- Additional details on the greenhouse effect can be found at the following websites.

  NASA: http://gcmd.nasa.gov/Resources/pointers/glob_warm.html

  The National Climatic Data Center: www.ncdc.noaa.gov/oa/climate/globalwarming.html

  The Australian Greenhouse Office: www.greenhouse.gov.au. (38.3, 38.4)

- In 2007, former U.S. Vice President Al Gore and the Intergovernmental Panel on Climate Change (IPCC) received the Nobel Peace Prize "for their efforts to build up and disseminate greater knowledge about man-made climate change, and to lay the foundations for the measures that are needed to counteract such change." The full statement of the Nobel Prize committee can be found at http://nobelprize.org/nobel_prizes/peace/laureates/2007/. (38.3, 38.4)

- Students are unlikely to enter your course with a prior understanding of the diverse impacts of global climate change on ecosystems and individual species. Concepts such as the increased spread of disease vectors, the shifting of natural ranges and breeding seasons, and the spread of invasive species will likely be new to them, and taking it all in can be overwhelming. However, an awareness of the impact of global climate change can also be motivating. Consider ending your class sessions by discussing positive actions that students can take to make a difference. A few websites that provide related suggestions follow.

www.liveneutral.org

www.green-e.org

www.stopglobalwarming.org

www.sierraclub.org/energy/. (38.5, 38.6)

- Consider challenging your students to find at least one scholarly article online that documents the impact of climate change on at least one species. They could email the link to you as their assignment. (38.6)

Conservation Biology and Restoration Ecology (38.7–38.13)

Student Misconceptions and Concerns

- Although they are typically sympathetic to efforts at species conservation, students often do not understand the complexity of the issues involved. The final section of this chapter helps to describe some of the recent efforts to conserve biodiversity and their challenges. A class discussion about the difficulties of conservation can help students realize that there are no simple solutions, and that interventions must be carefully planned and monitored. (38.7–38.13)

- Learning about current environmental problems, such as climate change and declining biodiversity, can be extremely discouraging to students entering adulthood. Providing students with examples of successful interventions and suggestions for actions they can take as individuals, while honestly describing the challenges still to be met, may be the best way to help them engage these issues. (38.7–38.13)

Teaching Tips

- Consider referencing some of the following websites for basic ideas on what individuals can do to help address environmental problems.

  California Environmental Protection Agency: www.arb.ca.gov/html/brochure/50things.htm

  Pennsylvania Dept. of Environmental Protection: www.dep.state.pa.us/earthdaycentral/96/business/FS1977.htm

  Environment Canada: www.ec.gc.ca/education/default.asp?lang=En&n=826B95C3-1 (38.7–38.13)

- The World Resource Institute provides information, ideas, and solutions to global environmental problems. Their website at www.wri.org/ is an excellent resource for additional information. (38.7–38.13)

- The IUCN Red List of threatened and endangered species can be accessed at www.iucnredlist.org/. (38.7)

- If a short field trip is possible, you might wish to take students into a nearby wooded area to compare the diversity of life at the edge of the woods and deep within it. (38.8)

- In some ways, highways are types of movement corridors between populations of people living in cities. (38.8)

- The Conservation International website highlights biodiversity hot spots at www.biodiversityhotspots.org/Pages/default.aspx. (38.9)

- Zoned reserves illustrate one successful avenue of conservation in which efforts are developed in recognition of social demands. The recent increase in the use of green technology and consumer interest in green products reveals the potential for cooperative progress. Challenge your students to consider careers that might allow them to contribute to the development of sustainable solutions beneficial to the environment, industry, and society. Recycling programs, energy conservation, and the development of renewable energy sources can be cost-effective alternatives that help minimize human impact on the environment. (38.10)

- Conservation efforts such as Y2Y require careful consideration of diverse points of view. Consider challenging your class to represent the perspectives of a rancher, a parent of small children, and a park ranger with regard to the expanding range of wolves, perhaps in the form of a staged debate. What issues might be most important to each of these people? What policies could be developed to address their concerns? (38.11)

- The Kissimmee River Restoration Project's website is www.saj.usace.army.mil/Divisions/Everglades/Branches/ProjectExe/Sections/UECKLO/KRR.htm. The website, sponsored by US Army Corps of Engineers, includes a large photo gallery detailing the historical changes to the river system, maps, and many related details of the project. (38.12)

- The chapter's final module reflects upon the broader goals of biology and conservation, providing an opportunity to discuss what it means to be educated and why knowledge matters. As the text's penultimate paragraph notes, "We are most likely to save what we appreciate, and we are most likely to appreciate what we understand." Consider leaving your students with this empowering message that our world can be better, and our future brighter, if we continue to learn and apply our knowledge appropriately. (38.13)

Key Terms

biodiversity hot spots	extinction	ozone layer
biological magnification	extirpation	phenotypic plasticity
conservation biology	landscape	restoration ecology
ecotourism	landscape ecology	zoned reserve
endemic species	movement corridor	

Word Roots

bio- = life (*biodiversity hot spots*: a small geographic area with an exceptional concentration of endangered and threatened species, especially endemic species)

end- = within (*endemic species*: a species whose distribution is limited to a specific geographic area)

pheno- = appear (*phenotypic plasticity*: an individual's ability to change phenotype in response to local environmental conditions)